NEW ELEMENTARY MATHEMATICS

SYLLABUS D

2

D1284415

Sin Kwai Meng
M. Sc., Cert. Ed.

General Editor
Dr Wong Khoon Yoong
Ph. D., B.Sc. (Hons), Dip. Ed.

PAN PACIFIC PUBLICATIONS (S) PTE LTD

An imprint of SNP Panpac Pte Ltd

SNP Panpac Pte Ltd
97 Ubi Avenue 4
Singapore 408754

© SNP Panpac Pte Ltd

Website: http://www.snpcorp.com
Email: panpmktg@snpcorp.com

All rights reserved. No part of this publication may be reproduced, stored in a retrieval system, or transmitted in any form or by any means, electronic, mechanical, photocopying, recording or otherwise, without the prior written permission of the publishers.

First published 1992
Reprinted 1993
Reprinted 1994
Reprinted 1995
Reprinted 1996
New edition 1997
Reprinted 1998
Reprinted 1999
Reprinted 2000
Reprinted 2003

Printed by Utopia Press Pte Ltd

ISBN 981-208-460-6

PREFACE

THE SERIES

NEW ELEMENTARY MATHEMATICS is a series of six course books. The first two books follow closely the latest Mathematics Syllabus for Lower Secondary Schools issued by the Ministry of Education, Singapore, for use from 1992. Books 3A, 3B, 4A and 4B cover the Singapore-Cambridge G.C.E. 'O' Level Mathematics Syllabus D.

THE APPROACH

Throughout the series, emphasis is placed on the development of better understanding of mathematical concepts and their applications, as well as on proficiency in problem solving, mathematical reasoning and higher order thinking.

To facilitate this, we have included the following:

- **investigative work**
- **communication skills in mathematics**
- **appropriate computational and estimation skills**
- **mental calculation and**
- **problem-solving heuristics**

THE FEATURES

EXERCISES

Numerous exercises are provided for students of varied abilities and the problems are **graded**. The more difficult questions are marked with asterisks (*).

CHAPTER REVIEW

At the end of every chapter, there is a *Chapter Review* which **recapitulates concepts** learnt.

CHALLENGER

This section just after the *Chapter Review* is specially designed to provide **interesting and challenging problems** on that particular chapter topic for the abler and more adventurous students.

PROBLEM SOLVING

Problem Solving exercises are given to enable students to practise their problem-solving skills.

REVISION EXERCISES

Sets of **revision exercises** are also included at appropriate intervals to provide students with the necessary **practice and reinforcement**.

MISCELLANEOUS EXERCISES

These exercises are given at chapter intervals. They provide students with many questions in which to apply various concepts learnt.

INVESTIGATION

Problems in the *Investigation* section provide opportunities for students to **explore, experiment with and discuss mathematical ideas**.

MATHSTORY

A story or history on mathematics is given at the side margin where appropriate. This section is meant to enrich students with the knowledge of how mathematics develops over the years.

It is hoped that this series will help students gain confidence in and better insights into the subject, and above all, that students will look upon Mathematics as something both exciting and rewarding.

I am grateful to all those who have, in one way or another, rendered assistance and offered invaluable suggestions.

I am also grateful to the University of Cambridge Local Examinations Syndicate and EPB Publications Pte Ltd for permission to reproduce some of the examination questions.

Sin K. M.

CONTENTS

PROBLEM SOLVING TIPS FOR THE STUDENT

In this book, you will have an opportunity to apply several strategies to solve interesting problems. These problems are given at the end of each chapter.

Checklist for Solving Problems

1. **Accept the problem**
   - Accept the challenge to solve unfamiliar or difficult problems.

2. **Understand the problem**
   - Read the question carefully several times and understand the key words.
   - Ascertain what is given, what is the unknown and what are the conditions.
   - Draw a diagram, make a model or act it out.
   - Describe the problem in your own words.

3. **Devise a plan**
   - Search for information to relate relevant data to the unknown.
   - Use strategies such as:
     (i) Guess and check with logical thinking.
     (ii) Simplify the problem, use tabulation or look for a pattern.
     (iii) Think of a related problem.
     (iv) Use a diagram or a model.

4. **Carry out the plan**
   - Apply the strategies and monitor your progress.
   - Check each step carefully.
   - Read the question again to make sure that you are on the right track.
   - Avoid getting stuck in one method for too long. Try another method.
   - If you are still stuck, take a break. Do something different and come back to the problem later.

5. **Look back**
   - Reflect, extend and seek improvement.
   - Check the result. (Is it reasonable? Does it satisfy the given conditions?)
   - Check the solution. (Can I do it a different way?)
   - Improve on the method used.
   - Extend the method. (How do I solve the problem if some of the conditions are changed?)

The checklist has been prepared to help you improve your problem-solving skills. This is what you should do:

- Copy the checklist onto a card.
- Keep it in your exercise book.
- Refer to it frequently when you solve problems.
- Add your own notes to the card when you learn or discover new strategies.

In learning to solve problems, it is important to take time to think about what you have done. At the end of each practice session, ask yourself some of the following questions.

1. What do I like most about the problem?
2. What strategies did I use? Why?
3. What did I do when I got stuck? Which strategy helped me to get started?
4. Did I check my work carefully.
5. What kind of mistakes did I make?
6. What were the easiest and hardest problems I solved? Why were they easy or hard?
7. Did I feel frustrated, scared or bored concerning these problems? What did I do to overcome these bad feelings?
8. Did I feel satisfied, happy and excited after doing these problems?

You may write down your thoughts in a notebook. At the end of the term, see how much you have improved in your problem-solving skills.

ENJOY SOLVING THE PROBLEMS!

Chapter 1

Indices

Chapter Highlights

- Using positive, zero and negative integral indices
- Using the laws of indices
- Simplifying expressions involving indices
- Understanding the definition of the standard form
- Using and computing numbers in standard form

1.1 POSITIVE INTEGRAL INDICES

We know that 7^5 means $7 \times 7 \times 7 \times 7 \times 7$. The number 7 is called the **base** and the number 5 is called the **index** or **exponent**.

7^5 (base, index or exponent)

7^5 is read as '*the 5th power of 7*' or '*7 to the power 5*'. Similarly, 10^4 is read as '*the 4th power of 10*' or '*10 to the power 4*'.

The exponent tells you how many times a number, or base, is used as a factor.

Numbers in index notation with the same base 7 such as 7^5, 7^9 and 7^{12} are referred to as **powers** of 7. Similarly, 10^4, 10^8 and 10^{11} are powers of 10.

MATHSTORY

The French mathematician René Descartes (1596–1650) introduced the use of Hindu-Arabic numerals as exponents on a given base.

Examples

(a) Consider $7^3 \times 7^2$.
We have $7^3 \times 7^2 = (7 \times 7 \times 7) \times (7 \times 7)$
$= 7^5$

Notice that 7^5 can be written as 7^{3+2}.
So we have $7^3 \times 7^2 = 7^{3+2}$.
In general, we have the first Law of Indices:

$$a^m \times a^n = a^{m+n}$$

(b) Consider $\dfrac{3^6}{3^4}$.

We have $\dfrac{3^6}{3^4} = \dfrac{3 \times 3 \times 3 \times 3 \times 3 \times 3}{3 \times 3 \times 3 \times 3}$
$= 3 \times 3$
$= 3^2$

Notice that 3^2 can be written as 3^{6-4}.

So we have $\dfrac{3^6}{3^4} = 3^{6-4}$.

In general, we have the second Law of Indices:

$$\frac{a^m}{a^n} = a^{m-n}$$

Note: We assume that $m > n$ since negative indices are not dealt with in this section.

(c) Consider $(5^2)^3$.
We have $(5^2)^3 = 5^2 \times 5^2 \times 5^2$
$= (5 \times 5) \times (5 \times 5) \times (5 \times 5)$
$= 5^6$

Notice that 5^6 can be written as $5^{2 \times 3}$.
So we have $(5^2)^3 = 5^{2 \times 3}$.

In general, we have the third Law of Indices:

$$(a^m)^n = a^{mn}$$

(d) Consider $3^4 \times 5^4$.

We have $3^4 \times 5^4 = (3 \times 3 \times 3 \times 3) \times (5 \times 5 \times 5 \times 5)$

$= (3 \times 5) \times (3 \times 5) \times (3 \times 5) \times (3 \times 5)$

$= (3 \times 5)^4$

In general, we have the fourth Law of Indices:

$$a^m \times b^m = (a \times b)^m$$

(e) Consider $\frac{2^3}{7^3}$.

We have $\frac{2^3}{7^3} = \frac{2 \times 2 \times 2}{7 \times 7 \times 7}$

$= \left(\frac{2}{7}\right) \times \left(\frac{2}{7}\right) \times \left(\frac{2}{7}\right)$

$= \left(\frac{2}{7}\right)^3$

In general, we have the fifth Law of Indices:

$$\frac{a^m}{b^m} = \left(\frac{a}{b}\right)^m$$

Notice that the first, second and third laws are to be used for powers of the same base and the fourth and fifth laws for powers that have the same index.

Class Activity 1

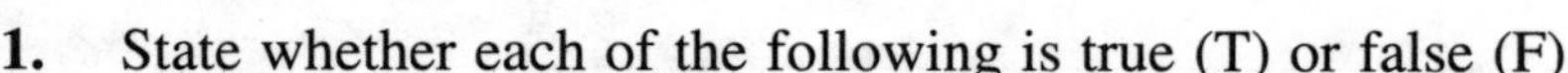

1. State whether each of the following is true (T) or false (F).

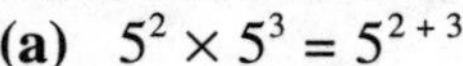

(a) $5^2 \times 5^3 = 5^{2+3}$ **(b)** $2^5 \times 3^5 = 5^{2+3}$
(c) $5^2 \times 5^3 = 5^{2\times 3}$ **(d)** $4^2 \times 2^2 = 2^{4+2}$
(e) $5^2 + 5^3 = 5^{2+3}$ **(f)** $2^5 + 3^5 = (2+3)^5$
(g) $(2^2)^3 = 2^{2+3}$ **(h)** $(2^3)^2 = 2^{3\times 2}$
(i) $5^3 \times 6^3 = (5 \times 6)^3$ **(j)** $(5^3)^2 = (5^2)^3$
(k) $4^6 \div 4^3 = 4^{6\div 3}$ **(l)** $6^4 \div 3^4 = 4^{6-3}$
(m) $4^6 \div 4^3 = 4^{6-3}$ **(n)** $5^4 \div 5^2 = 5^{4\div 2}$
(o) $4^6 - 4^3 = 4^{6-3}$ **(p)** $6^4 \div 3^4 = (6 \div 3)^4$
(q) $(8 \div 4)^3 = 3^{8\div 4}$ **(r)** $8^2 - 3^2 = (8-3)^2$
(s) $7^{2+3} = 7^2 \times 7^3$ **(t)** $7^{3\times 2} = (7^3)^2$

2. By inspection, match each expression in column A with its equivalent in Column B. State the law of indices used in each case.

Example

The first expression (i) in Column A is equivalent to the expression (a) in Column B. The law used is the second law of indices.

Column A	Column B
(i) $\frac{7^5}{7^2}$	**(a)** 7^{5-2}
(ii) $\frac{5^7}{2^7}$	**(b)** 2^{7+5}
(iii) $7^5 \times 7^2$	**(c)** 5^{7+2}
(iv) $5^7 \times 5^2$	**(d)** 7^{5+2}
(v) $(5^2)^7$	**(e)** $\left(\frac{5}{2}\right)^7$
(vi) $(7^5)^2$	**(f)** $2^{7\times5}$
(vii) $5^7 \times 2^7$	**(g)** $7^{5\times2}$
(viii) $2^5 \times 7^5$	**(h)** 5^{7-2}
(ix) $\frac{5^7}{5^2}$	**(i)** $(2 \times 7)^5$
(x) $2^7 \times 2^5$	**(j)** $\left(\frac{2}{7}\right)^5$
(xi) $(2^7)^5$	**(k)** $5^{2\times7}$
(xii) $7^2 \times 5^2$	**(l)** $(7 \times 5)^2$
(xiii) $\frac{2^5}{7^5}$	**(m)** $(5 \times 2)^7$
(xiv) $\frac{7^2}{5^2}$	**(n)** $\left(\frac{7}{5}\right)^2$
(xv) $\frac{2^7}{2^5}$	**(o)** 2^{7-5}

3. Do the five laws of indices also apply to **negative** bases? Investigate.

Worked Example 1

Simplify the following and express your answers in index form.

(a) $2^3 \times 2^4 \times 2^5$ **(b)** $(7^2 \times 7^3)^2$

(c) $\dfrac{19^6 \times 19^3}{11^5 \times 11^3}$ **(d)** $\dfrac{3^2 \times 5^4 \times 3^7}{5^2}$

Solution:

(a) $2^3 \times 2^4 \times 2^5 = 2^{3+4+5}$
$= 2^{12}$

(b) $(7^2 \times 7^3)^2 = (7^{2+3})^2$
$= (7^5)^2$
$= 7^{5 \times 2}$
$= 7^{10}$

(c) $\dfrac{19^6 \times 19^3}{11^5 \times 11^3} = \dfrac{19^{6+3}}{11^{5+3}}$
$= \dfrac{19^9}{11^8}$

(d) $\dfrac{3^2 \times 5^4 \times 3^7}{5^2} = \dfrac{3^2 \times 3^7 \times 5^4}{5^2}$
$= 3^{2+7} \times 5^{4-2}$
$= 3^9 \times 5^2$

Worked Example 2

Simplify the following and express your answers in index form.

(a) $\dfrac{3^7 \times 2^7}{2^3 \times 2^4}$ **(b)** $\dfrac{6^5 \times 2^4}{3^5 \times 2^2}$

Solution:

(a) $\dfrac{3^7 \times 2^7}{2^3 \times 2^4} = \dfrac{(3 \times 2)^7}{2^{3+4}}$
$= \dfrac{6^7}{2^7}$
$= \left(\dfrac{6}{2}\right)^7$
$= 3^7$

(b) $\dfrac{6^5 \times 2^4}{3^5 \times 2^2} = \dfrac{6^5}{3^5} \times \dfrac{2^4}{2^2}$
$= \left(\dfrac{6}{3}\right)^5 \times 2^{4-2}$
$= 2^5 \times 2^2$
$= 2^{5+2}$
$= 2^7$

Alternative solution:

(a) $\dfrac{3^7 \times 2^7}{2^3 \times 2^4} = \dfrac{3^7 \times 2^7}{2^{3+4}}$
$= \dfrac{3^7 \times 2^7}{2^7}$
$= 3^7 \quad \left(\text{since } \dfrac{2^7}{2^7} = 1\right)$

Alternative solution:

(b) $\dfrac{6^5 \times 2^4}{3^5 \times 2^2} = \dfrac{(2 \times 3)^5 \times 2^4}{3^5 \times 2^2}$
$= \dfrac{2^5 \times 3^5 \times 2^4}{3^5 \times 2^2}$
$= 2^{5+4-2}$
$= 2^7 \quad \left(\text{since } \dfrac{3^5}{3^5} = 1\right)$

Note: In section 1.2, you will learn that the law $\dfrac{a^m}{a^n} = a^{m-n}$ can be used to simplify $\dfrac{2^7}{2^7}$ or $\dfrac{3^5}{3^5}$.

Worked Example 3

By using a calculator, verify that:

(a) $(-3)^4 \times (-3)^3 = (-3)^7$

(b) $(-4)^5 \times (-7)^5 = [(-4) \times (-7)]^5$

Solution:

(a) LHS $= 81 \times (-27) = -2\ 187$

RHS $= -2\ 187$

$\therefore$ LHS = RHS

(b) LHS $= -1\ 024 \times (-16\ 807) = 17\ 210\ 368$

RHS $= 28^5 = 17\ 210\ 368$

$\therefore$ LHS = RHS

Exercise 1.1

answers on p. 425

1. Simplify the following and express your answers in index form.

(a) $11^3 \times 11^4$ **(b)** $\frac{5^6}{5^3}$

(c) $(18^4)^3$ **(d)** $6^3 \times 6^4$

(e) $\frac{7^6}{7^4}$ **(f)** $(13^6)^2$

(g) $2^2 \times 2^5 \times 2^6$ **(h)** $\frac{2^5 \times 2^6}{2^7}$

(i) $(7^2 \times 7^3)^5$ **(j)** $5^6 \times 5^7 \times 5^2$

(k) $\frac{5^4 \times 5^5}{5^6}$ **(l)** $(5^6 \times 5^2)^3$

(m) $7^4 \times 11^2 \times 11^5 \times 7^2$ **(n)** $\frac{11^4}{11^2 \times 5^2 \times 5^3}$

(o) $\frac{3^6 \times 3^5}{2^4 \times 2^5}$ **(p)** $17^2 \times 11^4 \times 17^3 \times 11^5$

(q) $\frac{17^5}{7^2 \times 7^5 \times 17^3}$ **(r)** $\frac{7^9 \times 2^5}{2^4 \times 7^2}$

2. Simplify the following and express your answers in index form.

(a) $3^3 \times 4^3$ **(b)** $\frac{42^2}{6^2}$ **(c)** $\frac{6^3}{9^3}$

(d) $3^3 \times 2^3$ **(e)** $\frac{24^4}{8^4}$ **(f)** $\frac{35^2}{42^2}$

(g) $\frac{6^2 \times 6^4}{2^3 \times 3^3}$ **(h)** $\frac{3^2 \times 2^4 \times 3^5}{6^4}$ **(i)** $\frac{(3^2)^3 \times 4^6}{2^6}$

(j) $\dfrac{2^9 \times 3^5}{2^2 \times 6^5}$ **(k)** $\dfrac{6^7}{6^2 \times 3^3 \times 2^3}$ **(l)** $\dfrac{3^6 \times 4^4}{3^2 \times 2^4}$

(m) $\dfrac{4^5 \times 3^5}{2^3 \times 2^2}$ **(n)** $\dfrac{6^7}{3^2 \times 3^3 \times 2^7}$ **(o)** $\dfrac{4^{10}}{(2^3)^2 \times 2^4}$

(p) $\dfrac{4^7 \times 3^4}{4^3 \times 6^4}$ **(q)** $\dfrac{5^3 \times 2^5 \times 3^3}{2^2}$ **(r)** $\left(\dfrac{3}{2}\right)^5 \times \dfrac{6^5}{3^2}$

3. Use a calculator to verify the following.

(a) $(-7)^3 \times (-7)^2 = (-7)^5$ **(b)** $\dfrac{(-3)^6}{(-3)^4} = (-3)^2$

(c) $[(-5)^2]^3 = (-5)^6$ **(d)** $(-3)^4 \times (-5)^4 = [(-3) \times (-5)]^4$

(e) $\dfrac{(-2)^3}{(-7)^3} = \left(\dfrac{-2}{-7}\right)^3$

4. **(a)** Write the value of $\left(\dfrac{2}{3}\right)^4$ as a fraction.

(b) Simplify $\left(\dfrac{2}{3}\right)^6 \times \left(\dfrac{2}{3}\right)^{10}$ as a power of $\dfrac{2}{3}$.

1.2 ZERO AND NEGATIVE INTEGRAL INDICES

We have seen in section 1.1 the second law of indices:

$$\frac{a^m}{a^n} = a^{m-n}, \ (m > n).$$

The condition $m > n$ can be omitted if we include the use of zero and negative indices in this law. But what do zero and negative indices mean? Let us look at the following examples.

Examples

(a) What is the meaning of (i) 2^0 and (ii) 3^0?

(i) Let us assume that $\dfrac{a^m}{a^n} = a^{m-n}$ is true for $m = n$, and take $m = 3$, $n = 3$ and $a = 2$, then

$$\frac{2^3}{2^3} = 2^{3-3}$$

$$1 = 2^0$$

or

$$2^0 = 1$$

(ii) Similarly, if we take $m = 5$, $n = 5$ and $a = 3$, then

$$\frac{3^5}{3^5} = 3^{5-5}$$

$$1 = 3^0 \quad \text{or} \quad 3^0 = 1$$

In general,

$$\mathbf{a^0 = 1 \qquad (a \neq 0)}$$

(b) What is the meaning of (i) 7^{-2} and (ii) 6^{-5}?

(i) Let us assume that $\frac{a^m}{a^n} = a^{m-n}$ is true for $m < n$, and take $m = 3$, $n = 5$ and $a = 7$, then

$$\frac{7^3}{7^5} = 7^{3-5}$$

$$\frac{7 \times 7 \times 7}{7 \times 7 \times 7 \times 7 \times 7} = 7^{-2}$$

$$\frac{1}{7^2} = 7^{-2} \quad \text{or} \quad 7^{-2} = \frac{1}{7^2}$$

(ii) Similarly, if we take $m = 2$, $n = 7$ and $a = 6$, then

$$\frac{6^2}{6^7} = 6^{2-7}$$

$$\frac{6 \times 6}{6 \times 6 \times 6 \times 6 \times 6 \times 6 \times 6} = 6^{-5}$$

$$\frac{1}{6^5} = 6^{-5} \quad \text{or} \quad 6^{-5} = \frac{1}{6^5}$$

In general,

$$\mathbf{a^{-n} = \frac{1}{a^n} \qquad (a \neq 0)}$$

Listed below are the definitions for a^0 and a^{-n} and the five laws of indices that we have learnt:

Definitions	Laws of Indices
$a^0 = 1$ $a^{-n} = \frac{1}{a^n}$	**Law 1:** $a^m \times a^n = a^{m+n}$ **Law 2:** $\frac{a^m}{a^n} = a^{m-n}$ **Law 3:** $(a^m)^n = a^{mn}$ **Law 4:** $a^m \times b^m = (ab)^m$ **Law 5:** $\frac{a^m}{b^m} = \left(\frac{a}{b}\right)^m$

It can be shown that all the five laws of indices apply to zero and negative indices and **also to negative bases, but the base of a^{-n} or $\frac{1}{a^n}$ must not be zero since 0^{-n} or $\frac{1}{0^n}$ is undefined.**

Worked Example 1

Simplify the following and show your answers in positive index form.

(a) $\dfrac{3^5 \times 3^{-3}}{3^9}$ **(b)** $\dfrac{7^{10}}{7^2 \times 7^{-3}}$

(c) $2^{-5} \times 3^7 \times 3^{-2} \times 2^2$ **(d)** $\dfrac{(-7)^9}{3^0 \times 3^{-8} \times (-7)^{-3}}$

Solution:

(a)
$$\begin{aligned}\frac{3^5 \times 3^{-3}}{3^9} &= \frac{3^{5+(-3)}}{3^9}\\ &= \frac{3^2}{3^9}\\ &= 3^{2-9}\\ &= 3^{-7}\\ &= \frac{1}{3^7}\end{aligned}$$

(b)
$$\begin{aligned}\frac{7^{10}}{7^2 \times 7^{-3}} &= \frac{7^{10}}{7^{2+(-3)}}\\ &= \frac{7^{10}}{7^{-1}}\\ &= 7^{10-(-1)}\\ &= 7^{10+1}\\ &= 7^{11}\end{aligned}$$

(c)
$$\begin{aligned}2^{-5} \times 3^7 \times 3^{-2} \times 2^2 &= 2^{-5} \times 2^2 \times 3^7 \times 3^{-2}\\ &= 2^{(-5)+2} \times 3^{7+(-2)}\\ &= 2^{-3} \times 3^5\\ &= \frac{1}{2^3} \times 3^5\\ &= \frac{3^5}{2^3}\end{aligned}$$

(d)
$$\begin{aligned}\frac{(-7)^9}{3^0 \times 3^{-8} \times (-7)^{-3}} &= \frac{(-7)^{9-(-3)}}{3^{-8}}\\ &= \frac{(-7)^{12}}{\frac{1}{3^8}}\\ &= (-7)^{12} \times 3^8 = 7^{12} \times 3^8\end{aligned}$$

Worked Example 2

Evaluate the following.

(a) $3^{-3} \times 4^{-3}$

(b) $\dfrac{10^{-3}}{5^{-3}}$

(c) $\dfrac{3^2 \times 6^{-3}}{10^{-3} \times 5^2}$

Solution:

(a) $3^{-3} \times 4^{-3} = (3 \times 4)^{-3}$
$= 12^{-3}$
$= \dfrac{1}{12^3}$
$= \dfrac{1}{1\ 728}$

(b) $\dfrac{10^{-3}}{5^{-3}} = \left(\dfrac{10}{5}\right)^{-3}$
$= 2^{-3}$
$= \dfrac{1}{2^3}$
$= \dfrac{1}{8}$

(c) $\dfrac{3^2 \times 6^{-3}}{10^{-3} \times 5^2} = \dfrac{3^2}{5^2} \times \dfrac{6^{-3}}{10^{-3}}$
$= \dfrac{3^2}{5^2} \times \left(\dfrac{6}{10}\right)^{-3}$
$= \dfrac{3^2}{5^2} \times \left(\dfrac{3}{5}\right)^{-3}$
$= \dfrac{3^2}{5^2} \times \dfrac{3^{-3}}{5^{-3}}$
$= \dfrac{3^{2+(-3)}}{5^{2+(-3)}}$
$= \dfrac{3^{-1}}{5^{-1}}$
$= \left(\dfrac{3}{5}\right)^{-1}$
$= \dfrac{1}{\frac{3}{5}}$
$= \dfrac{5}{3}$
$= 1\dfrac{2}{3}$

Questions:
For non-zero bases, are the following true?

$\left(\dfrac{a}{b}\right)^{-1} = \dfrac{b}{a}$

$\left(\dfrac{a}{b}\right)^{-2} = \left(\dfrac{b}{a}\right)^2$

Note: The solutions can be presented in fewer steps if mental calculation is used.

Alternative solution:

(c) $\dfrac{3^2 \times 6^{-3}}{10^{-3} \times 5^2} = \left(\dfrac{3}{5}\right)^2 \times \left(\dfrac{6}{10}\right)^{-3}$

$= \left(\dfrac{3}{5}\right)^2 \times \left(\dfrac{3}{5}\right)^{-3}$

$= \left(\dfrac{3}{5}\right)^{2+(-3)}$

$= \left(\dfrac{3}{5}\right)^{-1}$

$= \dfrac{5}{3}$

$= 1\dfrac{2}{3}$

Note: This solution shows that the laws of indices still apply even if the base is *not* an integer.

Exercise 1.2

answers on p. 425

1. Simplify the following and express your answers in positive index form.

(a) $11^{-3} \times 11^5$ **(b)** $\dfrac{7^{-7}}{7^9}$ **(c)** $(5^4)^{-3}$

(d) $5^{-5} \times 5^2$ **(e)** $\dfrac{3^{-4}}{3^{-6}}$ **(f)** $(7^{-2})^{-3}$

(g) $7^{-2} \times 7^0$ **(h)** $\dfrac{5^0}{5^4}$ **(i)** $(3^{-4})^2$

(j) $\dfrac{2^2 \times 2^{-6}}{2^3}$ **(k)** $\dfrac{3^8}{3^2 \times 3^{-4}}$ **(l)** $(3^4 \times 3^0)^3$

(m) $\dfrac{5^{-6} \times 5^2}{5^{-7}}$ **(n)** $\dfrac{7^{-7}}{7^{-2} \times 7^4}$ **(o)** $(2^{-3} \times 2^7)^2$

(p) $\dfrac{7^{-2} \times 7^8}{7^{12}}$ **(q)** $\dfrac{5^{-10}}{5^2 \times 5^4}$ **(r)** $(5^8 \times 5^{-4})^{-3}$

2. Simplify the following and express your answers in positive index form.

(a) $5^{-5} \times 5^{-6} \times 2^7 \times 2^{-3}$ **(b)** $\dfrac{5^5}{3^8 \times 5^3 \times 3^{-7}}$

(c) $7^{20} \times 11^{-7} \times 7^{-22} \times 11^9$ **(d)** $\dfrac{7^0}{7^2 \times 17^3 \times 17^0}$

(e) $2^7 \times 5^4 \times 5^0 \times 2^{-9}$ **(f)** $\dfrac{5^2 \times 2^{14} \times 5^{-4}}{2^{-6}}$

(g) $\dfrac{3^{-6} \times 3^2}{2^{-4} \times 2^6}$ **(h)** $\dfrac{7^{-8} \times 3^{-9} \times 7^4}{3^7}$

(i) $\dfrac{5^{-10} \times 5^{15}}{7^2 \times 7^{-4}}$ **(j)** $\dfrac{5^{-10} \times 11^7 \times 5^4}{11^{-4}}$

(k) $\dfrac{2^{-8} \times 2^{-4}}{7^6 \times 7^4}$ **(l)** $\dfrac{2^3 \times 7^{-10} \times 2^{-8}}{7^2}$

3. Evaluate the following.

(a) $3^{-2} \times 5^{-2}$ **(b)** $\dfrac{10^{-5}}{2^{-5}}$ **(c)** $\dfrac{9^{-3}}{6^{-3}}$

(d) $2^{-5} \times 3^{-5}$ **(e)** $\dfrac{8^{-4}}{4^{-4}}$ **(f)** $\dfrac{2^3 \times 4^{-4}}{6^{-4} \times 5^3}$

(g) $4^{-3} \times 3^{-3}$ **(h)** $\dfrac{6^{-5}}{2^{-5}}$ **(i)** $\dfrac{3^3 \times 4^3}{2^{-3} \times 5^{-3}}$

(j) $5^{-2} \times 6^{-2}$ **(k)** $\dfrac{2^{-2}}{6^{-2}}$ **(l)** $\dfrac{3^{-3} \times 3^4}{5^{-3} \times 2^4}$

4. Simplify the following and express your answers in positive index with a positive base.

(a) $(-3)^4 \times (-3)^3$ **(b)** $(-2)^6 \times (-2)^{-4}$ **(c)** $(-2)^5 \times (2)^5$
(d) $(-3)^{-4} \times (-2)^{-4}$ **(e)** $(-5)^7 \div (-5)^3$ **(f)** $(-6)^4 \div (-3)^4$

5. Evaluate the following.

(a) $\left[\dfrac{15}{8} - \left(\dfrac{4}{5}\right)^{-1}\right] + \left(\dfrac{5}{2}\right)^{-1}$ **(b)** $\dfrac{5^{-1}}{3} \times \left(\dfrac{8}{15}\right)^{-4} \times \left(\dfrac{15}{16}\right)^{-3}$

1.3 INDICES INVOLVING VARIABLES

A variable is a symbol, usually a letter, that represents numbers.

Worked Example 1

Simplify the following.

(a) $(a^3)(a^5)(a^7)$ **(b)** $(p^2q^3)(q^4p^6)$

(c) $\dfrac{t^4}{t^2}$ **(d)** $(x^2)^3(x^5)$

Solution:

(a) $(a^3)(a^5)(a^7) = a^{3+5+7}$
$= a^{15}$

(b) $(p^2q^3)(q^4p^6) = (p^{2+6})(q^{3+4})$
$= p^8q^7$

(c) $\dfrac{t^4}{t^2} = t^{4-2}$
$= t^2$

(d) $(x^2)^3(x^5) = (x^{2\times 3})(x^5)$
$= x^{6+5}$
$= x^{11}$

Worked Example 2

Simplify the following and express your answers in positive index form.

(a) $(a^3)(a^{-5})(a^4)$ **(b)** $(r^3s^4)(s^{-6}r^0)$

(c) $\dfrac{(-x)^9}{x^{15}}$ **(d)** $(y^2)^2(y^{-5})$

Solution:

(a) $(a^3)(a^{-5})(a^4) = a^{3+(-5)+4}$
$= a^2$

(b) $(r^3s^4)(s^{-6}r^0) = (r^3s^4)(s^{-6} \times 1)$
$= r^3 \times s^{4+(-6)}$
$= r^3 \times s^{-2}$
$= r^3 \times \dfrac{1}{s^2}$
$= \dfrac{r^3}{s^2}$

(c) $\dfrac{(-x)^9}{x^{15}} = \dfrac{-x^9}{x^{15}}$ Note: $(-x)^9 = -x^9$
$= -x^{9-15}$
$= -x^{-6}$
$= -\dfrac{1}{x^6}$

(d) $(y^2)^2(y^{-5}) = (y^{2\times 2})(y^{-5})$
$= (y^4)(y^{-5})$
$= y^{-1}$
$= \dfrac{1}{y}$

Exercise 1.3

answers on p. 425

1. Simplify the following.

(a) $(a^2)(a^3)(a^4)$ **(b)** $(p^3)(p^4)(p^6)$
(c) $(x^5)(x^6)(x^2)$ **(d)** $(b^2)(b^4)(b^6)$
(e) $(y^3)(y^5)(y^7)(y^9)$ **(f)** $(a^2b^3)(b^4a^3)$
(g) $(x^4y^3)(y^6x^8)$ **(h)** $(m^3n^5)(m^7n^9)$
(i) $(p^4q^2)(q^3p^5)$ **(j)** $(r^2s^3t^3)(r^3s^4t^2)(r^3s^4t^5)$
(k) $\dfrac{a^3}{a^2}$ **(l)** $\dfrac{(-t)^5}{(-t)^3}$
(m) $\dfrac{a^4}{a^2}$ **(n)** $\dfrac{x^5}{x^2}$
(o) $\dfrac{(-a)^2b^5}{(-b)^2}$ **(p)** $\dfrac{m^7n^3}{m^2}$
(q) $(a^2)^3(a^4)$ **(r)** $(b^3)^2(b^3)$
(s) $(x^4)^2(x^3)$ **(t)** $(y^3)(y^2)^4$
(u) $(m^4)(m^2)^3$

2. Simplify the following and express your answers in positive index form.

(a) $(a^{-2})(a^{-3})(a^{4})$ **(b)** $(b^{5})(b^{6})(b^{-7})$ **(c)** $(c^{-8})(c^{6})(c^{-2})$

(d) $(p^{3})(p^{4})(p^{-6})(p^{0})$ **(e)** $(a^{2}b^{-3})(b^{-4}a^{4})$ **(f)** $(r^{-5}s^{-2})(s^{5}r^{-2})$

(g) $(x^{-10}y^{7})(y^{-8}x^{4})$ **(h)** $(p^{4}q^{-3})(q^{7}p^{-6})$ **(i)** $(t^{4}u^{-8})(u^{5}t^{0})(t^{-5}u^{0})$

(j) $\dfrac{b^{-2}}{b^{4}}$ **(k)** $\dfrac{p^{-6}}{p^{-4}}$ **(l)** $\dfrac{q^{-7}}{q^{-7}}$

(m) $\dfrac{r^{-6}}{r^{6}}$ **(n)** $\dfrac{a^{2}b^{-5}}{b^{2}}$ **(o)** $\dfrac{x^{-7}y^{5}}{x^{-2}}$

(p) $\dfrac{p^{-3}q^{-4}}{q^{5}}$ **(q)** $\dfrac{s^{5}t^{-7}}{t^{2}}$ **(r)** $\dfrac{u^{0}v^{4}}{u^{-2}}$

(s) $(u^{-2})^{3}(u)^{4}$ **(t)** $(w^{3})^{-2}(w)^{2}$ **(u)** $(x^{-4})^{-2}(x)^{2}$

(v) $(y^{4})^{4}(y^{-2})$ **(w)** $(z^{0})^{4}(z^{5})$ **(x)** $(r^{-11})^{0}(r^{0})^{50}$

1.4 STANDARD FORM

Scientists often use very large or very small measurements in their work.

For example, the distance of the sun from the earth as measured by an astronomer is about 149 000 000 km and the diameter of a yellow fever virus as measured by a biologist is about 0.000 018 mm.

Large numbers can be written in index form. This can be done in many ways. For example,

$$149\,000\,000 = 149 \times 1\,000\,000 = 149 \times 10^{6}$$
$$149\,000\,000 = 14.9 \times 10\,000\,000 = 14.9 \times 10^{7}$$
$$149\,000\,000 = 1.49 \times 100\,000\,000 = 1.49 \times 10^{8}$$
$$149\,000\,000 = 0.149 \times 1\,000\,000\,000 = 0.149 \times 10^{9}$$

Scientists adopt the form 1.49×10^{8} for 149 000 000 and refer to this as the **standard form** or **scientific notation**. The standard form is written as a product of a number and a power of 10, where the number must be less than 10 but not less than 1. Symbolically, this form is expressed as **$A \times 10^{n}$ where $1 \leqslant A < 10$ and n is an integer.**

Standard form, also called scientific notation, is a number written as the product of a number between one (inclusive) and ten and a power of ten.

Small numbers can also be written in the standard form. For example, to express 0.000 018 mm in standard form, we write

$$\begin{aligned} 0.000\,018 \text{ mm} &= \frac{18}{1\,000\,000} \text{ mm} \\ &= \frac{1.8}{100\,000} \text{ mm} \\ &= \frac{1.8}{10^{5}} \text{ mm} \\ &= 1.8 \times 10^{-5} \text{ mm} \end{aligned}$$

Suppose the population of a town is 759 980 and is rounded off to 760 000. This figure does not tell us exactly how many significant figures it has unless indicated. One way to indicate the number of significant figures is by using scientific notation. For example,

(a) 760 000, if correct to 2 significant figures, is written as 7.6×10^5.
(b) 760 000, if correct to 3 significant figures, is written as 7.60×10^5.
(c) 760 000, if correct to 4 significant figures, is written as 7.600×10^5.

Significant figures are the digits that are important in showing us the degree of accuracy.

Class Activity 2

1. Copy and complete the table below. Put in the table below 'T' to indicate true and 'F' to indicate false.

Number *A*	*A* is greater than or equal to 1	*A* is less than 10	*A* is greater than or equal to 1 and less than 10
(a) 2.12	T	T	T
(b) 12.01	T	F	F
(c) 1.0	T	T	T
(d) 0.17	F	T	F
(e) 9.36	T	T	
(f) 1.00	T	T	
(g) 0.37	F		F
(h) 10.00	T		F
(i) 5.07		T	T
(j) 3.00		T	T
(k) 0.06	F		
(l) 14.01			
(m) 8.88			
(n) 1.000			

2. Express the following in the form 10^n, where n is an integer.

(a) $\dfrac{10^3}{10^3}$ **(b)** $\dfrac{10^5}{10^6}$ **(c)** $\dfrac{10^{-5}}{10^8}$

(d) $\dfrac{10^7}{10^{-3}}$ **(e)** $\dfrac{10^{12}}{10^{-15}}$ **(f)** $\dfrac{10^{-6}}{10^{-9}}$

(g) $\dfrac{10^3 \times 10^5}{10^5}$ **(h)** $\dfrac{10^{-8} \times 10^2}{10^5}$ **(i)** $\dfrac{10^7}{10^{-2} \times 10^5}$

(j) $\dfrac{10^8 \times 10^{-11}}{10^3 \times 10^{-9}}$ **(k)** $\dfrac{10^{-2} \times 10^{-5}}{10^{-8} \times 10^{-12}}$ **(l)** $\dfrac{10^{-3} \times 10}{10^{-7} \times 10^3}$

3. Which of the following numbers are in the form $A \times 10^n$, where $1 \leqslant A < 10$ and n is an integer?

(a) 9.26×10^5 **(b)** 24.32×10^{-5} **(c)** 1.00×10^{-4}
(d) 3.001×10^6 **(e)** 10.26×10^5 **(f)** 0.16×10^2
(g) 4.20×10^{-5} **(h)** 9×10^{-1} **(i)** 1×10^{10}

Worked Example 1

Express the following in ordinary notation.

(a) 5.82×10^3 **(b)** 72×10^{-2} **(c)** 0.023×10^{-4}

Solution:

(a) $5.82 \times 10^3 = 5.82 \times 1\,000$
$= 5\,820$

(b) $72 \times 10^{-2} = 72 \times \frac{1}{10^2}$
$= \frac{72}{10^2}$
$= \frac{72}{100}$
$= 0.72$

(c) $0.023 \times 10^{-4} = 0.023 \times \frac{1}{10^4}$
$= \frac{0.023}{10^4}$
$= \frac{0.023}{10\,000}$
$= 0.000\,002\,3$

Worked Example 2

Rewrite the following in the form $A \times 10^n$, where $1 \leqslant A < 10$ and n is an integer.

(a) 182.3
(b) 0.003 5
(c) 32 000 000 (correct to 2 significant figures)
(d) 32 000 000 (correct to 3 significant figures)

Solution:

(a) $182.3 = 1.823 \times 100$
$= 1.823 \times 10^2$

(b) $0.003\,5 = 3.5 \times \frac{1}{1\,000}$
$= 3.5 \times \frac{1}{10^3}$
$= 3.5 \times 10^{-3}$

(c) $32\,000\,000 = 3.2 \times 10\,000\,000$
$= 3.2 \times 10^7$

(d) $32\,000\,000 = 3.20 \times 10\,000\,000$
$= 3.20 \times 10^7$

Worked Example 3

Express the following in standard form.

(a) 0.312×10^3

(b) 121×10^{-2}

(c) 24.3×10^{-3}

Solution:

(a) $0.312 \times 10^3 = 3.12 \times \frac{1}{10} \times 10^3$
$= 3.12 \times 10^{-1} \times 10^3$
$= 3.12 \times 10^2$

(b) $121 \times 10^{-2} = 1.21 \times 100 \times 10^{-2}$
$= 1.21 \times 10^2 \times 10^{-2}$
$= 1.21 \times 10^0$

(c) $24.3 \times 10^{-3} = 2.43 \times 10 \times 10^{-3}$
$= 2.43 \times 10^{-2}$

Reminder:
$10 = 10^1$
So
$10 \times 10^{-3} = 10^1 \times 10^{-3}$
$= 10^{-2}$

Worked Example 4

Evaluate the following and express the answers in standard form.

(a) $\dfrac{117 \times 10^{-3}}{6 \times 10^4}$

(b) $4.2 \times 10^3 + 3 \times 10^4$

(c) $3.1 \times 10^4 \times 4 \times 10^3$

Solution:

(a) $\dfrac{117 \times 10^{-3}}{6 \times 10^4} = \dfrac{117 \times 10^{-3} \times 10^{-4}}{6}$
$= 19.5 \times 10^{-7}$
$= (1.95 \times 10) \times 10^{-7}$
$= 1.95 \times 10^{-6}$

(b) $4.2 \times 10^3 + 3 \times 10^4 = 4.2 \times 10^3 + 30 \times 10^3$
$= (4.2 + 30)10^3$
$= 34.2 \times 10^3$
$= 3.42 \times 10^4$

(c) $3.1 \times 10^4 \times 4 \times 10^3 = 3.1 \times 4 \times 10^4 \times 10^3$
$= 12.4 \times 10^7$
$= 1.24 \times 10^8$

Note: For (b), rewrite the expression with the same power of 10 in each term before extracting the common factor.

Exercise 1.4

answers on p. 425

1. Express the following in ordinary notation (without indices).

(a) 5×10^5 **(b)** 4.28×10^{-4} **(c)** 1.690×10^{18}
(d) 5.01×10^8 **(e)** 2.386×10^5 **(f)** 7.75×10^3
(g) 1.2×10^{-9} **(h)** 2.01×10^{-6} **(i)** 3.50×10^7

2. Rewrite the following in the form $A \times 10^n$, where $1 \leqslant A < 10$ and n is an integer.

(a) 123.1
(b) 0.012
(c) 0.003 4
(d) 32.12
(e) 0.300 1
(f) 3 400 000 000 (correct to 2 significant figures)
(g) 3 400 000 000 (correct to 3 significant figures)
(h) 3 400 000 000 (correct to 6 significant figures)

3. Express the following in standard form.

(a) 235×10^2 **(b)** 129×10^4
(c) 12.45×10^3 **(d)** 29.03×10^4
(e) 0.123×10^3 **(f)** 0.23×10^2
(g) 212×10^{-2} **(h)** 912×10^{-3}
(i) 42.36×10^{-3} **(j)** 58.04×10^{-4}
(k) 0.421×10^{-3} **(l)** 0.042×10^{-2}

4. Multiply 6.32×10^4 by 7.71×10^{-3}, giving your answer in the form $A \times 10^n$ where $1 \leqslant A < 10$ and n is an integer. Give your answer correct to three significant figures.

5. Find the value of $\frac{2p}{q}$ when $p = 3.12 \times 10^{-5}$ and $q = 1.24 \times 10^{-7}$. Express your answer in the form $A \times 10^n$, where $1 \leqslant A < 10$ and n is an integer. Give your answer correct to three significant figures.

6. Express the following in standard form. Give the answers correct to three significant figures.

(a) $\dfrac{12.4 \times 10^3}{9 \times 10^{-2}}$ **(b)** $\dfrac{308.4 \times 10^{-6}}{17 \times 10^3}$

(c) $\dfrac{2.008 \times 10^{-8}}{4.02 \times 10^{-6}}$ **(d)** $\dfrac{30.7 \times 10^{-2} \times 123 \times 10^4}{4.23 \times 10^{-3}}$

(e) $\dfrac{3.14 \times 10^{-3} \times 1.26}{3.47 \times 10^{-7} \times 131 \times 10^2}$ **(f)** $\dfrac{1.21 \times 10^{-2} \times 1.31 \times 10^{-1}}{33 \times 10^{-7} \times 101 \times 10^5}$

7. **(a)** Express the speed of light which is $2.997\,9 \times 10^{10}$ cm/s in ordinary notation.

(b) In 1.008 g of hydrogen there are about 606 000 000 000 000 000 000 000 atoms. Express this in scientific notation. Give your answer correct to three significant figures.

(c) The edges of a rectangular block are of lengths 2 cm, 5 cm and 7 cm. Calculate its volume in cubic metres. Express your answer in standard form.

8. Evaluate the following and express the answers in scientific notation.

(a) $850 \times 0.000\,2 \times 100\,000$ (correct to 2 significant figures)
(b) $5.82 \times 0.05 \times 10\,000$ (correct to 3 significant figures)
(c) $9.004 \times 19.4 \times 100\,000$ (correct to 3 significant figures)
(d) $1.634 \times 22.42 \times 0.000\,001$ (correct to 2 significant figures)
(e) $6.401 \times 1.24 \times 0.000\,1$ (correct to 2 significant figures)

9. Evaluate the following and express the answers in standard form.

(a) $2.4 \times 10^4 + 4 \times 10^5$
(b) $2.4 \times 10^4 \times 4 \times 10^5$
(c) $24.3 \times 10^2 + 3 \times 10^3$
(d) $24.3 \times 10^2 \times 3 \times 10^3$
(e) $34.4 \times 10^{-4} + 6 \times 10^{-2}$
(f) $34.4 \times 10^{-4} \times 6 \times 10^{-2}$
(g) $1.02 \times 10^3 + 2.01 \times 10^4$
(h) $1.02 \times 10^3 \times 2.01 \times 10^4$
(i) $1.2 \times 10^{-3} + 2.1 \times 10^{-4}$
(j) $1.2 \times 10^{-3} \times 2.1 \times 10^{-4}$

Chapter Review

The Law of Indices

If m and n are integers and a and b are non-zero numbers, then:

- $a^m \times a^n = a^{m+n}$
- $\dfrac{a^m}{a^n} = a^{m-n}$
- $(a^m)^n = a^{mn}$
- $a^m \times b^m = (a \times b)^m$
- $\dfrac{a^m}{b^m} = \left(\dfrac{a}{b}\right)^m$
- $a^0 = 1$
- $a^{-n} = \dfrac{1}{a^n}$

The standard form or the scientific notation is written as $A \times 10^n$, where $1 \leqslant A < 10$ and n is an integer.

CHALLENGER 1

1. Evaluate $(81)^{-4(2^{-2})}$.

2. Find the value of x in $\left(\frac{2}{3}\right)^{-x} \times \left(\frac{8}{9}\right)^{x} = 2\frac{10}{27}$.

3. If $x * y$ means x^y, find the value of each of the following.
   (a) $3 * 2$
   (b) $2 * 3$
   (c) $(4 * 2) * 3$
   (d) $4 * (2 * 3)$

4. **(a)** If $25^x = 125^2$, find the value of x.
   (b) If $3^{2x} \times 9^{2x-3} = 1$, find the value of x.

5. If $A = 16^{18}$ and $B = 18^{16}$, determine, without using a calculator, which of these expressions has a greater value. $\left(\textit{Hint:} \text{ Find out whether the value of } \frac{A}{B} \text{ is greater than 1.}\right)$

6. Without evaluating the exact values, arrange the following in ascending order.

$$2^{100},\ 3^{75},\ 5^{50}$$

Problem Solving 1

Looking for Substitutes

$$\begin{array}{r} PLAY \\ +\ PLAY \\ \hline WASTE \\ \hline \end{array}$$

Substitute a digit chosen from 1 to 8 for each letter so that the addition is correct.

Rule: Replace the same letter by the same digit and different letters by different digits.

We infer that $W = 1$, $P = 6$ or 7 or 8. Now let us use the strategy of **guessing and checking** to solve the puzzle as follows:

- Try $P = 6$, $A = 2$, $L = 3$ or 4

$$\begin{array}{r} 6\;3\;2\;Y \\ +\quad 6\;3\;2\;Y \\ \hline 1\;2\;S\;T\;E \end{array} \qquad\qquad \begin{array}{r} 6\;4\;2\;Y \\ +\quad 6\;4\;2\;Y \\ \hline 1\;2\;8\;T\;E \end{array}$$

This trial fails since $S \neq 6$.

This trial fails since $T \neq 4$, and if $T = 5$, then $Y = 7$ and $E = 4$ (not admissible).

- Try $P = 6$, $A = 3$, $L = 7$ or 8

$$\begin{array}{r} {}^{1}6\;7\;3\;Y \\ +\quad 6\;7\;3\;Y \\ \hline 1\;3\;4\;T\;E \end{array} \qquad\qquad \begin{array}{r} {}^{1}6\;8\;3\;Y \\ +\quad 6\;8\;3\;Y \\ \hline 1\;3\;S\;T\;E \end{array}$$

This trial fails since $T \neq 6$ and $T \neq 7$.

This trial fails since $S \neq 6$.

- Try $P = 7$, $A = 4$, $L = 2$ or 3

$$\begin{array}{r} 7\;2\;4\;Y \\ +\quad 7\;2\;4\;Y \\ \hline 1\;4\;S\;T\;E \end{array} \qquad\qquad \begin{array}{r} 7\;3\;4\;Y \\ +\quad 7\;3\;4\;Y \\ \hline 1\;4\;6\;T\;E \end{array}$$

This trial fails since $S \neq 4$.

This trial fails since $T \neq 9$, and if $T = 8$, then $Y = 2$ and $E = 4$ (not admissible).

- Try $P = 7$, $A = 5$, $L = 6$ or 8

$$\begin{array}{r} {}^{1}7\;{}^{1}6\;5\;Y \\ +\quad 7\;6\;5\;Y \\ \hline 1\;5\;3\;T\;E \end{array} \qquad\qquad \begin{array}{r} {}^{1}7\;{}^{1}8\;5\;Y \\ +\quad 7\;8\;5\;Y \\ \hline 1\;5\;S\;T\;E \end{array}$$

This trial fails since $T \neq 0$ and $T \neq 1$.

This trial fails since $S \neq 7$.

- Try $P = 8$, $A = 6$, $L = 2$ or 3 or 4

$$\begin{array}{r} 8\;{}^{1}2\;{}^{1}6\;7 \\ +\quad 8\;2\;6\;7 \\ \hline 1\;6\;5\;3\;4 \end{array}$$

This trial is successful.

Looking back

Are there alternative solutions?
What if the condition of excluding the digits 0 and 9 is removed?

1. **Be Creative** Substitute a digit for each letter so as to make the following addition correct. (The same letter stands for the same digit. Different letters stand for different digits.)

$$\begin{array}{r} THINK \\ +\ THINK \\ \hline CREATE \\ \hline \end{array}$$

2. **The Right Order** Insert the appropriate brackets to make the following statement true.

$$5 - 1 \times 4 - 3 + 6 \div 8 = 7$$

3. **Last Digit** What is the last digit (i.e. the digit at the ones place) of 7^{100}?

4. **How Many Pages?** The number of digits used to number a book from page 1 to page 11 is 13 (e.g. 9 + 2 + 2). How many pages are there in a book if 2 862 digits are used to number its pages?

Chapter 2

Algebraic Manipulations

Chapter Highlights

- Using diagrams to establish special algebraic rules: $(a + b)^2 = a^2 + 2ab + b^2$, $(a - b)^2 = a^2 - 2ab + b^2$ and $a^2 - b^2 = (a + b)(a - b)$ where a and b are positive numbers and use these rules for calculations
- Using the distributive rule to establish the rules $a(b + c + d) = ab + ac + ad$ and $(a + b)(c + d) = ac + ad + bc + bd$
- Expanding products of algebraic expressions
- Using the distributive rule to factorise algebraic expressions, including use of brackets for grouping
- Expressing algebraic expressions in the forms $a^2 + 2ab + b^2$, $a^2 - 2ab + b^2$ and $a^2 - b^2$
- Factorising algebraic expressions of the forms $a^2 + 2ab + b^2$, $a^2 - 2ab + b^2$ and $a^2 - b^2$
- Demonstrating an understanding of the ideas of multiple and LCM of arithmetic and algebraic expressions
- Manipulating simple algebraic fractions
- Solving fractional equations involving numerical and linear algebraic denominators

2.1 SPECIAL ALGEBRAIC RULES FOR CALCULATIONS

Very often, algebraic manipulation can be explained with the aid of geometrical figures. The exercises given below illustrate this.

Class Activity 1

1. The figure on the right is a square made up of four parts A, B, C and D. The sides of the square are each $(a + b)$ units. Therefore the area is $(a + b)(a + b)$ or $(a + b)^2$ square units.
   (a) Is the area of A equal to a^2 square units?
   (b) Is the area of B equal to ab square units?
   (c) Is the area of C equal to ab square units?
   (d) Is the area of D equal to b^2 square units?
   (e) Is $(a + b)^2 = a^2 + ab + ab + b^2$ true?
   (f) Do you agree that $(a + b)^2 = a^2 + 2ab + b^2$?

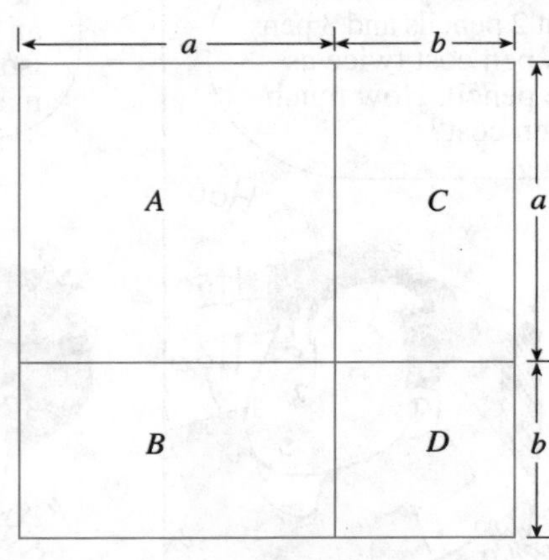

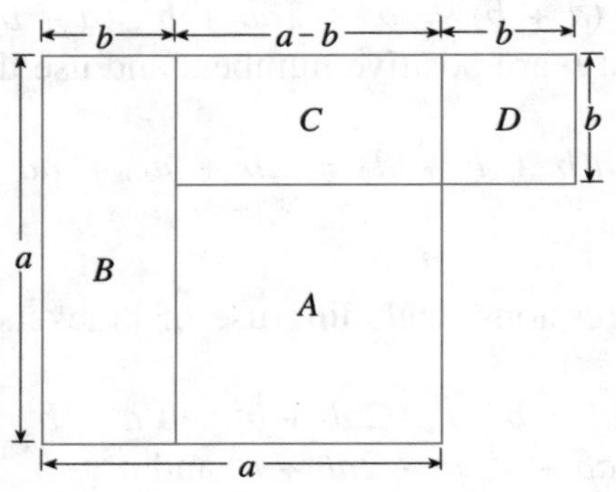

2. The figure on the left is made up of four parts A, B, C and D. The area of the square made up of A, B and C is a^2 square units.
   The area of D is b^2 square units. Therefore the total area of the figure is $(a^2 + b^2)$ square units.
   (a) Is the area of A equal to $(a - b)^2$ square units?
   (b) Is the area of B equal to ab square units?
   (c) Is the area of the rectangle made up of C and D equal to ab square units?
   (d) Is $a^2 + b^2 = (a - b)^2 + ab + ab$ true?
   (e) Is $(a - b)^2 = a^2 - 2ab + b^2$ true?

3. A small square (B) of area b^2 square units is removed from a bigger square of area a^2 square units as shown in the figure on the right. The area of the remaining figure (A) is $(a^2 - b^2)$ square units.

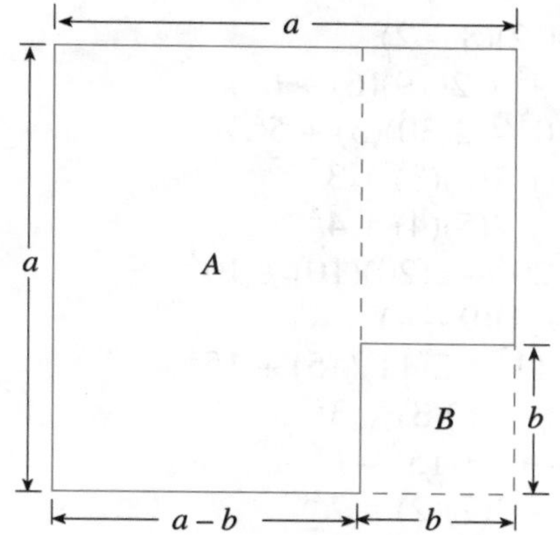

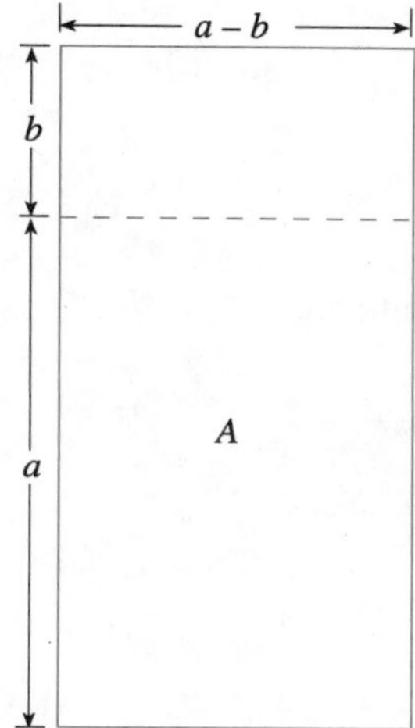

Suppose part A is cut into two portions and rearranged to form a rectangle as shown in the figure on the left.

(a) Is the area of the newly formed rectangle equal to $(a + b)(a - b)$ square units?

(b) Is $a^2 - b^2 = (a + b)(a - b)$ true?

The above exercises suggest the following three special algebraic rules for calculations:

$$(a + b)^2 = a^2 + 2ab + b^2$$
$$(a - b)^2 = a^2 - 2ab + b^2$$
$$a^2 - b^2 = (a + b)(a - b)$$

Class Activity 2

1. For each of the sentences from (a) to (u), state which of the following algebraic rules it belongs to:

(i) $(a + b)^2 = a^2 + 2ab + b^2$,
(ii) $(a - b)^2 = a^2 - 2ab + b^2$,
(iii) $a^2 - b^2 = (a + b)(a - b)$.

(a) $(7 + 2)^2 = 7^2 + 2(7)(2) + 2^2$
(b) $(16 - 4)^2 = 16^2 - 2(16)(4) + 4^2$
(c) $30^2 - 17^2 = (30 + 17)(30 - 17)$
(d) $9^2 + 2(9)(11) + 11^2 = (9 + 11)^2$
(e) $(18 - 7)^2 = 18^2 - 2(18)(7) + 7^2$
(f) $15^2 - 9^2 = (15 + 9)(15 - 9)$
(g) $(32 + 20)(32 - 20) = 32^2 - 20^2$
(h) $(20 + 13)^2 = 20^2 + 2(20)(13) + 13^2$
(i) $(36 + 2)^2 = 36^2 + 2(36)(2) + 2^2$

(j) $8^2 - 2^2 = (8 + 2)(8 - 2)$
(k) $(19 + 6)^2 = 19^2 + 2(19)(6) + 6^2$
(l) $(30 - 5)^2 = 30^2 - 2(30)(5) + 5^2$
(m) $(2 + 3)^2 = 2^2 + 2(2)(3) + 3^2$
(n) $(5 + 4)^2 = 5^2 + 2(5)(4) + 4^2$
(o) $(20 - 10)^2 = 20^2 - 2(20)(10) + 10^2$
(p) $9^2 - 4^2 = (9 + 4)(9 - 4)$
(q) $(11 + 15)^2 = 11^2 + 2(11)(15) + 15^2$
(r) $(5 - 3)^2 = 5^2 - 2(5)(3) + 3^2$
(s) $(15 + 6)(15 - 6) = 15^2 - 6^2$
(t) $(7 - 2)^2 = 7^2 - 2(7)(2) + 2^2$
(u) $31^2 - 22^2 = (31 + 22)(31 - 22)$

2. Match the expressions in Column *A* with those in Column *B* and state the rule used, e.g. (a)–(vi), $a^2 - b^2 = (a + b)(a - b)$.

Column *A*	Column *B*
(a) $40^2 - 15^2$	**(i)** $20^2 + 2(20)(3) + 3^2$
(b) $15^2 + 2(15)(12) + 12^2$	**(ii)** $(49 + 24)(49 - 24)$
(c) $(20 + 3)^2$	**(iii)** $(15 + 12)^2$
(d) $39^2 - 2(39)(4) + 4^2$	**(iv)** $21^2 - 11^2$
(e) $(15 - 4)^2$	**(v)** $(39 - 4)^2$
(f) $32^2 - 2(32)(26) + 26^2$	**(vi)** $(40 + 15)(40 - 15)$
(g) $49^2 - 24^2$	**(vii)** $42^2 + 2(42)(11) + 11^2$
(h) $(42 + 11)^2$	**(viii)** $(32 - 26)^2$
(i) $44^2 + 2(44)(20) + 20^2$	**(ix)** $45^2 - 2(45)(20) + 20^2$
(j) $(21 + 11)(21 - 11)$	**(x)** $15^2 - 2(15)(4) + 4^2$
(k) $(45 - 20)^2$	**(xi)** $(99 + 33)(99 - 33)$
(l) $99^2 - 33^2$	**(xii)** $(44 + 20)^2$

Examples

(a) Consider the expression $99^2 + 198 + 1$.

If we write $99^2 + 198 + 1$ as $99^2 + 2(99)(1) + 1^2$, we see that this is of the form:

$$a^2 + 2ab + b^2, \qquad \text{where } a = 99 \text{ and } b = 1.$$

So we can use the rule:

$$a^2 + 2ab + b^2 = (a + b)^2$$

to evaluate the expression $99^2 + 198 + 1^2$ as follows:

Putting $a = 99$ and $b = 1$ in the rule, we have

$$\begin{aligned} 99^2 + 2(99)(1) + 1^2 &= (99 + 1)^2 \\ &= (100)^2 \\ &= 10\ 000 \end{aligned}$$

Therefore $99^2 + 198 + 1 = 10\ 000$.
(Check the answer by using a calculator.)

(b) Consider the expression $(2x + 1)(2x - 1)$.

Notice that this is of the form $(a + b)(a - b)$, where $a = 2x$ and $b = 1$. So we can use the formula $(a + b)(a - b) = a^2 - b^2$ to remove the brackets as follows:

Putting $a = 2x$ and $b = 1$ in the rule, we have

$$\begin{aligned}(2x + 1)(2x - 1) &= (2x)^2 - (1)^2 \\ &= 4x^2 - 1\end{aligned}$$

Note that the expression $(2x + 1)(2x - 1)$ can be considered as a product of $(2x + 1)$ and $(2x - 1)$. When we express $(2x + 1)(2x - 1)$ in the form $4x^2 - 1$, we say that we are **expanding the product**.

Worked Example 1

Using the special algebraic rules, calculate the following.

(a) 405×395 **(b)** $68^2 - 32^2$ **(c)** $299^2 + 598 + 1$
(d) $1\ 999^2$ **(e)** $51^2 - 102 + 1$

Solution:

(a)
$$\begin{aligned}405 \times 395 &= (400 + 5)(400 - 5) \\ &= 400^2 - 5^2 \\ &= 160\ 000 - 25 \\ &= 159\ 975\end{aligned}$$
$(a + b)(a - b) = a^2 - b^2$

(b)
$$\begin{aligned}68^2 - 32^2 &= (68 + 32)(68 - 32) \\ &= (100)(36) \\ &= 3\ 600\end{aligned}$$
$a^2 - b^2 = (a + b)(a - b)$

(c)
$$\begin{aligned}299^2 + 598 + 1 &= (299 + 1)^2 \\ &= 300^2 \\ &= 90\ 000\end{aligned}$$
$a^2 + 2ab + b^2 = (a + b)^2$

Is 2(299)(1) equal to 598?

(d)
$$\begin{aligned}1\ 999^2 &= (2\ 000 - 1)^2 \\ &= 2\ 000^2 - 4\ 000 + 1 \\ &= 4\ 000\ 000 - 4\ 000 + 1 \\ &= 3\ 996\ 000 + 1 \\ &= 3\ 996\ 001\end{aligned}$$
$(a - b)^2 = a^2 - 2ab + b^2$

(e)
$$\begin{aligned}51^2 - 102 + 1 &= (51 - 1)^2 \\ &= 50^2 \\ &= 2\ 500\end{aligned}$$
$a^2 - 2ab + b^2 = (a - b)^2$

Is 2(51)(1) equal to 102?

Worked Example 2

Expand the following.

(a) $(2x+5)^2$ **(b)** $(3x-2y)^2$ **(c)** $(x^3+x)(x^3-x)$

Solution:

(a) $(2x+5)^2 = (2x)^2 + 2(2x)(5) + 5^2$
$= 4x^2 + 20x + 25$

Recall:
$(2x)^2 = (2x)(2x)$
$= 4x^2$

(b) $(3x-2y)^2 = (3x)^2 - 2(3x)(2y) + (2y)^2$
$= 9x^2 - 12xy + 4y^2$

(c) $(x^3+x)(x^3-x) = (x^3)^2 - x^2$
$= x^6 - x^2$

Study this expansion:
$(10x+5)^2$
$= (10x)^2 + 2(10x)(5) + 5^2$
$= 100x^2 + 100x + 25$
$= x(x+1)(100) + 25$

Hence complete the following:

$15^2 = [10(1)+5]^2$
$= (1)(2)(100) + 25$
$=$ ______ $+ 25$
$=$ ______

$25^2 = [10(2)+5]^2$
$= (2)(3)(100) + 25$
$=$ ______ $+ 25$
$=$ ______

Have you discovered a rule to evaluate the following mentally?
$35^2, 45^2, 55^2, 65^2, 75^2, 85^2$

Exercise 2.1

answers on p. 426

1. For each of the sentences from (a) to (i), state which of the following algebraic rules it belongs to:
(i) $(a+b)^2 = a^2 + 2ab + b^2$,
(ii) $(a-b)^2 = a^2 - 2ab + b^2$,
(iii) $(a+b)(a-b) = a^2 - b^2$.

(a) $(2x+3)^2 = (2x)^2 + 2(2x)(3) + 3^2$
(b) $4x^2 - 7^2 = (2x+7)(2x-7)$
(c) $(4x-3)^2 = (4x)^2 - 2(4x)(3) + 3^2$
(d) $(3x-2y)^2 = (3x)^2 - 2(3x)(2y) + (2y)^2$
(e) $(4x+3y)(4x-3y) = 16x^2 - 9y^2$
(f) $(5x+4y)^2 = (5x)^2 + 2(5x)(4y) + (4y)^2$
(g) $(7x+6y)^2 = (7x)^2 + 2(7x)(6y) + (6y)^2$
(h) $(5x^2+3y^2)(5x^2-3y^2) = 25x^4 - 9y^4$
(i) $(12x-7y)^2 = (12x)^2 - 2(12x)(7y) + (7y)^2$

2. Expand the following.
(a) $(3x+1)^2$ **(b)** $(5x+3)^2$ **(c)** $(6x+4)^2$ **(d)** $(2x+y)^2$
(e) $(4x+2y)^2$ **(f)** $(5x-1)^2$ **(g)** $(3x-2)^2$ **(h)** $(7x-5)^2$
(i) $(4x-y)^2$ **(j)** $(5x-3y)^2$ **(k)** $(x+1)(x-1)$ **(l)** $(x+6)(x-6)$
(m) $(x+y)(x-y)$ **(n)** $(3x+1)(3x-1)$ **(o)** $(2x+3y)(2x-3y)$ **(p)** $(5x+6y)^2$
(q) $(7x-9y)^2$ **(r)** $(8x-5y)^2$

3. Using the special algebraic rules, calculate the following.
(a) $25^2 - 15^2$ **(b)** $58^2 - 42^2$ **(c)** $(100+5)(100-5)$ **(d)** 105×95
(e) 301×299 **(f)** $999^2 - 998^2$ **(g)** 999^2 **(h)** $901^2 - 1\,802 + 1$
(i) 995^2 **(j)** $399^2 + 798 + 1$ **(k)** $499^2 + 998 + 1$ **(l)** 799^2
(m) $300^2 - 301 \times 299$ **(n)** $999^2 + 1\,999$
(o) $1\,234 \times 1\,232 - 1\,233^2 + 1$ **(p)** $501^2 - 499^2 - 998 - 1$

4. Do the following mentally.
(a) $99^2 - 1$ **(b)** $998^2 - 4$ **(c)** $998^2 \times 100 - 400$ **(d)** $99^2 + 2 \times 99 + 1$
(e) $99^2 + 200 - 1$ **(f)** $1\,001 \times 999 + 1$ **(g)** $101^2 - 201$ **(h)** $101 \times 99 + 1 - 99^2$

2.2 EXPANDING PRODUCTS

We have used special algebraic rules to expand products of algebraic expressions. We shall learn more about expanding products.

Examples

(a) Expand $a(b + c + d)$:
Fig. 2.1 shows a rectangle $ABCD$ that is divided into three parts. The areas of the parts X, Y and Z are ab, ac and ad square units respectively. But the area of rectangle $ABCD$ is equal to $AB \times AD$, that is $a(b + c + d)$ square units. So we have $a(b + c + d) = ab + ac + ad$. The is an extension of the **Distributive Law**.

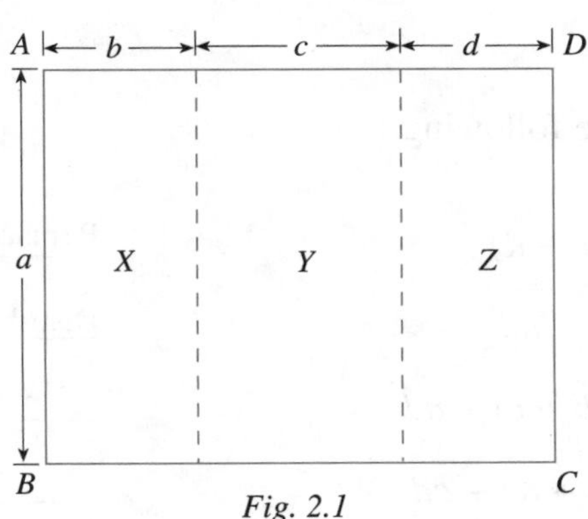

Fig. 2.1

(b) Expand $(a + b)(c + d)$:
Fig. 2.2 shows a rectangle $ABCD$ that is divided into four parts. The areas of the parts W, X, Y and Z are ac, ad, bc and bd square units respectively. But the area of rectangle $ABCD$ is equal to $AB \times BC$, that is $(a + b)(c + d)$ square units. So we have $(a + b)(c + d) = ac + ad + bc + bd$.

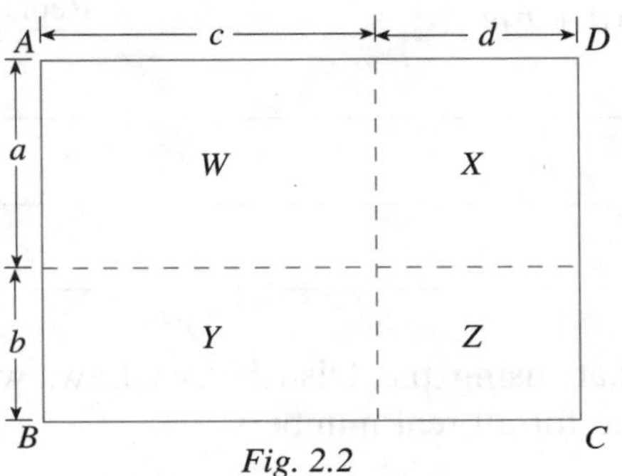

Fig. 2.2

Now study these rules again:

$$a(b + c + d) = ab + ac + ad$$
$$(a + b)(c + d) = ac + ad + bc + bd$$

$$a(\overset{1}{b} + \overset{2}{c} + \overset{3}{d}) = ab + ac + ad$$

$$(a + b)(\overset{1}{\underset{3}{c}} + \overset{2}{\underset{4}{d}}) = ac + ad + bc + bd$$

Note: The arrows indicate how each expansion is done step by step.

We have used geometrical methods to illustrate that the rules for expanding products are true for positive numbers a, b, c and d. If we use algebraic methods and assume that the Distributive Law is true for all real numbers, we can show that these rules are also true for all real numbers.

Class Activity 3

Copy and complete the following.

		Reason
1.	$a(b + c + d) = a(e + d)$	Replace $(b + c)$ by e.
	$= ae + ad$	Distributive Law
	$= a(b + c) + ad$	________
	$= ab + ac + ad$	________
2.	$(a + b)(c + d) = (a + b)e$	Replace $(c + d)$ by e.
	= ________	________
	= ________	________
	= ________	________

The activity shows that, using the Distributive Law, we can prove that the following rules are true for all real numbers.

$$a(b + c + d) = ab + ac + ad$$
$$(a + b)(c + d) = ac + ad + bc + bd$$

Worked Example

Expand the following.

(a) $3x(x + 5y - z)$ **(b)** $(a + b)(3c - 4d)$

(c) $(a - b)(c - a)$ **(d)** $(2x + 3)(x + 2)$

Solution:

(a) $3x(x + 5y - z) = 3x^2 + 15xy - 3xz$

(b) $(a + b)(3c - 4d) = 3ac - 4ad + 3bc - 4bd$

(c) $(a - b)(c - a) = ac - a^2 - bc + ab$

(d) $(2x + 3)(x + 2) = 2x^2 + 4x + 3x + 6$
$= 2x^2 + 7x + 6$

Exercise 2.2

answers on p. 426

1. Expand the following.

(a) $2x(y + z)$
(b) $3m(2p + q)$
(c) $4x(w + y + 2z)$
(d) $y^3(y^2 - y + 1)$
(e) $(7 - n + 2n^3)(-n^2)$
(f) $3a(a + 7)$
(g) $5p(2p + 5)$
(h) $4a^2(a - 8)$
(i) $7m(m^2 - m - 3)$
(j) $9v(v^3 + 3v^2 - 2v + 4)$
(k) $(x + y)(2p + 3q)$
(l) $(3a - b)(a^2 - b^3)$
(m) $(5m^2 - n)(m + n^2)$
(n) $(2x + 5)(x + 1)$
(o) $(3x - 2)(4x + 3)$
(p) $(3x + 2)(4x - 5)$
(q) $(2x - 5)(x - 3)$
(r) $(3x^2 - y)(6x^2 - 14y)$

2. Expand the following.

(a) $(a^2 - 2a + 4)(a + 3)$
(b) $(x^2 + x + 2)(x - 3)$
(c) $(2a^2 + 3a + 2)(a + 3)$
(d) $(x + 5)(x^2 + x - 1)$
(e) $(9a^2 + 12a + 4)(3a - 2)$
(f) $(2a - 3)(2 + a - 5a^2)$
(g) $(3x^2 - xy - 2y^2)(2x + 3y)$
(h) $(x^2 + xy + y^2)(x - 3y)$
(i) $(a + b + c)(x + y + z)$
(j) $(p^2 + q + r^3)(p + q^2 + r^2)$
(k) $(x^2 - x + 1)(x^3 + x^4 + 2)$
(l) $(3m^3 + 2m^2 + m + 2)(m + 3)$

3. Use the Distributive Law to show the following special rules.

$$(a + b)^2 = a^2 + 2ab + b^2$$
$$(a - b)^2 = a^2 - 2ab + b^2$$
$$(a + b)(a - b) = a^2 - b^2$$

2.3 FACTORISATION

Examples

(a) We can use the Distributive Law to expand the product $x(y + z)$ to $xy + xz$. Conversely, we can write $xy + xz$ as $x(y + z)$. This process is known as **factorisation**. Notice that x is found in both the terms xy and xz. We call x the **common factor**.

(b) Consider $3x + 6$. Is there a common factor? If we write $3x + 6$ as $3x + 3(2)$, we see that 3 is the common factor. So we can factorise $3x + 6$ as follows:

$$\begin{aligned} 3x + 6 &= 3x + 3(2) \\ &= 3(x + 2) \end{aligned}$$

(c) Consider $4a + 4$. If we write $4a + 4$ as $4a + 4(1)$, we see that 4 is the common factor. So we can factorise $4a + 4$ as follows:

$$\begin{aligned} 4a + 4 &= 4a + 4(1) \\ &= 4(a + 1) \end{aligned}$$

(d) Consider $x(x + 2) + 8(x + 2)$.

Let us denote $(x + 2)$ by a.
The expression can be written as $xa + 8a$.
We see that a is the common factor.
So we can factorise $x(x + 2) + 8(x + 2)$ as follows:

$$\begin{aligned} x(x + 2) + 8(x + 2) &= xa + 8a && \text{Replace } (x + 2) \text{ by } a. \\ &= a(x + 8) \\ &= (x + 2)(x + 8) && \text{Replace } a \text{ by } (x + 2). \end{aligned}$$

Worked Example 1

Factorise the following.

(a) $xy + xz + 2xw$ **(b)** $5ab + 15bc + 10bd$

(c) $x^2 + 2x + 8x + 16$ **(d)** $ax - bx + 2ay - 2by$

Solution:

(a) $xy + xz + 2xw = x(y + z + 2w)$

(b) $5ab + 15bc + 10bd = 5b(a + 3c + 2d)$

(c) $$\begin{aligned} x^2 + 2x + 8x + 16 &= (x^2 + 2x) + (8x + 16) \\ &= x(x + 2) + 8(x + 2) \\ &= (x + 2)(x + 8) \end{aligned}$$

(d) $$\begin{aligned} ax - bx + 2ay - 2by &= x(a - b) + 2y(a - b) \\ &= (a - b)(x + 2y) \end{aligned}$$

Worked Example 2

Factorise the following.

(a) $4x^2 - y^2$ **(b)** $4x^2 + 4xy + y^2$ **(c)** $9m^2 - 12mn + 4n^2$

Solution:

(a) $$\begin{aligned} 4x^2 - y^2 &= (2x)^2 - y^2 \\ &= (2x + y)(2x - y) \end{aligned}$$

(b) $$\begin{aligned} 4x^2 + 4xy + y^2 &= (2x)^2 + 2(2x)y + y^2 \\ &= (2x + y)^2 \end{aligned}$$

(c) $$\begin{aligned} 9m^2 - 12mn + 4n^2 &= (3m)^2 - 2(3m)(2n) + (2n)^2 \\ &= (3m - 2n)^2 \end{aligned}$$

Exercise 2.3

answers on p. 426

1. Factorise the following expressions.

(a) $mn + mp$ (b) $xy - xz$
(c) $pq + 2p$ (d) $3r - rs$
(e) $5x + 10$ (f) $7a + 7$
(g) $12p - 2$ (h) $x^2 + x$
(i) $y + yx$ (j) $3ab + 9ac + 6ad$
(k) $mn + mp + mq$ (l) $pq + pr + p$
(m) $3xy + 4yz - 5y$ (n) $ab + ac + 3ad$

2. Factorise the following expressions.

(a) $3x(x + 1) + 2(x + 1)$ (b) $7x(x - 2) + 2(x - 2)$
(c) $6x(x + 4) + 3(x + 4)$ (d) $6x^2 - 10x + 9x - 15$
(e) $4x^2 - 12x + 5x - 15$ (f) $2x(x - 1) + x - 1$
(g) $x^2 - x - 7x + 7$ (h) $3x^2 - 3x - x + 1$

3. Factorise the following expressions.

(a) $ax - bx + 3ay - 3by$ (b) $ax + bx - 7ay - 7by$
(c) $12ab - 12ac + bd - cd$ (d) $8ab - 8ac - bd + cd$
(e) $4mp + 3np + 8mq + 6nq$ (f) $6mp - 9np - 18mq + 27nq$
(g) $15ax - 10bx - 3ay + 2by$ (h) $55ax + 99bx - 15ay - 27by$
(i) $40px - 15qx - 64py + 24qy$ (j) $144ax - 72bx - 84ay + 42by$
(k) $5ax - 6by - 10bx + 3ay$ (l) $2mx - 20ny - 8nx + 5my$

4. Rewrite the expressions from (a) to (l) in the form:

(i) $a^2 + 2ab + b^2$,
(ii) $a^2 - 2ab + b^2$,
(iii) $a^2 - b^2$.

e.g. $25x^2 - 30x + 9 = (5x)^2 - 2(5x)(3) + 3^2$

(a) $16x^2 - 8xy + y^2$ (b) $36y^2 + 12y + 1$ (c) $9m^2 - 4n^2$
(d) $s^2 + 6st + 9t^2$ (e) $9x^2 - 6x + 1$ (f) $4s^2 - 36t^2$
(g) $16a^2 + 8ab + b^2$ (h) $49m^2 - 28mn + 4n^2$ (i) $y^2 - 6y + 9$
(j) $25p^2 + 20pq + 4q^2$ (k) $4x^2 - 36$ (l) $16x^2 - 9b^2$

5. Factorise the expressions in No. 4.

6. Factorise the following expressions.

(a) $25a^2 - 16b^2$ (b) $9m^2 + 12mn + 4n^2$
(c) $16p^2 - 24p + 9$ (d) $x^2 + 12x + 36$
(e) $49x^2 - 42xy + 9y^2$ (f) $36x^2 - 49$
(g) $25u^2 - 10uv + v^2$ (h) $81 - 64t^2$
(i) $1 + 30w + 225w^2$ (j) $(x + 1)^2 - 9$
(k) $(x - 1)^2 - (x + 1)^2$ (l) $(3 + x)^2 + 2(3 + x) + 1$
*(m) $x^2 + yz + xy + xz$ *(n) $p^2r^2 + p^2s^2 + q^2s^2 + q^2r^2$

*(o) $ab + b^2 - a - b$ *(p) $1 + a + a^2 + a^3$
*(q) $ab^2 - 1 + a - b^2$ *(r) $ac - a^2 + ad - cd$
*(s) $x^2 - 1 + xy - y$ *(t) $p^2 - q^2 - pr + qr$
*(u) $1 - a^2 - b - ba$ *(v) $3xy + yz - 9x^2 + z^2$

2.4 ADDITION AND SUBTRACTION OF ALGEBRAIC FRACTIONS

If a number can be expressed in the form $\frac{a}{b}$, where a and b are integers and $b \neq 0$, we call it a **rational number**.

A rational number is a number that can be written as a fraction or as an exact or recurring decimal.

If an algebraic expression is written in the form $\frac{A}{B}$, where A and B are algebraic expressions, we call it a **rational expression** or an **algebraic fraction**. For example, $\frac{a^2b}{c^3}$, $\frac{x-1}{x^2+1}$, $\frac{1}{x-1}$ and $\frac{3(b+9)}{(b-2)^2}$ are algebraic fractions.

Note: For a rational expression $\frac{A}{B}$ to be meaningful, it is assumed that the value of the expression B is not equal to zero.

The following example illustrates that adding algebraic fractions is similar to adding fractions in arithmetic.

Examples

Let us compare the following additions.

(a) $\frac{2}{5} + \frac{2}{7}$

(b) $\frac{x}{5} + \frac{x}{7}$

(c) $\frac{2}{a} + \frac{2}{b}$

For (a), the solution is

$$\frac{2}{5} + \frac{2}{7} = \frac{14}{35} + \frac{10}{35}$$
$$= \frac{24}{35}$$

Thinking process:

LCM of 5 and 7 is **35**.

$\frac{2}{5} = \frac{\mathbf{14}}{\mathbf{35}}$ ($\times 7$)

$\frac{2}{7} = \frac{\mathbf{10}}{\mathbf{35}}$ ($\times 5$)

For (b), the solution is

$$\frac{x}{5} + \frac{x}{7} = \frac{7x}{35} + \frac{5x}{35}$$
$$= \frac{12x}{35}$$

Thinking process:

LCM of 5 and 7 is **35**.

$$\frac{x}{5} \xrightarrow{\times 7} \frac{\mathbf{7x}}{\mathbf{35}}$$

$$\frac{x}{7} \xrightarrow{\times 5} \frac{\mathbf{5x}}{\mathbf{35}}$$

Notice that if we replace x by 2, both the question and solution in (b) will be the same as those in (a). Compare (b) with other examples by substituting other values of x.

For (c), the solution is

$$\frac{2}{a} + \frac{2}{b} = \frac{2b}{ab} + \frac{2a}{ab}$$
$$= \frac{2b + 2a}{ab}$$
$$= \frac{2(a+b)}{ab}$$

Thinking process:

LCM of a and b is $\boldsymbol{ab}$.

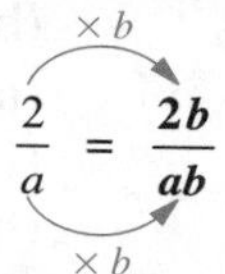

$$\frac{2}{a} \xrightarrow{\times b} \frac{\mathbf{2b}}{\mathbf{ab}}$$

$$\frac{2}{b} \xrightarrow{\times a} \frac{\mathbf{2a}}{\mathbf{ab}}$$

Notice also that if we replace a by 5 and b by 7, both the question and solution in (c) will be the same as those in (a). Compare (c) with other examples by substituting other values of a and b.

In Arithmetic, you have learnt how to find LCM. The following activity will help you discover how to find LCM in Algebra.

Class Activity 4

1. Which of the following are multiples of 7?

(a) 2×7 **(b)** 2×8
(c) $3 + 7$ **(d)** 7×4
(e) $2 \times 3 \times 7$ **(f)** $4 \times 7 \times 2$
(g) $3 \times 7 \times 7$ **(h)** $3 \times 4 \times 8$

2. Which of the following are multiples of a?

(a) $2a$ **(b)** $2b$
(c) $4 + a$ **(d)** $a \times 4$
(e) $2 \times 3a$ **(f)** $4a \times 2$
(g) $3 \times a^2$ **(h)** $3 \times 4b$

3. Consider the following products and answer the questions.

$$2 \times 4 \times 3, \qquad 3 \times 3 \times 4, \qquad 4 \times 4 \times 3, \qquad 4 \times 6 \times 3$$

(a) Is each product a multiple of 3?
(b) Is each product a multiple of 4?
(c) Are all the products common multiples of 3 and 4?
(d) Is $2 \times 4 \times 3$ the LCM of 3 and 4? Explain your answer.

4. Consider the following products and answer the questions.

$$2ba, \qquad 3ab, \qquad 4ba, \qquad b \times 6a$$

(a) Is each product a multiple of a?
(b) Is each product a multiple of b?
(c) Are all the products common multiples of a and b?
(d) Is $2ab$ the LCM of a and b? Explain your answer.

5. Find the LCM of the following.

(a) x, xy **(b)** $b, 4b$
(c) a, a^2 **(d)** $x, xy, 4x$
(e) $(x-1), (x+3)$ **(f)** $2(x+1), 3(2x-1)$
(g) $4(x-1), 2(x+2)$ **(h)** $4(x-1), 6(x+2)$
(i) $6(x+1), 9(x+1)$ **(j)** $(x+2), (x-3), (x-3)$

6. Copy and complete the following.

(a) $\dfrac{y}{x} = \dfrac{}{xy}$ **(b)** $\dfrac{2}{b} = \dfrac{}{4b}$

(c) $\dfrac{3}{4x} = \dfrac{}{4xy}$ **(d)** $\dfrac{2}{a} = \dfrac{}{a^2}$

(e) $\dfrac{2}{x-2} = \dfrac{}{(x-2)(x-1)}$ **(f)** $\dfrac{1}{2(x-1)} = \dfrac{}{6(x-1)(2x+1)}$

(g) $\dfrac{3}{4(x-1)} = \dfrac{}{12(x+2)(x-1)}$ **(h)** $\dfrac{5}{6(x+1)} = \dfrac{}{18(x+2)(x+1)}$

Worked Example 1
Simplify the following.

(a) $\dfrac{x}{2} + \dfrac{x}{5}$ **(b)** $\dfrac{x}{3} - \dfrac{x-5}{2}$ **(c)** $\dfrac{3(x+2)}{4} + \dfrac{4(3-x)}{5}$

Solution:

(a) $$\frac{x}{2} + \frac{x}{5} = \frac{5x}{10} + \frac{2x}{10} = \frac{7x}{10}$$

(b) $$\frac{x}{3} - \frac{x-5}{2} = \frac{2x}{6} - \frac{3(x-5)}{6} = \frac{2x - 3x + 15}{6} = \frac{15 - x}{6}$$

(c) $\dfrac{3(x+2)}{4} + \dfrac{4(3-x)}{5} = \dfrac{3(x+2)\times 5}{20} + \dfrac{4(3-x)\times 4}{20}$

$$= \frac{15x+30}{20} + \frac{48-16x}{20}$$

$$= \frac{15x+30+48-16x}{20}$$

$$= \frac{78-x}{20}$$

Worked Example 2

Simplify the following.

(a) $\dfrac{1}{a} + \dfrac{2}{b}$ **(b)** $\dfrac{3}{a} + \dfrac{5}{ab} - \dfrac{5}{3a}$ **(c)** $\dfrac{2}{x-1} + \dfrac{3}{x-2}$

Solution:

(a) $\dfrac{1}{a} + \dfrac{2}{b} = \dfrac{b}{ab} + \dfrac{2a}{ab}$

$$= \frac{b+2a}{ab}$$

(b) $\dfrac{3}{a} + \dfrac{5}{ab} - \dfrac{5}{3a} = \dfrac{3\times 3b}{3ab} + \dfrac{5\times 3}{3ab} - \dfrac{5b}{3ab}$

$$= \frac{9b}{3ab} + \frac{15}{3ab} - \frac{5b}{3ab}$$

$$= \frac{4b+15}{3ab}$$

(c) $\dfrac{2}{x-1} + \dfrac{3}{x-2} = \dfrac{2(x-2)}{(x-1)(x-2)} + \dfrac{3(x-1)}{(x-1)(x-2)}$

$$= \frac{2x-4+3x-3}{(x-1)(x-2)}$$

$$= \frac{5x-7}{(x-1)(x-2)}$$

Exercise 2.4

answers on p. 427

1. Simplify the following.

   (a) $\dfrac{x}{2} + \dfrac{y}{4}$ **(b)** $\dfrac{a}{3} - \dfrac{a}{5}$

   (c) $\dfrac{a+1}{3} + \dfrac{a}{2}$ **(d)** $a + \dfrac{3a}{5}$

(e) $\frac{a}{2} + \frac{3a}{5} - \frac{9a}{10}$

(f) $\frac{a}{3} - \frac{a+1}{5}$

(g) $\frac{a-b}{3} - \frac{a+b}{5}$

(h) $\frac{x}{3} - \frac{3-x}{5}$

(i) $\frac{3(x-3)}{4} + \frac{4(x+3)}{5}$

(j) $\frac{3x+2y}{4} + \frac{4x-3y}{6}$

(k) $\frac{3a-2}{4} - \frac{2(a+2)}{5} + \frac{a+5}{4}$

(l) $\frac{2x-1}{2} + \frac{3(x+2)}{3} - \frac{x+4}{4}$

(m) $\frac{2}{x} + \frac{2}{y}$

(n) $\frac{1}{xy} + \frac{y}{x}$

(o) $\frac{2}{b} + \frac{3}{4b}$

(p) $\frac{5}{x} + \frac{4}{xy} - \frac{3}{4x}$

(q) $\frac{1}{a} + \frac{1-a}{a^2}$

(r) $\frac{4a-b}{c} - \frac{a+b}{3c}$

2. Simplify the following.

(a) $\frac{1}{x-1} + \frac{2}{x+3}$

(b) $\frac{2}{x-2} + \frac{4}{x-1}$

(c) $\frac{1}{x-3} - \frac{2}{x-4}$

(d) $\frac{3}{x-2} + \frac{1}{x-1} + \frac{2}{x-1}$

(e) $\frac{1}{2(x-1)} + \frac{2}{3(2x+1)}$

(f) $\frac{2}{4(x+1)} - \frac{3}{2(x-2)}$

(g) $\frac{2}{4(x+1)} + \frac{1}{6(x-2)}$

(h) $\frac{3}{6(x-1)} - \frac{1}{9(x-1)}$

(i) $\frac{3}{(3x-1)} - \frac{2}{7(x-3)}$

(j) $\frac{3}{3x-2} + \frac{2}{4-6x}$

(k) $\frac{a}{a-b} - \frac{a}{a+b}$

(l) $a - \frac{ab}{b-a}$

(m) $\frac{m}{3m+n} - \frac{1}{3}$

(n) $\frac{m}{m-n} + \frac{m}{n-m}$

(o) $\frac{x-y}{x+y} + \frac{x+y}{x-y}$

(p) $\frac{b-a}{b+a} - \frac{b+a}{b-a}$

(q) $\frac{x+5}{x+2} - \frac{x+2}{x+5}$

(r) $\frac{2x}{3x-5y} - \frac{3y}{10y-6x}$

(s) $\frac{1}{a} + \frac{1}{b} - \frac{1}{a+b}$

(t) $\frac{5}{x-3} - \frac{1}{x+2} - \frac{1}{x}$

2.5 MULTIPLICATION AND DIVISION OF ALGEBRAIC FRACTIONS

MATHSTORY

Algebra was introduced in Europe in the 13th and 14th centuries by Leonardo of Pisa (also called Fibonacci). Algebra was occasionally referred to as 'the great art'. Both Diophantus (AD 250) and Francois Viete (1540–1603) have been called 'fathers of algebra': Diophantus, a Greek, wrote Arithmetica, a treatise originally in 13 books. Viete, a French lawyer, devoted his leisure time to mathematics. Not liking the word algebra, he referred to the subject as 'the analytic art'.

Worked Example 1

Simplify the following.

(a) $\left(\frac{3a}{5}\right)\left(\frac{7ab}{3}\right)$ **(b)** $\dfrac{\frac{2a}{3}}{\frac{4a}{9}}$

Solution:

(a) $\left(\frac{3a}{5}\right)\left(\frac{7ab}{3}\right) = \frac{21a^2b}{15}$

$= \frac{7a^2b}{5}$

(b) $\dfrac{\frac{2a}{3}}{\frac{4a}{9}} = \frac{2a}{3} \times \frac{9}{4a}$

$= \frac{3}{2}$

$= 1\frac{1}{2}$

Worked Example 2

Simplify the following.

(a) $\frac{a^2b^3}{b^2a^3} \times \frac{a^4b^5}{a^2b^4}$ **(b)** $\frac{a^3b^7}{b^8a^2} \div \frac{a^2b^6}{a^3b^4}$

(c) $\frac{3a-1}{2b^2} \times \frac{3a^2b}{9a-3}$

Solution:

(a) $\frac{a^2b^3}{b^2a^3} \times \frac{a^4b^5}{a^2b^4} = \frac{a^6b^8}{a^5b^6}$

$= ab^2$

(b) $\frac{a^3b^7}{b^8a^2} \div \frac{a^2b^6}{a^3b^4} = \frac{a^3b^7}{b^8a^2} \times \frac{a^3b^4}{a^2b^6}$

$= \frac{a^6b^{11}}{a^4b^{14}}$

$= \frac{a^2}{b^3}$

(c) $\frac{3a-1}{2b^2} \times \frac{3a^2b}{9a-3} = \frac{3a-1}{2b} \times \frac{3a^2}{3(3a-1)}$

$= \frac{a^2}{2b}$

Exercise 2.5

answers on p. 427

1. Simplify the following.

(a) $\left(\frac{2a}{5}\right)\left(\frac{5ab}{6}\right)$ **(b)** $\left(\frac{4x}{9}\right)\left(\frac{3xy}{8}\right)$ **(c)** $\left(\frac{2y}{3}\right)\left(\frac{9xy}{10}\right)$

(d) $\dfrac{\frac{3a}{4}}{\frac{9a}{10}}$ **(e)** $\dfrac{\frac{4x}{5}}{\frac{8x}{15}}$ **(f)** $\dfrac{\frac{x}{4}}{\frac{3x}{8}}$

2. Simplify the following.

(a) $\frac{x^2y^4}{x^5y^2} \times \frac{x^3}{y^4}$ **(b)** $\frac{a^8b^6}{b^4a^{10}} \times \frac{a^3}{b^2}$

(c) $\frac{p^6q^7}{q^8p^5} \times \frac{p^2q^3}{p^3q^6}$ **(d)** $\frac{t^4u^8}{t^7u^2} \times \frac{u^5t^4}{t^2u^6}$

(e) $\frac{x^4y^6}{x^5y^7} \div \frac{x^5y^4}{x^2y^7}$ **(f)** $\frac{a^3b^5}{b^4a^6} \div \frac{a^8b^6}{b^7a^9}$

(g) $\frac{a^{10}b^8}{a^5b^4} \div \frac{a^2b^4}{b^6a^5}$ **(h)** $\frac{x^9y^7}{x^2y^4} \div \frac{x^3y^2}{y^3x^4}$

(i) $\frac{p^{10}q^7}{p^4q^6} \div \frac{p^0q^6}{q^7p^4}$ **(j)** $\frac{p^5q^6}{q^2p^7} \div \frac{p^6q^8}{p^8q^5}$

3. Simplify the following.

(a) $\frac{6ab}{4bc} \div \frac{2ab^2}{8bc^2} \times \frac{bc^2}{b^2c}$ **(b)** $\frac{3a^3b^4}{b^2a^5} \times \frac{a^2b^3}{b^5a} \div \frac{3a}{6b^2}$

(c) $\frac{6x^2 \times 8xy}{9y^2 \times 4xz} \div \frac{1}{2}xy$ **(d)** $\frac{9x^2}{xy} \div \frac{6xy}{9yz} \div \frac{3z^2}{4x^2z}$

(e) $\frac{(3x-2)}{12yz} \times \frac{8xy}{6x-4}$ **(f)** $\frac{7x-y}{8x^2y} \div \frac{y-7x}{4yz^2}$

(g) $\frac{3ab}{a^2-b^2} \times \frac{a+b}{6b^2c}$ **(h)** $\frac{(3-2x)^2}{6y^2z} \div \frac{2(9-4x^2)}{9xy}$

2.6 FRACTIONAL EQUATIONS

Consider these equations.

$$9x + 5(x-2) = 60 \quad \text{.......................} \quad (1)$$

$$\frac{3x}{5} + \frac{x-2}{3} = 4 \quad \text{.......................} \quad (2)$$

Equation (1) is a simple equation. You have learnt this type of equation in Book 1. Equation (2) is a **fractional equation.**

You will notice that both equations have the same solution, $x = 5$. This means equations (1) and (2) are equivalent. We can convert equation (2) to equation (1) by multiplying every term by 15 (i.e. the LCM of 5 and 3) like this:

$$\frac{3x}{5} + \frac{x-2}{3} = 4$$

$$15 \times \frac{3x}{5} + 15 \times \frac{x-2}{3} = 15 \times 4$$

$$9x + 5(x-2) = 60$$

This suggests that to find the solution of a fractional equation, we first eliminate the denominators and then solve it in the usual way:

$$\begin{aligned} 9x + 5(x-2) &= 60 \\ 9x + 5x - 10 &= 60 \\ 14x &= 70 \\ x &= 5 \end{aligned}$$

Worked Example 1

Solve the following equations.

(a) $\frac{2x-1}{3} = 5$ **(b)** $\frac{2x}{5} - \frac{x-3}{7} = 2$

(c) $\frac{3(x+2)}{4} = \frac{1}{6} - \frac{4-x}{3}$

Solution:

(a)

$$\frac{2x-1}{3} = 5$$

$$3 \times \frac{2x-1}{3} = 3 \times 5 \qquad \text{Multiply each term by 3.}$$

$$\begin{aligned} 2x - 1 &= 15 \\ 2x &= 16 \\ x &= 8 \end{aligned}$$

(b)

$$\frac{2x}{5} - \frac{x-3}{7} = 2 \qquad \text{LCM of 5 and 7 = 35}$$

$$35 \times \frac{2x}{5} - 35 \times \frac{(x-3)}{7} = 35 \times 2 \qquad \text{Multiply each term by 35.}$$

$$\begin{aligned} 14x - 5(x-3) &= 70 \\ 14x - 5x + 15 &= 70 \\ 9x &= 55 \\ x &= 6\frac{1}{9} \end{aligned}$$

Note: $\frac{x-3}{7}$ should always be treated as $\frac{(x-3)}{7}$ before the denominator is 'eliminated'.

(c) $$\frac{3(x+2)}{4} = \frac{1}{6} - \frac{4-x}{3}$$ LCM of 3, 4 and 6 = 12

$$12 \times \frac{3(x+2)}{4} = 12 \times \frac{1}{6} - 12 \times \frac{(4-x)}{3}$$ Multiply each term by 12.

$$\begin{aligned} 9(x+2) &= 2 - 4(4-x) \\ 9x + 18 &= 2 - 16 + 4x \\ 9x - 4x &= -14 - 18 \\ 5x &= -32 \\ x &= -6\frac{2}{5} \end{aligned}$$

Note: After solving an equation, you should always check your answer by substitution. For example, you may check the answer for (c) using a calculator as follows:

$$\text{LHS} = \frac{3\left(-6\frac{2}{5} + 2\right)}{4} = -3\frac{3}{10} \qquad \text{RHS} = \frac{1}{6} - \frac{4 - \left(-6\frac{2}{5}\right)}{3} = -3\frac{3}{10}$$

Worked Example 2

Solve the following equations.

(a) $\frac{3}{x+2} = \frac{1}{2}$ **(b)** $\frac{2}{x-2} + \frac{3}{x-2} = 5$

Solution:

(a) $$\frac{3}{x+2} = \frac{1}{2}$$ LCM of $(x + 2)$ and $2 = 2(x + 2)$

$$2(x+2) \times \frac{3}{(x+2)} = 2(x+2) \times \frac{1}{2}$$ Multiply each term by $2(x + 2)$.

$$\begin{aligned} 6 &= x + 2 \\ \therefore x &= 6 - 2 = 4 \end{aligned}$$

(b) $$\frac{2}{x-2} + \frac{3}{x-2} = 5$$

$$(x-2) \times \frac{2}{(x-2)} + (x-2) \times \frac{3}{(x-2)} = (x-2) \times 5$$ Multiply each term by $(x - 2)$.

$$\begin{aligned} 2 + 3 &= 5x - 10 \\ 15 &= 5x \\ \therefore x &= 3 \end{aligned}$$

Exercise 2.6

answers on p. 427

Solve the following equations.

1. $\frac{x+3}{2} = 9$ **2.** $\frac{3x+2}{5} = 4$

3. $\frac{x+13}{6} = \frac{2}{3}$ **4.** $\frac{2x-5}{9} = \frac{1}{3}$

5. $\frac{3x}{5} + \frac{x+2}{7} = 4$

6. $\frac{2x}{3} - \frac{11-x}{5} = 3$

7. $\frac{4x}{5} - \frac{4+5x}{3} = 3$

8. $\frac{5x}{7} + \frac{3x+1}{2} = 16$

9. $\frac{x}{5} + \frac{1-x}{3} = \frac{1}{5}$

10. $\frac{2x}{3} - \frac{2x+1}{4} = \frac{5}{6}$

11. $\frac{3x}{8} - \frac{3-x}{4} = \frac{1}{6}$

12. $\frac{4x}{5} + \frac{2x-3}{4} = \frac{9}{10}$

13. $\frac{x}{3} + \frac{2(x+2)}{4} = \frac{1}{3} - \frac{x}{6}$

14. $\frac{3(2+x)}{4} - \frac{3(3-x)}{8} = \frac{5}{12}$

15. $\frac{2(x-1)}{3} - \frac{3(2x+1)}{5} = \frac{1}{3} - \frac{x}{5}$

16. $\frac{4(2x-1)}{5} + \frac{2(3-x)}{4} = \frac{3}{10} - \frac{2x}{5}$

17. $\frac{9}{x} = 3$

18. $\frac{6}{x} = \frac{5}{6}$

19. $\frac{2}{x-2} = \frac{1}{4}$

20. $\frac{6}{x+3} = \frac{2}{3}$

21. $\frac{5}{2(x-1)} = \frac{3}{5}$

22. $\frac{4}{3(2-x)} = 5$

23. $\frac{4}{x+3} = 3 - \frac{8}{x+3}$

24. $\frac{12}{2x-1} = 2 + \frac{2}{2x-1}$

25. $\frac{5}{2(1+2x)} = \frac{3}{2(1+2x)} - 2$

26. $3 + \frac{4}{x+4} = 1 - \frac{3}{x+4}$

***27.** $\frac{1}{x-3} + \frac{3}{x-2} = 0$

***28.** $\frac{2}{x-1} + \frac{4}{x-2} = 0$

***29.** $\frac{3}{x+2} - \frac{4}{x+3} = 0$

***30.** $\frac{4}{x-1} = 3 - \frac{2}{1-x}$

31. $\frac{2x+3}{x-4} = 3$

32. $\frac{42-7x}{27+5x} = \frac{1}{2}$

33. $\frac{5}{6x} + \frac{7}{9x} = 29$

34. $\frac{8}{9x} - \frac{7}{12x} = \frac{1}{36}$

***35.** $\frac{1}{2x} + \frac{2}{3x} - \frac{3}{4x} = \frac{5}{8}$

***36.** $\frac{2}{3x} - \frac{3}{7x} + \frac{1}{6x} = \frac{2}{7}$

***37.** $\frac{7}{3x-2} + \frac{9}{6x-4} = \frac{23}{26}$

***38.** $\frac{5}{21x-6} - \frac{9}{8-28x} = \frac{47}{60}$

2.7 PROBLEMS INVOLVING FRACTIONAL EQUATIONS

Worked Example 1

The difference between two numbers is $\frac{5}{12}$. If $\frac{3}{4}$ of the larger number is $\frac{3}{8}$ more than $\frac{1}{2}$ of the smaller, find the larger number.

Solution:

Let the larger number be x. Then the smaller number is $\left(x - \frac{5}{12}\right)$.

$$\frac{3x}{4} = \frac{3}{8} + \frac{1}{2}\left(x - \frac{5}{12}\right)$$

$$6x = 3 + 4\left(x - \frac{5}{12}\right) \quad \text{Multiply both sides by 8.}$$

$$6x = 3 + 4x - \frac{5}{3}$$

$$2x = \frac{4}{3}$$

$$\therefore x = \frac{2}{3}$$

The larger number is $\frac{2}{3}$.

Worked Example 2

The sum of two numbers is $1\frac{1}{4}$. If $\frac{3}{8}$ of the reciprocal of one number is equal to $\frac{1}{4}$ of the reciprocal of the other, find the two numbers.

Recall that the reciprocal of A is $\frac{1}{A}$ for $A \neq 0$ and the reciprocal of $\frac{B}{C}$ is $\frac{C}{B}$ for $B \neq 0$, $C \neq 0$.

Solution:

Let x be one of the numbers. Then the other number is $\left(\frac{5}{4} - x\right)$, i.e. $\frac{5 - 4x}{4}$.

$$\frac{3}{8}\left(\frac{1}{x}\right) = \frac{1}{4}\left(\frac{1}{\frac{5 - 4x}{4}}\right)$$

$$\frac{3}{8x} = \frac{1}{4}\left(\frac{4}{5 - 4x}\right)$$

$$\frac{3}{8x} = \frac{1}{5 - 4x}$$

$$5 - 4x = \frac{8x}{3}$$

$$15 - 12x = 8x$$

$$15 = 20x$$

$$\therefore x = \frac{3}{4}$$

$$\frac{5 - 4x}{4} = \frac{5 - 3}{4} = \frac{1}{2}$$

The two numbers are $\frac{3}{4}$ and $\frac{1}{2}$.

Note: We can also form the equation like this:

$$\frac{3}{8}\left(\frac{4}{5-4x}\right) = \frac{1}{4x}$$

which gives $x = \frac{1}{2}$ and $\frac{5-4x}{4} = \frac{3}{4}$.

Exercise 2.7

answers on p. 427

1. If x is subtracted from both the numerator and denominator of $\frac{3}{4}$, the result is $\frac{7}{10}$. Find x.

2. Two consecutive odd numbers are such that $\frac{7}{9}$ of the reciprocal of one is equal to the reciprocal of the other. Find the two odd numbers.

3. The sum of two numbers is $3\frac{3}{4}$. If $\frac{1}{3}$ of the larger number is $\frac{1}{2}$ more than $\frac{2}{3}$ of the smaller, find the numbers.

4. A rectangle has a perimeter of 34 cm. If $\frac{2}{3}$ of its length is equal to $\frac{3}{4}$ of its width, find the dimensions of the rectangle.

5. If $\frac{3}{4}$ of one of the acute angles of a right-angled triangle is $15\frac{1}{4}^{\circ}$ larger than $\frac{1}{6}$ of the other, find the acute angles.

6. A bottle $\frac{3}{4}$ filled with a liquid weighs $1\frac{1}{2}$ kg. The liquid alone weighs $\frac{3}{4}$ kg more than the empty bottle. If the bottle is completely filled, how much will the contents weigh?

7. The difference of two numbers is $\frac{13}{24}$. If $\frac{11}{12}$ of the reciprocal of one number is equal to $\frac{5}{9}$ of the reciprocal of the other, find the two numbers.

8. If $\frac{1}{2}$ of the complement of a certain angle is 1° more than $\frac{1}{6}$ of the supplement of the angle, find the angle.

9. Ali bought a total of 70 apples and pears. He paid \$12 for the apples and \$18 for the pears. A pear cost twice as much as an apple. If Ali bought x pears, form an equation in x and solve it.

10. Two cakes A and B weigh 13 kg altogether. $\frac{2}{3}$ of cake A and $\frac{3}{4}$ of cake B are sold. The remaining part of cake A is $\frac{4}{5}$ kg less than the remaining part of cake B. If cake A weighs x kg, form an equation in x and solve it.

11. Ann had \$20 less than Betty. Ann spent $\frac{3}{4}$ of her money and Betty spent $\frac{4}{5}$ of her money. Then Ann's remainder was $\frac{5}{6}$ of Betty's remainder. If Ann had \$$x$ originally, form an equation in x and solve it.

12. A, B and C are consecutive natural numbers. If $\frac{2}{7}$ of the reciprocal of A is equal to $\frac{1}{3}$ of the reciprocal of C, find B.

13. A school has 2 300 students. A total of 500 students cannot swim. This consists of $\frac{1}{5}$ of the boys and $\frac{1}{4}$ of the girls. If x boys can swim, form an equation in x and solve it.

14. At a party, $\frac{1}{3}$ of the people are children. There are $\frac{3}{5}$ as many men as women, and 5 more women than children. If the total number of people is x, form an equation in x and solve it.

Chapter Review

1. The following rules are useful for **expanding products** of algebraic expressions.
   - $a(b + c) = ab + ac$
   - $(a + b)^2 = a^2 + 2ab + b^2$
   - $(a - b)^2 = a^2 - 2ab + b^2$
   - $(a + b)(a - b) = a^2 - b^2$
   - $a(b + c + d) = ab + ac + ad$
   - $(a + b)(c + d) = ac + ad + bc + bd$

2. **Factorisation** is the reverse process of expanding products.

3. A **rational number** is a number that can be expressed in the form $\frac{a}{b}$, where a and b are integers and $b \neq 0$.

4. An **algebraic fraction** is an algebraic expression written in the form $\frac{A}{B}$, where A and B are algebraic expressions and the value of the expression B is not zero. $\frac{x^2y}{z}$, $\frac{a-1}{a^2+1}$, $\frac{1}{p-1}$, $\frac{4(x+5)}{(x-2)^2}$ are examples of algebraic fractions.

5. Fractions in Algebra are simplified in the same way as in Arithmetic.

6. To find the solution of a fractional equation, we first eliminate the denominators and then solve it in the usual way.

   Example:

   $\frac{x-1}{3} = \frac{1}{2}$ can be converted to $2(x-1) = 3$ by multiplying both sides by the LCM 6.

CHALLENGER 2

1. (a) If $a^2 + a + 1 = 0$, find the value of $1 - a - a^2$.
   (b) If $x + y = 1$ and $xy = -1$, find the value of $(x - y)^2$.

2. (a) If $a + \frac{1}{a} = 2$, find the value of $a^2 + \frac{1}{a^2}$.
   (b) If $\frac{1}{x} = a + b$ and $\frac{1}{y} = a - b$, find $\frac{x-y}{x+y}$ in terms of a and b.

3. (a) If $a^2 + a - 1 = 0$, find the value of $a^3 + 2a^2 + 2$.
   (b) If $a + b = 2$, find the value of $a^3 + 2a^2b + ab^2 + 2ab + 2b^2$.

4. Without using a calculator, state whether $\frac{10^{11}+1}{10^{10}+1}$ is greater than $\frac{10^{12}+1}{10^{11}+1}$. Explain your solution.

5. Which step of the following proof is not acceptable? Give reasons.
   Let $a = 1$ and $b = 1$, then:

$a = b$	.... (i)	$a^2 = ab$	.... (ii)
$a^2 - b^2 = ab - b^2$	.... (iii)	$(a + b)(a - b) = b(a - b)$	.... (iv)
$a + b = b$	.... (v)	$2 = 1$	.... (vi)

6. Which step of the following proof is not acceptable? Give reasons.
Let $a = 1$, $b = 2$ and $c = 3$, then:

$a + c = 2b$ ..... (i) $(a + c)(a - c) = 2b(a - c)$ ..... (ii)
$a^2 - c^2 = 2ab - 2bc$ ..... (iii) $a^2 - 2ab = c^2 - 2bc$ ..... (iv)
$a^2 - 2ab + b^2 = c^2 - 2bc + b^2$ ..... (v) $(a - b)^2 = (c - b)^2$ ..... (vi)
$a - b = c - b$ ..... (vii) $-1 = 1$ ..... (viii)

Problem Solving 2

Shaded Area

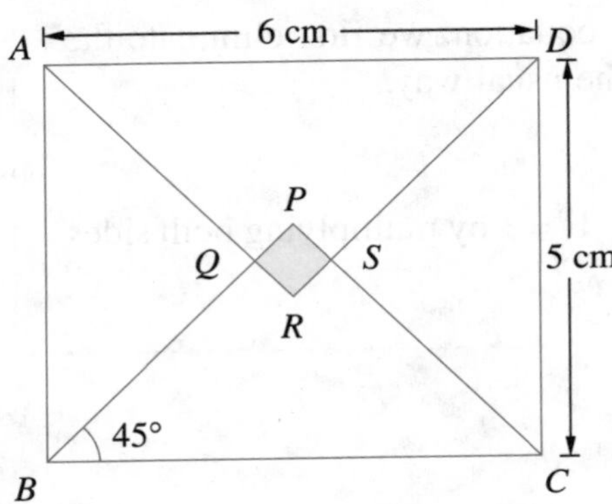

If the shaded region in the rectangle $ABCD$ is a square, calculate the area of the square.

Focus on one part of the problem first.
Find the height of $\triangle ABQ$ with AB as the base.

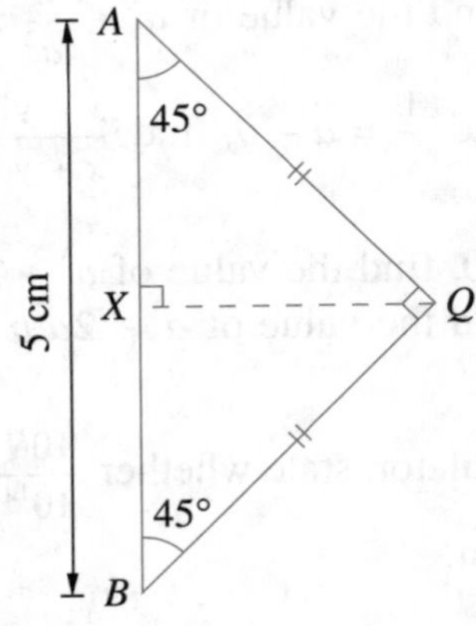

$QX = AX$ ($\triangle AQX$ is an isosceles triangle)

$= \frac{5}{2}$ cm

$= 2.5$ cm

Thus $QS = 6 - 2(2.5)$

$= 1$ cm

Also $PR = QS = 1$ cm

$\therefore$ Area of square $= 2(\triangle PQS)$

$= 2\left(\frac{1}{2} \times 1 \times \frac{1}{2}\right)$ cm^2

$= \frac{1}{2}$ cm^2

The strategy used is **solve part of the problem**

1. **Shaded Parts** In the diagram, the radius of the big circle is 7 cm. Find the total area of the shaded parts. $\left(\text{Take } \pi = \frac{22}{7}.\right)$

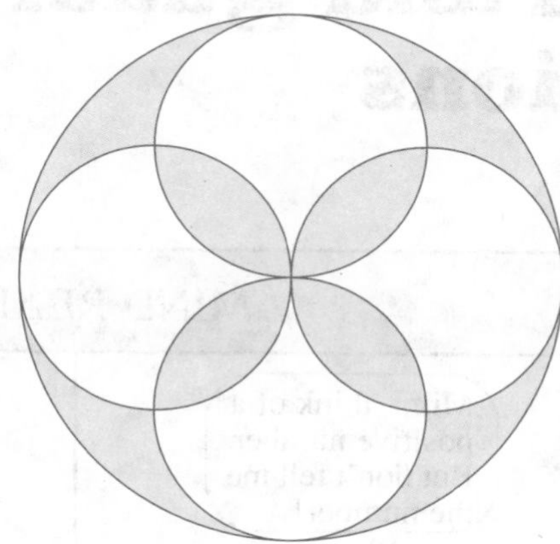

2. **Four Plus Five** Substitute a digit for each letter so as to make the following addition true. (The same letter stands for the same digit. Different letters stand for different digits.)

$$\begin{array}{r} F\ O\ U\ R \\ +\ F\ I\ V\ E \\ \hline N\ I\ N\ E \\ \hline \end{array}$$

3. **Common Part** Square $ABCD$ = square $EFGH$ = 16 cm^2. The vertex E of square $EFGH$ is the centre of square $ABCD$.
   (a) Find the area common to both squares (i.e. the shaded part).
   (b) If square $EFGH$ is rotated 30° clockwise about E, find the area of the part common to both the squares.

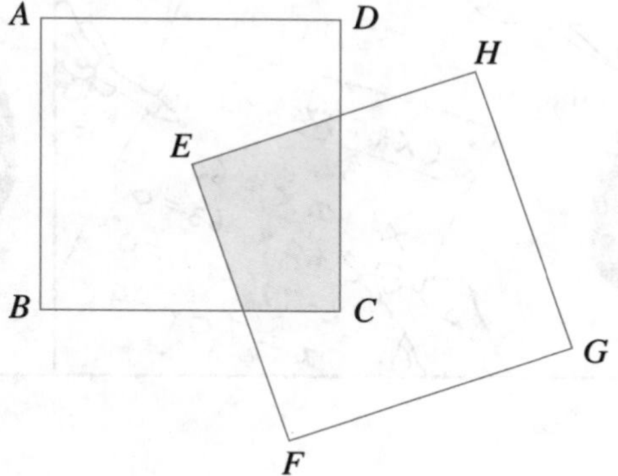

4. **Volume and Surface Area** The area of the top of a rectangular block is 192 cm^2, the area of the front of the block is 128 cm^2 and the area of the side is 96 cm^2. Find the volume of the block.

Chapter 3

Literal and Quadratic Equations

Chapter Highlights

- Solving literal equations, including applying the results to solve equations of the same form
- Transforming formulae, including changing the subject of a formula
- Solving quadratic equations of the form $(ax + b)(cx + d) = 0$
- Factorising quadratic expressions
- Solving quadratic equations by factorisation, including cases where brackets are involved
- Solving problems involving quadratic equations

3.1 LITERAL EQUATIONS

Consider this equation.

An equation is a statement that two quantities or expressions are equal.

$$2.1x + 1.701 = 1.3x + 2.071$$

Let us solve this equation using two methods.

Method 1

$$\begin{aligned} 2.1x + 1.701 &= 1.3x + 2.071 \\ 2.1x - 1.3x &= 2.071 - 1.701 \\ 0.8x &= 0.37 \\ x &= \frac{0.37}{0.8} \\ &= 0.462\ 5 \end{aligned}$$

Using a calculator
$2.1 - 1.3 = 0.8$
$2.071 - 1.701 = 0.37$
$0.37 \div 0.8 = 0.462\ 5$

Method 2

$$\begin{aligned} 2.1x + 1.701 &= 1.3x + 2.071 \\ 2.1x - 1.3x &= 2.071 - 1.701 \\ x(2.1 - 1.3) &= 2.071 - 1.701 \\ x &= \frac{2.071 - 1.701}{2.1 - 1.3} \\ &= 0.462\ 5 \end{aligned}$$

Using a calculator
$(2.071 - 1.701) \div (2.1 - 1.3)$
$= 0.462\ 5$

Notice that in Method 2, we leave the four known numbers to the final step before using the calculator. You will learn that Method 2 can also be used to solve **literal equations** such as $ax + b = cx + d$.

> **A literal equation is one in which letters are used to replace the numerical coefficients and the constant terms.**

Examples

(a) Solve this equation using Method 2.

$$5x + 2 = 3x + 6$$

(b) Find x in terms of a, b, c and d in this equation:

$$ax + b = cx + d$$

Let us compare the solutions for (a) and (b).

(a)
$$\begin{aligned} 5x + 2 &= 3x + 6 \\ 5x - 3x &= 6 - 2 \\ x(5 - 3) &= 6 - 2 \\ x &= \frac{6 - 2}{5 - 3} \\ &= 2 \end{aligned}$$

(b)
$$\begin{aligned} ax + b &= cx + d \\ ax - cx &= d - b \\ x(a - c) &= d - b \\ x &= \frac{d - b}{a - c} \end{aligned}$$

Notice that in the equation in (b), x is the unknown and a, b, c and d are treated as if they were 'known' numbers, just like those (5, 2, 3 and 6) in the equation in (a).

Worked Example 1
Express x in terms of a, b, c, d and e.
(a) $ax + b = cd + ex$
(b) $a(x + b) + c(x - d) = e$

Solution:
(a)
$$\begin{aligned} ax + b &= cd + ex \\ ax - ex &= cd - b \\ x(a - e) &= cd - b \\ x &= \frac{cd - b}{a - e} \end{aligned}$$

(b)
$$\begin{aligned} a(x + b) + c(x - d) &= e \\ ax + ab + cx - cd &= e \\ ax + cx &= e - ab + cd \\ x(a + c) &= e - ab + cd \\ x &= \frac{e - ab + cd}{a + c} \end{aligned}$$

Worked Example 2
Express x in terms of a, b and c.

(a) $\dfrac{a}{x} = b + c$

(b) $\dfrac{x}{3a} + \dfrac{x}{2b} = c$

Solution:

(a) $\frac{a}{x} = b + c$

$a = x(b + c)$

$x = \frac{a}{b + c}$

(b) $\frac{x}{3a} + \frac{x}{2b} = c$ LCM of $3a$ and $2b = 6ab$

$6ab \times \frac{x}{3a} + 6ab \times \frac{x}{2b} = 6ab \times c$ Multiply each term by $6ab$.

$2bx + 3ax = 6abc$

$x(2b + 3a) = 6abc$

$x = \frac{6abc}{2b + 3a}$

Exercise 3.1

answers on p. 427

1. **(a)** Find x in terms of a, p and q in this equation: $ax + p = q$.
(b) Solve $1.23x + 0.12 = 2.01$. Give your answer correct to 3 significant figures.

2. **(a)** Find x in terms of p, q, r and s in this equation: $px + q = rx - s$.
(b) Solve $2.01x + 2.12 = 1.32x - 1.25$. Give your answer correct to 3 decimal places.

3. **(a)** Find x in terms of m, n, p and q in this equation: $mx - n = px + q$.
(b) Solve $2.34x - 3.15 = 1.45x + 4.02$. Give your answer correct to 3 significant figures.

4. **(a)** Find x in terms of a, b, c and d in this equation: $ax - b = cx - d$.
(b) Solve $\frac{1}{3}x - \frac{4}{5} = \frac{2}{5}x - \frac{2}{3}$.

5. Express x in terms of a, b, c, d and e.
(a) $a(x - b) + c(x + d) = e$
(b) $b(a + x) + d(c - x) = ex$

6. Express x in terms of p, q, r and s.
(a) $p(x + q) + x + r = s$
(b) $q(x - p) - r(x + 2) = sx$

7. Express x in terms of a, b and c.

(a) $\frac{a}{x} = c + b$

(b) $\frac{b + c}{x} = a$

8. Express x in terms of a, b and c.

(a) $\frac{x}{2a} + \frac{x}{3b} = c$

(b) $\frac{x}{3a} - \frac{x}{2b} = 5c$

9. $ab + c = bd + e$

(a) Find b in terms of a, c, d and e.

(b) Find d in terms of a, b, c and e.

10. $ab - c = d + ae$

(a) Find a in terms of b, c, d and e.

(b) Find b in terms of a, c, d and e.

3.2 TRANSFORMATION OF FORMULAE

Consider the formula for the area of a trapezium.

$$A = \frac{1}{2}h(a + b)$$

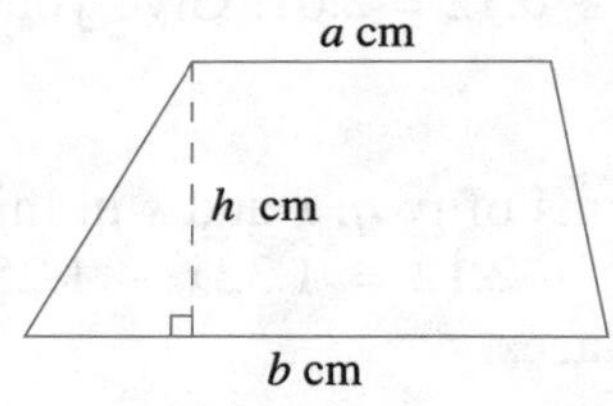

A formula is an equation that describes how one quantity is related to other quantities.

You can use this area formula to find the base b if the values of A, h and a are given.

For example, if $A = 32$, $h = 4$ and $a = 6$, then we have

$$A = \frac{1}{2}h(a + b)$$

$$32 = \frac{1}{2} \times 4(6 + b)$$

$$32 = 2(6 + b)$$

$$32 = 12 + 2b$$

$$20 = 2b$$

$$\therefore b = 10$$

$\therefore$ the base is 10 cm.

Suppose you are required to solve many problems of this type. Then you will find it convenient to make b the **subject of the formula**; that is, to express b in terms of A, h and a before replacing the variables with numbers.

Let us now transform the formula as follows:

$$A = \frac{1}{2}h(a + b)$$

$$2A = h(a + b) \qquad \text{Eliminate denominator.}$$

$$\frac{2A}{h} = a + b \qquad \text{Remove brackets.}$$

$$\therefore b = \frac{2A}{h} - a \qquad \text{Solve for } b.$$

Alternatively, we have

$$A = \frac{1}{2}h(a + b)$$

$$2A = h(a + b) \qquad \text{Eliminate denominator.}$$

$$2A = ha + hb \qquad \text{Remove brackets.}$$

$$2A - ha = hb \qquad \text{Solve for } hb.$$

$$\therefore b = \frac{2A - ha}{h} \qquad \text{Solve for } b.$$

Notice that the answer for b may have different forms.
Can you convert from one form to the other?

Worked Example 1

Make p the subject of the formula $d = \dfrac{p}{1 + p}$.

Solution:

$$d = \frac{p}{1 + p}$$

$$d(1 + p) = p \qquad \text{Eliminate denominator.}$$

$$d + dp = p \qquad \text{Remove brackets.}$$

$$d = p - dp \qquad \text{Group all terms in } p.$$

$$d = p(1 - d) \qquad \text{Extract factor } p.$$

$$\therefore p = \frac{d}{1 - d} \qquad \text{Solve for } p.$$

Worked Example 2

If $\frac{1}{u} + \frac{1}{v} = \frac{1}{f}$, express v in terms of f and u.

Solution:

$$\frac{1}{u} + \frac{1}{v} = \frac{1}{f}$$

$fv + fu = uv$ — Eliminate denominators.

$fu = uv - fv$ — Group all terms in v.

$fu = v(u - f)$ — Extract factor v.

$v = \frac{fu}{u - f}$ — Solve for v.

Alternative method:

$$\frac{1}{v} = \frac{1}{f} - \frac{1}{u}$$

$$\frac{1}{v} = \frac{u - f}{fu}$$

$v = \frac{fu}{u - f}$ — Solve for v.

Exercise 3.2

answers on p. 428

1. The volume V cm^3 of a circular cone of radius r cm and height h cm is given by the formula

$$V = \frac{1}{3}\pi r^2 h.$$

(a) Find the volume of the cone if $r = 6$ and $h = 14$. $\left(\text{Take } \pi = \frac{22}{7}.\right)$

(b) Make h the subject of the formula and hence find the depth of water in the inverted cone which is filled with water to the brim, given that its volume is 352 cm^3 and its radius is 4 cm.

2. There are N consecutive natural numbers. The sum S of these numbers is given by the formula

$$S = \frac{N}{2}(F + L),$$

where F is the first number (i.e. the smallest) and L is the last number (i.e. the largest).

(a) Find the sum of consecutive numbers from 12 to 38.

(b) Make F the subject of the formula. Hence find the first number of another set of 15 consecutive numbers arranged in ascending order, given that the sum is 150 and the last number is 17.

3. The formula for calculating the selling price, S, of an article is given by

$$S = C\left(1 + \frac{r}{100}\right),$$

where the cost price is C and the percentage profit is $r\%$.

(a) Find the cost price of an article if it is sold for \$138 at a profit of 20%.

(b) Make r the subject of the formula. Hence find the percentage profit when an article is sold for \$110, given that the cost price is \$88.

*4. A water tank is designed in such a way that just before the volume of water in it falls below 500 litres, a tap will automatically refill the tank at the rate of 20 litres per minute.

(a) If after T minutes of refilling, the volume of water in the tank is V litres, find a formula connecting V and T.

(b) Find the volume of water in the tank after 4 minutes of refilling.

(c) Rewrite the formula so that you can use it to find when the tank will be filled with a given volume of water. Use this to find in how many minutes the tank will be filled with 2 000 litres of water.

5. Rewrite each of the following formulae as indicated.

(a) $A = lw$. Express w in terms of A and l.

(b) $C = 2\pi r$. Make r the subject.

(c) $A = \frac{hb}{2}$. Express b in terms of A and h.

(d) $V = \pi r^2 h$. Make h the subject.

(e) $E = \frac{1}{2}n + a$. Express n in terms of E and a.

(f) $A = \frac{h}{2}(a + b)$. Express h in terms of A, a and b.

(g) If $A = h(R^2 - r^2)$, find h in terms of A, R and r.

(h) $P = 2(l + w)$. Make l the subject.

(i) $s = \pi r(r + h)$. Make h the subject.

(j) $x = \frac{S - s}{2p}$. Make S the subject.

(k) $\frac{1}{f} = \frac{1}{u} + \frac{1}{v}$. Make f the subject.

(l) $S = 2\pi r(r + h)$. Make h the subject.

(m) $S = \frac{1}{2}(u + v)t$. Make u the subject.

(n) $x = \frac{2p}{s - 1}$. Make s the subject.

(o) $x = \frac{2p}{p-1}$. Make p the subject.

(p) If $T = \frac{R+r}{R}$, find R in terms of T and r.

(q) If $\frac{1}{u} + \frac{1}{v} = \frac{1}{f}$, find u in terms of f and v.

(r) If $v = u + ft$, express t in terms of u, v and f.

(s) If $s = ut + \frac{1}{2}ft^2$, express f in terms of s, u and t.

(t) If $v^2 = u^2 + 2fs$, express s in terms of v, u and f.

(u) If $\frac{1}{t} = (u-1)\left(\frac{1}{r_1} + \frac{1}{r_2}\right)$, find t in terms of u, r_1 and r_2.

(v) If $\frac{b}{h} = r\left(1 + \frac{k}{h}\right)$, find r in terms of b, h and k.

3.3 QUADRATIC EQUATIONS

Consider the equation $(x-2)(x-5) = 0$.

The equation $(x-2)(x-5) = 0$ is of the form $p \times q = 0$ where $p = (x-2)$ and $q = (x-5)$. Notice that if either p or q is zero, then $p \times q$ is zero. Thus, the equation $(x-2)(x-5) = 0$ is satisfied if either $(x-2) = 0$ or $(x-5) = 0$. That is, the solutions are those numbers which make either $(x-2)$ or $(x-5)$ equal to zero. Therefore, the solutions are 2 and 5.

If we expand the left-hand side of the equation, we have $x^2 - 7x + 10 = 0$. Notice that the highest power of x is 2. We call equations of this type **quadratic equations**.

A quadratic equation is one in which the highest power that the variable is raised to is 2.

The general form of quadratic equations is

> **$ax^2 + bx + c = 0$, where a, b and c are constants and $a \neq 0$.**

Worked Example

Solve the equations.

(a) $(x-3)(2x+4) = 0$ (b) $x(2x+5) = 0$

Solution:

(a)
$$(x-3)(2x+4) = 0$$
$$x - 3 = 0 \quad \text{or} \quad 2x + 4 = 0$$
$$\therefore x = 3 \quad \text{or} \quad x = -2$$

(b)
$$x(2x+5) = 0$$
$$x = 0 \quad \text{or} \quad 2x + 5 = 0$$
$$\therefore x = 0 \quad \text{or} \quad x = -\frac{5}{2} = -2\frac{1}{2}$$

Remember to check your answer by substitution.

Exercise 3.3 

answers on p. 428

Solve the following equations.

1. $(x - 5)(x - 3) = 0$
2. $(x - 7)(x + 1) = 0$
3. $(2x - 7)x = 0$
4. $(x - 5)(x + 100) = 0$
5. $(3 - x)(3x - 1) = -11$
6. $(2x - 4)^2 = 0$
7. $(x + 0)(x - 3) = 0$
8. $x(x + 7) = 0$
9. $(x + 6)(2x - 11) = 0$
10. $(2x - 5)(4x + 7) = 0$
11. $(7 - 3x)(4x - 1) = 0$
12. $(x - 5)(x - 5) = 0$
13. $(x - 3)(x - 4) = 2$
14. $(x - 7)(x - 5) = 0$
15. $(x + 7)(x - 6) = -30$
16. $(x - 5)(x + 5) = 0$
17. $(x - 3)(x + 4) = 0$
18. $(x - 3)^2 = 36$
19. $(3x - 1)(4 - x) = 0$
20. $(4x + 3)(4x - 3) = 0$

3.4 QUADRATIC FACTORISATION

Cross-Multiplication Method

Let us look at the expansion of $(2x + 3)(x + 2)$.

$$\begin{aligned}(2x + 3)(x + 2) &= 2x^2 + 4x + 3x + 6 \\ &= 2x^2 + 7x + 6\end{aligned}$$

We can also do the expansion using a 'cross-multiplication chart' as follows:

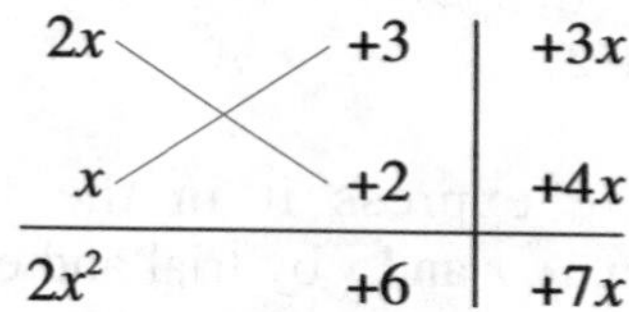

$$\begin{aligned}\therefore\ (2x + 3)(x + 2) &= 2x^2 + 6 + 7x \\ &= 2x^2 + 7x + 6\end{aligned}$$

Note: We multiply vertically to get $2x^2$ and $+6$. We 'cross multiply' and add the products to get $+7x$.

Class Activity

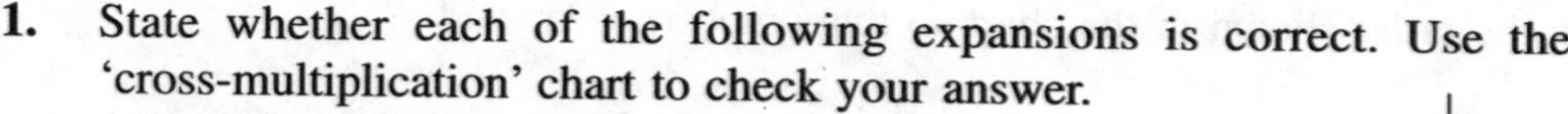

1. State whether each of the following expansions is correct. Use the

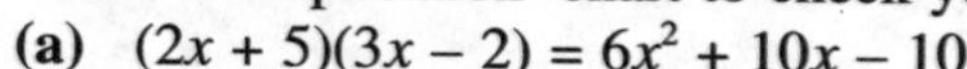

'cross-multiplication' chart to check your answer.

(a) $(2x + 5)(3x - 2) = 6x^2 + 10x - 10$
(b) $(2x + 5)(3x - 2) = 6x^2 - 10x - 10$
(c) $(2x + 5)(3x - 2) = 6x^2 + 11x - 10$
(d) $(2x + 5)(3x - 2) = 6x^2 - 11x - 10$

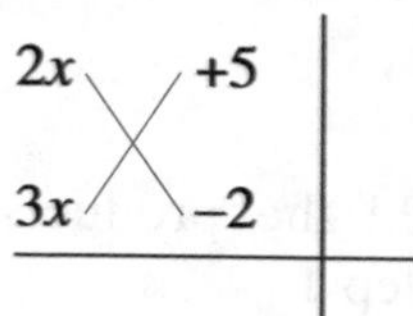

2. Complete the following charts.

(a) 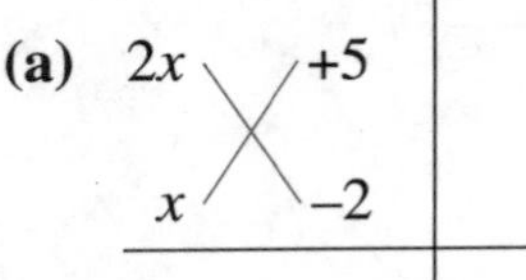

(b) 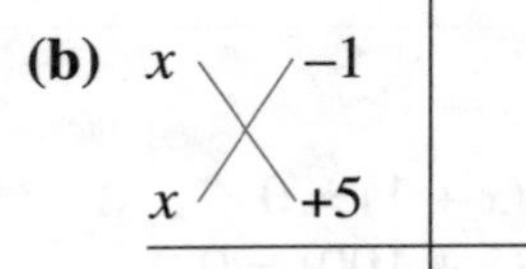

(c) $2x$ $+3$ / $3x$ -2

(d) 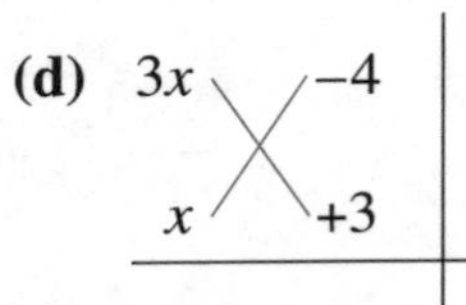

(e) 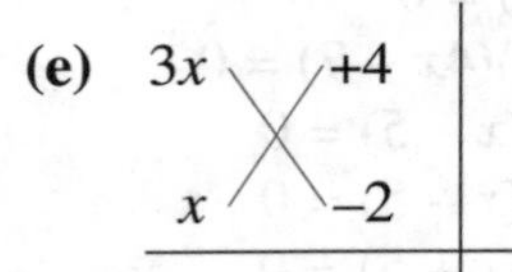

(f) 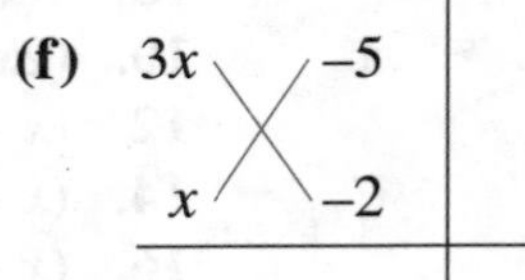

3. Use the 'cross-multiplication' chart to expand the following expressions.
(a) $(x + 5)(2x + 3)$ **(b)** $(2x - 3)(3x - 4)$
(c) $(5x + 2)(x - 2)$ **(d)** $(2 + 3x)(2x - 1)$

Factorisation

Expressions of the form $ax^2 + bx + c$ $(a \neq 0)$ are called **quadratic expressions** in x. For example, $2x^2 + 7x + 6$ is a quadratic expression in x. We can factorise the expression $2x^2 + 7x + 6$ if we write $7x$ as $4x + 3x$. Thus we have

$$\begin{aligned} 2x^2 + 7x + 6 &= 2x^2 + 4x + 3x + 6 \\ &= 2x(x + 2) + 3(x + 2) \\ &= (2x + 3)(x + 2) \end{aligned}$$

We can also factorise this expression if we express it in the form $(px + q)(rx + s)$ first and then find the values of p, q, r and s by trial and error. An easy way is to work backwards with the 'cross-multiplication' chart.

px	$+q$	$+rqx$
rx	$+s$	$+psx$
$2x^2$	$+6$	$+7x$

Step 1
Take note of the first term of the given quadratic expression, i.e. $2x^2$, and the constant term, i.e. $+6$. Write down, by trial and error, two terms px and rx and two integers q and s in the order shown in the chart so that $(px)(rx) = 2x^2$ and $qs = +6$.

Step 2
Cross multiply and add the products to check if $rqx + psx = +7x$. If $rqx + psx \neq 7x$, repeat Step 1.

Examples

(a) Factorise $3x^2 + 13x + 4$.

Notice that:
$3x^2 = (3x)(x)$
$4 = (+1)(+4)$
or $(+2)(+2)$
or $(-2)(-2)$

First trial

x	$+1$	$+3x$
$3x$	$+4$	$+4x$
		$+7x$

Check:
$7x \neq +13x$

Second trial

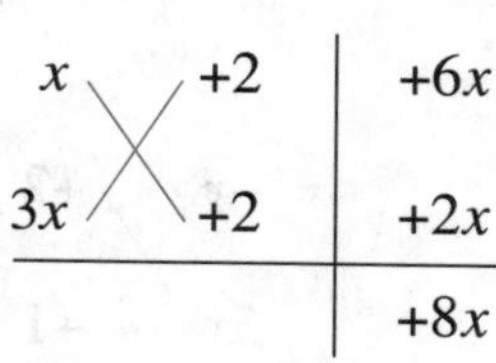

Check:
$8x \neq +13x$

Third trial

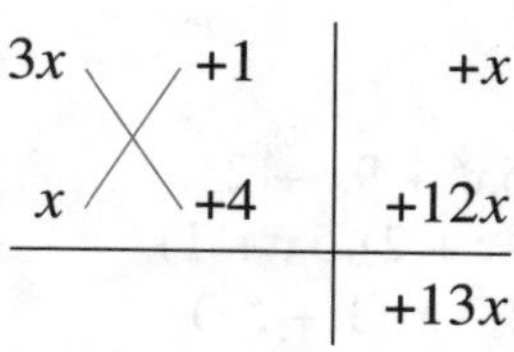

Check:
$13x = +13x$

The third trial is successful.
Thus $3x^2 + 13x + 4 = (3x + 1)(x + 4)$.

Note: In the charts above, we focus on the terms in x only. Make sure that the term in x^2 and the constant term are correct also.

(b) Factorise $8x^2 + 14x - 9$.

Notice that:
$8x^2 = (x)(8x)$
or $(2x)(4x)$
$-9 = (-1)(9)$
or $(1)(-9)$
or $(-3)(3)$

First trial

x	-1	$-8x$
$8x$	$+9$	$+9x$
		$+x$

Check:
$x \neq +14x$

Second trial

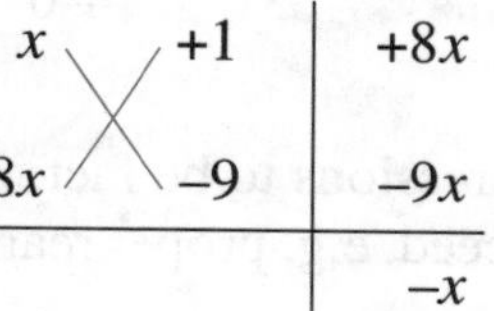

Check:
$-x \neq +14x$

Third trial

x	-3	$-24x$
$8x$	$+3$	$+3x$
		$-21x$

Check:
$-21x \neq +14x$

Fourth trial

x	$+3$	$+24x$
$8x$	-3	$-3x$
		$+21x$

Check:
$21x \neq +14x$

Fifth trial

$2x$	-1	$-4x$
$4x$	$+9$	$+18x$
		$+14x$

Check:
$14x = +14x$

The fifth trial is successful.
Thus $8x^2 + 14x - 9 = (2x - 1)(4x + 9)$.

Note: The unsuccessful trials need not be presented in the solution. After some practice, the possible combinations, cross-multiplying and checking can be done mentally.

Worked Example

Factorise the following.

(a) $2 + 9x - 5x^2$

(b) $3x^2 + 12x - 96$

(c) $3x^2 - 6 + 7x$

Solution:

(a) $2 + 9x - 5x^2 = -5x^2 + 9x + 2$
$= (-x + 2)(5x + 1)$
$= (2 - x)(1 + 5x)$

$-x$	$+2$	$+10x$
$5x$	$+1$	$-x$
$-5x^2$	$+2$	$+9x$

(b) $3x^2 + 12x - 96 = 3(x^2 + 4x - 32)$
$= 3(x + 8)(x - 4)$

x	$+8$	$+8x$
x	-4	$-4x$
x^2	-32	$+4x$

(c) $3x^2 - 6 + 7x = 3x^2 + 7x - 6$
$= (3x - 2)(x + 3)$

$3x$	-2	$-2x$
x	$+3$	$+9x$
$3x^2$	-6	$+7x$

Note: 1. It is useful to make sure that the expressions to be factorised are in the form $ax^2 + bx + c$ before you proceed, e.g. proper rearrangement is done in (a) and (c) in the 1st step.

2. If there is a common factor as in (b), extract the common factor first.

Exercise 3.4

answers on p. 428

1. Factorise the following.

(a) $x^2 + x - 12$ **(b)** $x^2 - 3x - 28$ **(c)** $x^2 - 14x - 32$

(d) $x^2 + 24x - 81$ **(e)** $x^2 - 28x + 192$ **(f)** $x^2 - 22x + 120$

(g) $x^2 - 10x - 119$ **(h)** $x^2 - 28x - 288$ **(i)** $x^2 - 5x - 150$

(j) $x^2 - 17x + 72$ **(k)** $x^2 + 12x - 133$ **(l)** $x^2 - 13x - 68$

2. Factorise the following.

(a) $2x^2 - 95x - 48$ **(b)** $2x^2 + 95x - 48$ **(c)** $2x^2 - 46x - 48$

(d) $2x^2 + 46x - 48$ **(e)** $2x^2 - 29x - 48$ **(f)** $2x^2 + 29x - 48$

(g) $2x^2 - 20x - 48$ **(h)** $2x^2 + 20x - 48$ **(i)** $2x^2 - 10x - 48$

(j) $2x^2 + 10x - 48$ **(k)** $2x^2 + 4x - 48$ **(l)** $2x^2 - 4x - 48$

3. Factorise the following.

(a) $x^2 - x - 2$	**(b)** $2 + x - 3x^2$	**(c)** $6x^2 + 5x - 4$
(d) $6x^2 - 2x - 20$	**(e)** $3x^2 + 12x - 15$	**(f)** $15x^2 - 13x + 2$
(g) $5x^2 - 14x + 8$	**(h)** $6x^2 - 11x - 7$	**(i)** $2 - 5x - 12x^2$
(j) $26x - 8x^2 - 6$	**(k)** $6 + x - x^2$	**(l)** $12 + 2x - 4x^2$
(m) $4x^2 + 2x - 20$	**(n)** $9x^2 - 6x - 24$	**(o)** $6x^2 - 22x + 20$
(p) $6x^2 + 5x - 6$	**(q)** $1 + 3x - 10x^2$	**(r)** $8x^2 + 8x + 2$
(s) $6x^2 - 3 - 17x$	**(t)** $12x^2 - 18x - 12$	**(u)** $8x - 10 + 2x^2$
(v) $12x^2 - 12 - 32x$	**(w)** $6x^2 - 16 + 20x$	**(x)** $3x^2 + 3 + 6x$

3.5 SOLVING QUADRATIC EQUATIONS BY FACTORISATION

We have seen that if a quadratic equation is written in the form $(ax + b)(cx + d) = 0$, the solution can be obtained easily. We shall now show how a quadratic equation not written in this form can be solved by factorisation.

Worked Example 1

Solve the following equations.

(a) $x^2 + 7x = 0$

(b) $x^2 - 9 = 0$

(c) $12x^2 + 7x - 10 = 0$

(d) $12x^2 - 26x - 10 = 0$

(e) $3x + 2 - 5x^2 = 0$

Solution:

(a)
$$x^2 + 7x = 0$$
$$(x + 7)x = 0$$
$$x + 7 = 0 \quad \text{or} \quad x = 0$$
$$\therefore x = -7 \quad \text{or} \quad x = 0$$

(b)
$$x^2 - 9 = 0$$
$$(x + 3)(x - 3) = 0$$
$$x + 3 = 0 \quad \text{or} \quad x - 3 = 0$$
$$\therefore x = -3 \quad \text{or} \quad x = 3$$

(c)
$$12x^2 + 7x - 10 = 0$$
$$(3x - 2)(4x + 5) = 0$$
$$3x - 2 = 0 \quad \text{or} \quad 4x + 5 = 0$$
$$\therefore x = \frac{2}{3} \quad \text{or} \quad x = -\frac{5}{4}$$
$$= -1\frac{1}{4}$$

$3x$	-2	$-8x$
$4x$	$+5$	$+15x$
		$+7x$

(d) $12x^2 - 26x - 10 = 0$

$6x^2 - 13x - 5 = 0$

$(3x + 1)(2x - 5) = 0$

$3x + 1 = 0$ or $2x - 5 = 0$

$\therefore x = -\frac{1}{3}$ or $x = \frac{5}{2}$

$= 2\frac{1}{2}$

$3x$	$+1$	$+2x$
$2x$	-5	$-15x$
		$-13x$

(e) $3x + 2 - 5x^2 = 0$

$-5x^2 + 3x + 2 = 0$

$(-x + 1)(5x + 2) = 0$

$-x + 1 = 0$ or $5x + 2 = 0$

$\therefore x = 1$ or $x = -\frac{2}{5}$

$-x$	$+1$	$+5x$
$5x$	$+2$	$-2x$
		$+3x$

Note: In (b), $x^2 - 9$ is a difference of squares, $x^2 - 3^2$.
In (d), we divide each term by 2 before we factorise.
In (e), we rearrange the terms in the equation before we factorise.

Worked Example 2

Solve the following equations.

(a) $(2x + 1)(3x - 1) = 14$

(b) $(x + 2)^2 = 2x + 7$

(c) $4(x + 1)(x - 4) + 25 = 0$

Solution:

(a) $(2x + 1)(3x - 1) = 14$

$6x^2 + x - 1 - 14 = 0$

$6x^2 + x - 15 = 0$

$(3x + 5)(2x - 3) = 0$

$3x + 5 = 0$ or $2x - 3 = 0$

$\therefore x = -\frac{5}{3}$ $x = \frac{3}{2}$

$= -1\frac{2}{3}$ $= 1\frac{1}{2}$

$3x$	$+5$	$+10x$
$2x$	-3	$-9x$
		$+x$

(b) $(x + 2)^2 = 2x + 7$

$x^2 + 4x + 4 = 2x + 7$

$x^2 + 2x - 3 = 0$

$(x + 3)(x - 1) = 0$

$x + 3 = 0$ or $x - 1 = 0$

$\therefore x = -3$ $x = 1$

x	$+3$	$+3x$
x	-1	$-x$
		$+2x$

(c) $4(x + 1)(x - 4) + 25 = 0$

$4(x^2 - 3x - 4) + 25 = 0$

$4x^2 - 12x - 16 + 25 = 0$

$4x^2 - 12x + 9 = 0$

$(2x - 3)(2x - 3) = 0$

$\therefore x = \frac{3}{2}$

$= 1\frac{1}{2}$ (repeated)

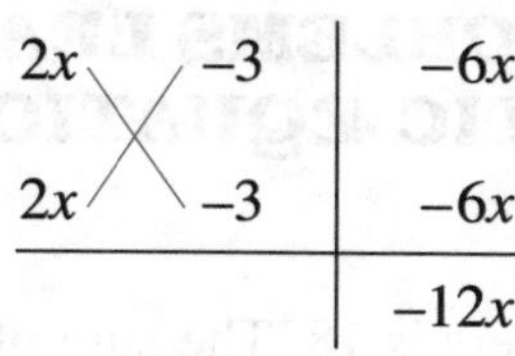

Note: The equation $4x^2 - 12x + 9 = 0$ is a special equation. It is of the pattern $(2x)^2 - 2(2x)(3) + (3)^2 = 0$. Recall that $a^2 - 2ab + b^2 = (a - b)^2$. Instead of using the trial and error method, we can simply write $4x^2 - 12x + 9 = 0$ as $(2x - 3)^2 = 0$.

Similarly, we can solve other special equations such as $x^2 + 6x + 9 = 0$ and $4x^2 - 25$ by using the rules $a^2 + 2ab + b^2 = (a + b)^2$ and $a^2 - b^2 = (a + b)(a - b)$ respectively.

Exercise 3.5

answers on p. 429

1. Solve the following equations.

(a) $3x^2 - 7x = 0$ **(b)** $2x^2 + x = 0$

(c) $28x^2 + 35x = 0$ **(d)** $x^2 - 36 = 0$

(e) $4x^2 - 49 = 0$ **(f)** $2c^2 - 3c - 9 = 0$

(g) $3d^2 - 2d = 8$ **(h)** $3x^2 = 8x + 3$

(i) $3p^2 + 10p - 8 = 0$ **(j)** $28a^2 + 39a + 5 = 0$

(k) $3x^2 = 27$ **(l)** $12y^2 + 55y + 63 = 0$

(m) $y^2 + 110y + 3\,000 = 0$ **(n)** $3p^2 + 34p + 91 = 0$

(o) $2c^2 + 3c - 2 = 0$ **(p)** $a^2 - 12a + 36 = 0$

(q) $25y^2 + 10y + 1 = 0$ **(r)** $x^2 + 6 = 5x$

(s) $3x^2 - 11x + 6 = 0$ **(t)** $3x^2 - 8x - 11 = 0$

(u) $12x = 4x^2 + 9$ **(v)** $3x^2 + 10x + 3 = 0$

(w) $5x^2 - 6x + 1 = 0$ **(x)** $7x^2 - 78x + 11 = 0$

(y) $12x^2 + 8 = 20x$ **(z)** $6x^2 - 12x + 6 = 0$

2. Solve the following equations.

(a) $(x + 2)(3 - x) + 6 = 0$ **(b)** $(3x - 7)(2x + 1) - 23 = 0$

(c) $(-x - 2)(x - 3) = 4$ **(d)** $(5x - 1)(3x - 2) = 22$

(e) $(x - 2)(5x - 4) + 1 = 0$ **(f)** $(x + 1)(x + 2) = 2(x + 2)$

(g) $(2x + 3)(3x - 2) + 2x + 3 = 0$ **(h)** $1 + (1 - x)(2x + 1) = x^2$

(i) $3(x - 1)^2 + 5x = 5$ **(j)** $4(x - 1)^2 - 12(x - 1) + 9 = 0$

3.6 WORD PROBLEMS LEADING TO QUADRATIC EQUATIONS

Worked Example

The sum of two numbers is 18. The sum of the squares of the numbers is 194. Find the two numbers.

Solution:

Let one of the numbers be x, then the other is $(18 - x)$. The sum of their squares is $x^2 + (18 - x)^2$. This sum is equal to 194.

$$\begin{aligned} x^2 + (18 - x)^2 &= 194 \\ x^2 + 324 - 36x + x^2 &= 194 \\ 2x^2 - 36x + 324 &= 194 \\ 2x^2 - 36x + 130 &= 0 \\ x^2 - 18x + 65 &= 0 \\ (x - 5)(x - 13) &= 0 \\ x - 5 = 0 \quad &\text{or} \quad x - 13 = 0 \\ x = 5 \quad &\text{or} \quad x = 13 \end{aligned}$$

x	-5	$-5x$
x	-13	$-13x$
		$-18x$

If we take $x = 5$, then the other number is $(18 - 5)$, i.e. 13.
If we take $x = 13$, then the other number is $(18 - 13)$, i.e. 5.
Therefore the two numbers are 5 and 13.

MATHSTORY

Many applied problems can be translated into a formula or statement that two quantities or expressions are equal. There is no shortcut for solving applied problems. A guideline to follow was proposed by George Polya (1887–1985) which uses 4 steps:

1. *Understand the problem.*
2. *Devise a plan.*
3. *Carry out the plan.*
4. *Look back and check.*

In essence, to solve an applied problem, we first translate the words of the problem into an algebraic equation and solve the equation.

Exercise 3.6

answers on p. 429

1. The sum of a number and its square is 156. Find the number.

2. The square of a number is equal to 17 times that number. What is the number?

3. The difference between two numbers is 7. The product of the numbers is 144. Find the smaller number.

4. The area of a rectangle is 84 cm^2. If the length is 5 cm longer than the width, find the length of the rectangle.

5. I think of a number and add 7 to it, then I multiply the sum by the original number and the result is 60. Find the number.

6. The square of a number is smaller than 12 times the number by 32. Find the number.

7. The area of a triangle is 24 cm^2. If its height is 2 cm longer than its base, find the base of the triangle.

8. The sum of the square of two consecutive odd numbers is 290. Find the two numbers.

9. The area of the shaded part is 112 cm^2. Find the value of x.

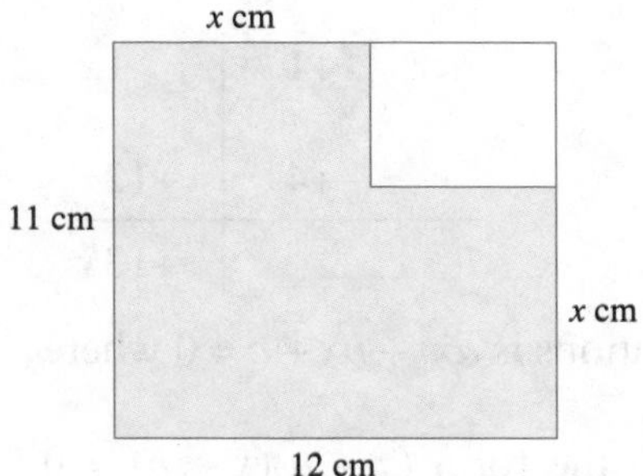

***10.** A farmer encloses a rectangular piece of land which has an area of 2 800 m^2 with a fence 220 m long. Find the length and the width of the piece of land.

***11.** A rectangular lawn, 36 m long and 15 m wide, has a path of uniform width around it. If the area of the path is 910 m^2, find the width of the path.

***12.** Mr Yang's daily wage was $5 more than Mr Chen's. Although Mr Yang worked 3 days less than Mr Chen, they earned $180 each. Find the number of days Mr Yang worked.

***13.** A car travelling uniformly covered 120 km from town A to town B. It would have saved 24 min, had it travelled 15 km/h faster. Find the speed of the car.

***14.** A man bought a number of pens for $63. If the cost per pen was reduced by $1, he would get 1 more pen by paying $1 more. Find the cost of each pen.

Chapter Review

1. A **literal equation** is one in which letters are used to replace the numerical coefficients and the constant terms.

   Example: $(ax + b) - cx = 0$

2. A **formula** may be transformed by making a specified variable as the subject of the formula.

   Example:

   $A = \frac{1}{2}h(a + b)$ can be transformed to $b = \frac{2A}{h} - a$ by making b the subject of the formula.

3. Expressions of the form $ax^2 + bx + c$ $(a \neq 0)$ are called **quadratic expressions** in x.
   - Quadratic expressions can be factorised by **cross-multiplication.**

   Example:
   $3x^2 + 13x + 4 = (3x + 1)(x + 4)$

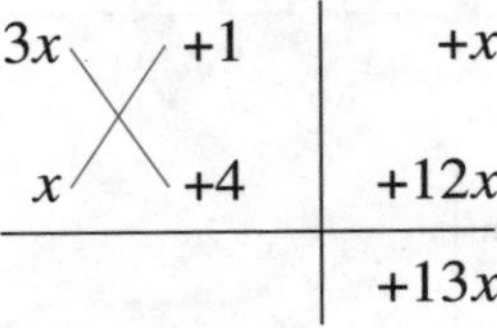

   - The general form of quadratic equations is $ax^2 + bx + c = 0$ where a, b, c are constants and $a \neq 0$.
   - A quadratic equation expressed in the form $(x - a)(x - b) = 0$ implies that either $x - a = 0$ or $x - b = 0$.
   - A quadratic equation expressed in the form $(x - a)(x - b) = c$ does **not** necessarily imply that $x - a = c$ or $x - b = c$.

CHALLENGER 3

1. State whether each of the following statements is true or false.
   If $(x - y)(y - z)(z - x) = 0$, then
   (a) all the variables must be zero,
   (b) all the variables must be equal,
   (c) at least two of the variables are equal,
   (d) at least one of the variables is zero.

2. Solve $1 - \cfrac{1}{1 - \cfrac{1}{1 - \cfrac{1}{x - 1}}} = 5$.

3. Solve the literal equation $ax^2 - bx + b - a = 0$.

4. If a, b and c are positive numbers, solve the literal equation
$$a(b + x) - b(c + x) - c(a + x) = a(x - c) - c(b + x).$$

5. If $a \neq 0$ and $b \neq 0$, solve the literal equation
$$(ax - b)^2 + (bx - a)^2 + 2x(a + b)^2 = 0.$$

6. **(a)** Solve $2^{2x} - 7(2^x) - 8 = 0$. (*Hint:* Let $y = 2^x$.)
   (b) Solve $2^{2x} + 2^{x+3} - 48 = 0$.

Problem Solving 3

Ten Matchsticks

Use not more than 10 matchsticks to form a rectangle each time. How many different rectangles can you form? Find their areas, taking 1 matchstick length as 1 unit.

We have $x + y \leqslant 5$

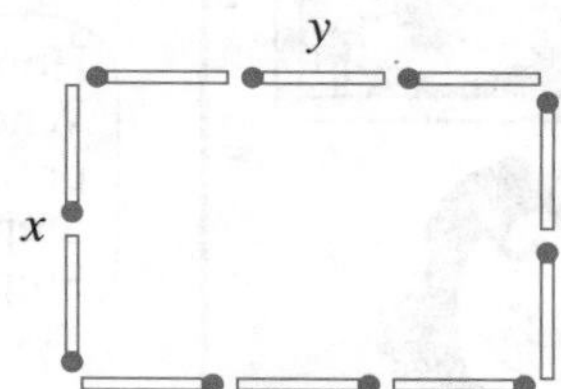

Then,
$x = 1, 1, 1, 1, 2, 2$
$y = 1, 2, 3, 4, 2, 3$

There are 6 different rectangles that can be formed. Their areas are:

1, 2, 3, 4, 4, 6 sq units

The strategies used are **consider a limiting case**, **draw a diagram** and **make a systematic list**.

1. **Twelve Sticks** Use not more than 12 sticks of length 2 cm each to form a different rectangle each time. Find the areas of all the rectangles.

2. **Forming Rectangles with Toothpicks** Use toothpicks as unit length to form a rectangle each time so that one side is less than 6 units and the other is not more than 2 units. Find the areas of all the rectangles formed.

3. **Price Increase** Last week, Mary paid \$60 for some meat at a market. This week, she got 2 kg less meat with the same amount of money due to a price increase of \$1 per kg. Find the new price of 1 kg of meat.

4. **Reflection** Take I to be 1 and substitute a digit for each of the other letters so as to make the following addition correct. (The same letter represents the same digit. Different letters represent different digits.)

$$\begin{array}{r} THINK \\ +\ RETHINK \\ \hline REFLECT \\ \hline \end{array}$$

Chapter 4

Word Problems

Chapter Highlights

- Demonstrating familiarity with the usage of the languages of fraction, percentage, ratio and rate and their connections
- Solving problems on rate, ratio and percentage
- Demonstrating familiarity with the terms percentage profit/gain/loss, percentage increase, decrease, discount, commission and depreciation
- Solving problems involving personal and household finance and simple financial transactions including currency exchange

4.1 PROBLEMS ON RATE, RATIO AND PERCENTAGE

Rate

Rate is used to describe how a quantity changes with respect to another quantity.

Rate is a comparison of two quantities that are not measured in the same units.

Example

A worker is paid \$84 for 6 hours of work. We say that he is paid \$ $\frac{84}{6}$ or \$14 for one hour of work or at the rate \$14/h.

Ratio

A ratio is used to compare the magnitudes of two similar quantities. It indicates what fraction one quantity is of the other, or how many times one quantity is as much as the other.

Ratio is a comparison of two quantities measured in the same units.

Example

A sum of money is shared between Mr X and Mr Y in the ratio 3 : 5. If Mr X gets \$$x$ and Mr Y gets \$$y$, then we write

$$x : y = 3 : 5 \quad \text{or} \quad y : x = 5 : 3$$

$$\frac{x}{y} = \frac{3}{5} \quad \text{or} \quad \frac{y}{x} = \frac{5}{3}$$

$$x = \frac{3}{5}y \quad \text{or} \quad y = \frac{5}{3}x$$

Percentage

'Per cent' means 'for each hundred' or 'out of a hundred'.

Percentage is a special fraction with one hundred as its denominator. It may be used to compare a part of a quantity to the whole quantity.

The short form of 'per cent' is %.

Percentages can be converted to decimals or fractions.

Examples

$$15\% = 15 \times \frac{1}{100} = \frac{15}{100} = 0.15$$

$$15\% = 15 \times \frac{1}{100} = \frac{15}{100} = \frac{3}{20}$$

Class Activity 1

State whether each of the following is true (T) or false (F).

1. A is $\frac{3}{4}$ of B means B is $\frac{4}{3}$ of A.

2. A is $\frac{3}{4}\%$ of B means B is $\frac{4}{3}\%$ of A.

3. If A is 5% more than B, then B is 5% less than A.

4. If A increases by 8% and then decreases by 8%, the result is equal to A.

5. If A increases by 10% and then further increases by 5%, the overall increase is 15% of A.

6. A is given a 5% increase followed by a 10% decrease. This is the same as when A is given a 10% decrease followed by a 5% increase.

7. If A increases by 10%, its value becomes B. Then A is 90% of B.

8. If A increases by 10%, its value becomes B. Then B is 110% of A.

9. If A is 35% of B, then $A : B$ is $35 : 100$.

10. If A is 35% of B, then $B : A$ is $65 : 35$.

11. $A : B$ is $3 : 4$ means A is $\frac{3}{7}$ of B.

12. $A : B$ is $3 : 4$ means A is 75% of B.

13. $A : B$ is $3 : 4$ means B is 75% of A.

14. In a class, the ratio of the number of boys to the number of girls is $3 : 4$. This means the number of boys is $\frac{3}{4}$ the number of girls.

15. In a class, the number of boys to the number of girls is $3 : 4$. This means the number of boys is 75% of the number of students in the class.

16. In a class, the number of boys to the number of girls is $3 : 4$. This means the number of girls is 75% of the number of students in the class.

17. A increases in the ratio $5 : 4$ means A increases by $\frac{5}{4}\%$.

18. A increases in the ratio 5 : 4 means A increases by 125%.

19. A increases in the ratio 5 : 4 means A increases by 25%.

20. The fee charged at a rate of $5 per hour means the ratio of the fee charged in dollars to the number of hours spent is 1 : 5.

21. If $A : B = \frac{1}{x} : \frac{1}{y}$, then $A : B = y : x$.

22. The number of boys in a class is a% and the number of girls is $(a + 10)$%. This means the number of girls is 10% more than the number of boys.

23. If there are more girls than boys in a class and the difference in percentage is 10%, then the number of girls is more than the number of boys by 10% of the class.

24. A is 200% of B means A is twice B.

25. A is 200% more than B means A is twice B.

26. The rate of consumption of petrol by a car is 12.5 l per 100 km. This means it uses petrol at a rate of 0.125 l/km.

27. The consumption of petrol by a car is 12.5 l per 100 km. This means it travels at a rate of 8 km/l.

28. In a class, there are 20% more girls than boys. This means 60% of the class are girls and 40% are boys.

Worked Example 1

Ali takes 15 minutes to walk from the school to the MRT station. Bala takes 20 minutes to walk from the school to the station. If the difference in their speeds is 2 km/h, how far is the MRT station from the school?

Solution:

Let x km be the distance between the school and the MRT station.

Ali's speed = $\left(x \div \frac{1}{4}\right)$ km/h = $4x$ km/h

Bala's speed = $\left(x \div \frac{1}{3}\right)$ km/h = $3x$ km/h

So $4x - 3x = 2$

$x = 2$

$\therefore$ the distance is 2 km.

Worked Example 2

Car A travelled along a straight road from town X to town Y at a constant speed of 75 km/h. Car B travelled from town Y to town X at a constant speed of 65 km/h. Both started their journeys at the same time and travelled on the same road. If they passed each other after travelling $2\frac{3}{4}$ hours, find the distance between X and Y.

Solution:

In 1 hour, car A covered 75 km.

In $2\frac{3}{4}$ hours, car A covered $\left(\frac{11}{4} \times 75\right)$ km.

In 1 hour, car B covered 65 km.

In $2\frac{3}{4}$ hours, car B covered $\left(\frac{11}{4} \times 65\right)$ km.

$$\therefore \text{ the distance between } X \text{ and } Y = \left[\left(\frac{11}{4} \times 75\right) + \left(\frac{11}{4} \times 65\right)\right] \text{ km}$$

$$= 385 \text{ km}$$

Worked Example 3

A sum of money is divided equally among Ann, Betty and Carol. An equal sum of money is divided among David, Eddie and Frederick in the ratio 2 : 3 : 5. If Ann receives $28 more than David, how much does Frederick receive?

Solution:

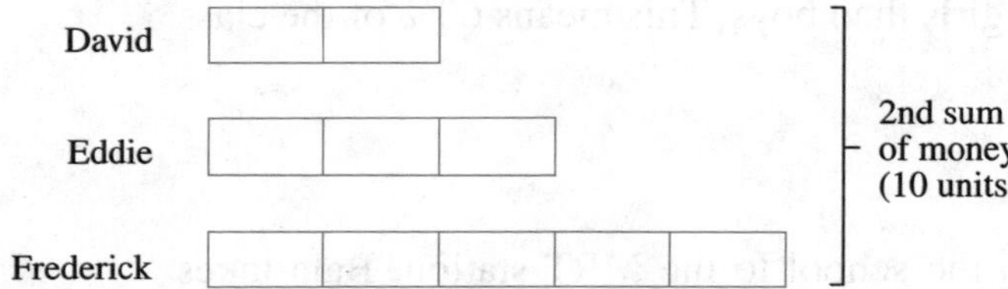

David's share = 2 units

Since the two sums of money are equal,

$$\text{Ann's share} = \frac{10}{3} \text{ units}$$

So $$\left(\frac{10}{3} - 2\right) \text{ units} = \$28$$

$$\frac{4}{3} \text{ units} = \$28$$

$$1 \text{ unit} = \$21$$

$$\text{Frederick's share} = 5 \text{ units}$$

$$= 5 \times \$21$$

$$= \$105$$

Alternative solution:

Let each sum of money be $\$x$.

Ann's share = $\$\left(\frac{x}{3}\right)$

David's share = $\$\left(\frac{2x}{10}\right) = \$\left(\frac{x}{5}\right)$

So
$$\frac{x}{3} - \frac{x}{5} = 28$$
$$2x = 28 \times 15$$
$$x = 210$$
$$\text{Frederick's share} = \$\left(\frac{5x}{10}\right)$$
$$= \$105$$

Worked Example 4

25% of a class of 40 students were girls. When some new girls joined the class, the percentage of girls increased to 40%. How many new girls joined the class?

Solution:

In the original class, number of girls $= \frac{25}{100} \times 40$
$= 10$

Let x be the number of new girls who joined the class.

Then
$$\text{number of girls} = 10 + x$$
$$\text{number of students} = 40 + x$$
$$10 + x = 40\% \times (40 + x)$$
$$= \frac{40}{100} \times (40 + x)$$
$$= \frac{160 + 4x}{10}$$
$$100 + 10x = 160 + 4x$$
$$6x = 60$$
$$x = 10$$

$\therefore$ 10 new girls joined the class.

Alternative solution:

Let x be the number of new girls who joined the class.
Number of boys remains unchanged.

$75\% \times 40 = 60\% \times (40 + x)$
$30 = 24 + 0.6x$
$6 = 0.6x$
$x = 10$

$\therefore$ 10 new girls joined the class.

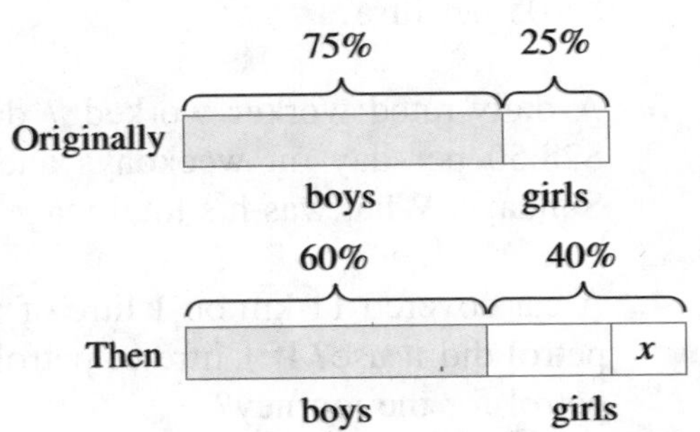

Worked Example 5

Solution A contains 40% of concentrated acid and solution B contains 60% of the same concentrated acid. How many cubic centimetres of each type are needed to produce 1 000 cm^3 of mixture containing 55% of concentrated acid?

Solution:

Let the volume of solution A in the mixture be x cm^3.
Then the volume of solution B in the mixture is $(1\,000 - x)$ cm^3.

x cm^3 of solution A contains $\frac{40}{100}x$ cm^3 of concentrated acid.

$(1\,000 - x)$ cm^3 of solution B contains $\frac{60}{100}(1\,000 - x)$ cm^3 of concentrated acid.

But the mixture contains $\left(\frac{55}{100} \times 1\,000\right)$ cm^3 of concentrated acid.

$$\frac{40}{100}x + \frac{60}{100}(1\,000 - x) = \frac{55}{100} \times 1\,000$$
$$4x + 6\,000 - 6x = 5\,500$$
$$-2x = -500$$
$$x = 250$$

$\therefore$ the mixture contains 250 cm^3 of solution A and 750 cm^3 of solution B.

Exercise 4.1

answers on p. 429

1. Under an employment contract, a daily-rated worker was to work 6 days a week for 52 weeks a year. For the first 26 weeks, he was paid \$15.70 per day. His daily wage was increased to \$18.00 for the rest of the year. Find the amount he earned for the whole year.

2. A salesman found that he had to travel 45 km each working day in the week (excluding Sundays). At this rate, what would his petrol bill for 4 weeks be if his car travelled 9 km on 1 litre of petrol, and the petrol cost \$1.05 per litre?

3. A daily-rated worker worked 7 days a week for 3 weeks. He was paid \$28.50 per day on weekdays and Saturdays and twice this amount on Sundays. What was his total wage?

4. A car covered 11 km on 1 litre of petrol. If it covered 418 km, how much petrol did it use? If 1 litre of petrol cost \$1.05, how much was the cost of petrol for the journey?

5. An express train left station X at 09 00 and arrived at station Y at 11 30. If it travelled at a constant speed of 55 km/h, what was the distance travelled?

6. Find the average speed of an aeroplane if it left airport P at 07 45 and arrived at airport Q at 09 00, the distance travelled being 750 km.

7. Town A was 364 km away from town B. A car left town A for town B at 10 30. If it travelled at a constant speed of 56 km/h, at what time would it arrive at B?

8. The speed of a car is 90 km/h. Express the speed in
(a) km/min, **(b)** m/s.

9. **(a)** A late night radio programme began at 22 45 one evening and finished at 03 20 the following morning. For how many minutes did the programme last?
(b) A small bird enters its nest to feed its young, on average, every 40 seconds. How many visits to the nest does the bird make, on average, each hour?
(C)

10. Mary works five days each week. She starts work at 08 30, has a lunch break of one hour and finishes work at 17 55.
(a) How many hours does she work each week?
(b) If she is paid a rate of \$7.60 an hour excluding lunch break, calculate her weekly wage.

11. Walking at an average speed of 5 km/h, Alan took 24 minutes to travel from home to his office and arrived at 07 55.
(a) Find the time at which he left home.
(b) Calculate how far he had to walk.

12. A man walks a distance of 600 m at an average speed of 4 km/h and then, without stopping, jogs a further distance of 1.4 km in 7 minutes. Calculate
(a) the time, in minutes, he takes to walk the 600 m,
(b) his jogging speed in km/h,
(c) his average speed for the whole journey in km/h.

13. The speed of light is given as 3.00×10^8 m/s. Light takes 5.00×10^2 seconds to travel from the Sun to the Earth.
(a) Calculate, in km, the distance between the Earth and the Sun, giving your answer in standard form, correct to 2 significant figures.
(b) How long does light take to travel from the Sun to Jupiter if the distance between them is given as 7.78×10^8 km? Give your answer correct to 3 significant figures.

14. Alice and Betty work part time in a restaurant. Each of them is paid \$6.40 an hour. Alice works $2\frac{1}{2}$ hours every day of the week except Sunday. Betty works 5 hours on Saturday and $6\frac{3}{4}$ hours on Sunday. The rate of pay for Sunday is \$10.60 an hour.

(a) How much does Alice earn each week?
(b) How much longer does Alice work each week than Betty?
(c) On a Saturday, how much more money does Betty earn than Alice?
(d) How much does Betty earn each week?

15. The table gives the annual rates of road tax for private cars in 1988.

Engine capacity in cubic centimetres (cc)	Cents per cubic centimetre
1 000 and below	70
1 001 to 1 600	90
1 601 to 2 000	105
2 001 to 3 000	125
Above 3 000	175

(a) Find, in dollars, the annual road tax for a car with engine capacity 1 400 cc.
(b) A man has a car with an engine capacity of 2 000 cc. His wife has a car with an engine capacity of 2 200 cc. Calculate in dollars, how much more road tax the woman has to pay each year than her husband.
(C)

16. Cyclist *A* took 3 h to travel from town *X* to town *Y*. Cyclist *B* took 45 min less to cover the same distance as he travelled at a speed faster by 3 km/h. Find the distance from town *X* to town *Y*.

17. A motorist travelled along a straight road from town *A* to town *B* at 70 km/h. A motorcyclist travelled from town *B* to town *A* at 80 km/h. Both started the journeys at the same time and travelled on the same road.
(a) If they passed each other after travelling for 1 hour 40 minutes, find the distance between town *A* and town *B*.
(b) How long did the motorcyclist take to travel his whole journey?

18. At 09 00, car *A* started its journey and travelled at 70 km/h. At 10 30, car *B* started from the same place and travelled steadily on the same road. Car *B* took $3\frac{1}{2}$ h to catch up with car *A*.
(a) Find the speed of car *B*.
(b) At 15 24, car *B* reached its destination. When did car *A* reach the same destination?

19. Divide \$63 among three men in the ratio $\frac{1}{2} : \frac{1}{4} : \frac{1}{8}$. How much will each get?

20. Divide \$88 between *A* and *B* so that for every \$3 received by *A*, *B* will receive \$5. How much will each get?

21. The monthly salaries of 3 men are \$500, \$700 and \$900 respectively. Divide a bonus of \$1 050 among them in proportion to their salaries. How much bonus will each get?

22. The total prize money for the first three placings in a competition was \$14 000. If the winner received twice as much as the one in the second placing and four times as much as the one in the third placing, how much did each receive?

23. It took 6 men to complete a certain job in 3 hours and 20 minutes. How long will it take 8 men, working at the same rate, to complete the same job?

24. David works 20 days in order to earn \$1 360. Assuming the same rate of pay per day, calculate
(a) how much he will earn in 14 days,
(b) how many days he will have to work in order to earn \$612.

25. A sum of money is divided among Alan, Bill and Carl in the ratio 2 : 4 : 7. If Carl receives \$27 more than Bill, how much more does Bill receive than Alan?

26. **(a)** Find the larger share when 18.6 kg is divided in the ratio 2 : 3 : 5.
(b) A sum of money was divided among John, Paul and Robert in the ratio 2 : 4 : 5. Had the sum of money been divided equally among them, John's share would have been larger by \$50. What was the total sum of money?

27. 9 men can unload 450 kg of goods in 2 hours. If, after having unloaded 150 kg of goods, 5 men were asked to do other jobs, how many more hours are needed for the remaining 4 men to unload the rest of the goods?

28. 4 skilled workers can do a job in 5 days. 5 semi-skilled workers can do the same job in 6 days. How long does it take 1 semi-skilled and 2 skilled workers to do the job working together?

29. A telephone directory has 743 pages and an average of 380 entries on each page.
(a) Find, correct to the nearest thousand, the number of entries in the directory.
(b) If 17% of the subscribers do not have their telephone numbers listed in the directory, find the total number of subscribers. Give your answer correct to the nearest thousand.

30. A concert hall has seats for an audience of 240. Calculate
(a) the number of people in the hall when $\frac{5}{8}$ of the seats are occupied,
(b) the percentage of seats which are occupied when there are 204 people at the concert.

31. **(a)** The area of a square is 225 cm^2. Find the length of one side of the square.
(b) If the length is now increased by 20%, find the area of the new square.

32. The intake of a certain school in the year 1997 was 75 students more than that of 1996. If the intake of students in 1996 was 500, what was the percentage increase?

33. The enrolment of a school was 480 in 1987. By 1997, the enrolment had increased by 20%. What was the enrolment in 1997?

34. In 1987, the population of a town was 72 000. In 1997, the population had risen to 88 000. Find the percentage increase in population. Give your answer correct to 1 decimal place.

35. In an examination, 80 problems were given and all the problems carried equal marks.
(a) A boy had 28 problems correct. What percentage was this?
(b) In order to pass the examination, it is necessary to answer at least 45% of the problems correctly. What was the lowest number of correct answers needed to pass?

36. How much water must be added to 960 m*l* of acid which contains 10% pure acid to obtain a solution containing 8% of pure acid?

***37.** 70 g of sugar is added to 400 g of water to produce a solution. How much more sugar must be added to the solution so that it contains 20% of sugar?

***38.** An alloy of copper and silver containing 64% of pure silver is mixed with another alloy also of copper and silver containing 70% of pure silver. How much of each type of alloy is needed to produce 1 500 kg of alloy containing 68% of pure silver?

***39.** 60 ml of solution A is mixed with 120 ml of solution B to produce solution C which contains 8% of pure acid. If 80 ml of solution A is mixed with 40 ml of solution B, a solution D containing 10% of pure acid can be produced. Find the percentage of pure acid in solution A.

***40.** x ml of pure alcohol from a bottle containing 2 l of pure alcohol is replaced by water. Again, x ml of the diluted alcohol from the bottle is replaced by water. If the bottle now contains 81% of pure alcohol, find the value of x.

4.2 PROBLEMS INVOLVING FINANCIAL TRANSACTIONS

Class Activity 2

1. Copy and complete the sentences in Column B so that each has the same meaning as in Column A.

	Column A	Column B
(a)	The percentage profit is 10%.	The profit is 10% of the ________.
(b)	The percentage increase or decrease is 10%.	The increase or decrease is 10% of the ________.
(c)	An increase or decrease of 10%.	An increase or decrease by 10% of the ________.
(d)	A discount of 10%.	A discount equal to 10% of the ________.
(e)	A gain or loss of 10%.	A gain or loss equal to 10% of the ________.
(f)	A is 10% more or less than B.	A is more or less than B by 10% of ________.
(g)	A commission of 10%.	A commission equal to 10% of the ________.
(h)	A depreciation of 10%.	A decrease in value equal to 10% of the ________.
(i)	16 of the 40 students are girls. What percentage are girls?	16 of the 40 students are girls. What percentage of ________ are girls?
(j)	The percentage of boys in a class is 10%.	10% of ________ are boys.

2. State whether each of the following is true (T) or false (F).

(a) To find the percentage profit means to find the profit and then express it as a percentage of the cost price.

(b) To express x as a percentage of y means to divide x by y and then multiply by 100% to obtain the percentage.

(c) If the percentage profit is a%, then the selling price is $(100 + a)$% of the cost price.

(d) If the percentage profit is a%, then the cost price is $(100 - a)$% of the selling price.

(e) If the percentage loss is a%, then the selling price is $(100 - a)$% of the cost price.

(f) If the percentage loss is a%, then the cost price is $(100 - a)$% of the selling price.

(g) If the percentage gain is a%, then the cost price is $\frac{100}{100 + a}$ of the selling price.

(h) If the percentage loss is a%, then the cost price is $\frac{100}{100 - a}$ of the selling price.

(i) If the percentage gain is a%, then the cost price is the quotient of dividing the selling price by $(100 + a)$%.

(j) If the percentage loss is a%, then the cost price is the quotient of dividing the selling price by $(100 - a)$%.

Worked Example 1

The usual price of an article was \$200. A man bought it at a discount of 15%. How much did he pay for it?

Solution:

Reduced price = usual price – discount
= \$200 – 15% of usual price

$$= \$200 - \left(15 \times \frac{1}{100} \times \$200\right)$$

= \$200 – \$30
= \$170

$\therefore$ he paid \$170 for the article.

Alternative solution:

Reduced price = 85% × \$200
= 0.85 × \$200
= \$170

Worked Example 2

By selling goods for \$336, a trader made a profit of 12%. How much did the goods cost?

Solution:
If the cost of goods was x dollars,
then the profit was $(336 - x)$ dollars.

The profit of 12% of x can be expressed as $\frac{12}{100}x$ or $\frac{3}{25}x$.

We have
$$\begin{aligned} 336 - x &= \frac{3}{25}x \\ 25(336 - x) &= 3x \\ 25 \times 336 - 25x &= 3x \\ 8\,400 &= 28x \\ \frac{8\,400}{28} &= x \\ x &= 300 \end{aligned}$$

$\therefore$ the goods cost \$300.

Alternative solution:
Let the cost of goods be x dollars.
$x : 336 = 100\% : 112\%$

$$\begin{aligned} x &= \frac{100}{112} \times 336 \\ &= 300 \end{aligned}$$

Worked Example 3
On a certain day, the exchange rates of currency were as follows:

Foreign currencies	Singapore dollars (S$)
100 baht (Thailand)	5.60
100 pesos (Philippines)	5.70
100 rupiah (Indonesia)	0.06
100 ringgit (Malaysia)	58.00

Convert
(a) S\$25 to baht (to the nearest baht),
(b) S\$50 to pesos (to the nearest peso),
(c) 1 500 rupiah to S\$,
(d) 750 ringgit to S\$.

Solution:
(a) S\$5.60 = 100 baht

$$\text{S\$1} = \frac{100}{5.60} \text{ baht}$$

$$\therefore \text{S\$25} = \left(\frac{100}{5.60} \times 25\right) \text{ baht} = 446 \text{ baht}$$

You may first estimate the answer mentally:

(a) $\$25 = \frac{100}{5.60} \times 25$ baht
$\approx \frac{100}{6} \times 24$ baht
$=$ 400 baht

(b) $S\$5.70 = 100 \text{ pesos}$

$$S\$1 = \frac{100}{5.70} \text{ pesos}$$

$$\therefore S\$50 = \left(\frac{100}{5.70} \times 50\right) \text{ pesos} = 877 \text{ pesos}$$

$$\$50 = \frac{100}{5.70} \times 50 \text{ pesos}$$
$$\approx \frac{5\ 400}{6} \text{ pesos}$$
$$= 900 \text{ pesos}$$

(c) $100 \text{ rupiah} = S\$0.06$

$$1 \text{ rupiah} = S\$\left(\frac{0.06}{100}\right)$$

$$\therefore 1\ 500 \text{ rupiah} = S\$\left(\frac{0.06}{100} \times 1\ 500\right) = S\$0.90$$

$$1\ 500 \text{ rupiah} = S\$\left(\frac{0.06}{100} \times 1\ 500\right)$$
$$= S\$\frac{6 \times 15}{100}$$
$$= S\$0.90$$

(d) $100 \text{ ringgit} = S\$58$

$$1 \text{ ringgit} = S\$\left(\frac{58}{100}\right)$$

$$\therefore 750 \text{ ringgit} = S\$\left(\frac{58}{100} \times 750\right) = S\$435$$

$$750 \text{ ringgit} = S\$\left(\frac{58}{100} \times 750\right)$$
$$\approx S\$\frac{60}{100} \times 750$$
$$= S\$450$$

Worked Example 4

A lady paid \$1 250 cash for a colour television set. A man bought an identical set on hire purchase. He paid a deposit of \$312.50 and the balance in 12 monthly instalments of \$85.50. How much more did he pay than the lady?

Solution:

Deposit = \$312.50

12 monthly instalments of \$85.50 = \$85.50 × 12
= \$1 026

The hire purchase price = \$312.50 + \$1 026
= \$1 338.50

The difference between the cash price and hire purchase price
= \$1 338.50 – \$1 250
= \$88.50

∴ he paid \$88.50 more.

Worked Example 5

Ali and Bala decided to start a business. Ali invested \$24 000 and Bala invested \$18 000. They agreed to share the profit of the business in the same ratio as their investments. In 1996, the total profit was \$10 500.

(a) Find Ali's share of the profit in 1996.

(b) The total profit made in 1996 was 25% greater than in 1995. Find the total profit made in 1995.

(c) The total profit made in 1997 was 15% greater than in 1996. After sharing the profit, Bala sold his share to Ali for \$19 800. Calculate Bala's total profit made in three years.

Solution:

(a) Ali's share : Bala's share = 24 000 : 18 000 = 4 : 3

In 1996, Ali's profit $= \$10\ 500 \times \frac{4}{7}$

$= \$6\ 000$

(b) Total profit in 1995 $= \$10\ 500 \div 125\%$
$= \$8\ 400$

(c) Total profit in 1997 $= \$10\ 500 \times 115\%$
$= \$12\ 075$

In three years,
total profit of business $= \$8\ 400 + \$10\ 500 + \$12\ 075$
$= \$30\ 975$

Bala's share of the profit $= \frac{3}{7} \times \$30\ 975$
$= \$13\ 275$

$\therefore$ Bala's total profit made in three years $= \$13\ 275 + \$19\ 800 - \$18\ 000$
$= \$15\ 075$

Exercise 4.2

answers on p. 429

1. An article costs \$72.80. If the cost is increased by 25%, find the new cost.

2. If a man's salary is increased from \$500 to \$625, find the percentage increase in his salary.

3. An article costs 85 cents. What will be the new cost if the cost is decreased by 5%? Give your answer to the nearest cent.

4. A man bought an article for \$250 and sold it for \$280. Find his percentage gain.

5. A shopkeeper bought 40 pens of the same type for \$600 and sold them at \$18 each. What was his percentage gain or loss?

6. A merchant made 15% profit by selling his goods for \$92. How much did he pay for the goods?

7. The usual price of a dress was \$250. A lady bought it at a discount of 12%. How much did she pay for it?

8. A bookseller sold 300 identical pencils at 25 cents each and made a profit of $15. What was his percentage profit?

9. A man bought a second-hand car for $8 500, spent $1 500 on repairs and then sold it for $12 000. What was his percentage profit?

10. A shopkeeper made a profit of 20% when he sold an article for $24.48. How much did the article cost?

11. A man bought an article for $120. At what price must he sell it in order to make a profit of 15%?

12. Find the percentage discount for the following articles. Give each answer correct to the nearest per cent.

	Usual price	Sale price
(a)	$10.90	$ 9.50
(b)	$ 1.60	$ 1.05
(c)	$ 5.90	$ 4.90
(d)	$ 3.60	$ 2.60
(e)	$ 3.10	$ 2.15
(f)	$27.00	$16.90

13. How much would it cost a man in one year if he bought the following?

Daily newspapers (Monday to Saturday) at 60 cents each
Sunday papers at 65 cents each
Weekly reviews at $1.50 each
Monthly magazines at $3.50 per copy

(Assume that in 1 year, there are 365 days with 52 Sundays.)

14. A man bought 15 boxes of oranges at $20.50 per box. It cost him $16 to transport these oranges. Find his net profit if he sold all his oranges for $385.

15. On a certain day, the exchange rates of currency were as follows:

100 units of foreign currencies	Singapore dollars
Thai baht	5.60
Philippine peso	5.70
Indonesian rupiah	0.06
Malaysian ringgit	58.00

Convert

(a) 1 Singapore dollar to Thai baht (to the nearest baht),
(b) 1 000 Philippine pesos to Singapore dollars,
(c) 50 Singapore dollars to Malaysian ringgit (to the nearest ringgit),
(d) 1 000 Indonesian rupiah to Singapore dollars.

16. A shopkeeper allows his customers to pay for the following articles in two ways.

Article	Cash	Hire purchase
Electric oven	$ 350	Deposit $80 and 12 monthly instalments of $26.
Refrigerator	$1 200	Deposit $300 and 24 monthly instalments of $45.
Video recorder	$ 2 270	Deposit $570 and 24 monthly instalments of $78.

For each of the articles, find the difference between the cash price and the hire purchase price.

17. At a restaurant, a 12% service charge is added to the basic food bill. Calculate
(a) the service charge on a basic food bill which amounts to $125,
(b) the basic food bill on which a service charge of $8.40 is included.

18. The perimeter of a rectangular floor, of length 6 m, is 22 m. Calculate
(a) the area of the floor,
(b) the cost of carpeting this floor if the cost of a carpet is $25 per square metre.

19. A wholesaler sells a roll of 20-m curtain material at $160. A retail store sells the same material at $12 per metre.
(a) How much will 20 m of curtain material cost at the retail store?
(b) How much will be saved if 20 m of material are bought from the wholesaler?
(c) Express the amount saved as a percentage of the price at the retailer.

20. A doctor's prescription states that the medicine prescribed should be diluted with water in the ratio of two parts medicine to three parts water.
(a) If there are 120 m*l* of medicine, how much water will have been used when the patient has completed taking the medicine?
(b) If the patient must take 5 m*l* of medicine three times a day, how much water is taken with the medicine each day?
(c) At the above rate, how many days will the patient take to finish the medicine?

21. Mr Li bought 15 badminton rackets for $232.50.
(a) Find the cost of each racket.
(b) If he sells each racket for $19, how much profit will he make on each one?
(c) Express his total profit as a percentage of his cost. (Give your answer correct to the nearest per cent.)

22. Tom bought a new motorcycle for $5 200.
(a) Calculate the decrease in value if it is worth 20% less after one year.
(b) After another year, the value decreased further by 10%. Calculate the value of the motorcycle after two years.

23. Look at this figure and answer the following questions.

(a) How much more must be paid if the microwave oven is bought by instalment?
(b) Express the difference between paying by cash and paying by instalments as a percentage of the cash price.

24. Peter and Paul shared the profits from their two food stalls in the ratio 3 : 4.
(a) Calculate Paul's share if the profit from the first stall was $4 550.
(b) Peter received $550 less than Paul from the profit of the second stall. Calculate the profit made from the second stall.

25. Patrick bought a car for $38 000. He owned it for one year and then sold it for $32 300.
(a) Calculate the loss in value of the car as a percentage of the purchase price.
(b) The amounts of money he spent on the car for the year were as follows:

Road tax	$1 200
Insurance	$ 450
Repairs	$ 150
Petrol	910 litres at an average cost of $1.20 per litre
Parking fees	$592

Calculate the total cost of owning and maintaining the car, including the depreciation in value.

26. The exchange rates for one American dollar (US$1.00) are shown in the table.

Australia	1.53 dollars	Italy	1 616 lira
Austria	11.46 schillings	Japan	106 yen
Canada	1.34 dollars	Malaysia	2.55 ringgit
Denmark	6.69 krone	New Zealand	1.83 dollars
France	5.73 francs	Netherlands	1.82 guilders
Germany	1.61 marks	Singapore	1.55 dollars
Great Britain	0.662 pounds	Spain	127 pesetas
Hong Kong	7.78 dollars	Switzerland	1.41 francs

Change
(a) US$96 into Danish krone,
(b) US$96 into French francs,
(c) 220 marks into American dollars,
(d) 2 050 schillings into lira.
Write all your answers correct to two decimal places.

27. **(a)** A sum of money is divided among Joan, Jean and Janice in the ratio 3 : 5 : 8. If Jean's share is $36 less than Janice's share, calculate how much money Joan receives.
(b) If the interest earned in 1 year on $1 000 is $42.50, calculate how much would be earned in 2 years on $40 000 at the same rate of simple interest.

28. **(a)** Calculate the simple interest on $200 at 4% per annum for 5 years.
(b) The exchange rate between the English pound (£) and the American dollar ($) during one summer was £1 to $1.60.
(i) How many dollars would an Englishman get for £400?
(ii) How many pounds would an American get for $800? (*C*)

29. Each of the 50 seats at the front of a cinema sells for half the price of one of the remaining seats. There are 200 seats altogether and when every seat is sold the takings are $525.
(a) Find the price of a seat at the front of the cinema.
(b) The prices of all the seats are then increased by 20%. Calculate the new takings when all the seats are sold. (*C*)

30. The owner of a sportshop made a profit of 35% on every item which he sold.
(a) Find the selling price of a badminton racket which cost the shopkeeper $31.
(b) Find the cost price of a pair of dumbbells which the shopkeeper sold for $116.
(c) The shopkeeper made a profit of $84 when he sold a stopwatch. Calculate the selling price of the stopwatch.

31. A woman's basic weekly wage is \$140 and she receives this for working a 40-hour week.

(a) Calculate her hourly rate of pay.

(b) If she has to work overtime, she is paid one and a half times more. Calculate her hourly overtime rate of pay.

(c) Calculate the amount she would earn in a week in which she worked for 50 hours altogether.

(d) At the beginning of the year the woman opens a bank account and each month she pays \$20.50 into her account. After 6 months her account is credited with \$3.12 interest and, at the end of the year, her account is credited with a further \$10.08 interest. Calculate how much she has in her bank account at the end of the year.

(e) Each week, the woman sets aside $\frac{2}{5}$ of her basic wage of \$140 in order to pay her household bills. Calculate how much she spends, each week, on her household bills, giving your answer correct to the nearest \$10. *(C)*

32. During the course of a year, a motorist recorded that in successive periods of two months he had driven 640 km, 1 200 km, 2 000 km, 4 000 km, 2 800 km and 880 km. Calculate

(a) the average monthly distance driven,

(b) the fuel bill for the year if the cost of petrol is \$1.20 for every 16 km driven,

(c) what the average monthly distance would have to be, if the cost of petrol increased by 25% and the fuel bill for the year remained the same. *(C)*

33. Mr Brown, Mr Jones and Mr Smith each decided to buy a television.

(a) Mr Brown decided to buy one which was priced at \$540 and he offered to pay cash for it. He was given a discount of $7\frac{1}{2}$%. Calculate how much he actually paid for this television.

(b) Mr Jones decided to buy a set priced at \$714 on hire purchase. He agreed to pay a deposit of one-third of the shop price and 24 equal monthly repayments. Given that he paid \$874 altogether for his television, calculate the amount of one of his monthly repayments.

(c) Mr Smith was interested in a television which was priced at \$600 but, by the time he had decided to buy it, the price had increased by 5%. Mr Smith also decided to pay cash for his television and, like Mr Brown, he was given a discount of $7\frac{1}{2}$%. Calculate how much he paid for his television. *(C)*

34. **(a)** Calculate $\frac{0.163}{0.185 \times 632}$, giving your answer correct to 2 significant figures.

(b) In 1985 Angela and John decided to start a business. Angela invested \$240 000 and John invested \$160 000. They agreed that all the profits should be divided in the same ratio as the sums of money they invested. In 1990 the total profit was \$15 000.

(i) How much was John's share of the 1990 profit?

(ii) The total profit in 1991 was 40% greater than that made in 1990. Calculate the total profit made in 1991.

(iii) The total profit in 1990 was 20% greater than that made in 1989. Calculate the total profit made in 1989.

(iv) Express the total profit in 1991 as a percentage of the total profit in 1989. *(C)*

35. The cash price of a television set is \$750. Robert buys it on hire purchase and pays a deposit of 25% of the cash price, and interest is charged at $8\frac{1}{2}\%$ per year on the balance. He pays the rest in 24 monthly instalments.

(a) Calculate the deposit Robert has to pay.

(b) Calculate the interest he will be charged.

(c) Calculate the monthly instalment, correct to the nearest 10 cents.

(d) Express the amount he would have saved by paying cash as a percentage of the total amount he has to pay by hire purchase.

Chapter Review

1. **Rate**

Rate is used to describe how a quantity changes with respect to another quantity.

Examples:

(a) If A is paid \$120 for 8 hours of work, we say A is paid \$$\frac{120}{8}$ for one hour or at a rate of \$15/h.

(b) If A buys US\$300 from a bank with S\$423, we say the exchange rate of currency is S\$1.41 to US\$1.

2. Ratio

A ratio indicates what fraction one quantity is of the other or how many times one quantity is as much as the other.

Example:

The ratio of A's salary to B's salary is 4 : 5. If A receives \$$a$ and B receives \$$b$, we write

$$a : b = 4 : 5 \quad \text{or} \quad b : a = 5 : 4$$

$$\frac{a}{b} = \frac{4}{5} \quad \text{or} \quad \frac{b}{a} = \frac{5}{4}$$

$$a = \frac{4}{5}b \quad \text{or} \quad b = \frac{5}{4}a$$

3. Percentage

'Per cent' means 'for each hundred' or 'out of a hundred'.
The short form of 'per cent' is %.

Example:

8% of a quantity is $\frac{8}{100}$ of it.

4. Speed

It is a rate of distance travelled per unit of time.

$$\text{Speed} = \frac{\text{Distance travelled}}{\text{Time taken}}$$

Example: The rate of 55 kilometres in 1 hour or 55 km/h is a speed.

CHALLENGER 4

1. A small amount of prune juice is poured into a glass of water. The same amount of the mixture is poured back into the bottle of prune juice. If the bottle of prune juice contains 2 ml of water now, what is the amount of prune juice contained in the glass of water? Give reasons for your answer.

2. A motorist travelled from town A to town B at a certain speed. On his way back, he travelled faster by 10 km/h and saved $12\frac{1}{2}$% of his travelling time. Find his speed from town A to town B.

3. In a 50-metre swimming event, when Anne completed her race, Betty was 5 m behind Anne. By the time Betty completed her race, Carol was 5 m behind Betty. How far behind Anne was Carol when Anne touched the finish?

4. If 8 men take 12 days to do $\frac{4}{7}$ of a job, how many more men are needed to complete the job in 4 more days?

5. Ali travelled at a uniform speed from town A to town B and returned immediately to town A. At the same time, Bill travelled uniformly on the same road from town B to town A and returned immediately to town B. They first met at a point X, 12 km from town B. On their way back, they met again at a point Y, 8 km from town A. Find the distance from town A to town B.

6. A mug was filled with pure alcohol poured from a bottle containing 2 litres of pure alcohol. The bottle, with some pure alcohol remaining, was then topped up with water to 2 litres again. A second mug of the same capacity as the first mug was filled with the diluted alcohol poured from the bottle again. If the bottle still contained 720 millilitres of pure alcohol, find the capacity of the mug.

Problem Solving 4

Pattern of Squares

How many matchsticks will there be in the 10th pattern?

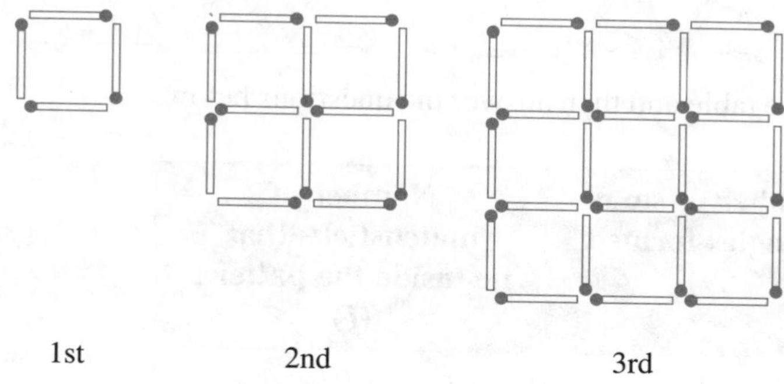

First **simplify** the problem to find the number of matchsticks needed for the 4th pattern. Draw this pattern. Then use **tabulation** to help you look for a **pattern** in the sequence.

We refer to this powerful combination of strategies as **STP**.

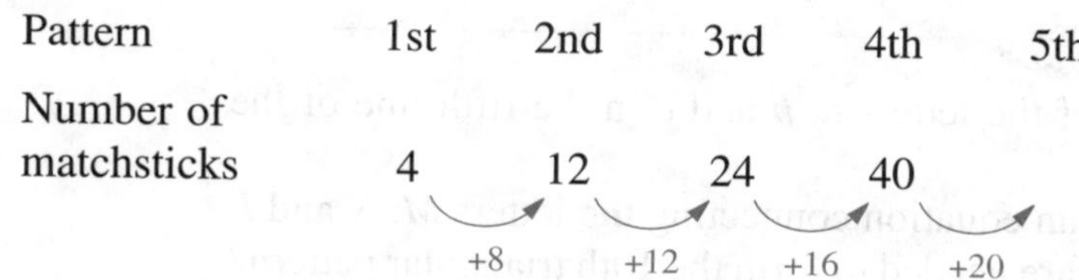

Pattern	1st	2nd	3rd	4th	5th
Number of matchsticks	4	12	24	40	

Observe that the 5th pattern should have 60 matchsticks. Draw the 5th pattern to check your guess. Now you may attempt to continue the following sequence.

$$4 + 8 + 12 + 16 + 20 + \ldots$$

or

$$4(1 + 2 + 3 + 4 + 5 + \ldots)$$

Thus, in the 10th pattern, the number of matchsticks is

$$4(1 + 2 + 3 + 4 + 5 + \ldots + 10) = 220$$

Ask yourself this question:
How many matchsticks are there in the nth pattern?

Problems...

1. Pattern of Triangles Matchsticks are used to make a series of triangular patterns.

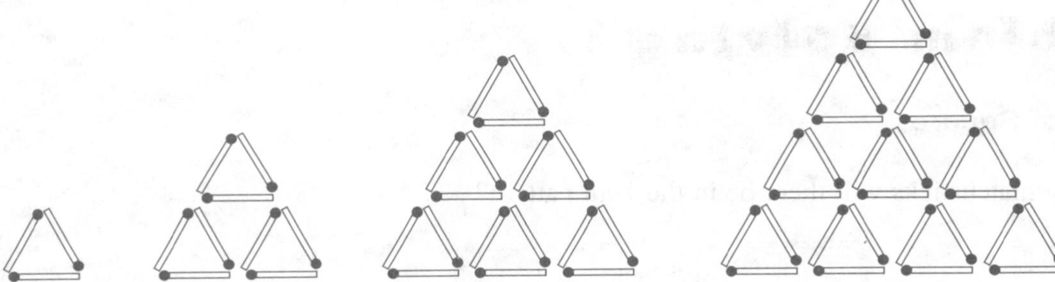

Study the number patterns in the table and then answer the questions below.

Number of matchsticks used (M)	Number of small triangles formed (N)	Number of matchsticks that lie inside the pattern (I)
3	1	0
9	4	3
18	9	9
30	16	18
a	b	c

(a) Write down the value of the letters a, b and c in the fifth line of the table.
(b) Form, and write down, an equation connecting the letters M, N and I.
(c) How many matchsticks are needed to form the 10th triangular pattern?

2. Euclid's Donkey Euclid asked the following problem more than two thousand years ago: A mule and a donkey, laden with wheat, were going to the market. The mule said, 'If you give me one measure, I would carry twice as much as you, but if I give you one, we would have equal burdens.' How many measures was each carrying on its burden?

3. Necklace A necklace is made out of square beads and round beads.

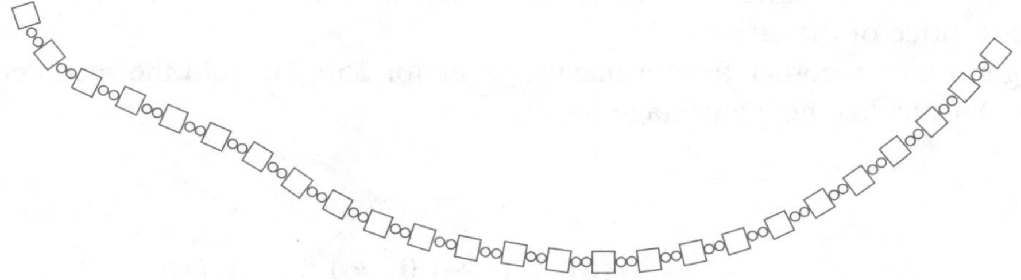

(a) Count the number of square beads and the number of round beads in the drawing.

Similar necklaces were made to the same pattern, always with a square bead at each end.

(b) If 6 square beads were used, how many round beads would be needed?

(c) If 36 round beads were used, how many square beads would be needed?

(d) If s square beads and r round beads were used, write down a formula connecting s and r.

(e) If a necklace had 121 beads on it altogether, find how many square beads and how many round beads there would be. *(C)*

4. Three Plus Four If T is taken to be 2, what do the other letters represent to make the addition correct?

$$\begin{array}{r} THREE \\ +\quad FOUR \\ \hline SEVEN \\ \hline \end{array}$$

Rule: The same letter represents the same digit. Different letters represent different digits.

REVISION EXERCISE 1

Revision 1A *(answers on p. 430)*

1. Multiply (5.23×10^4) by (7.31×10^{-2}). Write your answer in the form $A \times 10^n$, where A is a number between 1 and 10 and n is a whole number. Give your answer correct to 3 significant figures. *(C)*

2. **(a)** When a shopkeeper sells an article for \$3.15, he makes a profit of 5% of the cost price. Calculate the cost price of the article.

(b) A retailer bought a tape recorder from a manufacturer for \$50. He sold the recorder to a customer for \$80. Calculate his percentage profit.

3. Solve the equations.

(a) $\frac{3a}{5} + \frac{a-2}{3} = 4$ **(b)** $2.1x + 1.07 = 1.3x + 1.710$

4. Express x in terms of a, b and c.

(a) $\frac{a}{x} = \frac{b-c}{2x+1}$ **(b)** $\frac{x}{a} + \frac{x}{2b} = c$

5. Factorise the following.

(a) $49x^2 - 70xy + 25y^2$ **(b)** $(x + 2y)^2 - 4y^2$

6. Solve the equations.

(a) $2x^2 + 7x + 6 = 0$ **(b)** $6x^2 + 9x + 3 = 0$

7. The length of a rectangle is 6 cm more than its width. If the area is 40 cm^2, find the length and breadth of the rectangle.

8. **(a)** A man bought an article for \$340 and sold it for \$391. Find his percentage gain.

(b) A gown was priced at \$210. A lady bought the gown at 15% discount. How much did she pay?

9. **(a)** A train leaves a station at 08 42 and arrives at its destination at 11 17. How many minutes does the journey take?

(b) On the return journey the train leaves at noon. It takes exactly the same time as it did on the outward journey. Write down, using the 24 hour clock notation, the time at which it arrives back at its starting point. *(C)*

10. A man buys a video camera for \$2 088. He pays a deposit of \$288 and he is to pay the amount outstanding plus interest in 12 equal monthly instalments. If the interest is charged at 12% per annum for the full period of 12 months, find the amount of each instalment.

Revision 1B *(answers on p. 430)*

1. Given that $x - y = 2z$, express
   (a) x in terms of y and z,
   (b) z in terms of x and y,
   (c) y in terms of x and z.

2. (a) A certain type of rice costs 78 cents per kilogram. What will be the new cost, to the nearest cent, if its cost is decreased by 5%?
   (b) A manufacturer gives a retailer a discount of 40% on the list price. What is the list price of an item for which the retailer pays \$72?

3.

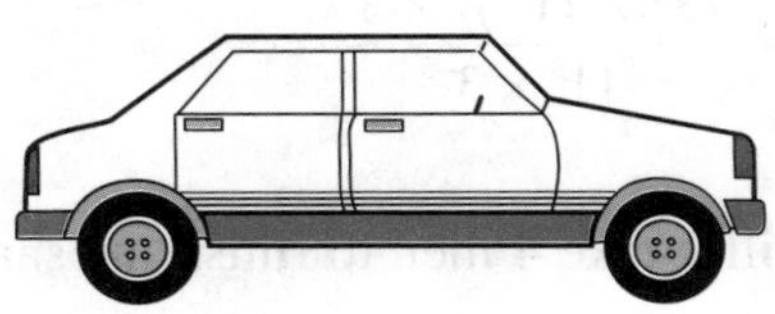
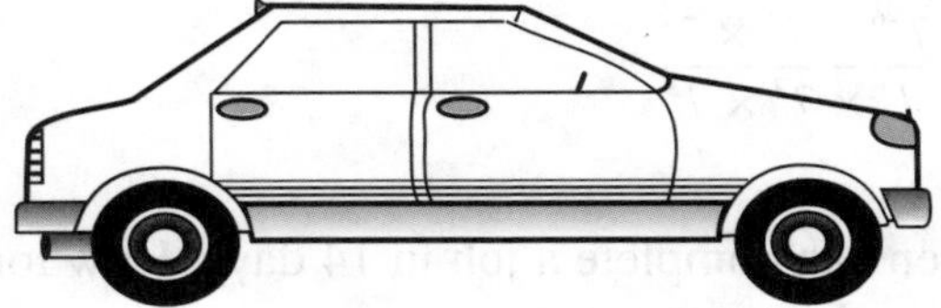

   The smaller car is about 3.5 metres long.
   (a) Estimate the length of the larger car.
   (b) Write down the scale used in the form $1 : n$.

4. The population of a school in 1997 was 1 800, which was 123 students more than that in 1996. Express the population of the school in 1996 as a percentage of that in 1997.

5. A man saved \$300 in a certain month.
   (a) In the following month, he saved \$225. What was the percentage decrease in his savings?
   (b) In the third month, he saved \$270. What was the percentage increase in his savings?

6. Solve the equations.
   (a) $4x^2 - 15x + 9 = 0$
   (b) $27a^2 - 6a - 8 = 0$

7. Simplify the following.
   (a) $\dfrac{x+1}{3} + \dfrac{x}{2} - \dfrac{3x}{4}$
   (b) $\dfrac{3a+2b}{4} + \dfrac{4a-3b}{6} - \dfrac{2(a+2)}{5}$

8. Find the value of $\dfrac{2a}{b}$ where $a = 2.21 \times 10^{-6}$ and $b = 1.23 \times 10^{-8}$. Write your answer in the form $A \times 10^n$, where n is an integer and $1 \leqslant A < 10$. Give your answer correct to 3 significant figures.

9. When a sum of money \$$P$ is invested at R% simple interest for T years, the amount of money, \$$A$, is calculated by using the formula $A = P + \dfrac{PRT}{100}$.
   (a) Jose invests \$4 000 at 12% simple interest. Calculate the amount of money he will have at the end of 3 years.
   (b) Make T the subject of the formula $A = P + \dfrac{PRT}{100}$. *(C)*

10. A path 2 m wide surrounds a square field. If the total area of the path and field is $10\frac{1}{4}\%$ more than the area of the field, find the perimeter of the field.

Revision 1C *(answers on p. 430)*

1. Find the exact value of $\frac{0.03 \times 0.49}{42}$, expressing your answer in the standard form.

2. Simplify the following, leaving your answer in an index form.

(a) $\frac{7^{-6} \times 7^4 \times 7^2}{7^3 \times 7^7 \times 7^3}$ **(b)** $\frac{(3^2 \times 11^{-3})^2 \times 3^{-7}}{11^3 \times 3^{-5}}$

3. 10 men can complete a job in 14 days. How long will it take 4 men to finish the same job if they work at the same rate?

4. Factorise the following.
(a) $3a^2 + 18ab - 81b^2$ **(b)** $36x^2 - y^2 + 12x - 2y$

5. The height of a triangle is 5 cm less than its base. If the area is 52 cm^2, find its base.

6. In an election, there were two candidates. Candidate A received 65% of the votes cast and secured 2 400 votes more than candidate B. How many people voted?

7. Simplify the following.

(a) $\frac{x}{2} + \frac{3x}{5} - \frac{9x}{10}$ **(b)** $\frac{3x - 2}{4} - \frac{2(x + 2)}{5} + \frac{x + 5}{4}$

8. Write as a single fraction.

(a) $\frac{2}{a} + \frac{1}{2a}$ **(b)** $3y + \frac{1}{2y}$

9. Given $ab + 2a = 21$,
(a) express a in terms of b,
(b) find the value of b when $a = 2$.

10. The insurance premium for Samy's car is \$1 280 per year. As the car is a sports-model, there is a 5% surcharge on the premium. However, as Samy has not made any claims for the last two years, he is entitled to a 30% no claims bonus on the total premium. How much does he pay for the year's insurance?

Revision 1D *(answers on p. 430)*

1. Express 0.027 684
 (a) as a decimal, correct to three decimal places,
 (b) as a decimal, correct to four significant figures,
 (c) in the form $A \times 10^n$ where A is a number between 1 and 10, and n is an integer.

2. **(a)** A shopkeeper bought 50 pens for \$1 250 and sold them at \$30 each. What was his percentage gain or loss?
 (b) A merchant made 12% by selling goods for \$168. How much did he pay for the goods?

3. Simplify the following.
 (a) $\dfrac{m^{-7} \times m^{16}}{m^7 \times m^{-10}}$
 (b) $\dfrac{a^7 \times b^3}{a^{-7} \times b^{-3}}$
 (c) $\dfrac{s^6 t^7}{t^5}$

4. The perimeter of a field is 316 m. If the area is 6 192 m^2, find the length and breadth of the field.

5. Simplify the following.
 (a) $\dfrac{x - y}{3} - \dfrac{x + y}{5}$
 (b) $\dfrac{2a - 1}{2} + \dfrac{3(a + 2)}{3} - \dfrac{a + 4}{4}$

6. **(a)** Equal marks were allocated to each of the 30 questions in a class test. A boy answered 18 questions correctly. What percentage was this?
 (b) To pass the test, a student must answer at least 40% of the questions correctly. Find the least number of correct answers needed to pass.

7. Expand
 (a) $3(4x - 5y)(5x + 4y)$,
 (b) $2x(x + y)(x - y + 1)$.

8. **(a)** Factorise $x^2 - y^2 - 3x + 3y$.
 (b) Find the exact value of $2\,340\,004^2 - 2\,340\,003^2$.
 (c) Given that $x^2 + y^2 = 15$ and $xy = 5$, calculate $(x + y)^2$.

9. **(a)** Given that $t = \dfrac{d}{100}\left(1 - \dfrac{t_1}{100}\right)$, express t_1 in terms of t and d.
 (b) Given that $R = R_0(1 + at)$, express t in terms of R, R_0 and a.
 (c) Given that $R = \dfrac{R_1 R_2}{R_1 + R_2}$, express R_1 in terms of R and R_2.

10.

Hazel Green sells $2\frac{1}{2}$ litre tins of paint in her shop for $14.30 each.

(a) **(i)** Express this price in dollars per litre.
(ii) At this price, how many millilitres of paint do you get for $1?

(b) Hazel makes a profit of 30% on the cost price of the tin of paint. Calculate the cost price.

(c) In a sale, she reduces the price of the tin of paint to $11.44. Calculate
(i) the percentage reduction in the selling price of the tin of paint,
(ii) the percentage profit she now makes on the cost price.

(d) A 5-litre tin of paint is priced in the sale at $21.12. Calculate the price of this tin in pounds sterling, given that £1 = $1.65. *(C)*

Revision 1E *(answers on p. 430)*

1. Factorise the following.
(a) $9m^2 + 6mt - 24t^2$ **(b)** $9xk - 4yk - 9xh + 4yh$

2. The area of a rectangle is 12 m² and the length of the base is x m.
(a) Express the height of the rectangle in terms of x.
(b) Express the perimeter of the rectangle in terms of x.
(c) If the perimeter is 49 m, what are the dimensions of the rectangle?

3. For each of the following, find the difference between the cash price and the hire purchase price.
(a) An electric oven to be sold for $320 cash or a deposit of $80 and 12 monthly instalments of $25.
(b) A motor scooter to be sold for $2 400 cash or a deposit of $400 and 24 monthly instalments of $95.
(c) A copying machine to be sold for $5 000 cash or a deposit of $1 000 and 24 monthly instalments of $180.

4. Solve the equations.
(a) $(a + 3)(4 - a) + 8 = 0$ **(b)** $(4x - 7)(2x + 1) - 18 = 0$

5. **(a)** A tourist wished to change 15 000 rupiah for Singapore dollars from a bank. How many Singapore dollars would he get if the exchange rate was 100 rupiah to S$0.10?
(b) He also wished to buy US dollars with 24 000 rupiah. If the exchange rate was US$1 to S$1.41, how many US dollars would he buy?

6. Simplify each of the following.

(a) $3ab \times 2b^2$

(b) $\dfrac{5a^2b \times 6ab^2}{21a^2b^2}$

(c) $3ab(1 - b) + 5ab^2$

(d) $\dfrac{a(b - 3c)}{3} + ac$

7. A has x number of stamps and B has y number of stamps. If A gives B 1 stamp, then B will have twice as many stamps as A. Write down an equation in x and y.

8. Expand
(a) $(3x^2y + y^2)(x^2 - 3xy^2)$,
(b) $3xy(z + 4y - 3x + 1)$.

9. **(a)** Factorise $x^2 - 2xy + y^2 - 1$.
(b) Given that $x^2 + y^2 = 20$ and $xy = 7$, calculate $(x - y)^2$.

10. A man is trying to decide whether to buy or to rent a new radio set. The model he wants costs \$400 and the dealer charges an additional $3\frac{1}{2}$% of this cost to install it. During the first year no charge will be made for repairs. After this the man estimates that repairs will cost \$20 for each of the next four years, and then \$35 for each of the following three years. At the end of these eight years he expects to receive a trade-in value of \$20 for the set when he buys a new one. Calculate
(i) the installation charge,
(ii) the total estimated repair cost and
(iii) the estimated net cost of the set over the eight years (that is, the total he expects to pay less the trade-in value).

The cost to rent the same set is \$8.40 per month during the first year but $7\frac{1}{2}$% discount is allowed if the year's rental is paid in advance. Calculate the rental for this year if it is paid in advance. For the second and subsequent years the rental is reduced to \$7.60 per month but no discount is allowed. Calculate the rental for the second year. Hence evaluate the total rental if the set is kept for eight years, the first year's rental being paid in advance. (*C*)

MISCELLANEOUS EXERCISE 1

(answers on p. 431)

1. Without using a calculator, simplify $(-2)^3 + (-2)^{-4} + \left(-\frac{1}{2}\right)^{-2} - \left(-\frac{1}{2}\right)^2$.

2. Without using a calculator, simplify $(7 \times 17^{-1} - 7^{-1} \times 17)(7^{-1} - 17^{-1})^{-1}$.

3. **(a)** Find, without using a calculator, the last digit (i.e. the digit at the 'ones' place) of each of the following.
(i) 19^2 **(ii)** 19^3 **(iii)** 19^4 **(iv)** 19^5 **(v)** 19^{19}
(b) Find the last digit of 1998^{1998}.

4. Find the value of $\frac{x}{y}$ if $3x^2 - 4xy + y^2 = 0$.

5. Solve $\left(x + \frac{1}{x}\right)^2 - \left(x + \frac{1}{x}\right) - 6 = 0$. $\left(\textit{Hint:} \text{ Let } y = x + \frac{1}{x}.\right)$

6. If $(2a)^{2b} = (a^b)(x^b)$, find x in terms of a.

7. If a, b and c are prime numbers such that $a = b^2 - c^2$, find a.

8. When Abu's age was x years, his father's age was 3 years more than twice his age. Abu's age is now y years. Find an expression for his father's present age.

9. **(a)** Given that $a + b = 3$ and $a - b = -7$, find the value of $a^2 - b^2$.
(b) Given that $x^2 + y^2 = 25$ and $xy = 12$, find the value of
(i) $(x + y)^2$,
(ii) $(x - y)^2$.

10. **(a)** If the product of two possible integers is a prime number, what must be the value of the smaller integer?
(b) Given that x and y are positive integers, solve
(i) $(x + y)(x - 3y) = 17$,
(ii) $x^2 - 4y^2 = 13$.

11. If $2x - 3y + 1 = 0$, express $3x - y$
(a) in terms of x,
(b) in terms of y.

12.

Köln (Cologne)	13 03	13 31	13 53	14 00	14 09	14 53	15 00
Bonn	13 24		14 13	14 20	14 30	15 13	15 20
Koblenz	13 59	14 39	14 47	14 53	15 16	15 47	15 53
Mainz	14 49	15 34		15 43	16 15		16 43
Frankfurt			16 11	16 13	16 43	17 11	17 13
Mannheim	15 31	16 35			17 48		

Part of the timetable for trains travelling from Köln is shown above.

(a) During this period
  (i) how many of the trains stop at Bonn,
  (ii) how many of the trains stop at both Koblenz and Mannheim?

(b) How long does it take the 13 03 train from Cologne to travel to Mannheim?

(c) A woman arrives at Bonn station at 13 40. At what time would she arrive in Frankfurt assuming her train is on time?

(d) According to the timetable what is the longest time it takes for a train to travel from Köln to Mannheim?
(C)

13. Mary has a recipe to make a dessert. The ingredients to be used are as follows:

Self-raising flour	480 g
Sugar	365 g
Butter	115 g
Plums	1 320 g
Add water to make up a total of 2.5 kg.	

(a) How much water, in m*l*, is required? (Take the mass of 1 m*l* of water to be 1 g.)

(b) If 990 g of plums are used, calculate the amount of the other ingredients required.

(c) Mary's mother wants to alter the original recipe by using less sugar but more plums. If 10% less sugar is used, find the percentage increase in the use of plums so that the ingredients still add up to 2.5 kg. Give your answer correct to the nearest one per cent.

14. **(a)** In 1996, a family spent one-sixth of their income on rent, one quarter on food, and two-ninths on clothes. They spent a total of \$8 740 on these three items.
  (i) What was their total income?
  (ii) How much more money did they spend on food than on clothes?

(b) In 1997 their income increased to \$15 000. What percentage increase was this? Give your answer correct to one decimal place.

(c) Also in 1997, their total expenditure on rent, food and clothes increased by 5%. If the rent remained the same, and food costs increased by 10%, by what percentage did the cost of clothes increase?
(C)

15.

January

S	M	T	W	T	F	S
				1	2	3
4	5	6	7	8	9	10
11	12	13	14	15	16	17
18	19	20	21	22	23	24
25	26	27	28	29	30	31

The figure shows the calendar of the month of January in 1998.

(a) Draw a square enclosing 9 numbers so that the sum of the numbers at the 4 corners is 80.

(b) Draw a square enclosing 16 numbers so that the sum of the numbers at the 4 corners is 68.

(c) Draw a rectangle enclosing 15 numbers so that the sum of the numbers at the 4 corners is 88.

INVESTIGATION 1

1. Take any 2-digit number as your starting number. Then follow the instructions below to get the next number.

- If it is an even number, divide it by 2.
- If it is an odd number, multiply it by 3 and add 1 to it.

Then get your 3rd, 4th, . . . numbers in the same manner until a pattern is observed.

(a) Describe your observations.
(b) Investigate using other numbers.
(c) What is your conclusion?
(d) Would you get the same result if you use 27 as your starting number?

2. **(a)** Copy and complete the following.

$26^2 - 24^2 =$ ________

$27^2 - 23^2 =$ ________

$28^2 - 22^2 =$ ________

$29^2 - 21^2 =$ ________

$30^2 - 20^2 =$ ________

$31^2 - 19^2 =$ ________

$32^2 - 18^2 =$ ________

$33^2 - 17^2 =$ ________

$34^2 - 16^2 =$ ________

Describe your observations.
Have you discovered a rule?

(b) Is there a rule to help you do the following subtractions quickly? Investigate.

$3.5^2 - 1.5^2 =$ ________

$3.6^2 - 1.4^2 =$ ________

$3.7^2 - 1.3^2 =$ ________

$3.8^2 - 1.2^2 =$ ________

3.

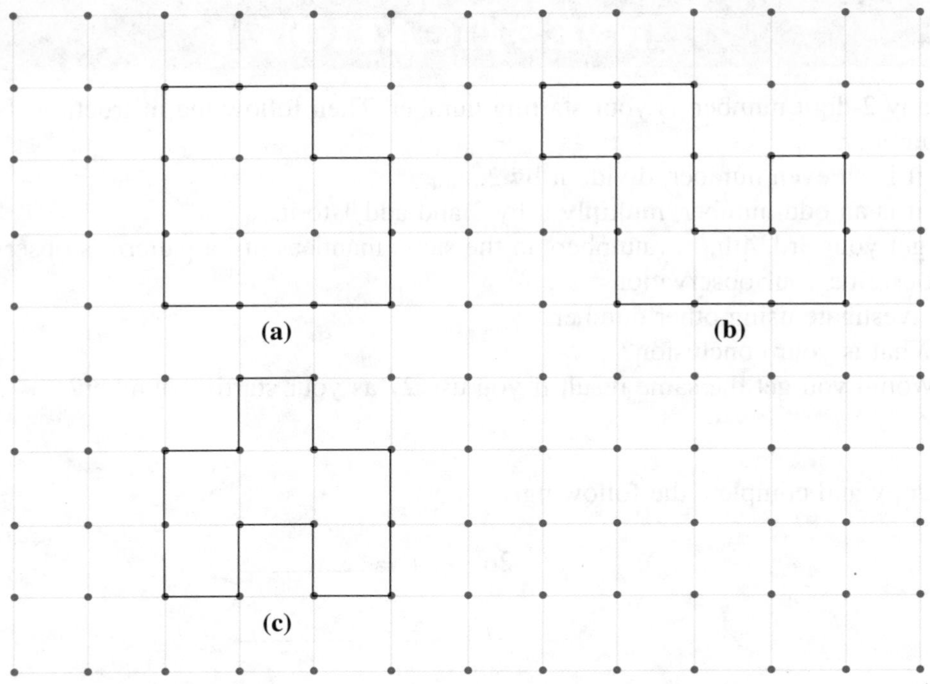

(a) Arrange the figures in ascending order
(i) by area, **(ii)** by perimeter.
Do you agree that for two given regions, the one with a greater area must have the greater perimeter?

(b) Draw a number of rectangles such that each of them has 20 cm as its perimeter. What is the greatest area that can be obtained with this perimeter?

(c) Investigate how you would form a 'quadrilateral' with a piece of wire of given length so that the figure formed has the maximum area.

4. A line segment joining two points on a circle is called a chord. A chord divides the inside of a circle into two parts.

(a) Copy and complete the following table.

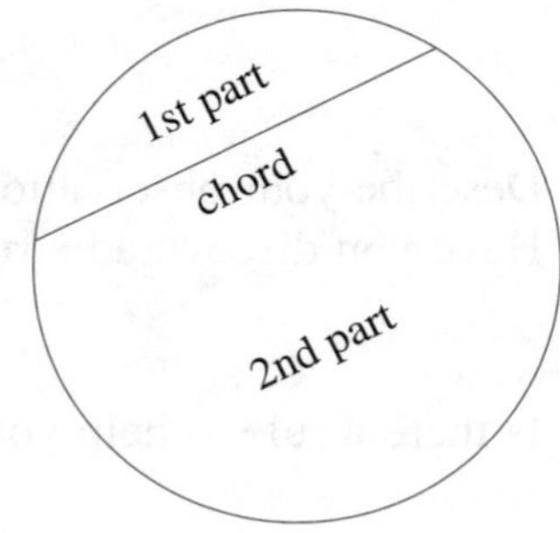

Number of chords	1	2	3	4	5	6	7	8	9	10
Maximum number of parts	2	4	7							

(b) How many parts will you get if 20 chords are drawn? Investigate.

Chapter 5

Graphs I

Chapter Highlights

- Using ordered pairs of numbers to describe positions
- Using Cartesian coordinates in two dimensions
- Identifying simple rules connecting pairs of values of x and y
- Completing table of values of x and y for a given rule (equation) in x and y including plotting the points for the ordered pairs defined by the table
- Drawing graphs of linear equations
- Interpreting and drawing graphs in practical situations including conversion graphs
- Interpreting and drawing travel graphs
- Recognising that a point on a straight line graph represents an ordered pair of numbers satisfying the equation of the straight line and that the point of intersection of two straight lines represents an ordered pair of numbers satisfying the equations of the two lines simultaneously
- Solving simultaneous linear equations by graphs
- Recognising that the graph of $y = x^2$ is a curve with a line of symmetry and that the curve does not lie below the x-axis, including writing the equation for the line of symmetry
- Using the graph of $y = x^2$ to find the squares and square roots of numbers
- Recognising that the graph of $y = -x^2$ is a curve with a line of symmetry and that the curve does not lie above the x-axis
- Drawing quadratic graphs, including describing how the values of y change with the values of x, and naming the point whose y coordinate is the smallest or the greatest
- Drawing quadratic graphs, including finding the corresponding value of y when the value of x is given and vice versa

5.1 THE COORDINATE PLANE

Class Activity 1

1. At the beginning of the school year, Mr Li, the language teacher, prepared a plan of the seating arrangement of the class.

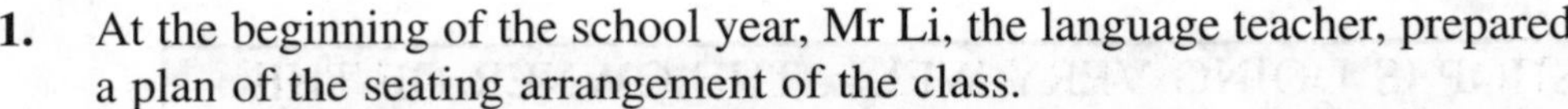

Here is his plan.

Pingfen	Kim	Jinfa	Suyin	John	Lihua
Ruilan	Ali	Huaming	Xiulin	Mary	Mingyin
David	Shunfu	Devi	Guoliang	Xingfa	Fatimah
Suming	Afu	Meimei	Tony	Kumar	Weilin
Xiuzhu	Tina	Guanghua	Siti	Yaoxing	Sufen
Meiling	Ibrahim	Christine	Yingfu	Lilan	Wenliang

Teacher's Desk

Mr Wu, the mathematics teacher, did not draw any plan. Instead, he wrote a pair of numbers against each student's name in the class list like this:

Xingfa (5, 4), Ali (2, 5), Suming (1, 3), Devi (3, 4) and so on.

For each pair, the first number was to tell which row from the left, and the second number, which desk down the row.
Thus Xingfa's seat was at (row 5, desk 4),
Ali's seat was at (row 2, desk 5),
Suming's seat was at (row 1, desk 3),
Devi's seat was at (row 3, desk 4).

(a) Who occupied the following seats?

(2, 3) (5, 2) (6, 4) (5, 5) (4, 1) (3, 2)
(4, 4) (2, 6) (3, 3) (3, 5) (3, 6) (2, 4)

(b) What pair of numbers did Mr Wu write against the following names? Pingfen, Tony, Mingyin, Kumar, Suyin, Siti, Ruilan, Xiulin, Tina, David.

(c) Did Mr Wu use the pairs of numbers (2, 1) and (1, 2) to refer to the same seat? If not, who occupied the seats numbered (2, 1) and (1, 2)?

2. (a)

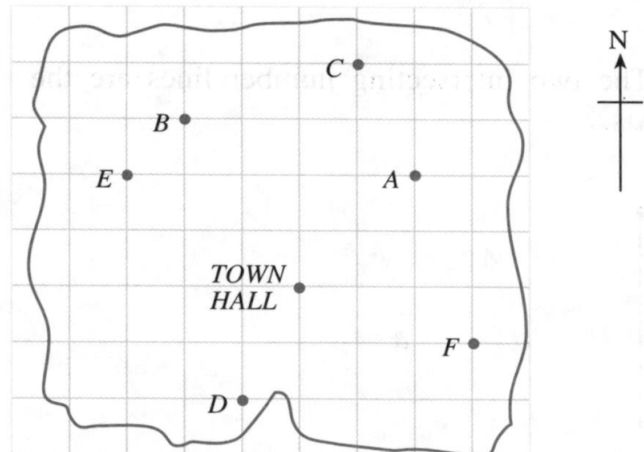

The map shows the locations of the air raid shelters of a town from the Town Hall.
Shelter A is located 2 km east followed by 2 km north. We write (2 East, 2 North).
Shelter B is located 2 km west followed by 3 km north. We write (2 West, 3 North).

Copy and complete the following.

(i) The position of shelter C is (______, ______).

(ii) The position of shelter D is (______, ______).

(iii) The position of shelter E is (______, ______).

(iv) The position of shelter F is (______, ______).

(b) We can also make use of a pair of numbers to locate the positions of the shelters as follows:
The position of shelter A is (2, 2),
i.e. 2 units east followed by 2 units north.

The position of shelter B is (–2, 3),
i.e. 2 units west followed by 3 units north.

Note: We use (–2, 3) to denote (2 west, 3 north).

Copy and complete the following.

(i) The position of shelter C is (___, ___).

(ii) The position of shelter D is (___, ___).

(iii) The position of shelter E is (___, ___).

(iv) The position of shelter F is (___, ___).

Ordered Pairs

Fig. 5.1 shows a number plane. The two intersecting number lines are the **horizontal axis** and the **vertical axis.**

An axis is a line of reference used to help locate a point in the coordinate plane.

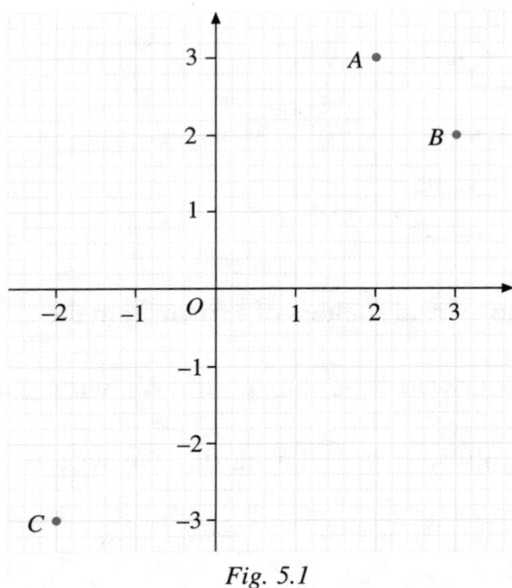

Fig. 5.1

The point A is 2 units to the right of the vertical axis and 3 units above the horizontal axis and so its position can be described by using a number pair (2, 3). Number pairs such as (2, 3) are called **ordered pairs** because the order of the numbers is important. For example, the pair (3, 2) is different from (2, 3) because (3, 2) represents the point B which is 3 units to the right of the vertical axis and 2 units above the horizontal axis. The point C is 2 units to the left of the vertical axis and 3 units below the horizontal axis, and its position is indicated by the ordered pair (–2, –3).

The point of intersection of the two *axes* is called the **origin**. The origin is represented by the ordered pair (0, 0).

The origin is a point of reference with coordinates (0, 0). It helps to locate a point in the coordinate plane.

Coordinates

In Fig. 5.2, P is represented by (4, 3). We refer to the number 4 as the *first coordinate* and the number 3 as the *second coordinate*.

By convention, the horizontal axis is called the *x-axis* and the vertical axis, the *y-axis*. The first coordinate is called the x coordinate and the second coordinate, the y coordinate.

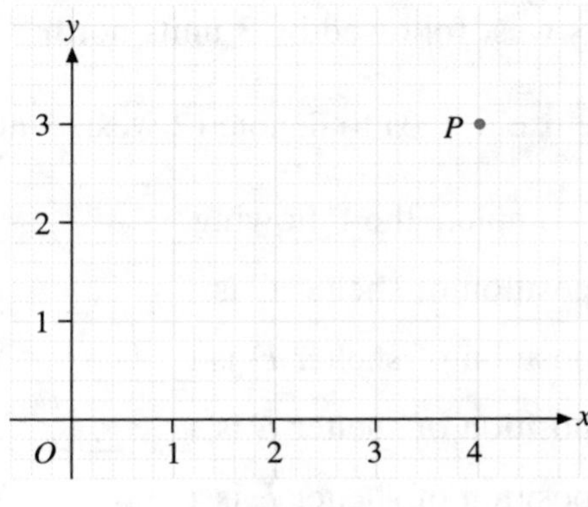

Fig. 5.2

Coordinates is a pair of numbers that locate a point in the coordinate plane.

Exercise 5.1

answers on p. 431

1. Study the figure on the right. Then copy and complete the table below.

Point	Ordered Pair
P	(2, 3)
Q	
R	
S	
T	
U	
V	
W	

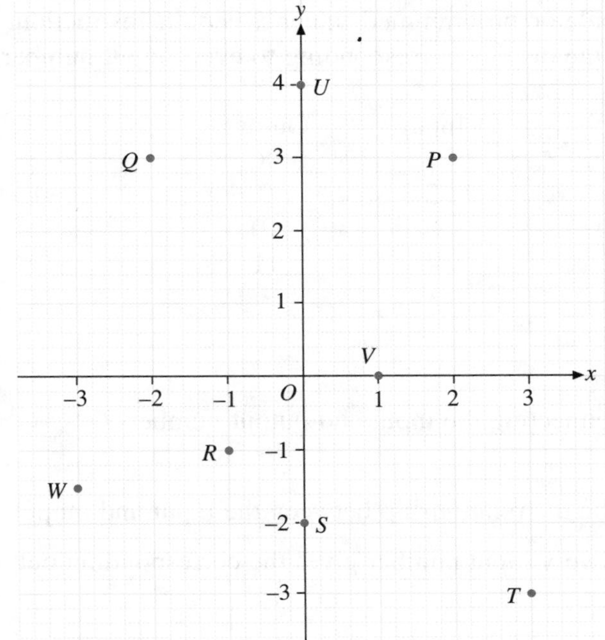

2. Draw a set of axes at right angles on your graph paper. Using 1 cm to represent 1 unit along both axes, plot and label the points represented by the following ordered pairs of numbers.

$C(0, 3)$ $D(3, 0)$ $E(-2, 2)$ $F(6, 2)$

$G(-2, 5)$ $H(0, 0)$ $I(-7, -4)$ $J\left(2\frac{1}{2}, 3\right)$

3. Substitute the x and y coordinates of each ordered pair below for x and y respectively in the equation $y = x + 3$. Then state which of the ordered pairs below satisfy the equation.

(a) (0, 3) **(b)** (1, 4) **(c)** (2, 5) **(d)** (3, 6)
(e) (4, 7) **(f)** (5, 8) **(g)** (6, 10) **(h)** (7, 11)

4. Do the following on the same graph paper.

(a) Plot the points $A(3, 5)$, $B(2, 3)$, $C(3, 1)$ and $D(4, 3)$. Join AB, BC, CD and AD. Name the geometrical figure that you have drawn.

(b) Plot the points $E(-5, 4)$, $F(-6, 2)$, $G(-2, 2)$ and $H(-1, 4)$. Join EF, FG, GH and EH. Name the geometrical figure that you have drawn.

(c) Plot the points $J(-5, -2)$, $K(-6, -4)$, $L(-4, -2)$ and $M(-3, -4)$. Join JK, KM, ML and LJ. Name the geometrical figure that you have drawn.

(d) Plot the points $N(2, -2)$, $O(2, -4)$, $P(6, -4)$, and $Q(6, -2)$. Join NO, OP, PQ and NQ. Name the geometrical figure that you have drawn.

5.2 GRAPHS OF LINEAR EQUATIONS IN TWO VARIABLES

A man has a calculator programmed under a certain instruction. It gives an output number on the display corresponding to every input number as follows:

Input		Output
1	$\to$	8
2	$\to$	9
3	$\to$	10
4	$\to$	11
.		.
.		.

What is the rule connecting the input and output numbers?

One way to describe the relationship between the input and output numbers is:

'Adding 7 to every input number gives the corresponding output number.'

We can also say:

'If the input number is x, then the output number is $x + 7$.'

Another way to describe this is:

'For every input number x, the corresponding output number is y, where $y = x + 7$.'

Then the input and output numbers can be listed as follows:

x		y
1	$\to$	8
2	$\to$	9
3	$\to$	10
4	$\to$	11
.		.
.		.

Or we make a horizontal table like this:

x	1	2	3	4	......
y	8	9	10	11	......

Class Activity 2

1. A calculator is programmed under different rules in the following three cases. The tables show the values of x and the corresponding values of y. Write down the rule connecting x and y in each case.

(a)

x	1	2	3	4	5	6	7
y	2	4	6	8	10	12	14

(b)

x	1	2	3	4	5	6	7
y	–3	–2	–1	0	1	2	3

(c)

x	1	2	3	4	5	6	7
y	$\frac{2}{3}$	$1\frac{1}{3}$	2	$2\frac{2}{3}$	$3\frac{1}{3}$	4	$4\frac{2}{3}$

2. A special calculator is programmed under different rules which connect the input x and the output y as indicated.

(a) Copy and complete the following tables.

(i) Rule: $y = 2x + 5$

x	1	2	3	4	5	6
y			11			17

(ii) Rule: $y = 3x - 1$

x	1	2	3	4	5	6
y		5			14	

(iii) Rule: $y = x^2 + 1$

x	1	2	3	4
y	2		10	

(b) Using 1 cm to represent 1 unit along both axes, plot the points that correspond to the ordered pairs in your tables. What do you notice?

You have seen that the graphs of equations such as $y = 2x + 5$ and $y = 3x - 1$ are straight lines and you have noticed that these equations are of the form $y = mx + c$ where m and c are constants. Equations of these types are called **linear equations** because their graphs are straight line graphs.

Equations involving a term in x^2 such as $y = x^2 + 1$ are not linear equations. You will learn more about this type of equations later.

Exploring:
Before drawing the graphs, can you predict whether a linear equation has an 'up-hill' graph or a 'down-hill' graph? Explain your findings.

Examples

(a) Consider $5x + 2y - 3 = 0$.
Then $2y = -5x + 3$

$$y = -\frac{5}{2}x + \frac{3}{2}$$

This is of the form $y = mx + c$ $\left(\text{where } m = -\frac{5}{2} \text{ and } c = \frac{3}{2}\right)$.

Thus $5x + 2y - 3 = 0$ is a linear equation.

(b) Consider $7x - y = 0$.
Then $y = 7x$.
This is of the form $y = mx + c$ (where $m = 7$ and $c = 0$).
Thus $7x - y = 0$ is a linear equation.

(c) Consider $y + 3 = 0$.
Then $y = -3$.
This is of the form $y = mx + c$ (where $m = 0$ and $c = -3$).
Thus $y + 3 = 0$ is a linear equation.
Note that the ordered pairs $(1, -3)$, $(2, -3)$, $(3, -3)$, $(4, -3)$ and so on satisfy the equation $y + 3 = 0$.
The graph of this equation is a straight line parallel to the x-axis, 3 units below it.

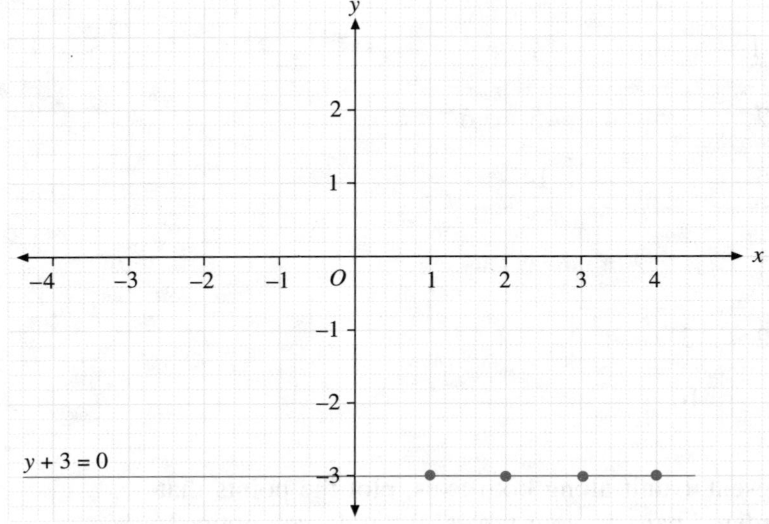

(d) Consider $2x - 5 = 0$.
Although this cannot be written in the form $y = mx + c$, the ordered pairs (2.5, 1), (2.5, 2), (2.5, 3), (2.5, 4) and so on satisfy the equation $2x - 5 = 0$. The graph of this equation is a straight line parallel to the y-axis, 2.5 units to the right of it.

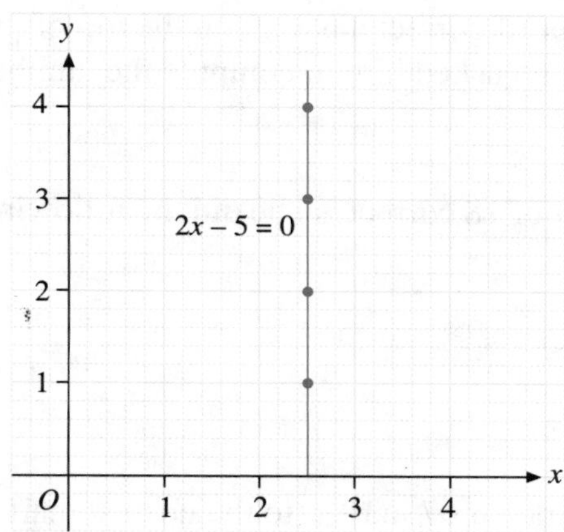

Exercise 5.2

1. For each of the following, make up a table of five ordered pairs. Then plot the points in each case on a separate sheet of graph paper. The points in each case should appear to lie on a straight line. Draw a straight line through these points.
(a) $y = x + 2$ **(b)** $y = x - 2$ **(c)** $y = -x + 4$

2. Draw the straight line graphs of the following equations on the same sheet of graph paper using two ordered pairs of your choice for each line.
(a) $y = x$ **(b)** $y = -x + 6$ **(c)** $y = -x + 2$

3. For each of the following equations, can you tell whether its graph is an up-hill graph (／) or a down-hill graph (＼) or a vertical line or a horizontal line?
(a) $y = 2x + 3$ **(b)** $y = 5x + 2$
(c) $y = -3x + 9$ **(d)** $y = -2x$
(e) $y = 3x + 2$ **(f)** $y = -2x + 7$
(g) $5x + 2y - 3 = 0$ **(h)** $x - 2y - 3 = 0$
(i) $x - 3y = 0$ **(j)** $7x - y = 0$
(k) $y - 2x - 3 = 0$ **(l)** $4y - 7x = 0$
(m) $x + 9 = 0$ **(n)** $2y - 1 = 0$

4. Draw a graph for each of the equations in question 3 using two ordered pairs of your choice.

5.3 SIMPLE APPLICATIONS OF STRAIGHT LINE GRAPHS

Example

A class of 43 students took a test which consisted of 18 questions. The teacher corrected each script and wrote the number of correct answers on the top of the script. Then he gave the scripts to Arthur and asked him to compute the number of marks out of 100.

The first script Arthur looked at had 12 out of 18 correct, so he did the following calculation:

18 correct answers give 100 marks.

1 correct answer gives $\frac{100}{18}$ marks.

12 correct answers give $\frac{100}{18} \times 12$ marks or 67 marks (to the nearest mark).

The next script had 10 correct answers, so Arthur wrote $\frac{100}{18} \times 10$ and the number of marks for this script was 56.

Arthur began to feel that this was too much work. After thinking for a minute, he discovered that if x was the number of correct answers, then the number of marks for the script would be $\frac{100}{18}x$ or $\frac{50}{9}x$.

Arthur took another script and found that this script had 14 correct answers, so he replaced x by 14 in his 'formula' and worked out the marks. The number of marks for this script was $\frac{50}{9} \times 14$ or 78 marks.

Arthur still had 40 scripts to go when he began to think, "If I let the number of marks scored be y, then I will get a linear equation $y = \frac{50}{9}x$. Since the graph of this equation is a straight line, maybe I could use it."

So he drew the x-axis and the y-axis on a large piece of graph paper and marked the scales. What scales do you think he should choose on the axes?

Then he thought to himself, "(0, 0) and (18, 100) have to be points on the graph. Yes, I need 18 units on the x-axis and 100 units on the y-axis." So he used 1 cm to represent 5 units on the y-axis and 1 cm to represent 1 unit on the x-axis to draw the graph.

Exercise 5.3

answers on p. 431

1. Use Arthur's last method mentioned above to find the scores for 10 scripts having the following number of correct answers: 4, 5, 6, 7, 8, 9, 11, 13, 15, 16. (Out of 18 possible correct answers.)

2. Out of a possible 80 marks, 8 students obtained the following marks: 28, 60, 72, 50, 40, 64, 52, 42. Their marks are to be recorded in percentages in the record book. Choose your own scales which would enable you to get quite accurate results. Draw a conversion graph to find the number of marks each would get out of 100.

3. It is given that US$1 = S$1.40.

(a) If US$$x$ = S$$y$, write down the equation connecting x and y.

(b) Copy and complete the table.

x (US$)	0	
y (S$)		140

(c) Plot a straight line graph for the table with the following scales: 1 cm represents US$10 along the x-axis and S$10 along the y-axis. Use it to answer the questions in (d).

(d) Copy and complete the following. (Give your answers correct to the nearest dollar.)

(i) US$25 = S$ ________ **(ii)** US$80 = S$ ________

(iii) S$50 = US$ ________ **(iv)** S$155 = US$ ________

4. It is given that 1 km/h = 0.3 m/s, correct to 1 decimal place.

(a) If x km/h = y m/s, write down the equation connecting x and y.

(b) Copy and complete the table.

x (km/h)	0	
y (m/s)		30

(c) Plot a straight line graph for the table with the following scales:

1 cm along the x-axis represents 1 km/h

2 cm along the y-axis represent 1 m/s

Use it to answer the questions in (d).

(d) Copy and complete the following. (Give your answers correct to 1 decimal place.)

(i) 0.8 m/s = ________ km/h **(ii)** 0.6 m/s = ________ km/h

(iii) 3.2 m/s = ________ km/h **(iv)** 4.8 m/s = ________ km/h

(v) 3 km/h = ________ m/s **(vi)** 8.4 km/h = ________ m/s

(vii) 11.2 km/h = ________ m/s **(viii)** 15.6 km/h = ________ m/s

5. It is given that a car can cover 48 km with 4.5 litres of petrol.

(a) With x litres of petrol, the car can travel a distance of y km. Write down an equation connecting x and y.

(b) Copy and complete the table.

x (litres)	0	
y (km)		192

(c) Plot a straight line graph for the table with the following scales:

1 cm on the x-axis represents 2 litres
1 cm on the y-axis represents 15 km

Use it to answer the questions in (d) and (e).

(d) Find, correct to the nearest km, the distance the car can travel with **(i)** 12 litres of petrol, **(ii)** 18 litres of petrol, **(iii)** 25 litres of petrol.

(e) Find, correct to the nearest litre, the quantity of petrol needed by the car to travel **(i)** 100 km, **(ii)** 150 km, **(iii)** 280 km.

6. A man hired a car from a car rental company. He was charged as follows:

$50 for the rental plus $1.50 for every kilometre travelled.

If he travelled x kilometres, he had to pay a total of $$y$.

(a) Write down an equation connecting x and y.

(b) Copy and complete the following.

x (km)	0	
y (dollars)		200

(c) Plot a straight line graph for the table in (b) using scales of your choice. Use the graph to answer the questions in (d), (e) and (f).

(d) How much had he to pay the company if he travelled **(i)** 80 km, **(ii)** 120 km, **(iii)** 148 km?

(e) What distance had he travelled if he paid the company **(i)** $92, **(ii)** $128, **(iii)** $266?

(f) If petrol cost $1.40 per litre and the car could run 12 km with each litre of petrol, find the total cost (including the rental) if he travelled 144 km.

7. (a) Draw a conversion graph for selling price against cost price from $10 to $26, given that the percentage profit is 30%.

(b) Find the selling price if the cost price is $16.

(c) Find the cost price if the selling price is $28.

8. (a) Draw a conversion graph for GST against selling price from $44 to $66, given that the GST is 3% of the selling price.

(b) Find the GST if the selling price is $46.

(c) Find the selling price if the GST is $1.86.

9. **(a)** Draw a conversion graph for kilogram (kg) against pound (lb) from 0 lb to 20 lb, given that 1 lb $\approx$ 0.45 kg.
(b) Convert 14 lb to kg.
(c) Convert 8.1 kg to lb.

10. **(a)** Draw a conversion graph for litre against gallon from 0 gallon to 4 gallons, given that 1 gallon $\approx$ 4.5 litres.
(b) Convert $2\frac{3}{4}$ gallons to litres (correct to 1 decimal place).
(c) Convert 14.6 litres to gallons $\left(\text{correct to the nearest } \frac{1}{4} \text{ gallon}\right)$.

5.4 TRAVEL GRAPHS

A graph which shows the relationship between the distance travelled and the time taken in a journey is known as a **travel graph**.

Examples

(a)

x (minutes)	0	10	20	30	40	50	60
y (km)	0	5	10	15	20	25	30

The table shows the distance-time relationship of a journey made by a truck. *y* represents the number of kilometres travelled and *x* the number of minutes taken. The total distance is 30 km and the truck takes 60 minutes to reach the destination. Thus the average speed is 30 km/h.

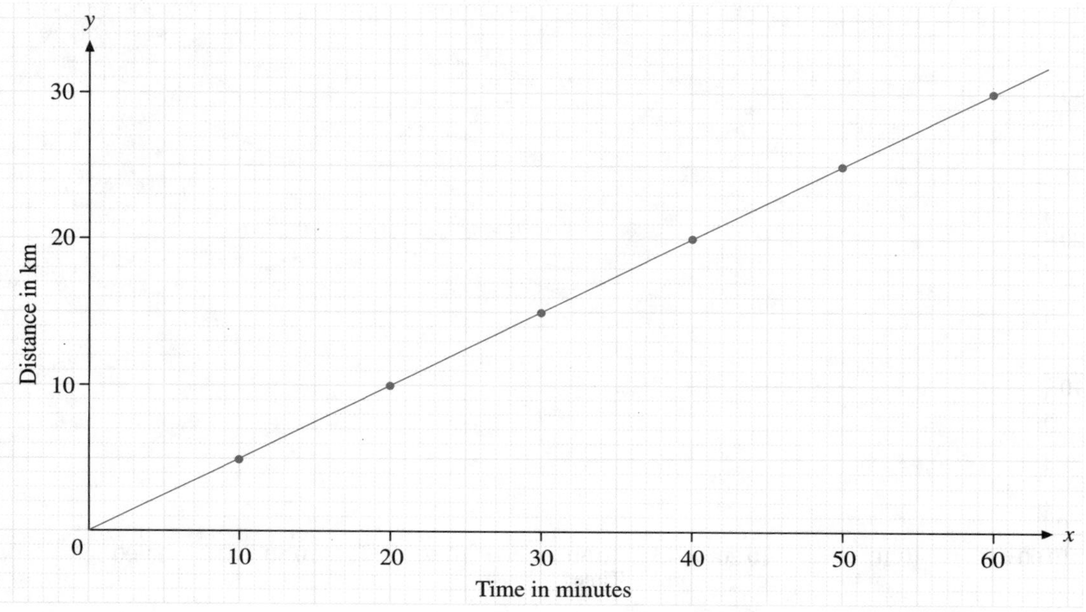

The figure shows the graph of the journey. The graph is represented by a straight line. It tells us that the truck is travelling at a constant speed of 30 km/h. If you study the table, you will notice that the ratio $\frac{y}{x}$ is constant. Let $\frac{y}{x} = k$. Thus the equation of the graph is $y = kx$ where k is a constant.

The graph, being a straight line, implies that the speedometer shows 30 km/h at every instant. This is not true in reality. Strictly, the parts of the graph corresponding to the beginning and end of the journey should be somewhat curved, but since we want to make it simpler, we have ignored these details.

From the graph, we see that when $x = 12$, $y = 6$. This means that the truck has travelled 6 km in 12 minutes.

Suppose the journey begins at noon. We know that the truck is 6 km away from the starting point at 12 12.

(b)

Time	10 00	10 05	10 10	10 20	10 30	10 40	10 50	11 00
Distance (km)	0	5	10	10	15	20	25	30

The table above is the distance-time table of a car journey. This journey is represented by the graph below.

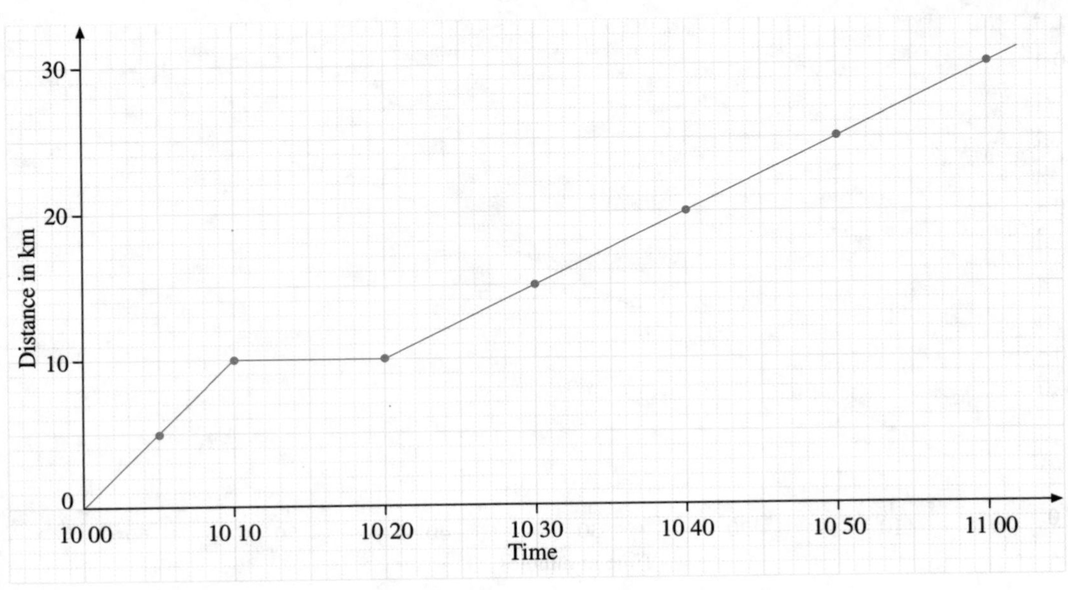

From the graph, we observe the following.

(i) From time 10 00 to 10 10, the car covers 10 km in 10 min.
The straight line shows that the car is travelling at a constant speed for the first 10 minutes.

$$\begin{aligned}\text{Constant speed} &= \frac{\text{distance travelled}}{\text{time taken}}\\ &= \frac{10}{10}\text{ km/min}\\ &= 1\text{ km/min}\\ &= 60\text{ km/h}\end{aligned}$$

(ii) From time 10 10 to 10 20, the distance covered remains unchanged. This means that the car is not moving during this period of time.

(iii) From time 10 20 to 11 00, the car covers 20 km travelling at a constant speed of $\left(20 \div \frac{2}{3}\right)$ km/h, i.e. 30 km/h.

(iv) $$\begin{aligned}\text{Average speed of the car for the whole journey} &= \frac{\text{total distance travelled}}{\text{total time taken}}\\ &= \frac{30}{1}\text{ km/h}\\ &= 30\text{ km/h}\end{aligned}$$

(c) The graph below shows the journeys of a van and a car. They start from the same point A and travel by the same route.

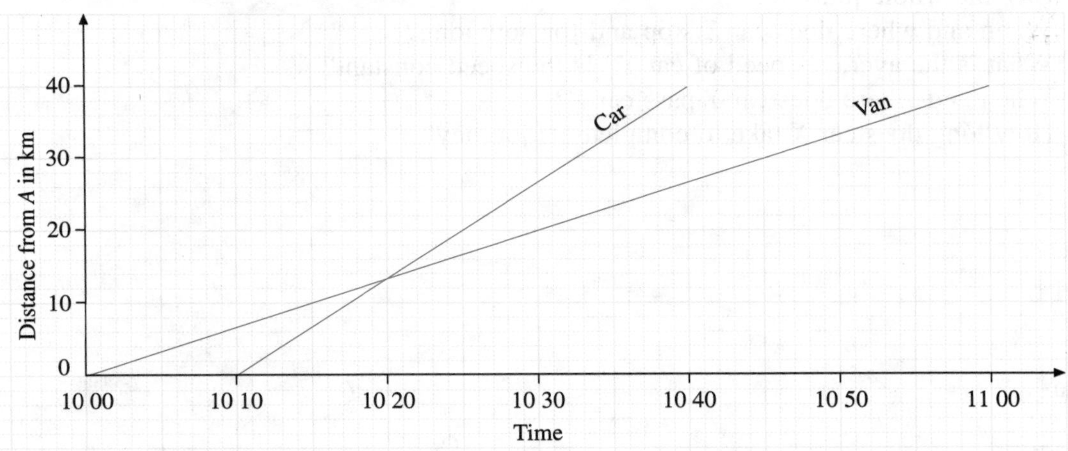

From the graph, we observe the following.

(i) From time 10 00 to 11 00, the van covers 40 km in one hour. Thus the speed is 40 km/h.

(ii) From time 10 10 to 10 40, the car covers 40 km in 30 minutes.

Thus the speed is $\left(40 \div \frac{1}{2}\right)$ km/h, i.e. 80 km/h.

(iii) The car overtakes the van at 10 20.

(iv) The car overtakes the van at a point 13 km from the starting point A.

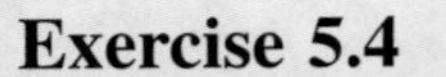

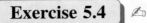

answers on p. 432

1.

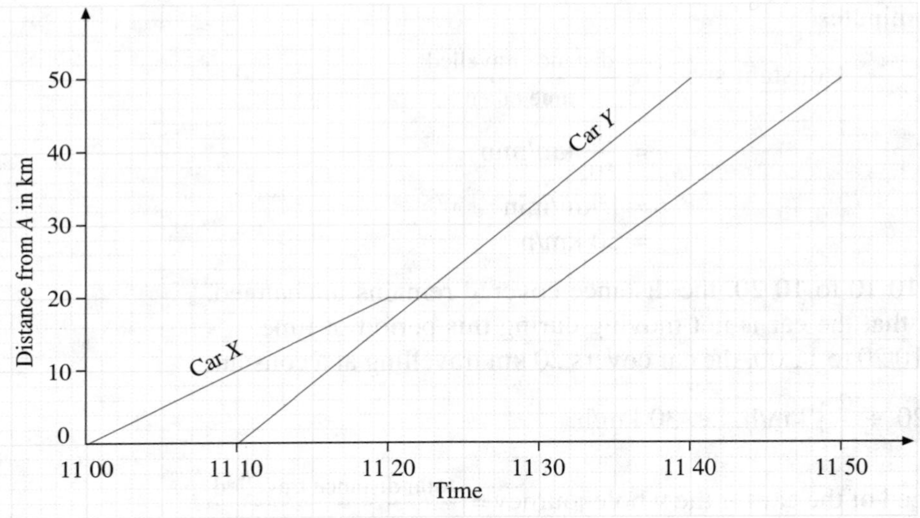

The graph above shows that two cars X and Y start from the same point A. They travel by the same route.

(a) What is the average speed of car X for
  (i) the first 20 minutes of its journey,
  (ii) the last 20 minutes of its journey,
  (iii) the whole journey?

(b) When and where does car X stop and for how long?

(c) What is the average speed of car Y? Is the speed constant?

(d) When and where does car Y pass car X?

(e) How long does car X take to complete its journey?

2.

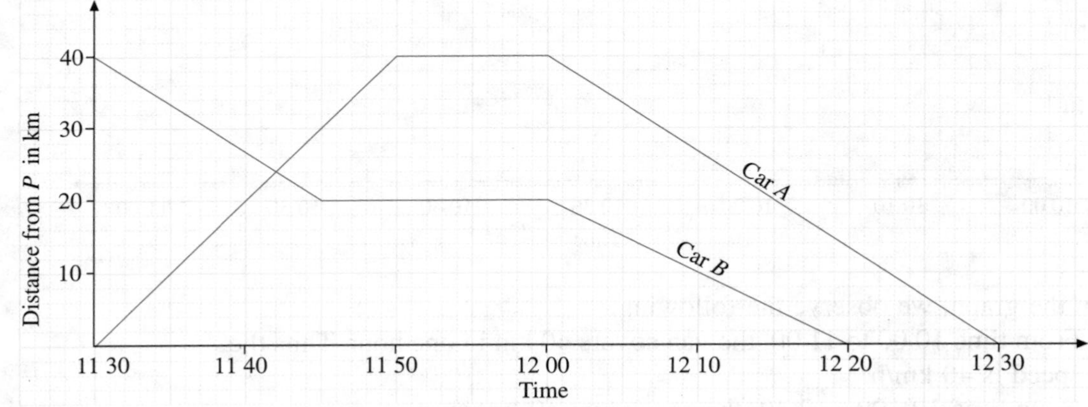

The graph above shows the journeys of two cars. Car A travels from point P to point Q and returns to P. Car B travels from Q by the same route to P.

(a) What is the total distance travelled by car A?

(b) What is the average speed of car A for the whole journey?

(c) How long does car B take to complete its journey?
(d) What is the average speed of car B for the whole journey?
(e) When and where does car B stop and for how long?
(f) When and where does car B meet car A? (Give the distance from the starting point.)

3.

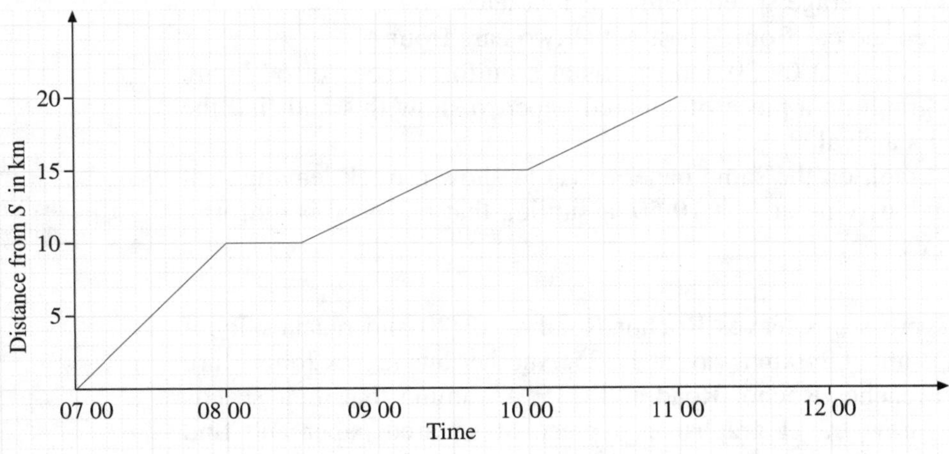

The graph above is a travel graph describing Salleh's trip to Kaifa's house which is 20 km away from his home S. Answer the following questions based on the graph.

(a) When did Salleh leave his house and when did he arrive at Kaifa's house?
(b) For how long did he travel?
(c) How far did he travel and what was his average speed?
(d) Did he travel at a constant speed throughout?
(e) How many times did he rest and for how long altogether?
(f) What was his average speed in the last part of his journey? Was the speed constant?
(g) When did he travel the fastest?

4.

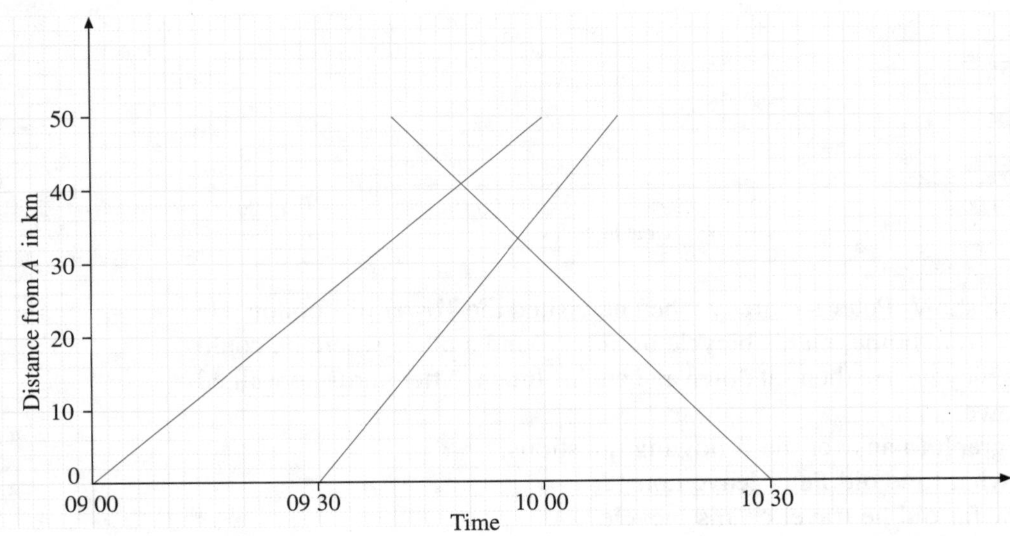

The line graphs represent three car journeys between town A and town B which are 50 km apart. Answer the following questions from the graphs.

(a) Are the speeds of the three cars uniform?
(b) Do all the cars travel from A to B?
(c) What is the average speed of each of the two cars leaving A?
(d) What is the average speed of the car that leaves B?
(e) State when the car from B passes the two cars from A.
(f) A van leaves B at 09 30 and travels at a uniform speed of 60 km/h. Draw a graph on a piece of squared paper to show this and find the time of its arrival at A.
(g) Draw a graph on the same paper as (f) to show a truck leaving A at 10 00 and arriving at B at 10 50, assuming that its speed is uniform. What is its speed?

5. The Johor Express bus leaves Rochor Road at 13 30 and reaches Johor Baru, which is about 27 km away, at 14 25. Another bus leaves Johor Baru at 13 45 and reaches Rochor Road at 14 35. Assuming that their speeds are uniform, draw travel graphs on a piece of squared paper and find approximately the average speed of each bus and the time at which they pass each other.

6.

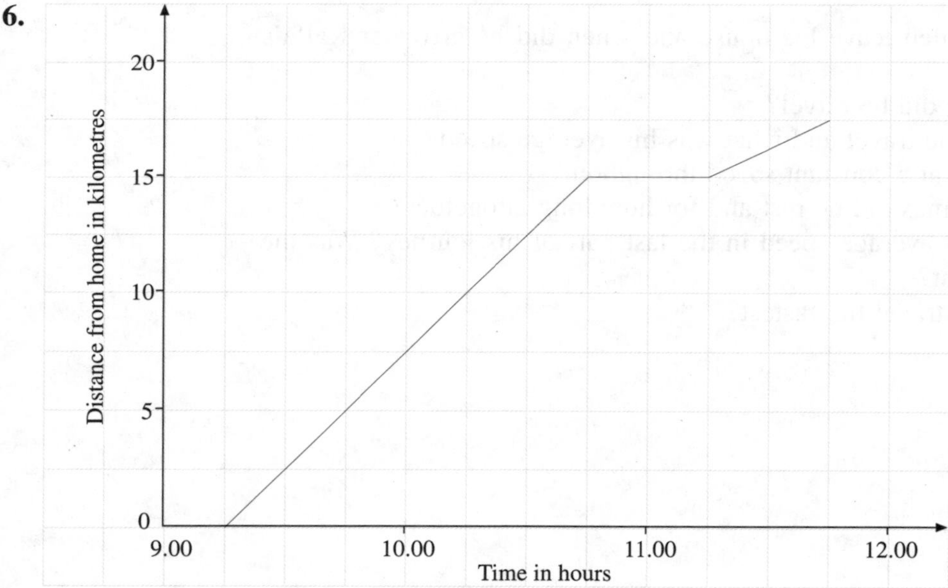

The graph shows Peter's journey when he visited the Tower of London. He travelled, from home, on his bicycle until he found a place where he could leave his bicycle. He then sat down and ate his lunch. Afterwards he walked to the Tower.

Use the graph to answer the following questions.

(a) At what time did Peter leave home?
(b) How far did he travel on his bicycle?

(c) How many minutes did it take him to eat his lunch?
(d) At what average speed, in km/h, did he walk to the Tower?
(e) Assuming Peter travelled home by the same route, and that he walked 5 km in the Tower itself, find how far he travelled altogether on this day trip. *(C)*

7.

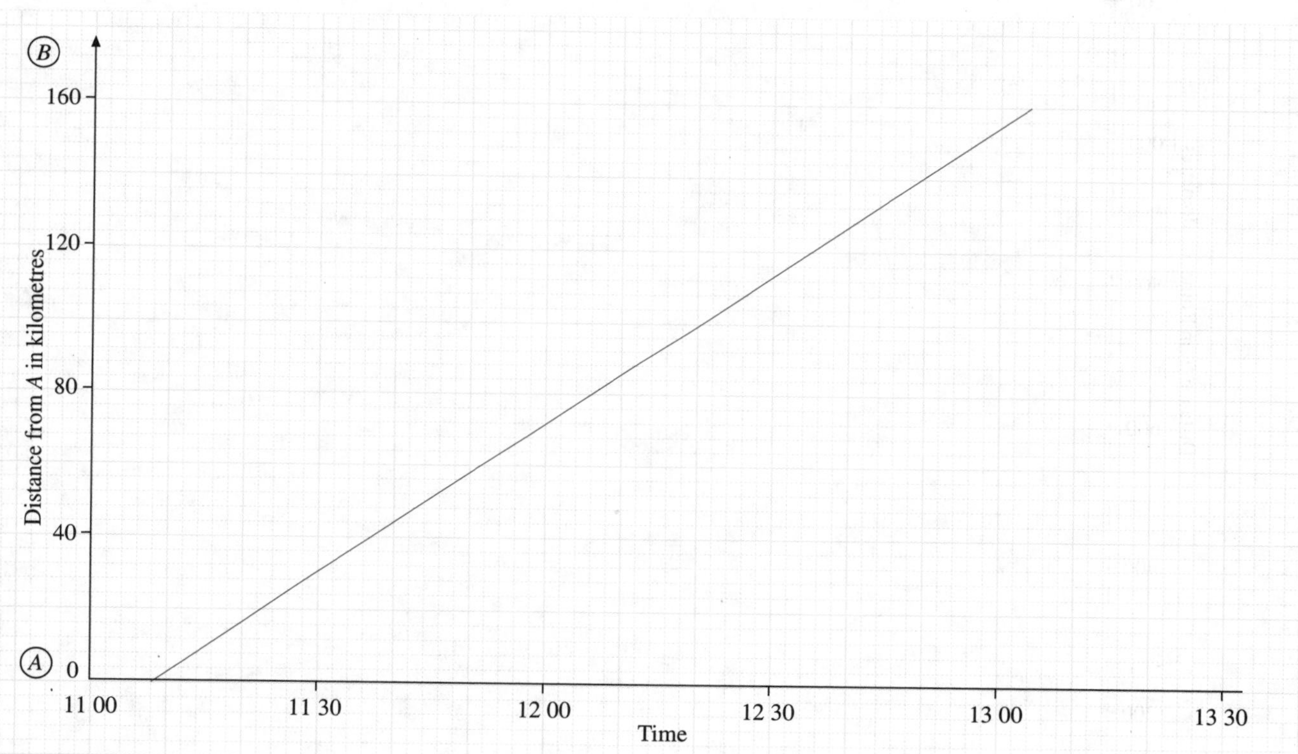

The graph above shows two autobahn stops, Ⓐ and Ⓑ, 160 kilometres apart. The line on the graph represents the journey of a car which leaves Ⓐ at 11 08 and is driven to Ⓑ, without stopping, at a constant speed. It arrives at Ⓑ at 13 04.

Note: An autobahn is a German motorway.

(a) Calculate the average speed of the car for this journey.
(b) A second car arrives at Ⓐ at 13 24, having been driven from Ⓑ at a constant speed of 80 kilometres per hour.
  (i) Copy the graph and draw the graph of this journey on your diagram.
  (ii) How far from Ⓑ are the two cars when they pass one another? *(C)*

8.

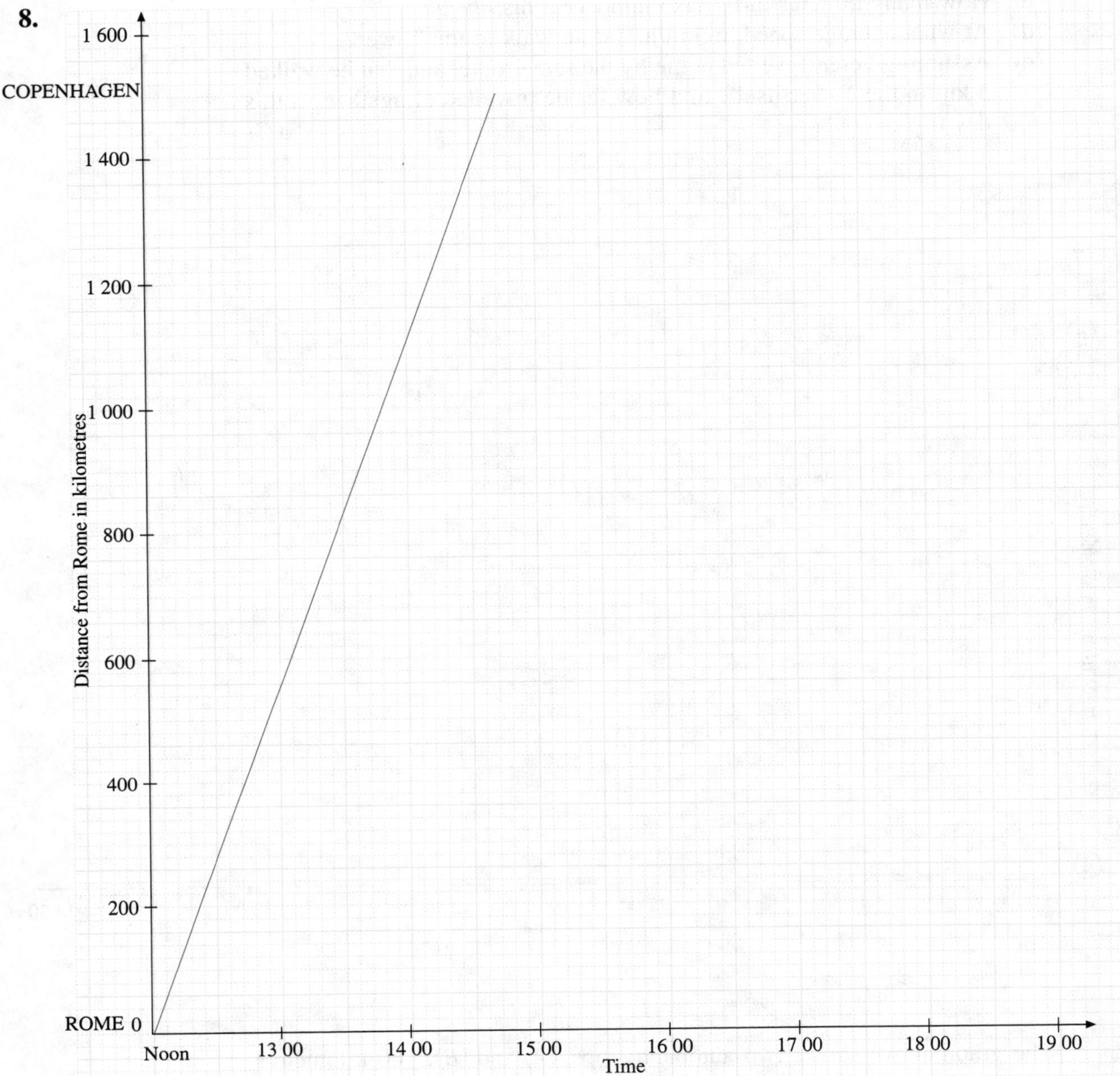

Copy the graph which represents the flight of an aircraft which leaves Rome at noon and arrives in Copenhagen at 14 42. It crosses no time zones.

(a) How long does the flight take?

(b) Use your graph to find the distance from Rome to Copenhagen.

(c) Calculate the average speed of the flight, in kilometres per hour.

From the return flight to Rome, the aircraft departs at 16 15, and takes exactly the same time for the journey.

(d) Draw lines on your graph to represent

  (i) the time the aircraft is on the ground in Copenhagen,

  (ii) the return journey.

(e) How long is the aircraft on the ground in Copenhagen?
(f) At what time does the aircraft arrive back in Rome? (*C*)

9.

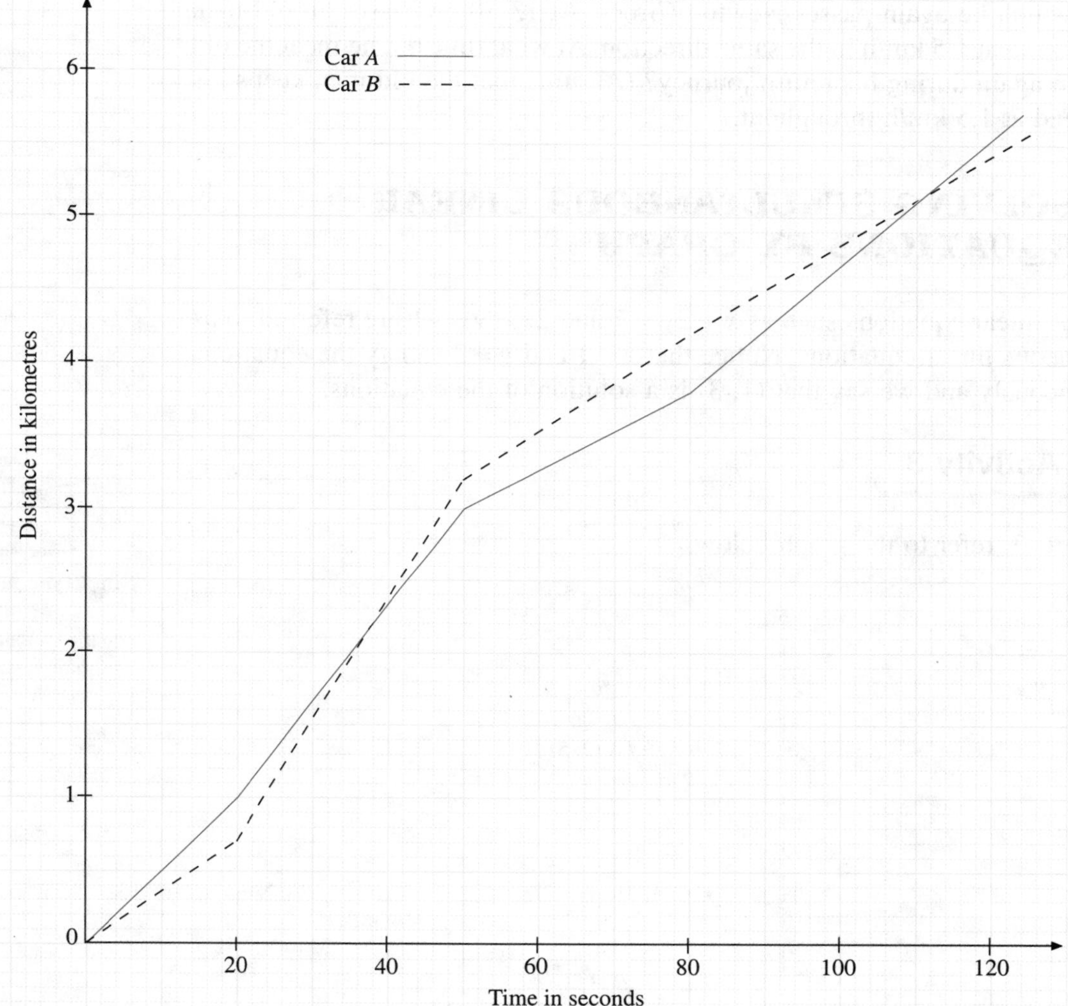

The graph shows the progress of the two leading cars during the first two minutes of a Grand Prix race.

(a) Which car first goes into the lead?
(b) What happens about 38 seconds after the start?
(c) After 50 seconds,
  (i) what is the distance, in metres, between the cars,
  (ii) which car is in the lead?
(d) For the period of time between 50 seconds and 80 seconds, write a comment on
  (i) the distance between the cars, **(ii)** the speed of the cars.
(e) How many seconds after the start of the race does car *A* regain the lead?
(f) Calculate, in kilometres per hour, the average speed of car *A* during the first two minutes. (*C*)

10. A man walks steadily along Bukit Timah Road at 3.5 km/h, passing Newton Circus at 13 20. He continues to walk until 14 20 and then turns back and walks at 4 km/h. Draw a travel graph and find approximately the time at which he again passes Newton Circus. At 13 30 he passes an old man walking at 1.5 km/h in the same direction. At what time did he meet the old man again during his return journey? (Assume that the old man keeps his speed at 1.5 km/h throughout.)

5.5 SOLVING SIMULTANEOUS LINEAR EQUATIONS BY GRAPHS

A pair of linear equations such as $x + 2y = 7$ and $2x - y = -1$ are referred to as simultaneous linear equations. Notice that $x = 1$ and $y = 3$ satisfy the equations simultaneously and we say that (1, 3) is a solution of the equations.

Class Activity 3

Simultaneous equations are a set of equations that contain common variables.

For No. 1–3, refer to the graph below.

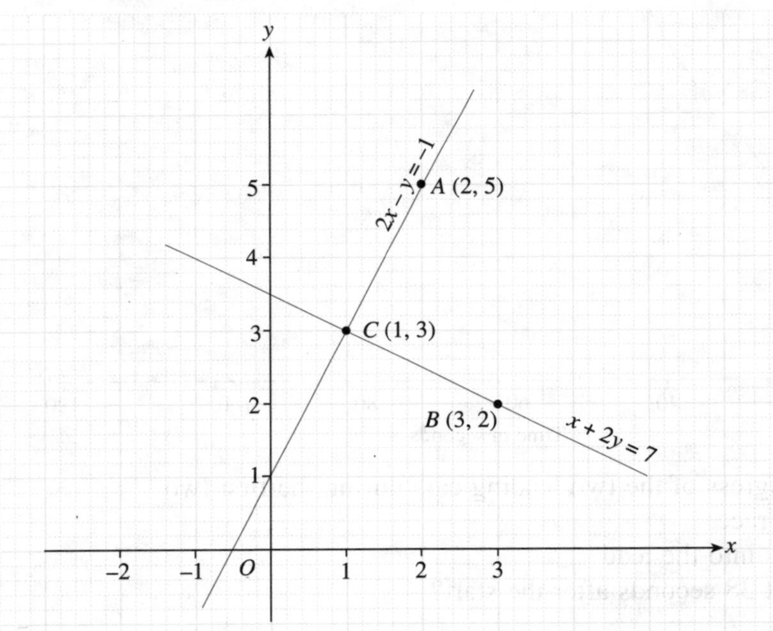

1. **(a)** Does the ordered pair (2, 5) satisfy the equation $2x - y = -1$?
(b) Does the ordered pair (2, 5) satisfy the equation $x + 2y = 7$?
(c) Does the ordered pair (2, 5) satisfy both the equation $2x - y = -1$ and $x + 2y = 7$?

2. **(a)** Does the ordered pair (3, 2) satisfy the equation $x + 2y = 7$?
(b) Does the ordered pair (3, 2) satisfy the equation $2x - y = -1$?
(c) Does the ordered pair (3, 2) satisfy both the equations $x + 2y = 7$ and $2x - y = -1$?

3. **(a)** Does the ordered pair (1, 3) satisfy the equation $2x - y = -1$?
(b) Does the ordered pair (1, 3) satisfy the equation $x + 2y = 7$?
(c) Does the ordered pair (1, 3) satisfy both the equations $2x - y = -1$ and $x + 2y = 7$?
(d) Study the graph. Do you agree that the coordinates of the point of intersection of the lines $2x - y = -1$ and $x + 2y = 7$ satisfy the following simultaneous equations?

$$2x - y = -1$$
$$x + 2y = 7$$

4. **(a)** Draw the lines $5x - y = 6$ and $3x - y = -10$ on the same axes.
(b) Find from your graph, the point of intersection of these two lines.
(c) Write down the two numbers that satisfy the simultaneous equations

$$5x - y = 6$$
$$3x - y = -10.$$

(d) Check your answer in (c) by calculation.

Worked Example

Using a scale of 1 cm to 1 unit on each axis, draw the graphs of the following pair of simultaneous equations for values of x from –3 to 3. Use your graphs to solve the equations:

$9x - 10y = -3$
$2x + 5y = 9$

Solution:

$9x - 10y = -3$

x	–3	3
y	–2.4	3

$2x + 5y = 9$

x	–3	3
y	3	0.6

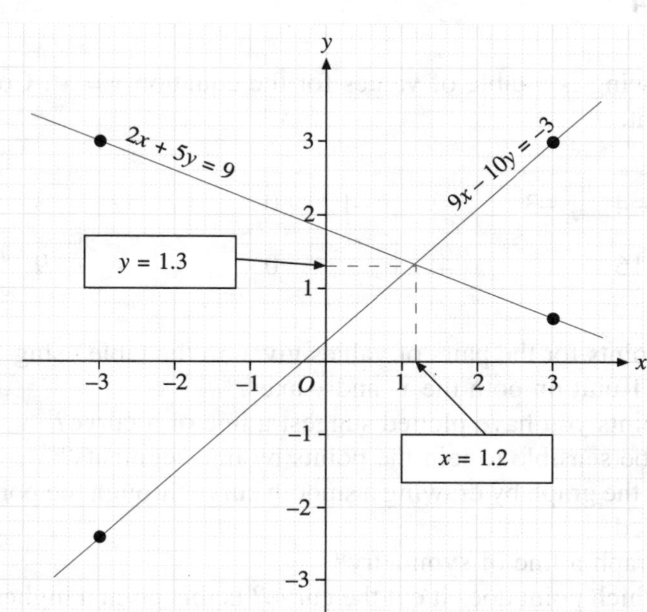

From the graph, we have $x = 1.2$ and $y = 1.3$.

Note: A graphical method gives only approximate answers. In this case, the answer is given to one decimal place.

Exercise 5.5

answers on p. 432

Using a scale of 2 cm to 1 unit on each axis, draw the graphs of the following pairs of simultaneous equations for values of x from –3 to 3. Use your graphs to solve the simultaneous equations. (Give your answers correct to 1 decimal place where necessary.)

1. $3x + 5y = -4$
$x - 2y = -1$

2. $4x - 10y = -13$
$x + 2y = 5$

3. $4x - 5y = 2$
$7x - 10y = 2$

4. $7x - 10y = -9$
$3x + 5y = -1$

5. $9x - 10y = 3$
$3x + 5y = -1$

6. $7x - 10y = -13$
$3x + 10y = -1$

7. $5x - 10y = -1$
$4x + 5y = 7$

8. $7x - 10y = 9$
$x + 2y = -1$

9. $x - y = 1$
$3x + 5y = -6$

10. $4x - 5y = -2$
$x + 5y = 3$

5.6 QUADRATIC GRAPHS

Class Activity 4

1. **(a)** The following is a table of values for the equation $y = x^2$. Copy and complete it.

x	–4	–3	–2	–1	0	1	2	3	4
y	16		4		0		4	9	

(b) Plot the points for the pairs of values given in the table using 1 cm to represent 1 unit on both the x- and y-axes.

(c) Do the points you have plotted suggest a line or a curve? Would it be sensible to join the points by line segments?

(d) Complete the graph by drawing a smooth curve through the points you have plotted.

(e) Has the graph a line of symmetry? If so, at which point does it cut the curve? Is this point a highest point or lowest point of the curve? What is the equation of the line of symmetry?

(f) Do you agree that the y coordinate of any point of this curve is always positive?

(g) Notice that the curve does not lie below the x-axis. If you were to draw the curve for x from -10 to 10, do you agree that all points of this curve still do not lie below the x-axis? What if we take the values of x from -100 to 100?

(h) From the graph, find the values of y when $x = 1.5$ and $x = -1.5$.

(i) From the graph, find the values of x when $y = 8$.

(j) From the graph, find the squares of 1.8 and -3.5.

(k) From the graph, find the square roots of 6, 11 and 15.

2. (a) Draw the graph $y = -x^2$ for values of x from -4 to 4.

(b) Has the graph a line of symmetry? If so, does it pass the highest or lowest point of the curve? What is the equation of the line of symmetry?

(c) Do you agree that the y coordinate of any point of the curve is negative?

(d) Do you think that all points of the curve (including those beyond the range from -4 to 4) do not lie above the x-axis?

3. (a) The following is a table of values for the equation $y = x^2 - 8x + 17$. Copy and complete it.

x	0	1	2	3	4	5	6	7	8
y	17		5		1		5	10	

(b) Plot the points for the values given in the table using 1 cm to represent 1 unit on both the x- and y-axes.

(c) Complete the graph by drawing a smooth curve through the points you have plotted.

(d) As x increases from 0 to 4, does the value of y increase or decrease, and from what value to what value does it change?

(e) As x further increases from 4 to 8, does the value of y increase or decrease, and from what value to what value does it change?

(f) Name the point of the curve whose y coordinate is the smallest.

4. (a) The following is a table of values for the equation $y = -x^2 + 8x + 1$. Copy and complete it.

x	0	1	2	3	4	5	6	7	8
y	1		13		17		13	8	

(b) Plot the points for the value given in the table using 1 cm to represent 1 unit on both the x- and y-axes.

(c) Complete the graph by drawing a smooth curve through the points you have plotted.

(d) As x increases from 0 to 4, does the value of y increase or decrease, and from what value to what value does it change?

(e) As x further increases from 4 to 8, does the value of y increase or decrease, and from what value to what value does it change?

(f) Name the point of the curve whose y coordinate is the greatest.

Worked Example

(a) The following is a table of values for the equation $y = 1 + x - 3x^2$. Copy and complete it.

x	–3	–2	–1	0	1	2	3
y		–13		1			–23

(b) Using 2 cm along the x-axis to represent 1 unit and 1 cm along the y-axis to represent 5 units, draw the graph of $y = 1 + x - 3x^2$.

(c) From your graph, find

(i) the value of y when $x = 2.8$,

(ii) the value of x when $y = -8$.

Solution:

(a)

x	–3	–2	–1	0	1	2	3
y	–29	–13	–3	1	–1	–9	–23

(b) Graph of $y = 1 + x - 3x^2$.

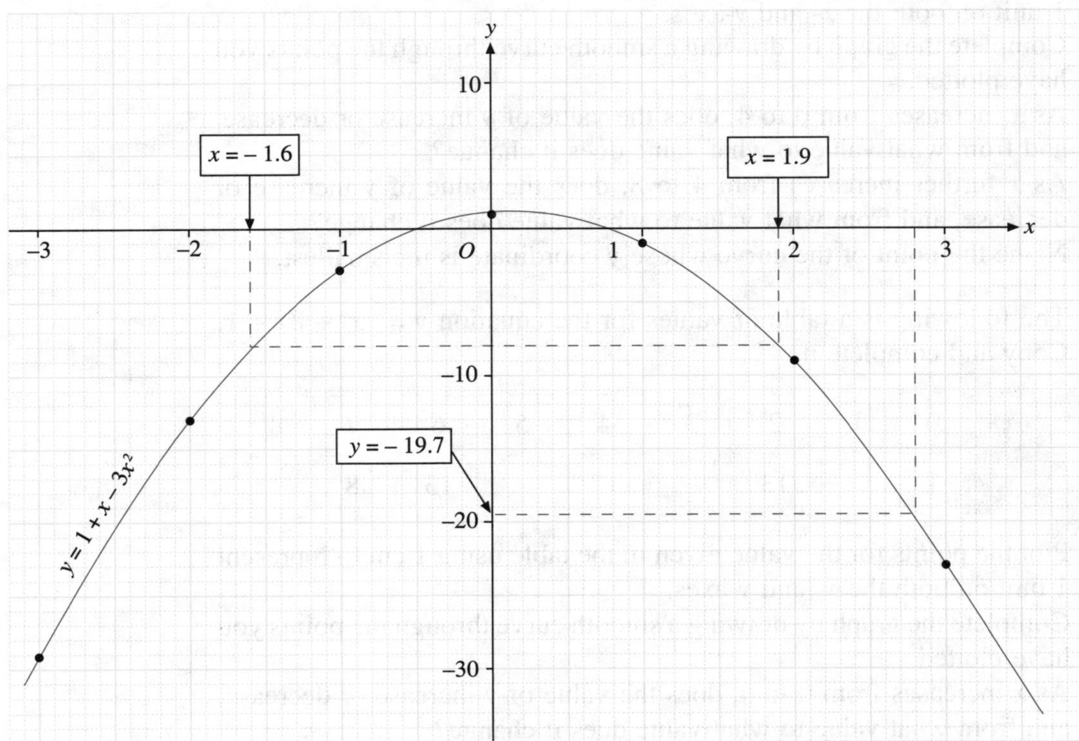

Exercise 5.6

answers on p. 432

1. **(a)** Given that $y = 25 + 4x - 3x^2$, copy and complete the table below.

x	–3	–2	–1	0	1	2	3	4	5
y	–14	5				21		–7	–30

(b) Taking 2 cm to represent 1 unit of x and 2 cm to represent 10 units of y, draw the graph of $y = 25 + 4x - 3x^2$ from $x = -3$ to $x = 5$.

(c) From the graph, find

(i) the value of y when $x = -1.2$,

(ii) the values of x when $y = 21.5$.

2. **(a)** Copy and complete the following table of values for the graph $y = 2x^2 + 5x - 7$ for values of x between –1 and 4.

x	–1	0	1	2	3	4
y	–10		0		26	45

(b) Using a scale of 2 cm to 1 unit on the x-axis and 2 cm to 10 units on the y-axis, draw the graph of $y = 2x^2 + 5x - 7$ for values of x between –1 and 4.

(c) From the graph, find

(i) the value of y when $x = 2.5$,

(ii) the value of x when $y = 3.5$.

3. **(a)** Given that $y = 3x^2 + 3x - 5$, copy and complete the table below.

x	–2	–1	0	1	2	3
y	1		–5	1		31

(b) Using a scale of 2 cm to 1 unit on the x-axis and 2 cm to 10 units on the y-axis, draw the graph of $y = 3x^2 + 3x - 5$ for values of x between –2 and 3.

(c) From the graph, find

(i) the value of y when $x = 1.8$,

(ii) the value of x when $y = 5.5$.

4. Plot the following graphs using suitable scales and answer the questions that follow. (*Hint:* Since the scale is not given, choose a scale which includes the values you need to find. For example, in (a) $x = 1.5$ and $y = 12.5$.)

(a) $y = 2x^2 + 2x - 5$
 (i) Find y when $x = 1.5$.
 (ii) Find x when $y = 12.5$.

(b) $y = x^2 + 3x + 1$
 (i) Find y when $x = 1.3$.
 (ii) Find x when $y = 12.4$.

(c) $y = 5x^2 + 6x - 8$
 (i) Find y when $x = -1.4$.
 (ii) Find x when $y = 19$.

(d) $y = 2x^2 + 5x - 4$
 (i) Find y when $x = 0.5$.
 (ii) Find x when $y = -6.3$.

(e) $y = 2x^2 + 15x - 4$
 (i) Find y when $x = 1.1$.
 (ii) Find x when $y = 9.3$.

(f) $y = 3x^2 + 4x + 1$
 (i) Find y when $x = -1.8$.
 (ii) Find x when $y = 4.5$.

Chapter Review

1. A point on a number plane is represented by an ordered pair.

   Example:

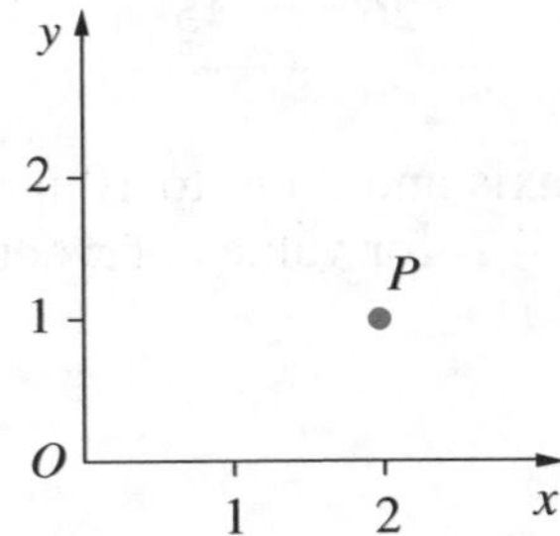

   P is represented by the ordered pair (2, 1) where the number 2 is the x coordinate and the number 1 is the y coordinate. We read the x coordinate of a point first followed by the y coordinate.

2. Linear equations are of the form $y = mx + c$ where m and c are constants.

   Example: $y = 2x + 4$

3. Equations involving a term x^2 are not linear equations.

4. Graphs of linear equations are straight lines.

5. A travel graph is one which shows the relationship between the distance from a point and the travelling time.

6. The solution of a pair of simultaneous equations is represented by the coordinates of the point of intersection of the graphs of the two equations.

7. Quadratic equations are of the form

$$y = ax^2 + bx + c \ (a \neq 0).$$

8. Graphs of quadratic equations in two variables are quadratic graphs.

9. A quadratic graph has a line of symmetry passing through the highest or lowest point of the curve.

CHALLENGER 5

1. $A(1, p)$ and $B(q, 7)$ are points on the curve $y = 3 + 4x - x^2$ as shown.
   (a) Calculate the values of p and q.
   (b) If the area bounded by the curve AB, the line segments AC and BD and the x-axis is $6\frac{2}{3}$ square units, calculate the area bounded by the curve AB, the line segments AE and BF and the y-axis.

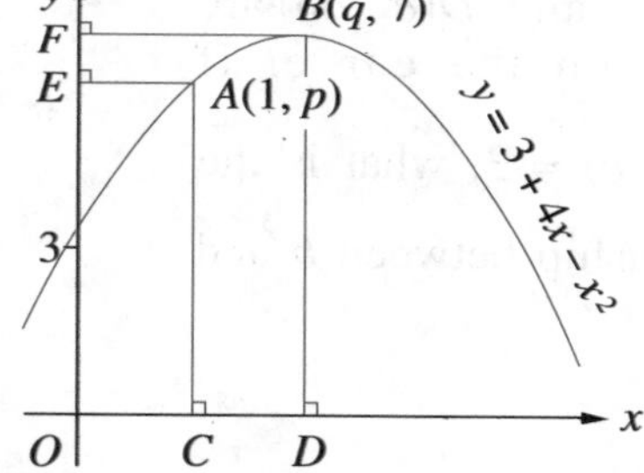

2. A piece of wire 60 cm long is bent to make a rectangular frame. If the base of the frame is x cm and the area enclosed is y cm^2,
   (a) show that $y = 30x - x^2$,
   (b) find graphically the greatest possible area enclosed.

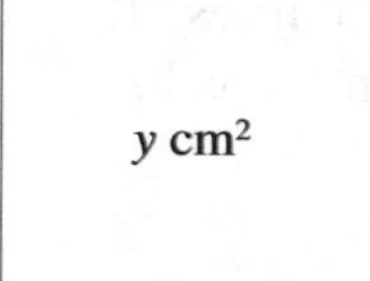

3. Ali's house was 3 km from his school. One day, Ali left his house at 10 15 and walked steadily at a speed which would bring him to school for library duty at 11 00. On his way, he met Bala, who left the school at 10 00 and walked at 5 km/h towards Ali's house. They stopped and talked for 5 minutes when they met. Ali then learnt that Menghui was waiting for him to discuss a soccer match. At what speed did Ali have to walk so that he could spend 10 minutes with Menghui before he began his library duty? Solve the problem graphically.

4. **(a)** In the figure, the y-axis is the line of symmetry of the curve which passes through $A(2, 8)$ and $B(p, 8)$.

(i) Write down the value of p.

(ii) If C and D are two other points on the curve such that their y coordinates are equal, what is the relationship between their x coordinates?

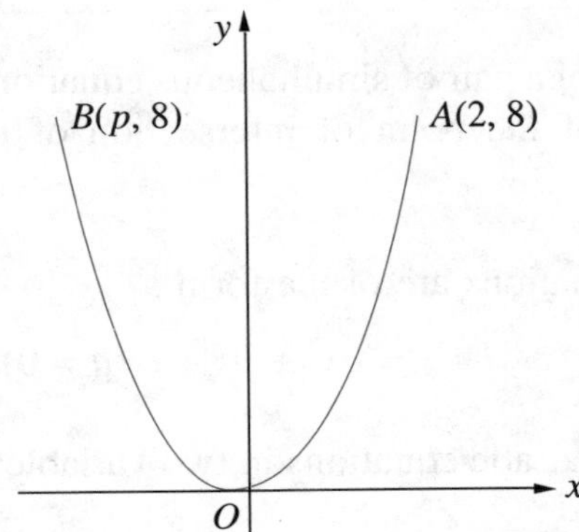

(b) In the figure, the line $x = 3$ is the line of symmetry of the curve which passes through $A(5, 6)$ and $B(p, 6)$.

(i) Write down the value of p.

(ii) $C(a, b)$ and $D(c, d)$ are points on the curve. If $\frac{1}{2}(a + c) = 3$, what is the relationship between b and d?

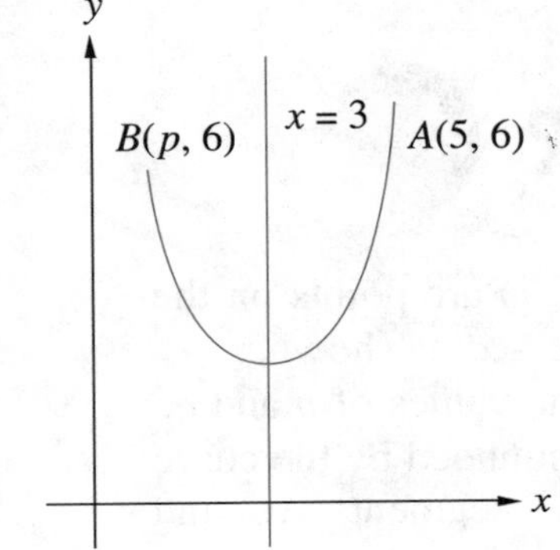

5. The curve $y = x^2 + kx + 18$ is symmetrical about the line $x = 4$. Find the value of k. (*Hint:* $A(a, b)$ and $B(c, d)$ are points on the curves. If $b = d$ and $a = 1$, write down the value of c.)

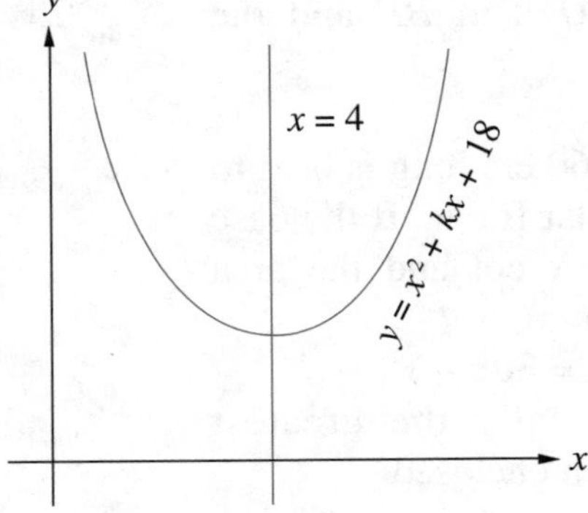

6. A motorist left town X at 08 15 to travel to town Y, which was 120 km away. He drove steadily at a speed which would bring him to town Y at 10 15. But on his way, his car had a puncture. He stopped for 20 minutes to change the wheel and then drove at a speed 20 km/h higher than before. He arrived at town Y at 10 25. How far had he driven when the puncture occurred? Solve the problem graphically.

Problem Solving 5

Father and Son

Two years ago, a man was 5 times as old as his son. In two years' time, the man will be 4 times as old as his son. How old is the son now?

Let us use the strategies **use a model** and **use an equation**.

Suppose the son's age is x years old now.

2 years ago:

$x - 2$

B [ ] ←— Difference —→

F [ ][ ][ ][ ][ ]

$x - 2$ $x - 2$ $x - 2$ $x - 2$ $x - 2$

2 years' time:

$x + 2$ $x + 2$ $x + 2$ $x + 2$

F [ ][ ][ ][ ]

B [ ] ←— Difference —→

$x + 2$

Since the difference in their ages remains unchanged, we have

$$4(x - 2) = 3(x + 2)$$
$$\therefore x = 14$$

So the son is 14 years old now.

Ask yourself: Can I form the equation without drawing the model?
How would I find the man's present age?

Problems...

1. **Fish and Prawns** Mary bought 2 kg of fish and 1 kg of prawns for \$24. Ann spent \$27 for 1 kg of fish and 2 kg of prawns from the same stall. Find the prices for each kilogram of fish and prawns.

2. **Swapping Digits** A two-digit integer is divisible by 3 but not by 6. If the digits are reversed, the new number is 18 more than the original. What is the integer? (*Hint:* If the 'tens' digit is x and the 'ones' digit is y, then the number is $10x + y$. What is the number with the digits reversed?)

3. **Turfing** Two fields A and B had to be turfed by one work team. On the first day, the whole team worked on field A. On the second day, half the team worked on field A and the other half on field B. The job in field A was completed by the end of the second day. On the third day, only one worker from the team worked on field B to finish off the turfing. If the areas of fields A and B are in the ratio 5 : 2, find the number of workers in the team.

4. **An Urgent SOS** What do the letters represent to make the addition correct?

$$\begin{array}{r} SEND \\ +\ MORE \\ \hline MONEY \\ \hline \end{array}$$

Rule: The same letter represents the same digit. Different letters represent different digits.

Chapter 6

Simultaneous Linear Equations

Chapter Highlights

- Solving simultaneous linear equations in two variables by elimination
- Solving simultaneous linear equations in two variables by substitution
- Solving problems involving simultaneous linear equations

6.1 SIMPLE ELIMINATION METHOD

We have seen that simultaneous linear equations can be solved by using graphs. We shall now learn how they can be solved by using an algebraic method known as the elimination method.

Examples

(a) Consider these simultaneous linear equations.

$$6x + 4y = 24 \quad \text{.......................} \quad (1)$$
$$7x - 4y = 2 \quad \text{.......................} \quad (2)$$

As the terms $+4y$ and $-4y$ are found in equation (1) and equation (2), the variable y can be eliminated easily by forming a new equation as follows:

$$(1) + (2): \qquad (6x + 4y) + (7x - 4y) = 24 + 2 \quad \text{.....................} \quad (3)$$
$$13x = 26$$
$$\therefore\ x = 2$$

Notice that the left-hand side of equation (3) is the sum of the left-hand sides of equations (1) and (2). The right-hand side of equation (3) is similarly obtained.

To find the value of y, we take x to be 2 in either equation (1) or equation (2). Thus if we replace x by 2 in equation (1), we have

$$\begin{aligned} (6 \times 2) + 4y &= 24 \\ 12 + 4y &= 24 \\ 4y &= 24 - 12 \\ 4y &= 12 \\ \therefore\ y &= \frac{12}{4} \\ &= 3 \end{aligned}$$

$\therefore$ the solutions are $x = 2$ and $y = 3$.

Check: $7x - 4y = 7 \times 2 - 4 \times 3 = 2$, as in equation (2).

Note: We use equation (2) for the check because the value of y was found by putting $x = 2$ in equation (1).

(b) Consider these simultaneous equations.

$$2x + y = 10 \quad \text{.......................} \quad (1)$$
$$2x - 3y = 2 \quad \text{.......................} \quad (2)$$

As the term $2x$ is found in both equations (1) and (2), the variable x can be eliminated easily as follows:

(1) – (2): $(2x + y) - (2x - 3y) = 10 - 2$ .... (3)

$$2x + y - 2x + 3y = 8$$
$$4y = 8$$
$$y = 2$$

Replacing y by 2 in equation (1), we have

$$2x + 2 = 10$$
$$2x = 8$$
$$x = 4$$

Check: $2x - 3y = (2 \times 4) - (3 \times 2) = 2$, as in equation (2).

Exercise 6.1

answers on p. 432

Find the solutions of each of the following pairs of simultaneous equations. Decide which unknown can be eliminated more easily first.

1. $7x - 2y = 29$
$7x + y = 38$

2. $10x - 3y = 18$
$8x + 3y = 36$

3. $5x - 6y = 8$
$7x + 6y = 40$

4. $x + 6y = 10$
$x - 9y = -20$

5. $5x + 3y = 30$
$x - 3y = -12$

6. $6x + y = 32$
$6x - 3y = 24$

7. $2x + 6y = 20$
$2x + 5y = 17$

8. $3y + 4x = 9$
$3y + 5x = 12$

9. $8x + 4y = 36$
$8x + 3y = 33$

10. $10x + 7y = -31$
$15x + 7y = -36$

11. $4x + 6y = -4$
$9x + 6y = 6$

12. $7y - 5x = 1$
$7y + 8x = 53$

6.2 ELIMINATION METHOD

Examples

(a) Consider these simultaneous equations.

$3x + 2y = 12$ .... (1)

$7x - 4y = 2$ .... (2)

Notice that we cannot obtain a new equation with only one variable simply by addition or subtraction. However, if you multiply both sides of equation (1) by 2 (usually indicated as (1) × 2), we will obtain

$$6x + 4y = 24 \quad \text{.......................} \quad (3)$$

We can now proceed to solve equations (2) and (3) by addition.

(b) Consider these simultaneous equations.

$$7x + 4y = 57 \quad \text{.......................} \quad (1)$$
$$5x + 6y = 47 \quad \text{.......................} \quad (2)$$

Suppose we wish to eliminate y. We form an equivalent pair of simultaneous equations by multiplying each side of the equations by a suitable number.

(1) × 3: $\quad 21x + 12y = 171 \quad$ .... (3)
(2) × 2: $\quad 10x + 12y = 94 \quad$ .... (4)

We can eliminate y by taking (3) – (4) and then solve for x and y.

Note: To eliminate y, we must decide what 'suitable numbers' we can use as the multipliers to obtain equations in which the coefficients of y are numerically equal. We study the coefficients of the terms in y in equations (1) and (2) and find the LCM of the coefficients. The LCM of 4 and 6 is 12. Hence we multiply each side of equation (1) by 3 and each side of equation (2) by 2 to create the term $12y$ in both equations (3) and (4).

(c) Consider these simultaneous equations.

$$3x + 2y = 3 \quad \text{.......................} \quad (1)$$
$$6x + 4y = 9 \quad \text{.......................} \quad (2)$$

(1) × 2: $\quad 6x + 4y = 6 \quad$ .... (3)
(2) – (3): $\quad 0 = 3$

This is impossible, so there is no solution.

Note: The graphs of equations (1) and (2) are a pair of parallel lines.

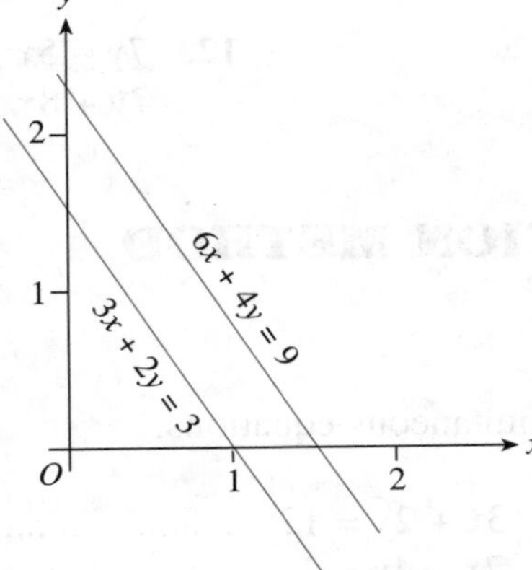

(d) Consider these simultaneous equations.

$$x + y = 2 \quad \dots\dots\dots\dots\dots\dots \quad (1)$$
$$2x + 2y = 4 \quad \dots\dots\dots\dots\dots\dots \quad (2)$$

If you multiply both sides of equation (1) by 2, you will get an equation identical to equation (2). This means that equation (2) and equation (1) are equivalent.

If $x = 1$ and $y = 1$, both equations (1) and (2) are satisfied. Therefore $x = 1$ and $y = 1$ are solutions of the equations.

You will notice that there are many other pairs of solutions, e.g.

$x = 2$ and $y = 0$,
$x = 3$ and $y = -1$,
$x = 4$ and $y = -2$, and so on.

In fact, these equations have an infinite number of solutions.

Note: You will notice that the graphs of equations (1) and (2) coincide.

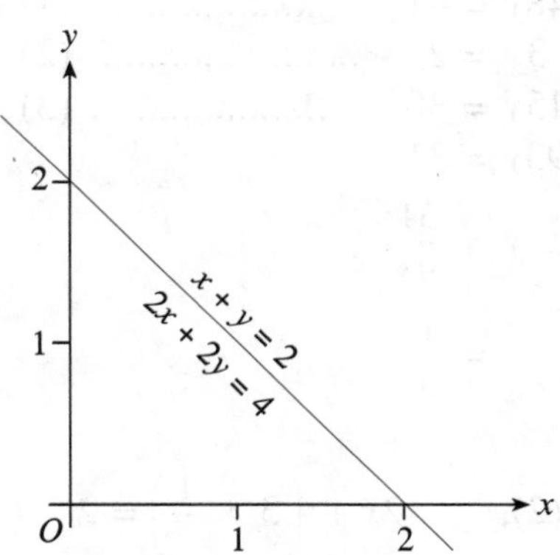

Worked Example 1

Solve these equations.

$3x + 5y = 9$
$-5x + 2y = 16$

Solution:

	$3x + 5y = 9$	.... (1)
	$-5x + 2y = 16$	.... (2)
(1) × 5:	$15x + 25y = 45$	.... (3)
(2) × 3:	$-15x + 6y = 48$	.... (4)
(3) + (4):	$31y = 93$	
	$\therefore y = \frac{93}{31}$	
	$= 3$	

Substituting $y = 3$ in (1),

$$
\begin{aligned}
3x + (5 \times 3) &= 9 \\
3x &= 9 - 15 \\
3x &= -6 \\
\therefore x &= \frac{-6}{3} \\
&= -2
\end{aligned}
$$

Thus the solutions are $x = -2$ and $y = 3$.

Note: It is a good habit to check your answers. This can be done as rough work even though it is not a required part of the solution.

Worked Example 2

Solve these equations.

$30x - 48y = -1$

$2x + 3y = 2$

Solution:

$$
\begin{aligned}
30x - 48y &= -1 \quad \dots\dots\dots\dots \text{(1)} \\
2x + 3y &= 2 \quad \dots\dots\dots\dots \text{(2)} \\
\text{(2)} \times 15: \quad 30x + 45y &= 30 \quad \dots\dots\dots\dots \text{(3)} \\
\text{(3)} - \text{(1)}: \quad 93y &= 31 \\
\therefore y &= \frac{31}{93} \\
&= \frac{1}{3}
\end{aligned}
$$

Substituting $y = \frac{1}{3}$ in (2),

$$
\begin{aligned}
2x + \left(3 \times \frac{1}{3}\right) &= 2 \\
2x + 1 &= 2 \\
2x &= 1 \\
\therefore x &= \frac{1}{2}
\end{aligned}
$$

Thus the solutions are $x = \frac{1}{2}$ and $y = \frac{1}{3}$.

Exercise 6.2

answers on p. 432

Solve the following equations.

1. $3x - 2y = 7$
$4x + 5y = 40$

2. $2x - 7y = 1$
$5x + 17y = 37$

3. $8x + 2y = 13$
$16x + y = 14$

4. $12x + 10y = 30$
$27x - 5y = 315$

5. $-7x + 12y = -11$
$50x + 9y = 47$

6. $12x + 3y = 36$
$5x + y = 15$

7. $6x - 5y = 3$
$3x + 11y = -39$

8. $3x - 5y = 21$
$x - 4y = 3$

9. $2x + 6y = 13$
$8x + y = 6$

10. $x + 3y = 5$
$7x - 6y = 44$

11. $12x + 4y = 5$
$2x + 3y = 3$

12. $5x - 2y = 0$
$3x + 5y = 31$

13. $9x + 24y = -13$
$15x - 12y = 13$

14. $6x - 5y = -3$
$x + y = 5$

15. $7x + 4y = 20$
$3x + 2y = 8$

16. $3x + 7y = 8$
$2x + 2y = 12$

17. $12x + 3y = 4$
$4x + y = 1$

18. $2x - 6y = -2$
$x - 3y = -1$

19. $3x - 5y = 11$
$6x - 10y = 21$

20. $7x + 3y = -11$
$14x - 6y = 22$

21. $21m + 7n + 7 = 0$
$28m + 8n + 12 = 0$

22. $7p - 5q - 31 = 0$
$16p + 15q - 18 = 0$

23. $3a + 14b + 27 = 0$
$12a - 25b - 135 = 0$

24. $8r - 11s + 65 = 0$
$12r + 13s + 9 = 0$

6.3 SUBSTITUTION METHOD

Consider these simultaneous equations.

$$2x + y = 10$$
$$2x - 3y = 2$$

You have seen in Section 6.1 how these equations were solved by using the elimination method. We shall now solve these equations by using the substitution method.

Now $\qquad 2x + y = 10 \quad \ldots\ldots\ldots\ldots\ldots\ldots\ldots \quad (1)$

$\qquad 2x - 3y = 2 \quad \ldots\ldots\ldots\ldots\ldots\ldots\ldots \quad (2)$

From (1), we have $\qquad y = 10 - 2x \quad \ldots\ldots\ldots\ldots\ldots\ldots\ldots \quad (3)$

Substituting $y = 10 - 2x$ in (2), we have

$$\begin{aligned} 2x - 3(10 - 2x) &= 2 \\ 2x - 30 + 6x &= 2 \\ 8x &= 32 \\ x &= 4 \end{aligned}$$

Substituting $x = 4$ in (3), we have

$$\begin{aligned} y &= 10 - 8 \\ &= 2 \end{aligned}$$

Check: $2x - 3y = 8 - 6 = 2$, as in equation (2).

Note: We use equation (2) for the check and not equation (1) because the value of y was found by putting $x = 4$ in equation (3), which is equivalent to equation (1).

Worked Example 1

Solve the following equations.

$5x + 2y = 27$

$2x + 3y = 2$

Solution:

$$5x + 2y = 27 \quad \dots\dots\dots\dots\dots\dots\dots\dots \quad (1)$$

$$2x + 3y = 2 \quad \dots\dots\dots\dots\dots\dots\dots\dots \quad (2)$$

From (1):

$$2y = 27 - 5x$$

$$y = \frac{27 - 5x}{2} \quad \dots\dots\dots\dots\dots\dots\dots\dots \quad (3)$$

Substituting $y = \dfrac{27 - 5x}{2}$ in (2),

$$\begin{aligned} 2x + \frac{3(27 - 5x)}{2} &= 2 \\ 4x + 81 - 15x &= 4 \\ -11x &= -77 \\ x &= 7 \end{aligned}$$

Substituting $x = 7$ in (3),

$$\begin{aligned} y &= \frac{27 - 35}{2} \\ &= -4 \end{aligned}$$

Thus the solutions are $x = 7$ and $y = -4$.

Worked Example 2
Solve the following equations.

$\frac{5}{6}x - \frac{9}{10}y = -2$

$\frac{1}{3}x + \frac{2}{5}y = 3$

Solution:

$$\frac{5}{6}x - \frac{9}{10}y = -2 \quad \text{.......................} \quad (1)$$

$$\frac{1}{3}x + \frac{2}{5}y = 3 \quad \text{.......................} \quad (2)$$

(1) × 30: $25x - 27y = -60$ .... (3)

(2) × 15: $5x + 6y = 45$ .... (4)

From (4):

$$6y = 45 - 5x$$

$$y = \frac{45 - 5x}{6} \quad \text{.......................} \quad (5)$$

Substituting $y = \dfrac{45 - 5x}{6}$ in (3),

$$\begin{aligned} 25x - \frac{27(45 - 5x)}{6} &= -60 \\ 25x - \frac{9(45 - 5x)}{2} &= -60 \\ 50x - 405 + 45x &= -120 \\ 95x &= 285 \\ x &= 3 \end{aligned}$$

Substituting $x = 3$ in (5),

$$\begin{aligned} y &= \frac{45 - (5 \times 3)}{6} \\ &= 5 \end{aligned}$$

Thus the solutions are $x = 3$ and $y = 5$.

Worked Example 3
Solve the following equations.

$2(x + 1) + (3y - 1) = 19$

$3(x + 2) - 2(y + 1) = 5$

Solution:

$$2(x + 1) + (3y - 1) = 19 \quad \text{.......................} \quad (1)$$
$$3(x + 2) - 2(y + 1) = 5 \quad \text{.......................} \quad (2)$$

From (1):
$$2x + 2 + 3y - 1 = 19$$
$$2x + 3y = 18 \quad \text{.......................} \quad (3)$$

From (2):
$$3x + 6 - 2y - 2 = 5$$
$$3x - 2y = 1 \quad \text{.......................} \quad (4)$$

From (3):
$$3y = 18 - 2x$$
$$y = \frac{18 - 2x}{3} \quad \text{.......................} \quad (5)$$

Substituting $y = \dfrac{18 - 2x}{3}$ in (4),

$$3x - 2\left(\frac{18 - 2x}{3}\right) = 1$$
$$9x - 36 + 4x = 3$$
$$13x = 39$$
$$x = 3$$

Substituting $x = 3$ in (5),

$$y = \frac{18 - (2 \times 3)}{3}$$
$$= 4$$

Thus the solutions are $x = 3$ and $y = 4$.

Exercise 6.3

answers on p. 433

Solve these equations using the elimination method or the substitution method.

1. $3x + y = 11$
$2x - y = 4$

2. $x + 3y = 13$
$x + 2y = 10$

3. $5x - y = 6$
$2x + y = 8$

4. $3x - 4y = 7$
$2x + y = 12$

5. $2x + 5y = 13$
$5x + 2y = 22$

6. $3x - 2y = 1$
$2x + 3y = 18$

7. $\frac{2}{5}x + \frac{1}{3}y = 1$
$\frac{3}{5}x - \frac{1}{9}y = 7$

8. $\frac{1}{4}x + \frac{2}{3}y = 5$
$\frac{3}{4}x + y = 6$

9. $\frac{2}{3}x + \frac{3}{4}y = 7$
$\frac{5}{6}x - \frac{1}{2}y = 3$

10. $\frac{7}{8}x + \frac{3}{5}y = 5$
$\frac{3}{5}x - \frac{4}{25}y = 2$

11. $2(x + 1) + 3(y - 1) = 12$
$(3x - 1) - (y - 2) = 4$

12. $2(y + 2) - 3(x - 1) = 1$
$3(2 + y) + 4(3 - x) = 11$

13. $(x - 3) - 2(y + 4) = -8$
$2(3 + 2x) - 5(4 - 3y) = 21$

14. $70(x - 1) + 90(y + 3) = 95$
$6(2x + 1) - 8(3y - 2) = 4$

15. $0.2x + 0.7y = 1$
$0.4x - 1.5y = -0.9$

16. $1.2x + y = 3.8$
$0.5x + 0.8y = 3.5$

17. $0.7x - 1.2y = -11.5$
$0.5x + 3.5y = 31$

18. $1.5x - 0.8y = 0.3$
$0.6x - 3.6y = -4.8$

19. $2p - 5q = 6p + 3q = 9$

20. $3c - d = 12c + 5d = 9$

6.4 WORD PROBLEMS USING SIMULTANEOUS EQUATIONS

Worked Example 1

A person bought 2 kg of fresh prawns and 10 kg of tomatoes for \$24. From the same stall, another person spent \$27 for 1 kg of fresh prawns and 20 kg of tomatoes. What were the prices for each kilogram of fresh prawns and tomatoes?

Solution:

If the fresh prawns cost \$$p$ per kilogram and the tomatoes cost \$$t$ per kilogram, then

$$2p + 10t = 24 \quad \text{.....................} (1)$$
$$p + 20t = 27 \quad \text{.....................} (2)$$

(1) – (2) × 2:
$$(2p + 10t) - 2(p + 20t) = 24 - (2 \times 27) \quad \text{.....................} (3)$$
$$2p + 10t - 2p - 40t = 24 - 54$$
$$-30t = -30$$
$$t = 1$$

Substituting $t = 1$ in (1),
$$2p + (10 \times 1) = 24$$
$$2p = 14$$
$$p = 7$$

Price of tomatoes: \$1 per kilogram

Price of prawns: \$7 per kilogram

Worked Example 2

Two years ago, a man was 7 times as old as his son, but in three years' time, he will be 4 times as old as the boy. How old is each of them now?

Let the man's present age be m years and the boy's present age be s years.

Then $\quad m - 2 = 7(s - 2)$ .... (1)

$\quad m + 3 = 4(s + 3)$ .... (2)

(2) – (1): $\quad 5 = 4(s + 3) - 7(s - 2)$

$\quad 5 = 26 - 3s$

$\quad s = 7$

Substituting $s = 7$ into (2), $\quad m + 3 = 4(7 + 3)$

$\quad m = 37$

Thus, the man is now 37 years old and the boy is 7 years old.

Exercise 6.4

answers on p. 433

1. The sum of two numbers is 23. Twice the larger number is 4 more than 4 times the smaller. What are the numbers?

2. One of the acute angles of a right-angled triangle is 16° larger than the other. How many degrees are there in each of the acute angles?

3. A bottle and its contents cost 60 cents but the contents cost 18 cents more than the bottle. How much does the bottle cost?

4. Two books cost \$15 altogether. One costs \$1.50 more than the other. How much does each book cost?

5. The sum of two numbers is $\frac{53}{24}$ and the difference of the same two numbers is $\frac{13}{24}$. What are the numbers?

6. A two-digit number is smaller by 27 than the number with the digits reversed. The sum of the digits is 13. Find the number.

7. There are 10 more boys than girls in a class. If one more girl joins the class, there will be twice as many boys as there are girls. How many boys and how many girls are there in the class?

8. A rope was cut into two pieces so that one piece was 18 m longer than the other. That piece was also three times as long as the other. How long was each piece and how long was the original rope?

9. An angle is three times its supplement. Find the angle. (*Note:* Two angles which add up to 180° are supplements of each other.)

10. Twice the length of a rectangle is three times the width. The perimeter is 320 cm. Find the dimensions of the rectangle.

11. If 5 is added to both the numerator and the denominator of a certain fraction, the result is $\frac{4}{7}$. If 1 is subtracted from both the numerator and the denominator, the result is $\frac{2}{5}$. Find the fraction.

12. A motor boat can travel 45 km downstream in 2 h and 30 min; and 39 km upstream in 3 h and 15 min. What is the speed of the boat in still water? What is the speed of the current?

13. Six oranges and four apples cost $3.20. One orange and five apples cost $2.05. What are the costs of an apple and an orange?

14. I think of two numbers. The first number plus three times the second number is 1. The first minus three times the second is 19. Find the numbers.

15. Ali bought 12 pencils and 10 rulers for $2.10. Paying the same price for each as Ali, I bought 20 pencils and 4 rulers for $1.60. What were the prices of a pencil and a ruler?

16. In triangle *ABC*, $\hat{A}$ is 20°. The number of degrees in $\hat{B}$ is 10 more than 9 times the number of degrees in $\hat{C}$. Find $\hat{B}$ and $\hat{C}$.

17. A boy walked for 4 h and cycled for 3 h, covering a total distance of 74 km. Later he walked for 2 h and cycled for 4 h, covering 82 km. What were his speed of walking and his speed of cycling if his speeds in the two cases were constant?

18. A carpenter can make a cabinet in 30 h. If he works for 21 h at the normal rate of pay and 9 h at the overtime rate, he will be paid $69. But if he works for 27 h at the normal rate and 3 h at the overtime rate, his earnings will be $63. Find his normal and overtime rates of pay.

19. In decimal numerals, if 36 is added to a certain two-digit number, the result is the number with the digits reversed. The 'ones' digit is 1 more than twice the 'tens' digit. What is the number?

20. Two trains leave two different stations 300 km apart; the first starts at noon and the second at 12 15 h. Travelling on parallel tracks, they meet each other at 15 00 h. Each train travels at a constant speed, the one leaving at 12 15 h moves at 15 km/h faster than the other. What are their speeds?

21. The total mass of a mixture of two liquids is 2.4 kg and the total volume is 1 000 cm^3. If 1 cm^3 of one of the liquids weighs 2 g and 1 cm^3 of the other liquid weighs 3 g, what volume of each liquid is present? What mass of each liquid is present?

22. Four years ago, a man was $2\frac{1}{2}$ times as old as his son, but in five years' time, he will be only twice as old as his son. How old is the man now?

Chapter Review

We can solve simultaneous equations by
- the elimination method or
- the substitution method.

Examples:

(a)

$$3x + 2y = 3 \quad \text{......} \quad (1)$$
$$2x + 3y = 7 \quad \text{......} \quad (2)$$

(1) × 2: $6x + 4y = 6$ ...... (3)

(2) × 3: $6x + 9y = 21$ ...... (4)

(3) – (4): $-5y = -15$

$$y = \frac{15}{5} = 3$$

Substituting $y = 3$ into (1),

$$3x + (2 \times 3) = 3$$
$$3x = 3 - 6$$
$$3x = -3$$
$$x = \frac{-3}{3} = -1$$

(b)

$$3x + 2y = 3 \quad \text{......} \quad (1)$$
$$2x + 3y = 7 \quad \text{......} \quad (2)$$

From (1), we have

$$2y = 3 - 3x$$
$$y = \frac{3 - 3x}{2} \quad \text{......} \quad (3)$$

Substituting $y = \frac{3 - 3x}{2}$ in (2), we have

$$2x + 3\left(\frac{3 - 3x}{2}\right) = 7$$

$$2x + \frac{9 - 9x}{2} = 7$$

$$4x + 9 - 9x = 14$$

$$-5x = 14 - 9$$

$$-5x = 5$$

$$x = -1$$

Substituting $x = -1$ into (3), we have

$$y = \frac{3 - 3(-1)}{2} = \frac{3 + 3}{2} = 3$$

- Always check your final answers against the given equations.

CHALLENGER 6

1. Solve the following simultaneous equations.

(a) $12x + 6y - 7 = 0$
$3x - 4y + 1 = 0$

(b) $\frac{12}{x} + \frac{6}{y} - 7 = 0$
$\frac{3}{x} - \frac{4}{y} + 1 = 0$

$\left(\textit{Hint:}\text{ Let } \frac{1}{x} = u \text{ and } \frac{1}{y} = v.\right)$

2. Solve the following simultaneous equations.

$$\frac{12}{x + y} + \frac{6}{x - y} - 7 = 0$$

$$\frac{3}{x + y} - \frac{4}{x - y} + 1 = 0$$

$\left(\textit{Hint:}\text{ Let } \frac{1}{x + y} = u \text{ and } \frac{1}{x - y} = v.\right)$

3. If $x = -1$ and $y = 2$ are the solutions of the simultaneous equations:

$$ax - by = -7$$

$$2x + by = 4a$$

find the values of a and b.

4. Solve the following simultaneous equations.

$$\frac{3}{xy} + \frac{2}{x+y} = \frac{14}{15}$$
$$\frac{1}{xy} - \frac{1}{x+y} = \frac{1}{30}$$

5. If $a \neq b \neq c$ such that

$$a + b = b$$
$$bc = b$$
$$c - b = b$$

find the values of a, b and c.

6. Solve the following simultaneous equations.

$$(2x + 3)^2 - 4y = 85$$
$$(x - 1)^2 - y = 5$$

Problem Solving 6

Oratory Competition

At the end of a school oratory competition, each contestant shook hands with every other contestant. The winner, Mary, shook hands with 3 times as many girls as boys. The runner-up, John, shook hands with 4 times as many girls as boys. How many contestants were there altogether?

The strategies to adopt are **use tabulation** and **use equations.**

	Number of boys	Number of girls	Ratio
Mary excluded	x	y	$\frac{x}{y} = \frac{1}{3}$
John excluded	$x - 1$	$y + 1$	$\frac{x-1}{y+1} = \frac{1}{4}$

From the table, we have

$$3x = y \qquad \text{..................... (1)}$$
$$4(x - 1) = y + 1 \qquad \text{..................... (2)}$$

(2) – (1): $4(x - 1) - 3x = 1$

$$x = 5$$
$$y = 15$$

$\therefore$ total number of contestants = 5 + 15 + 1 = 21

After you have checked your answer, think of alternative methods.

Example:

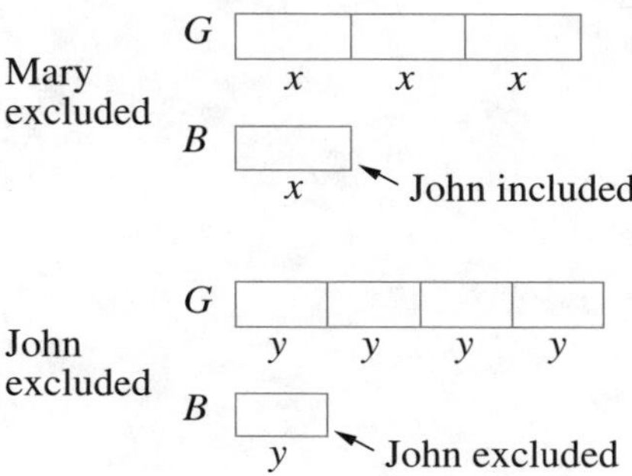

From the model, we have

$$x = y + 1 \quad \ldots\ldots\ldots\ldots\ldots\ldots \quad (1)$$
$$4x = 5y \quad \ldots\ldots\ldots\ldots\ldots\ldots \quad (2)$$

Solving (1) and (2), we have

$$y = 4$$

$\therefore$ total number of contestants = $5y + 1 = 21$

The strategies adopted are **use a model** and **use equations**.

1. **Members Come and Go** In the first term, the ratio of the number of boys to the number of girls in a computer club was 3 : 4. In the second term, 5 girls left the club but 3 boys joined the club. As a result, the ratio of the number of boys to the number of girls became 6 : 5. How many club members were there originally?

2. **Positive Integers** If x and y represent positive integers such that $(x + y)(2x - y) = 8$, find
   (a) the possible values of $(x + y)$ and $(2x - y)$,
   (b) the possible values of x and y.

3. **Buying Fish** With a fixed sum of money, a man can buy 3 more kilograms of fish if the price is decreased by $1 per kilogram, or 2 kilograms less if the price is increased by $1 per kilogram. How much is the fixed sum of money?

4. **Eighteen Prime Digits** Replace all the asterisks with prime numbers to make the multiplication correct.

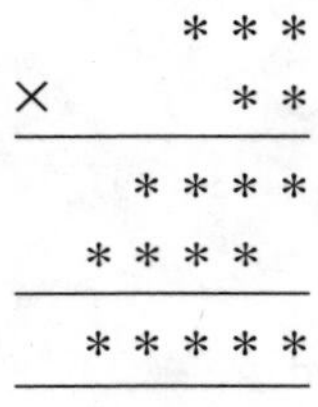

Chapter 7

Inequalities

Chapter Highlights

- Using the number line to illustrate solutions of inequalities including recognising the difference between positive integers, non-negative integers, negative integers, non-positive integers, integers, positive real numbers, non-negative real numbers, negative real numbers, non-positive real numbers and real numbers
- Using the inequality signs including converting equivalent inequalities in one variable
- Solving simple linear inequalities in one variable

7.1 SETS OF NUMBERS ON THE NUMBER LINE

The following examples illustrate how sets of numbers can be represented on number lines.

Examples

(a) If x represents positive integers, the set of values of x such that $x < 5$ is represented on a number line like this:

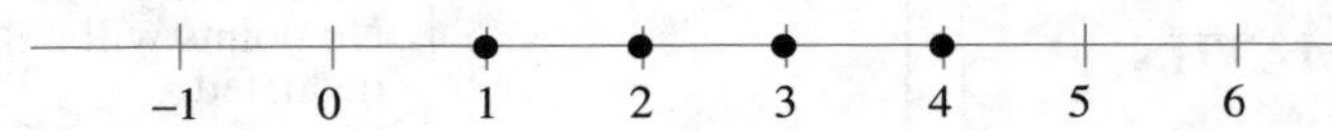

(b) If x represents negative integers, the set of values of x such that $x \geqslant -4$ is represented on a number line like this:

(c) If x represents integers, the set of values of x such that $x < 5$ and $x \geqslant -4$ is represented on a number line like this:

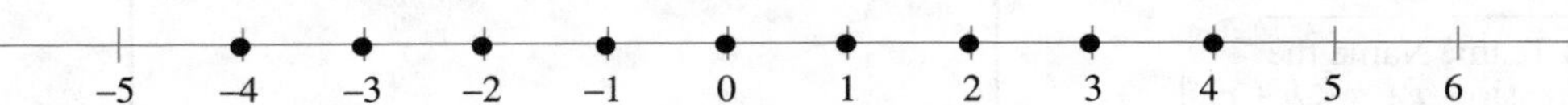

Note: The number zero is excluded in (a) and (b) because zero is neither positive nor negative.

(d) If x represents positive real numbers, the set of values of x such that $x < 5$ is represented on a number line like this:

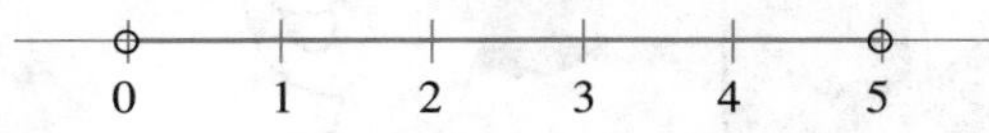

(e) If x represents positive real numbers, the set of values of x such that $x \leqslant 5$ is represented on a number line like this:

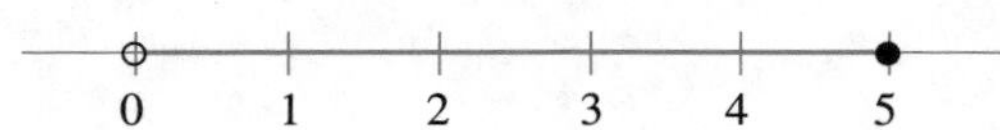

(f) If x represents non-negative real numbers, the set of values of x such that $x \leqslant 5$ is represented on a number line like this:

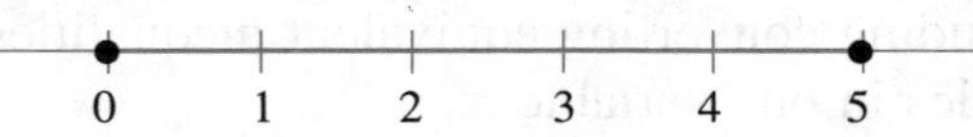

Note: In (d), the set of values of x is represented by a thick line excluding the end points 0 and 5, which are indicated by '○'.
In (e), the set of values of x is represented by a thick line excluding the end points 0 but including the end point 5 which is indicated by '●'.
In (f), the set of values of x is represented by a thick line including the end points 0 and 5.

(g) If x represents real numbers, the set of values of x such that $x < 5$ is represented on a number line like this:

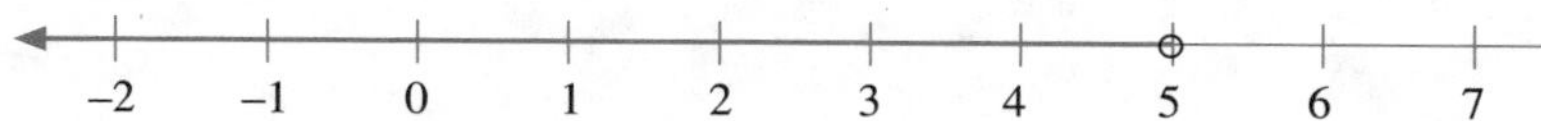

(h) If x represents real numbers, the set of values of x such that $x \leqslant 5$ is represented on a number line like this:

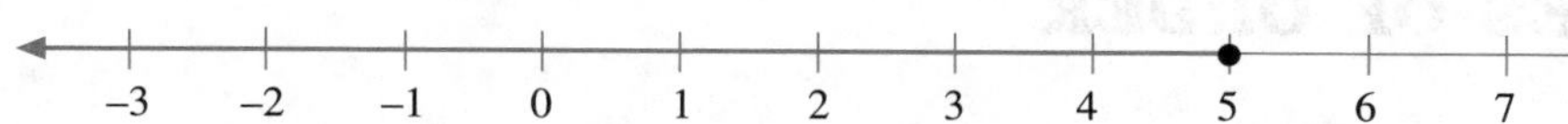

(i) If x represents real numbers, the set of values of x such that $x \geqslant -4$ is represented on a number line like this:

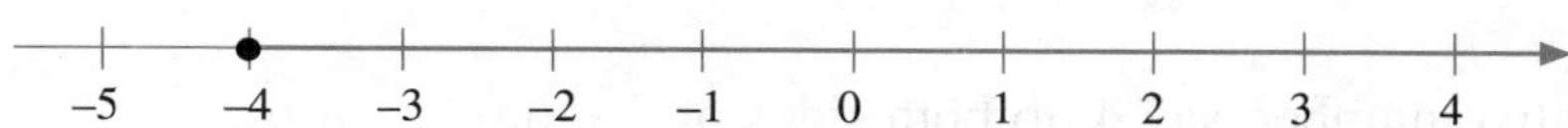

(j) If x represents real numbers, the set of values of x such that $x < 5$ and $x \geqslant -4$ is represented on a number line like this:

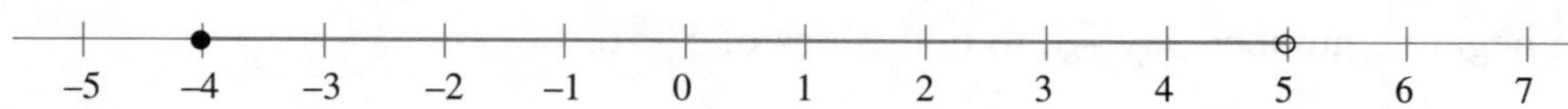

Note: The arrowhead indicates the direction in which the thick line extends indefinitely.

Exercise 7.1

answers on p. 433

1. Represent the set of values of x on a number line such that $x \leqslant 7$, if x represents
(a) positive integers,
(b) non-negative integers,
(c) positive real numbers,
(d) non-negative real numbers,
(e) real numbers.

2. Represent the set of values of x on a number line such that $x > -5$, if x represents
(a) negative integers,
(b) non-positive integers,
(c) negative real numbers,
(d) non-positive real numbers,
(e) real numbers.

3. Represent the set of values of x on a number line such that $x \geqslant -3$ and $x < 5$, if x represents
(a) integers,
(b) real numbers.

7.2 PROPERTIES OF ORDER

Examples

(a) Consider the sentence, $5 < 6$.

This sentence is true.

Suppose we add a positive number, say 4, to both sides of $5 < 6$.

Then we have $5 + 4 < 6 + 4$
or $9 < 10$ which is again true.

Suppose we add a negative number, say -3, to both sides of $5 < 6$.

Then we have $5 + (-3) < 6 + (-3)$
or $2 < 3$ which is again true.

In general, we have:

If a, b and c are numbers and $a < b$, then $a + c < b + c$.

Properties of inequalities are often referred to as properties of order. We shall call this property the **addition property of order**.

(b) Consider $6 < 7$.

This statement is true.

Suppose we multiply both sides of $6 < 7$ by a positive number, say 2.

Then we have $2(6) < 2(7)$
or $12 < 14$ which is true.

Suppose we multiply both sides of $6 < 7$ by a negative number, say -4.

Then we have $-4(6) < -4(7)$
or $-24 < -28$ which is not true.

If we change the sign '<' to '>', we have $-24 > -28$, which is true.

It is easy to see that when we multiply both sides of an inequality by a negative number, it is necessary to change '<' to '>' or change '>' to '<' so as to ensure that we still have a true statement.

Let us state the **multiplication property of order** as follows:

If a, b and c are numbers and $a < b$, then
- **$ac < bc$ if c is positive and**
- **$ac > bc$ if c is negative.**

Equivalent Inequalities

Recall that equations such as $2x + 3 = 11$ and $2x = 8$, which have the same solution, are called equivalent equations. In the same way, any two inequalities with the same set of solutions are called **equivalent inequalities**.

Equivalent inequalities can be obtained by using the following rules.

Conversion of Equivalent Inequalities

- **Add the same number to both sides or subtract the same number from both sides.**
- **Multiply or divide both sides by the same positive number.**
- **Multiply or divide both sides by the same negative number and change '>' to '<' or '<' to '>'.**

Note: 1. We cannot multiply by zero. For example, if $x > 3$ and we multiply both sides of it by zero, we have $0 > 0$ which is simply a false statement.

2. We can write similar statements about equivalent inequalities using '$\leqslant$' or '$\geqslant$'.

Worked Example

For each pair of equivalent inequalities, show how the first inequality can be converted to the second.

(a) $x + 7 < 13$; $x < 6$ **(b)** $\frac{1}{4}x < 8$; $x < 32$ **(c)** $-3x \geqslant 27$; $x \leqslant -9$

Solution:

(a)

$$x + 7 < 13$$
$$x + 7 - 7 < 13 - 7 \quad \text{Add } -7 \text{ to both sides.}$$
$$x < 6$$

(b)

$$\frac{1}{4}x < 8$$
$$4\left(\frac{1}{4}x\right) < 4(8) \quad \text{Multiply both sides by 4.}$$
$$x < 32$$

(c)

$$-3x \geqslant 27$$
$$3x \leqslant -27 \quad \text{Multiply both sides by } -1 \text{ and reverse the sign.}$$
$$x \leqslant -9 \quad \text{Divide both sides by 3.}$$

Exercise 7.2

answers on p. 434

1. Which of the following inequalities are true?

(a) $3 > 2$
(b) $3(-1) > 2(-1)$
(c) $3(-1) < 2(-1)$
(d) $-3 < -2$
(e) $(-3)(-1) < (-2)(-1)$
(f) $-2 < 3$
(g) $(-2)(-1) > 3(-1)$
(h) $(-2)(-1) < 3(-1)$
(i) $2 < -3$
(j) $4 < 5$
(k) $4(2) < 5(2)$
(l) $4(-2) < 5(-2)$
(m) $4\left(-\frac{1}{2}\right) < 5\left(-\frac{1}{2}\right)$
(n) $4\left(-\frac{1}{2}\right) > 5\left(-\frac{1}{2}\right)$

2. For each pair of equivalent inequalities, show how the first inequality can be converted to the second.

(a) $x - 3 > 2, x > 5$
(b) $x + 2 \leqslant 1, x \leqslant -1$
(c) $x - 3 \geqslant 5, x \geqslant 8$
(d) $x - 4 > 2, x > 6$
(e) $x - 5 > 6, x > 11$
(f) $x + 2 \geqslant 4, x \geqslant 2$
(g) $x - 4 < -\frac{3}{2}, x < \frac{5}{2}$
(h) $x + 7 < \frac{11}{5}, x < -\frac{24}{5}$
(i) $x + \frac{1}{2} < \frac{5}{2}, x < 2$
(j) $x + \frac{2}{3} \geqslant \frac{5}{3}, x \geqslant 1$

3. For each pair of equivalent inequalities, show how the first inequality can be converted to the second.

(a) $2x < 2, x < 1$

(b) $-x \geqslant 2, x \leqslant -2$

(c) $3x > 5, x > \frac{5}{3}$

(d) $-3x > 5, x < -\frac{5}{3}$

(e) $3x < 2, x < \frac{2}{3}$

(f) $-2x > 1, x < -\frac{1}{2}$

(g) $\frac{1}{2}x \leqslant 6, x \leqslant 12$

(h) $\frac{2}{3}x \geqslant \frac{1}{2}, x \geqslant \frac{3}{4}$

(i) $\frac{x}{4} \leqslant -1, x \leqslant -4$

(j) $-3x > 0, x < 0$

7.3 SOLVING INEQUALITIES

Worked Example 1

Solve $-\frac{2}{3}x + 8 \geqslant 0$ and then draw the solution set on a number line.

Solution:

$-\frac{2}{3}x + 8 \geqslant 0$

$-\frac{2}{3}x \geqslant -8$ Subtract 8 from both sides.

$\frac{2}{3}x \leqslant 8$ Multiply both sides by –1 and reverse the sign.

$2x \leqslant 24$ Multiply both sides by 3.

$x \leqslant 12$ Divide both sides by 2.

The diagram of the solution set is

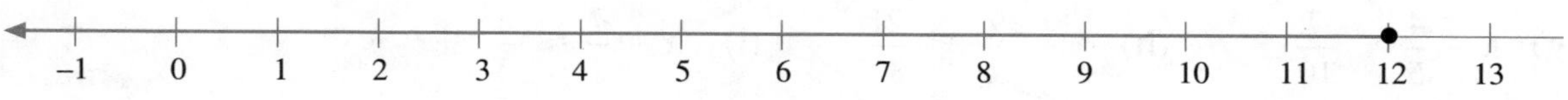

Worked Example 2

Solve $\frac{7}{2}x - \frac{4}{3} > \frac{3}{4}x + \frac{2}{3}$ and then draw the solution set on a number line.

Solution:

$\frac{7}{2}x - \frac{4}{3} > \frac{3}{4}x + \frac{2}{3}$

$12\left(\frac{7}{2}x - \frac{4}{3}\right) > 12\left(\frac{3}{4}x + \frac{2}{3}\right)$ Multiply both sides by 12, the LCM of 2, 3 and 4.

$42x - 16 > 9x + 8$

$33x - 16 > 8$ Subtract $9x$ from both sides.

$33x > 24$ Add 16 to both sides.

$x > \frac{24}{33}$ Divide both sides by 33.

$x > \frac{8}{11}$

The diagram of the solution set is

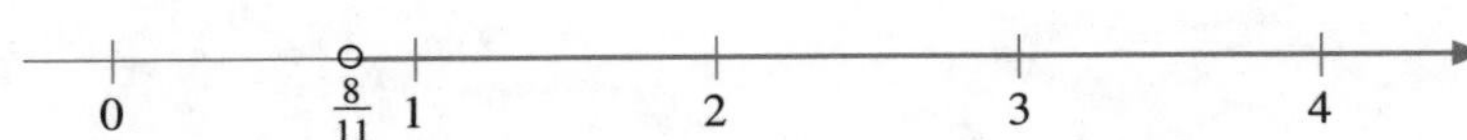

Note: After much practice, you may be able to solve the inequalities in fewer steps. Reasons given for the steps may be omitted.

Exercise 7.3

answers on p. 434

1. Solve each of the following inequalities and then draw the solution set on a number line.

(a) $x - 3 < 2$ **(b)** $x - 4 < 5$ **(c)** $x + 7 > 7$

(d) $x - 9 > 10$ **(e)** $x + 8 < 6$ **(f)** $x + 24 \geqslant 5$

(g) $x - 11 \leqslant 17$ **(h)** $x - 24 \geqslant 30$ **(i)** $x + 42 \leqslant 51$

2. Solve the following inequalities.

(a) $x + \frac{1}{2} > -\frac{2}{3}$ **(b)** $x - \frac{3}{4} < \frac{7}{2}$ **(c)** $x + \frac{4}{5} > \frac{6}{25}$

(d) $x - \frac{11}{8} > \frac{5}{24}$ **(e)** $x + \frac{9}{11} < \frac{3}{22}$ **(f)** $x + \frac{2}{3} \geqslant \frac{1}{3}$

(g) $x - \frac{4}{5} \leqslant \frac{7}{10}$ **(h)** $x + \frac{9}{16} \geqslant \frac{21}{32}$ **(i)** $x - \frac{7}{2} \leqslant \frac{8}{3}$

3. Solve the following inequalities.

(a) $3x > 8$ **(b)** $5x < -14$ **(c)** $6x \geqslant 19$

(d) $-7x < 8$ **(e)** $10x + 23 \leqslant -13$ **(f)** $3 - 4x > 4$

(g) $5 - 9x \leqslant -18$ **(h)** $2x + 7 > \frac{5}{2}$ **(i)** $3x + 5 \leqslant -\frac{1}{15}$

(j) $4 - 5x \leqslant \frac{1}{4}$ **(k)** $\frac{2}{3} - \frac{1}{3}x > \frac{4}{3}$ **(l)** $\frac{3}{4}x + \frac{1}{6} \leqslant -\frac{5}{4}$

(m) $\frac{4}{5} - \frac{1}{5}x \geqslant \frac{2}{7}$ **(n)** $\frac{1}{3} - \frac{2}{3}x < \frac{5}{6}$ **(o)** $\frac{5}{6}x - \frac{2}{3} \leqslant -\frac{5}{12}$

4. Solve the following inequalities.

(a) $3 - 3x \leqslant 4x + 7$ **(b)** $4x - 2 > 5 - 3x$

(c) $5 - 2x \leqslant 4x - 3$ **(d)** $3x \geqslant 2(8 + x)$

(e) $3(x - 3) < 4(2x + 3)$ **(f)** $\frac{2}{3} - \frac{1}{3}x > \frac{4}{3}x + \frac{2}{5}$

(g) $\frac{4}{5} - \frac{1}{5}x \geqslant \frac{2}{7} - \frac{2}{5}x$ **(h)** $\frac{1}{6}x - \frac{7}{2} < \frac{5}{6}x + \frac{3}{2}$

(i) $-\frac{1}{2}(2x - 5) \geqslant \frac{1}{3}(x + 3)$ **(j)** $\frac{3}{2}(4x - 7) \leqslant \frac{2}{3}(2x + 5)$

(k) $x + \frac{5}{3} < 3\left(2x - \frac{1}{5}\right)$ **(l)** $1 - \frac{x}{3} \geqslant \frac{2}{3}\left(2x - \frac{3}{4}\right)$

(m) $x - \frac{3}{4} < 7\left(\frac{x}{2} + 3\right)$ **(n)** $\frac{1}{3}\left(5x + \frac{1}{2}\right) \leqslant \frac{3}{4}\left(x + \frac{2}{7}\right)$

5. Given $37 - 3x \leqslant 15$,
(a) find the least value of x,
(b) find the least integer value of x.

6. Given $2x + 11 \leqslant 162$, find the largest value of x if
(a) x is a prime number,
(b) x is a multiple of 4.

***7.** Given that $x + y = 63$, x and y are positive integers divisible by 7 and that $x < y$, list the possible pairs of values of x and y.

***8.** Given that $2x + y = 63$, x and y are positive integers divisible by 3 and that $x \geqslant y$, list the possible pairs of values of x and y.

Chapter Review

1. The set of values in the solution of an equality is represented by a thick line.

2. If an end point is included in the solution, it is indicated by '●' or otherwise by '○' on the number line.

   Examples:

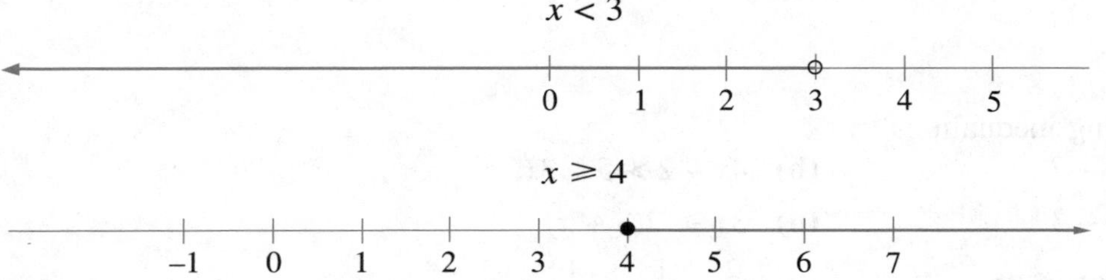

   The arrowhead indicates the direction in which the thick line extends indefinitely.

3. If a, b and c are numbers and $a < b$, then $a + c < b + c$.

4. If a, b and c are numbers and $a < b$, then
   - $ac < bc$ if c is positive and
   - $ac > bc$ if c is negative.

5. **Conversion of Equivalent Inequalities**
   - Add the same number to both sides or subtract the same number from both sides.
   - Multiply or divide both sides by the same positive number.
   - Multiply or divide both sides by the same negative number and change > to < or < to >.

CHALLENGER 

1. State whether each of the following statements is true or false. If $a > b$ and $c > d$, then:

(a) $ac > bd$ **(b)** $a - c > b - d$

(c) $a + c > b + d$ **(d)** $\frac{a}{c} > \frac{d}{b}$

2. State whether each of the following statements is true or false. If $a < b < -1$, then:

(a) $a > \frac{1}{b}$

(b) $\frac{1}{a} < \frac{1}{b}$

(c) $\frac{a}{b} > 1$

(d) $ab > 1$

3. Solve the inequality $2^{-x} > 64$.

4. If $1 \leqslant x \leqslant 3$ and $2 \leqslant y \leqslant 7$, find **(a)** the greatest value, **(b)** the smallest value of $\frac{y}{x} - \frac{x}{y}$.

5. If $-3 \leqslant x \leqslant 8$ and $-2 \leqslant y \leqslant 9$, find **(a)** the greatest value, **(b)** the smallest value of $y^2 - x^2$.

6. If $-5 \leqslant x \leqslant 9$ and $-8 \leqslant y \leqslant -1$, find **(a)** the greatest value, **(b)** the smallest value of $xy - \frac{1}{y}$.

Problem Solving 7

Income and Expenditure

In 1997, a family spent 19% of their income on rent, 26% on food, 30% on other items and saved the rest. In 1998, their income increased by 10%. If the cost of food increased by 10%, savings decreased by 4% and rent remained the same, by what percentage did the expenditure on other items increase?

The strategy to use is **use a diagram**

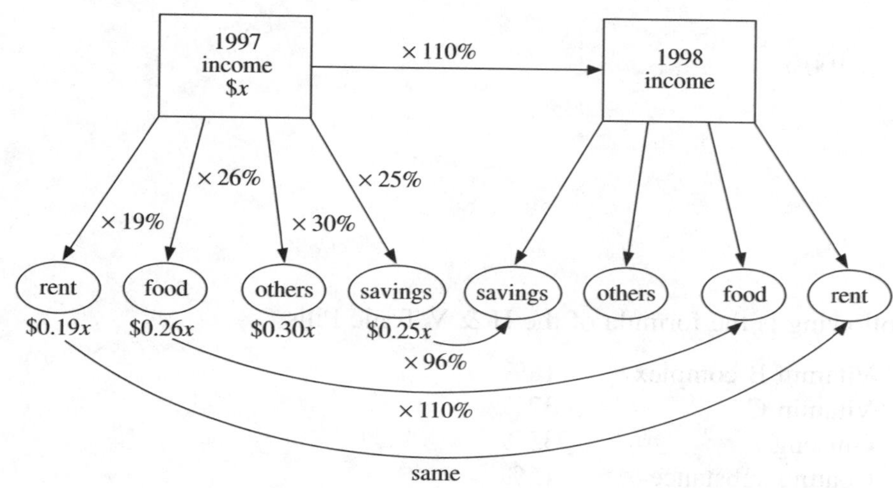

From the diagram, we can see that in 1998, income = $\$(1.1x)$

$$\begin{aligned} \text{savings} &= \$(0.96 \times 0.25x) \\ &= \$(0.24x) \\ \text{food} &= \$(1.1 \times 0.26x) \\ &= \$(0.286x) \\ \text{rent} &= \$0.19x \end{aligned}$$

So other expenditure = $\$(1.1x - 0.24x - 0.286x - 0.19x) = \$(0.384x)$

$$\text{Percentage increase} = \frac{0.384x - 0.30x}{0.30x} \times 100\% = 28\%$$

You may refer to this type of diagram as **arrow chart**.

Alternatively, you may **use tabulation**.

Let the income in 1997 be 100 units.

	1997	1998
Income	100	100 × 110% = 110
Rent	19	19
Food	26	26 × 110% = 28.6
Others	30	x
Savings	25	25 × 96% = 24

From the table, we have

$$x = 110 - 19 - 28.6 - 24 = 38.4$$

$$\begin{aligned} \text{Percentage increase} &= \frac{38.4 - 30}{30} \times 100\% \\ &= \frac{8.4}{30} \times 100\% \\ &= 28\% \end{aligned}$$

1. **Tonic Pills** The following is the formula of the H & V Tonic Pills.

Vitamin B complex	18%
Vitamin C	32%
Ginseng	35%
Coating substance	15%

The formula is recently improved as follows:

Vitamin B complex is increased by 10%.
Vitamin C is decreased by 5%.
Ginseng is increased by 12%.
Coating substance remains unchanged.

(a) By what percentage is the total mass of the pill increased?
(b) What is the proportion of the improved formula?
Give your answer correct to the nearest percent.

2. **Boys and Girls** In three classes A, B and C, there are altogether 126 students. $\frac{3}{4}$ of the students in class A, $\frac{2}{3}$ in class B and $\frac{1}{2}$ in class C are boys. The total number of boys is 81. If class B has 3 more girls than class A, find the number of girls in class A.

3. **Who is the Oldest?** Ann was born before Betty. Carol is older than Betty. The average age of Betty and Carol is more than that of Ann and Betty. If Dolly is younger than Betty, who is the oldest of the four?

4. **Nineteen Prime Digits** Replace all the asterisks by prime numbers to make the multiplication correct.

```
         * *
  ×    * * *
  ----------
       * * *
     * * *
   * * *
  ----------
   * * * * *
  ----------
```

Chapter 8

Congruent and Similar Triangles

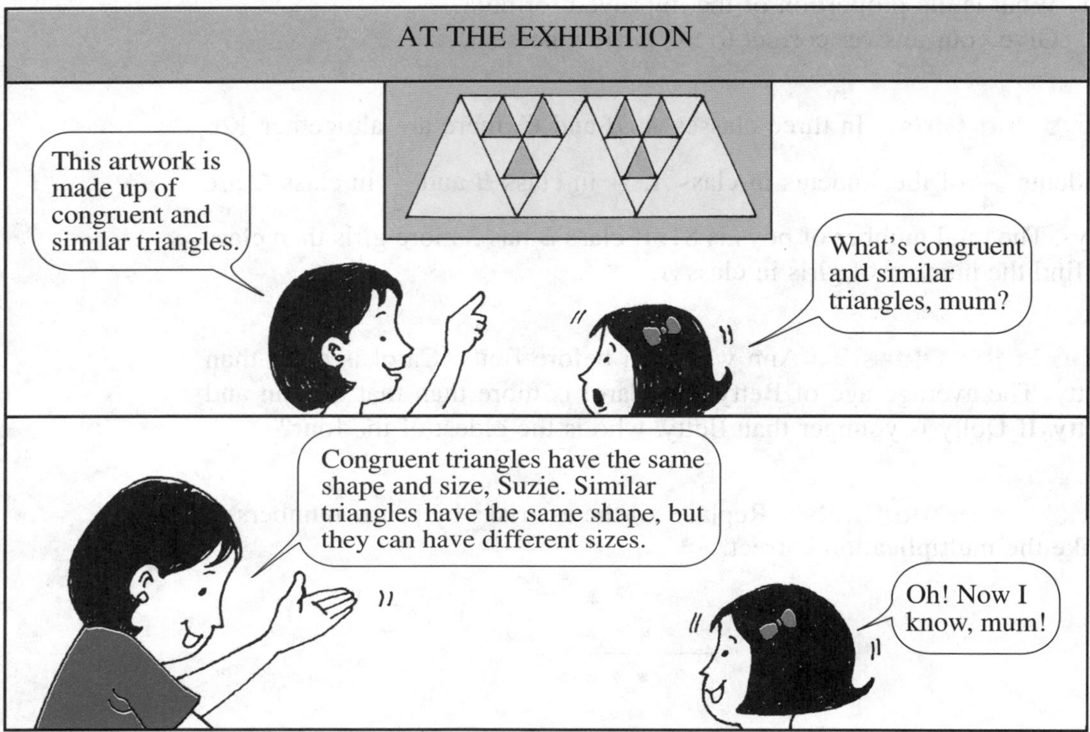

Chapter Highlights

- Writing statements of congruent triangles in the correct correspondence
- Recognising that corresponding sides and angles of congruent triangles are equal
- Demonstrating an understanding of the SAS, AAS, SSS and RHS tests for congruent triangles
- Identifying congruent triangles by using the tests for congruent triangles
- Finding unknown sides or angles of congruent triangles
- Using the Tests for Congruent Triangles to demonstrate an understanding of deductive reasoning
- Recognising that corresponding angles of similar triangles are equal and corresponding sides are proportional
- Drawing a triangle similar to a given triangle
- Demonstrating an understanding that two triangles are similar if their corresponding angles are equal or their corresponding sides are proportional or two pairs of their corresponding sides are proportional and the included angles are equal
- Identifying similar triangles, including writing ratio relationship with their sides and finding unknown angles and sides

8.1 CONGRUENT TRIANGLES

Two triangles are said to be congruent if they have the same shape and size. We can usually decide whether two triangles are congruent by placing one on top of the other to see if they fit. (Sometimes we may have to turn a triangle over.)

Congruent triangles are triangles which have the same shape and size.

If two triangles are congruent, obviously the six parts of one triangle (sides and angles) are equal to the corresponding parts of the other. For example, if $\triangle ABC$ and $\triangle PQR$ are congruent, then we have

$AB = PQ$, $\hat{A} = \hat{P}$,
$BC = QR$, $\hat{B} = \hat{Q}$,
$CA = RP$, $\hat{C} = \hat{R}$.

Notice that pairs of equal sides and equal angles are indicated by small marks on the figures.

The symbol '≡' (or '≅') is used as a short form for 'is congruent to'. Thus, '$\triangle ABC \equiv \triangle PQR$' is read as 'triangle ABC is congruent to triangle PQR'.

Note: 1. The statement '$\triangle ABC \equiv \triangle PQR$' tells us that triangles ABC and PQR are congruent. In addition, it also tells us that the parts of one triangle fit onto the parts of the other exactly by matching in a definite way as follows:

$$\hat{A} \longleftrightarrow \hat{P}, \quad \hat{B} \longleftrightarrow \hat{Q}, \quad \hat{C} \longleftrightarrow \hat{R},$$
$$AB \longleftrightarrow PQ, \quad BC \longleftrightarrow QR, \quad CA \longleftrightarrow RP.$$

We refer to this matching as a correspondence.

2. A simple way to remember the correspondence is by the diagram below.

$\triangle ABC \equiv \triangle PQR$

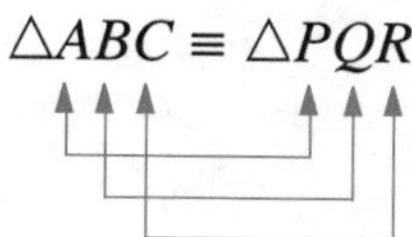

3. Keeping in mind the corresponding order of the vertices, we cannot write $\triangle ABC \equiv \triangle QRP$.

4. $\triangle ABC$ may also be called $\triangle BCA$. The statement '$\triangle ABC \equiv \triangle PQR$' may be written as '$\triangle BCA \equiv \triangle QRP$'.

MATHSTORY

Leibnitz (1646–1716) originated the use of the symbol ≈ for congruence. Gauss (1777–1855), the Prince of mathematicians, first used the symbol ≡ to indicate congruence in number theory.

5. The correspondences which we use are more than just a pairing of sides and angles. You should notice that the corresponding sides are opposite to the corresponding angles. For example, in the congruent triangles, ABC and PQR, $\hat{A}$ corresponds to $\hat{P}$ and the side opposite to $\hat{A}$ corresponds to the side opposite to $\hat{P}$, i.e. BC corresponds to QR.

Tests For Congruent Triangles

To test whether two triangles are congruent, you need not test all three sides and all three angles. The following class activity will help you discover some rules about congruent triangles.

Class Activity 1

1. In $\triangle ABC$, two sides and the included angle are given.

(a) Draw $\triangle PQR$ such that $\hat{P} = 30°$, $PQ = 4$ cm and $RP = 6$ cm.

(b) Is $\triangle PQR$ congruent to $\triangle ABC$?

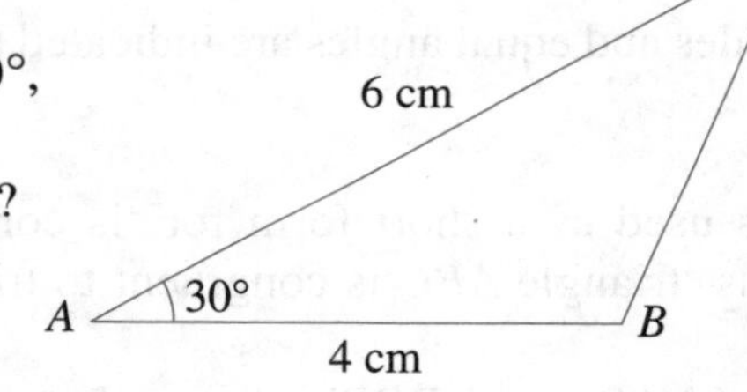

2. In $\triangle ABC$, two sides and a non-included angle are given.

(a) Draw $\triangle XYZ$ such that $\hat{Y} = 50°$, $YZ = 5$ cm and $ZX = 4$ cm.

(b) Is $\triangle XYZ$ congruent to $\triangle ABC$?

(c) Is $\triangle XYZ$ necessarily an acute-angled triangle?

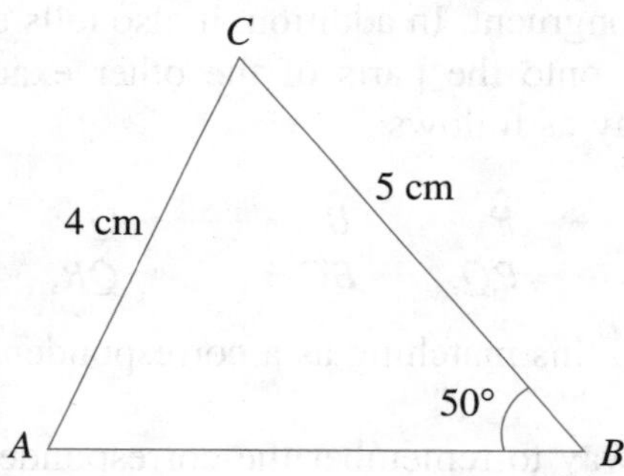

3. In $\triangle ABC$, two angles and one side are given.

(a) Draw $\triangle XYZ$ such that $\hat{X} = 60°$, $\hat{Y} = 50°$ and $ZX = 5$ cm.

(b) Is $\triangle XYZ$ congruent to $\triangle ABC$?

(c) Draw $\triangle PQR$ such that $\hat{P} = 60°$, $\hat{Q} = 50°$ and $PQ = 5$ cm.

(d) Is $\triangle PQR$ congruent to $\triangle ABC$?

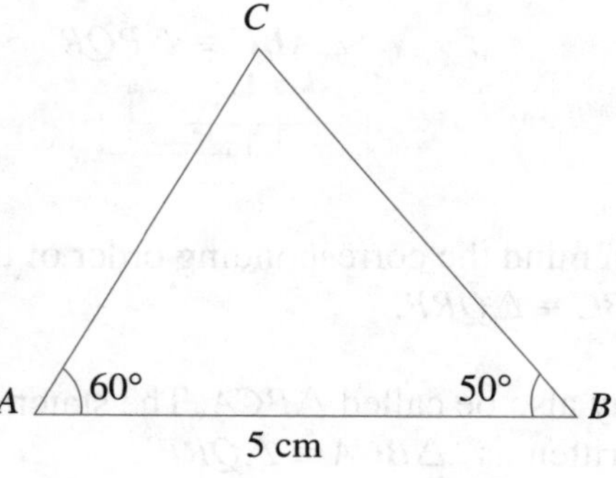

4. In $\triangle ABC$, three sides are given.
- **(a)** Draw $\triangle PQR$ such that $PQ = 5$ cm, $QR = 4$ cm and $RP = 6$ cm.
- **(b)** Is $\triangle PQR$ congruent to $\triangle ABC$?

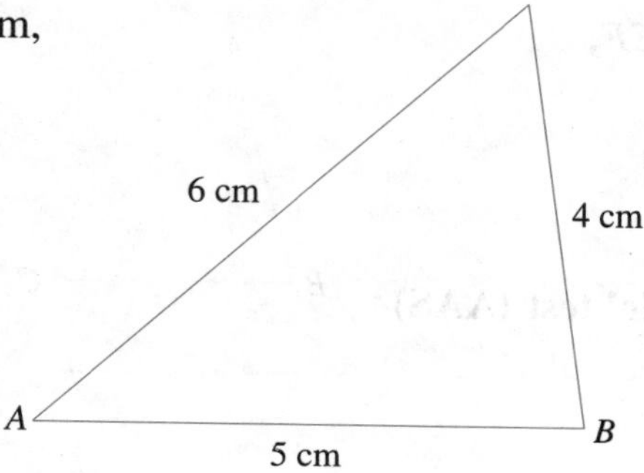

5. In $\triangle ABC$, three angles are given.
- **(a)** Draw $\triangle XYZ$ such that $\hat{X} = 70°$, $\hat{Y} = 50°$ and $\hat{Z} = 60°$.
- **(b)** Is $\triangle XYZ$ congruent to $\triangle ABC$?
- **(c)** Is $\triangle XYZ$ necessarily of the same size as $\triangle ABC$?

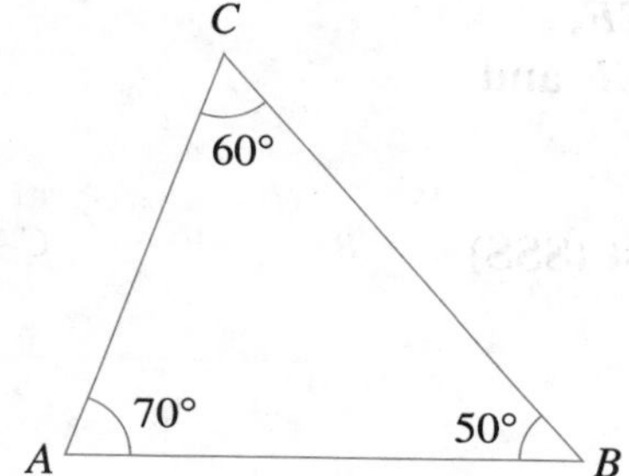

6. In $\triangle ABC$, one angle is a right angle, the hypotenuse (longest side) and another side are also given.
- **(a)** Draw $\triangle PQR$ such that $\hat{Q} = 90°$, $QR = 4$ cm and $RP = 7$ cm.
- **(b)** Is $\triangle PQR$ congruent to $\triangle ABC$?

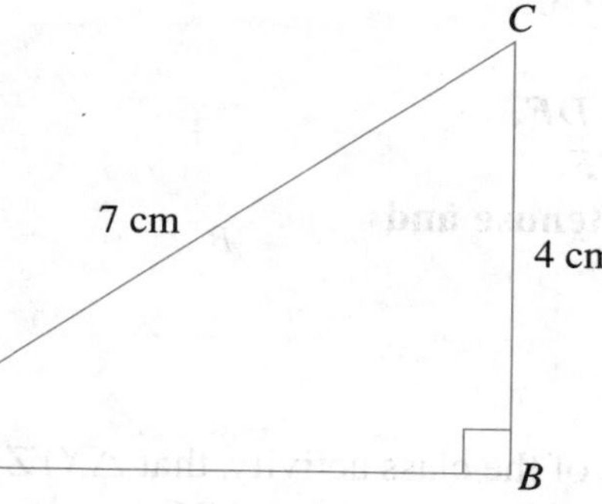

The results discovered from Class Activity 1 provide the following ***Tests For Congruent Triangles***:

In $\triangle ABC$ and $\triangle DEF$, if $AB = DE$, $\hat{B} = \hat{E}$ and $BC = EF$, then $\triangle ABC \equiv \triangle DEF$.
'Two Sides and the Included Angle' test (SAS)

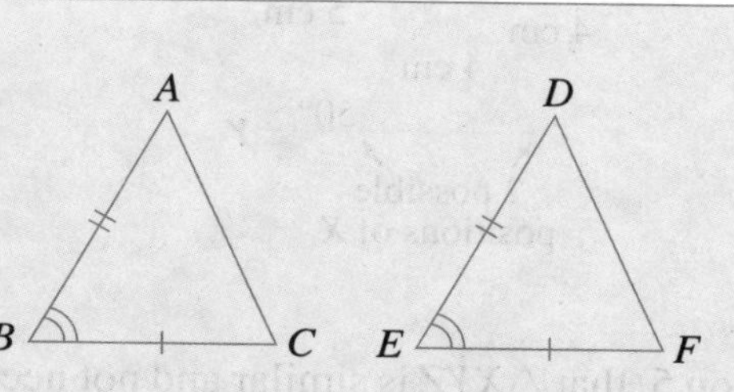

In $\triangle ABC$ and $\triangle DEF$,
if $\hat{B} = \hat{E}$, $\hat{C} = \hat{F}$
and $BC = EF$, then
$\triangle ABC \equiv \triangle DEF$.
'Two Angles and a Corresponding Side' test (AAS)

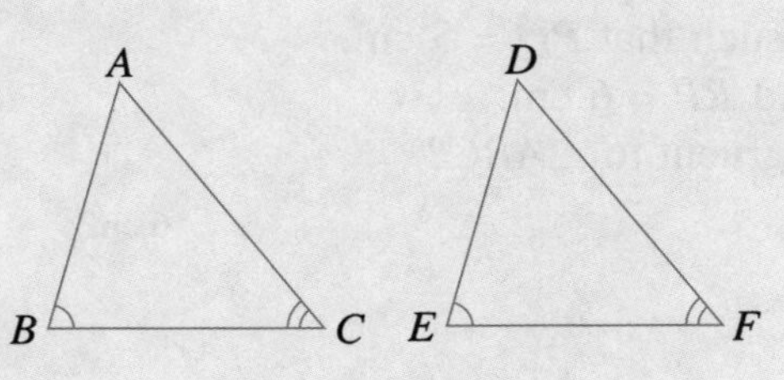

In $\triangle ABC$ and $\triangle DEF$,
if $AB = DE$, $BC = EF$ and
$CA = FD$, then
$\triangle ABC \equiv \triangle DEF$.
'Side-Side-Side' test (SSS)

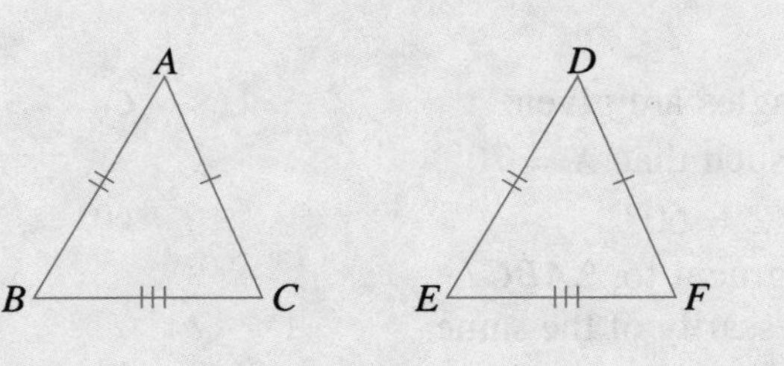

In $\triangle ABC$ and $\triangle DEF$,
if $\hat{B} = \hat{E} = 90°$,
$AB = DE$ and $AC = DF$,
then $\triangle ABC \equiv \triangle DEF$.
'Right angle, Hypotenuse and Side' test (RHS)

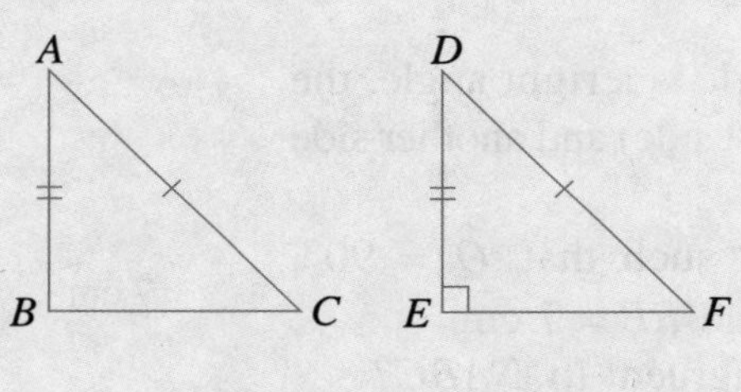

Notice, from question 2 of the class activity, that $\triangle XYZ$ which has two sides and a non-included angle equal to that of $\triangle ABC$ is not necessarily congruent to $\triangle ABC$ as there are two possible triangles that could be called $\triangle XYZ$ as shown.

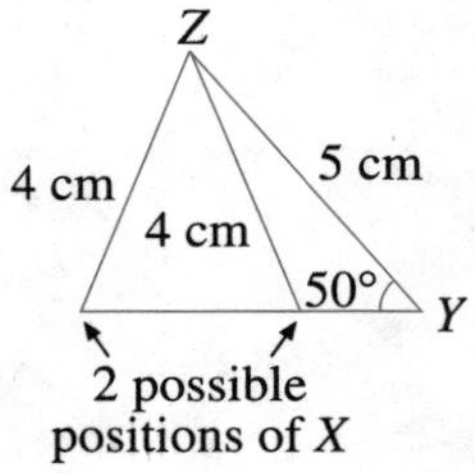

Also notice, from question 5, that $\triangle XYZ$ is similar and not necessarily congruent to $\triangle ABC$.

Exercise 8.1

answers on p. 434

1. Study each of the following figures (not drawn to scale). Must the triangles be congruent? Write, if applicable, a correct statement of congruence and state the test used.

(a)
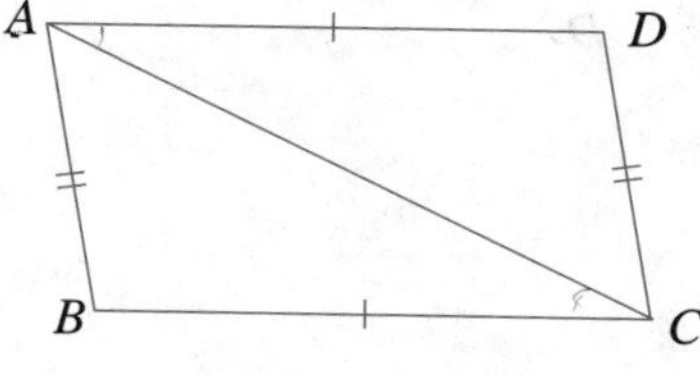

(b)
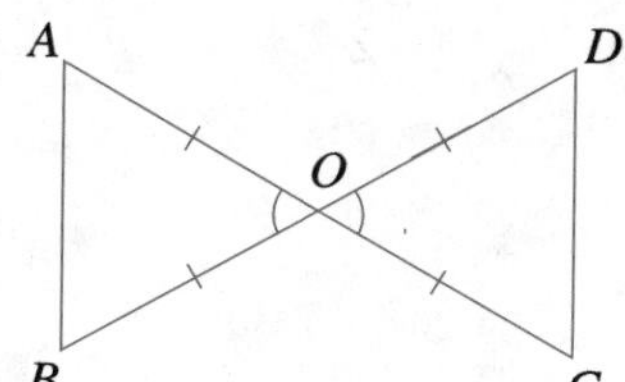

(c)
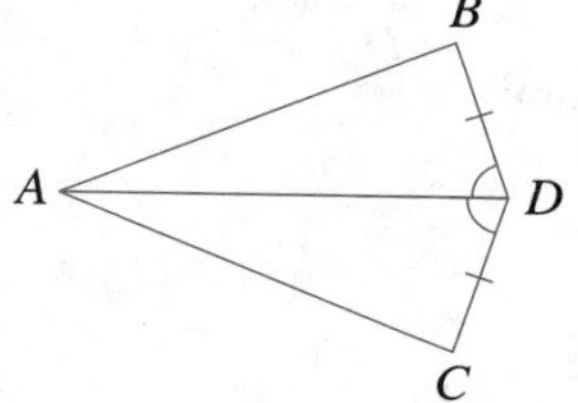

(d)
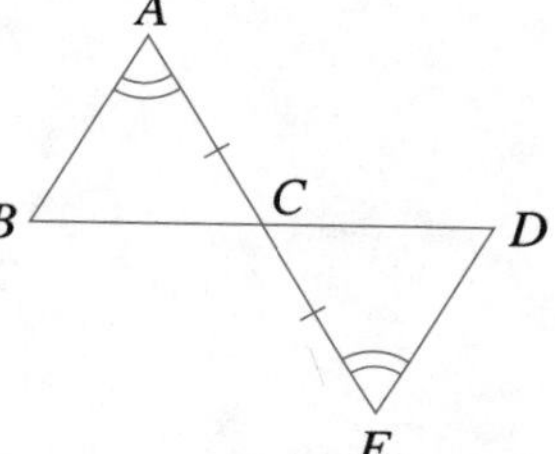

(e)
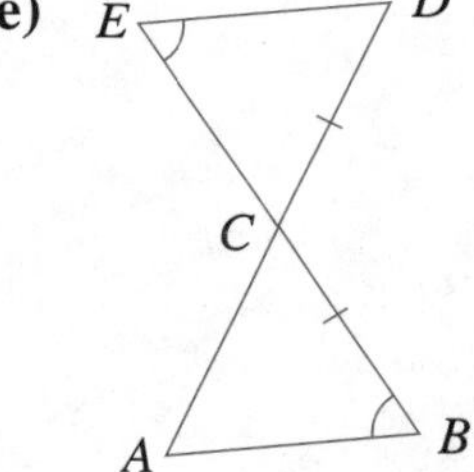

(f)
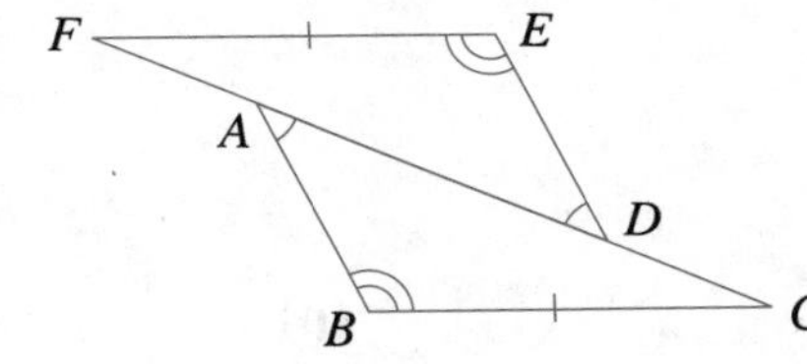

(g)
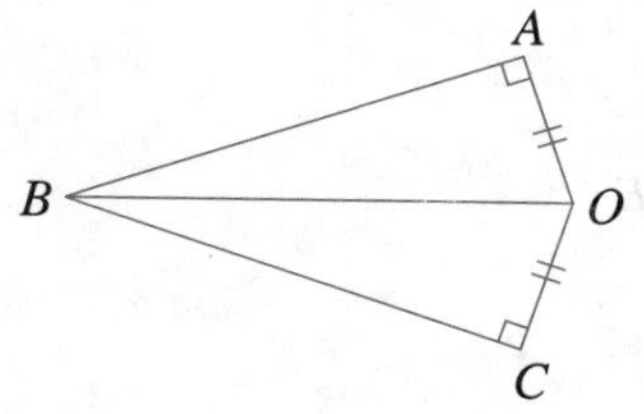

(h)
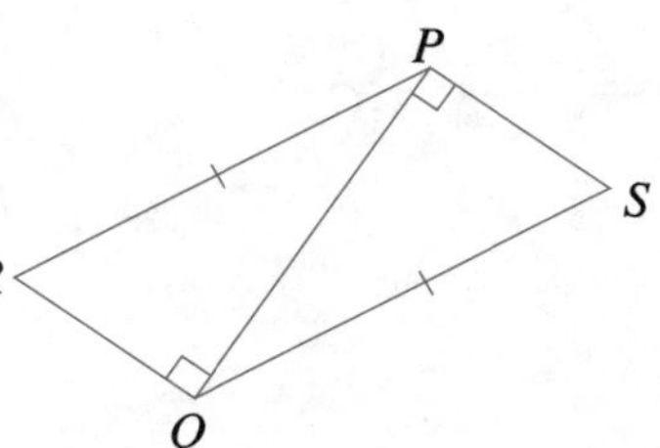

(i)
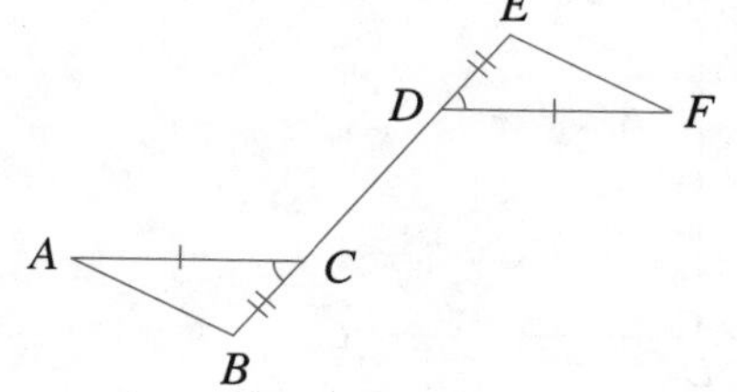

(j)
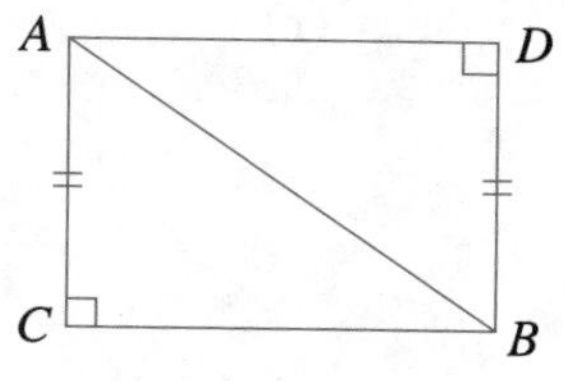

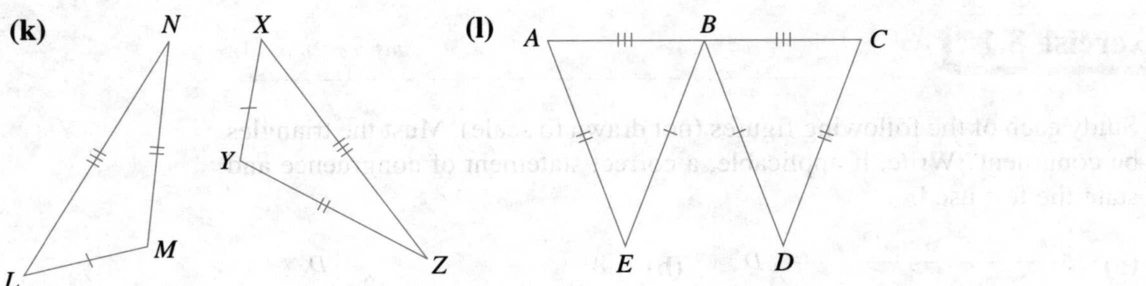
(k)
N
X
Y
M
L
Z
(l)
A
B
C
E
D

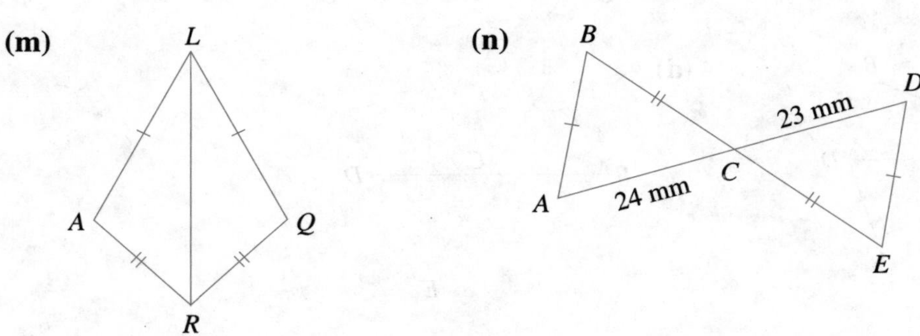
(m)
L
A
Q
R
(n)
B
D
23 mm
C
A
24 mm
E

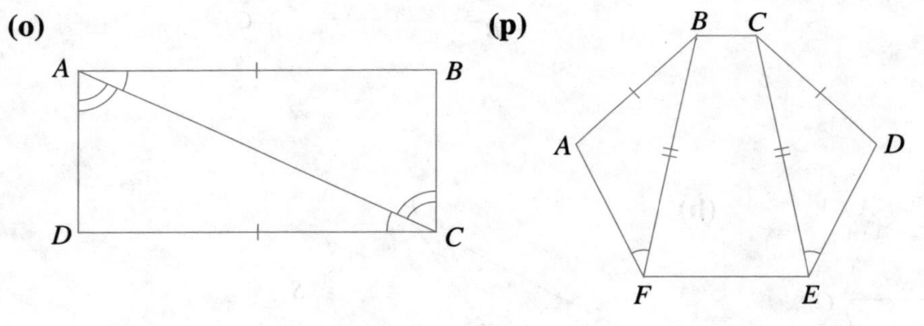
(o)
A
B
D
C
(p)
B
C
A
D
F
E

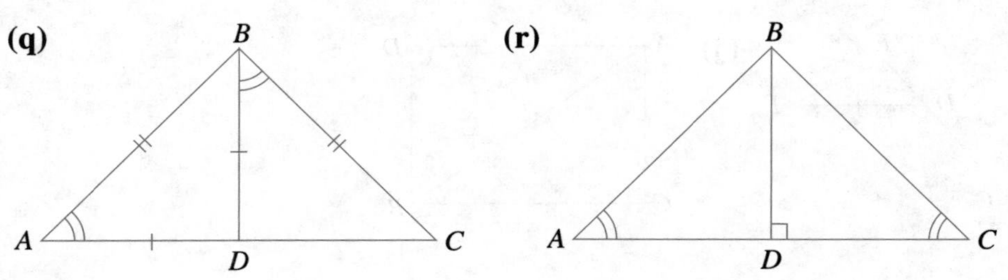
(q)
B
A
D
C
(r)
B
A
D
C

(s)

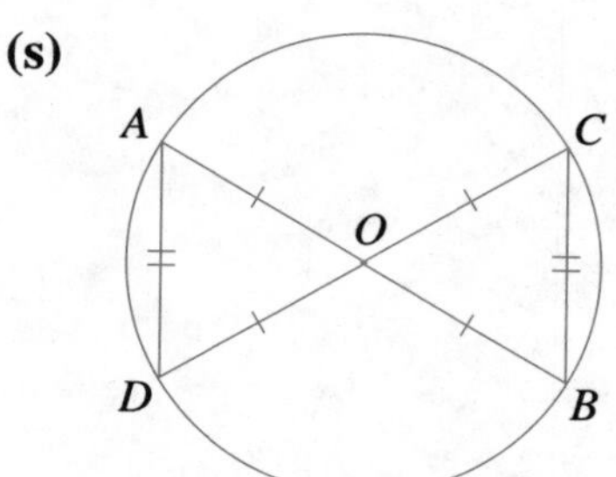

(t)

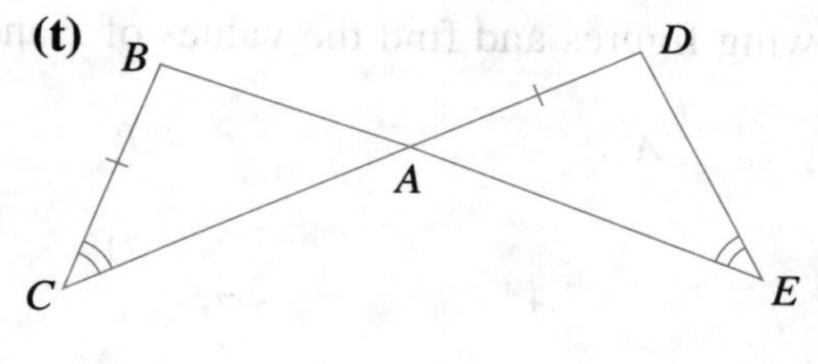

(u)

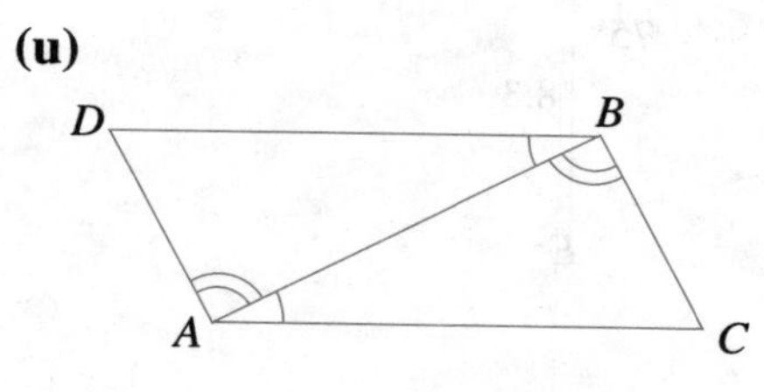

(v)

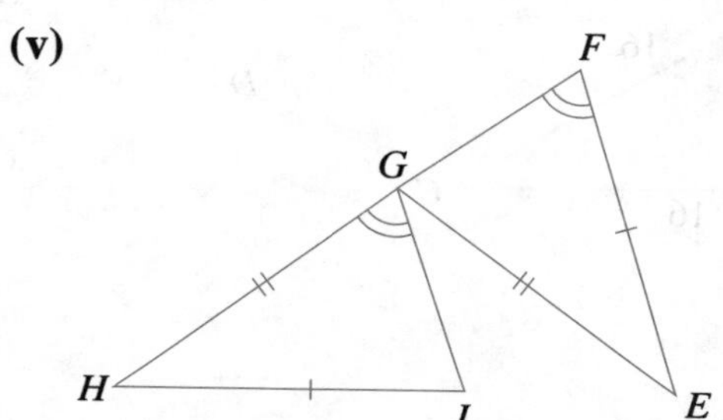

(w)

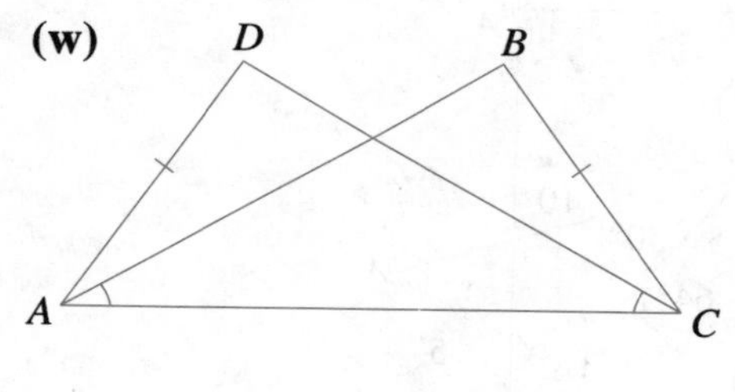

(x)

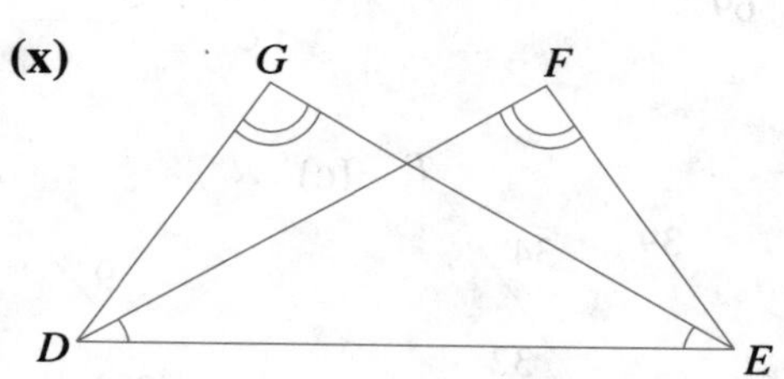

(y)

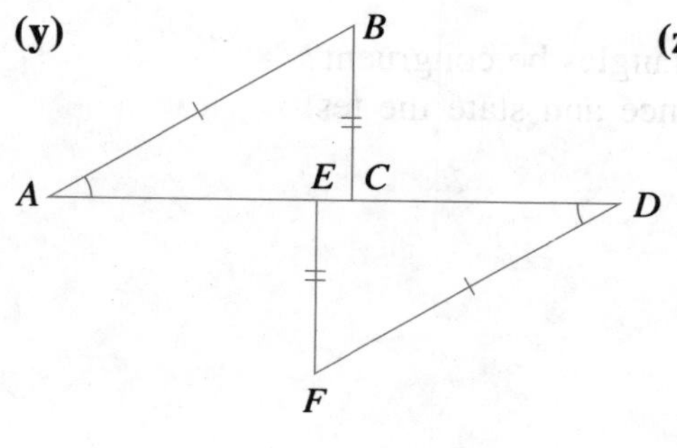

(z)

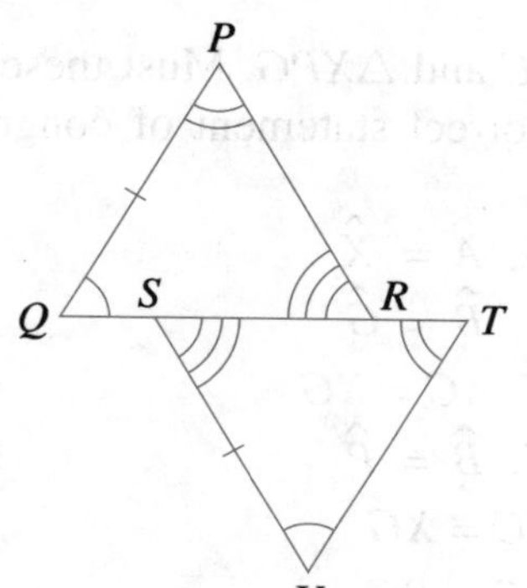

2. Study the following figures and find the values of x and y.

(a)

(b)

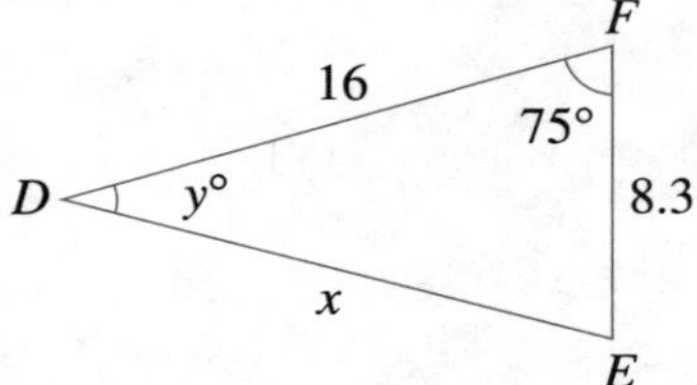

(c)

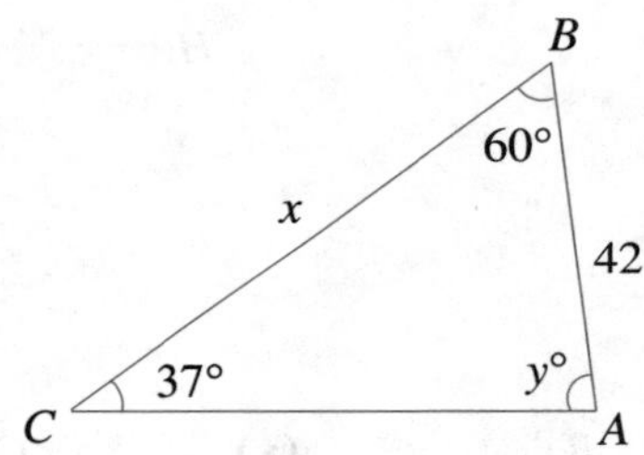

(d)

(e)

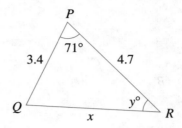

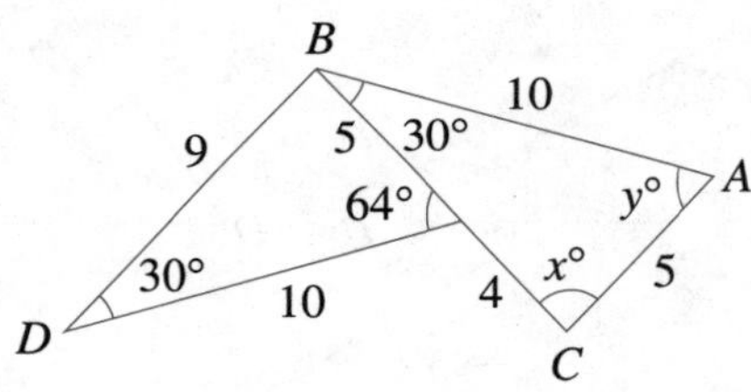

3. Study the data for $\triangle ABC$ and $\triangle XPG$. Must these triangles be congruent? Write, if applicable, a correct statement of congruence and state the test used.

(a) $AB = PX$, $AC = XG$, $\hat{A} = \hat{X}$

(b) $BC = PG$, $BA = XP$, $\hat{B} = \hat{G}$

(c) $AB = PG$, $BC = PX$, $AC = XG$

(d) $AB = XP$, $CA = GX$, $\hat{B} = \hat{P}$

(e) $\hat{B} = \hat{G}$, $\hat{C} = \hat{X}$, $BC = XG$

(f) $\hat{A} = \hat{X}$, $\hat{B} = \hat{P}$, $AC = PG$

Using Congruent Triangles

Worked Example 1

In $\triangle ABC$, $\hat{B} = \hat{C}$ and AD is the bisector of $\hat{A}$. Show that $AB = AC$.

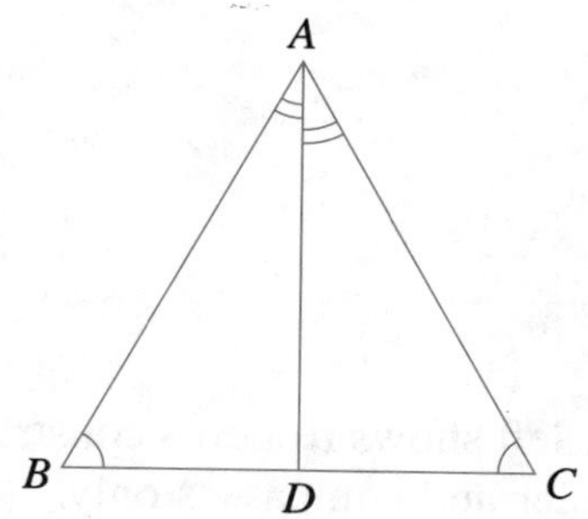

Solution:

In $\triangle ADB$ and $\triangle ADC$,

$$\begin{aligned} \hat{B} &= \hat{C} && \text{(given)} \\ B\hat{A}D &= C\hat{A}D && \text{(given)} \\ AD & \text{ is common.} \\ \therefore \triangle ADB &\equiv \triangle ADC && \text{(AAS)} \\ \therefore AB &= AC \end{aligned}$$

Worked Example 2

In the figure, $SB = RC$ and $PQRS$ is a rectangle. Explain why $\triangle ASR$ is an isosceles triangle.

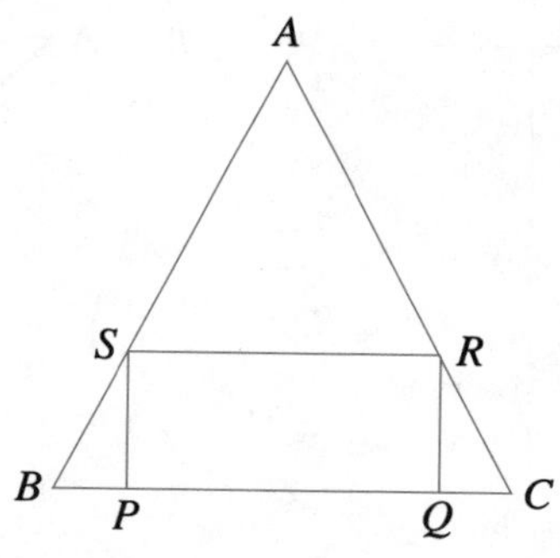

Solution:

In $\triangle BPS$ and $\triangle CQR$,

$$\begin{aligned} B\hat{P}S &= C\hat{Q}R = 90^\circ && \text{(prop. of rect.)} \\ SB &= RC && \text{(given)} \\ SP &= RQ && \text{(prop. of rect.)} \\ \therefore \triangle BPS &\equiv \triangle CQR && \text{(RHS)} \\ \therefore \hat{B} &= \hat{C} \end{aligned}$$

Now

$$\begin{aligned} A\hat{S}R &= \hat{B} && \text{(corr. } \angle\text{s } SR \,//\, PQ\text{, prop. of rect.)} \\ \therefore A\hat{R}S &= \hat{C} && \text{(corr. } \angle\text{s } SR \,//\, PQ\text{, prop. of rect.)} \\ \therefore A\hat{S}R &= A\hat{R}S \end{aligned}$$

So, $\triangle ASR$ is an isosceles triangle.

Exercise 8.2

answers on p. 435

1.

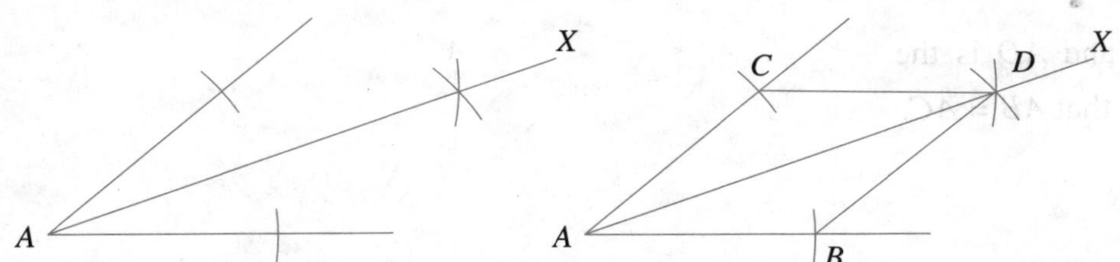

The figure on the left shows Robert's construction of the bisector of a given angle A, using ruler and compasses only.

(a) Describe briefly Robert's construction.

(b) Explain why Robert's construction is correct by using the triangles in the figure on the right.

2.

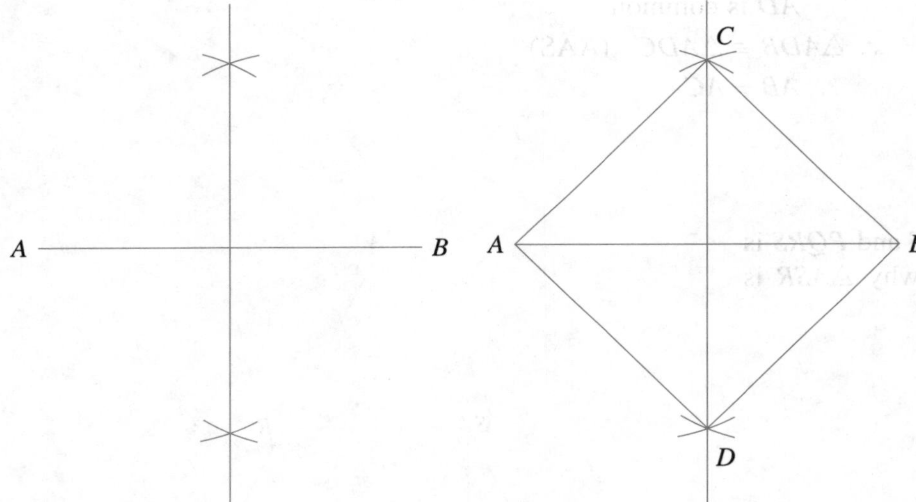

The figure on the left shows how the perpendicular bisector of AB is drawn, using ruler and compasses only.

(a) Describe briefly the construction.

(b) Prove that the construction is correct by using the figure on the right.

3. In the figure, AB // DC and AD // BC. Use congruent triangles to show that

(a) $AB = DC$,

(b) AC and BD bisect each other.

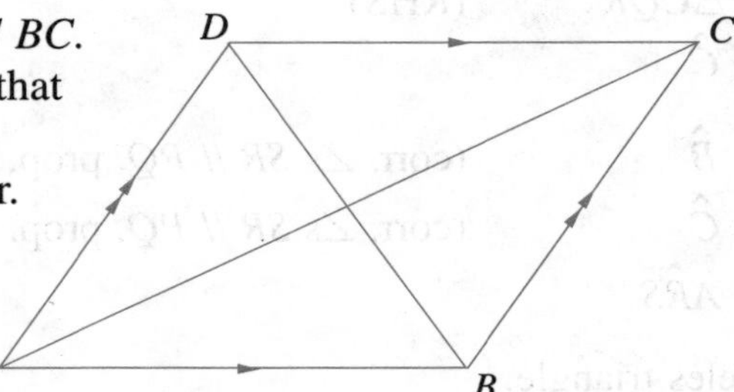

4. In the figure, $AD = CD$ and $AB = CB$.
Use congruent triangles to show that
   (a) BD bisects $A\hat{D}C$,
   (b) AC and DB are perpendicular to each other.

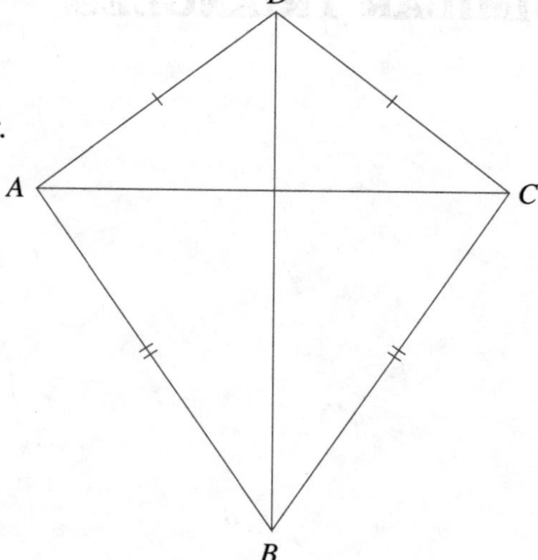

5. A rectangle is a special parallelogram with four right angles. Use congruent triangles to show that its diagonals are equal.

6. (a) Is $\triangle ADE$ congruent to $\triangle CBF$? Give reason.
   (b) Explain why
      (i) $\triangle DEF \equiv \triangle BFE$,
      (ii) $\triangle ABE \equiv \triangle CDF$.

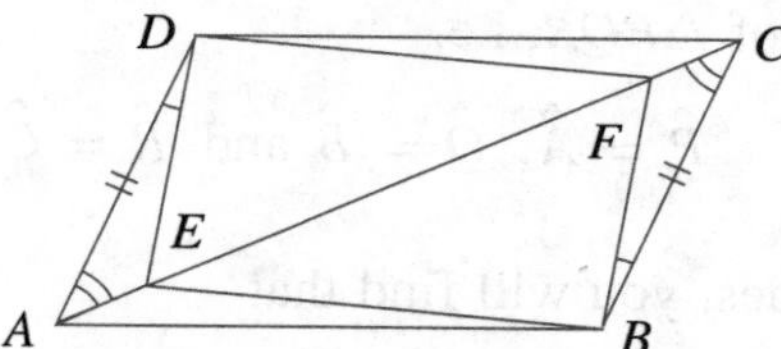

7. (a) Is $\triangle PAQ$ congruent to $\triangle QBO$? Give reason.
   (b) Show that
      (i) $\triangle PQR \equiv \triangle ORQ$,
      (ii) $\triangle PDR \equiv \triangle RCO$.

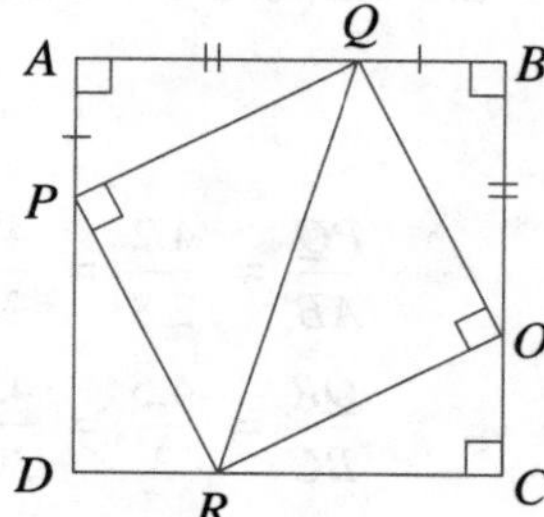

8. In the figure, $DE \parallel BC$ and $AD = AE$. Show that
   (a) $BD = CE$,
   (b) $BE = CD$.

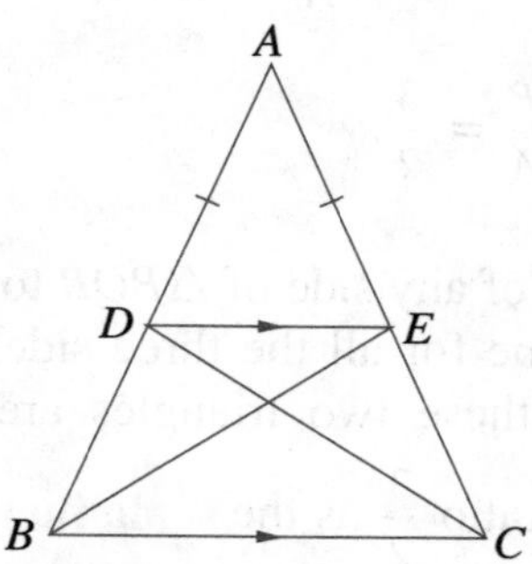

8.2 SIMILAR TRIANGLES

Example

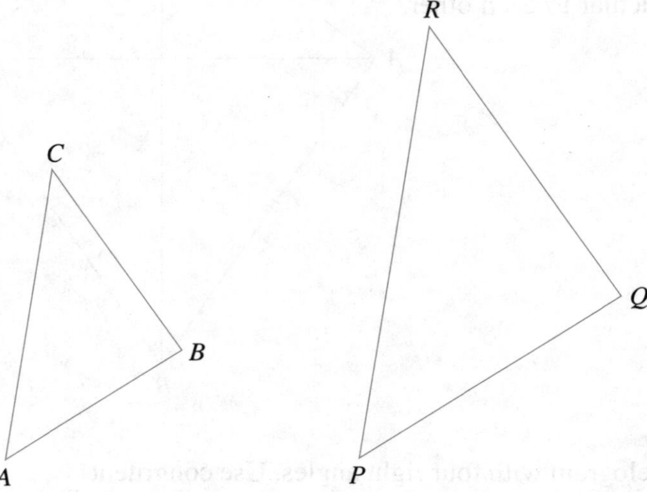

These two triangles have the same shape. We say that they are **similar triangles**. If you measure the angles, you will find that the angles of $\triangle ABC$ are equal to the corresponding angles of $\triangle PQR$, i.e.

Similar triangles are triangles which have the same shape but not the same size.

$$\hat{P} = \hat{A},\ \hat{Q} = \hat{B} \text{ and } \hat{R} = \hat{C}.$$

If you measure the sides, you will find that

$$PQ = 4.2 \text{ cm},\ QR = 4.5 \text{ cm},\ RP = 6 \text{ cm},$$
$$AB = 2.8 \text{ cm},\ BC = 3 \text{ cm and } CA = 4 \text{ cm}.$$

Notice that

$$\frac{PQ}{AB} = \frac{4.2}{2.8} = \frac{42}{28} = \frac{3}{2}$$

$$\frac{QR}{BC} = \frac{4.5}{3} = \frac{45}{30} = \frac{3}{2}$$

and

$$\frac{RP}{CA} = \frac{6}{4} = \frac{3}{2}$$

Thus $\dfrac{PQ}{AB} = \dfrac{QR}{BC} = \dfrac{RP}{CA} = \dfrac{3}{2}$.

Note: 1. The ratio of any side of $\triangle PQR$ to the corresponding side of $\triangle ABC$ is the same for all the three sides. We say that the corresponding sides of these two triangles are **proportional**. We refer to the constant ratio $\dfrac{3}{2}$ as the **scale factor**.

A scale factor is the ratio of the distance between two points on an image of an object and the distance between the corresponding points on the actual object.

2. When making statements about similar triangles such as '$\triangle PQR$ is similar to $\triangle ABC$', make sure that the letters P, Q and R match the letters A, B and C in the correct correspondence.

In general:

> **If two triangles are similar,**
> - **their corresponding angles are equal and**
> - **their corresponding sides are proportional.**

Tests For Similar Triangles

To test whether two triangles are similar, you need not test all the three sides and all the three angles. The following class activity will help you discover some rules for testing similar triangles.

Class Activity 2

1. $\triangle ABC$ is a given triangle.
You can draw a $\triangle XYZ$ such that $\hat{X} = \hat{A}$ and $\hat{Y} = \hat{B}$ by following the steps given below.

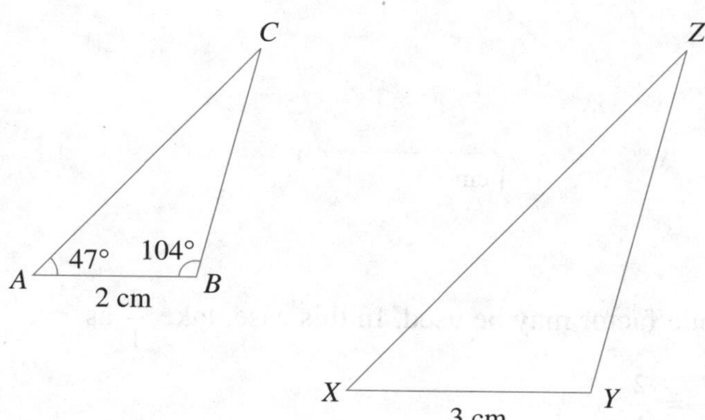

(a) Copy $\triangle ABC$. Draw XY of any length. In this case, take $XY = 3$ cm. Through X, draw a line such that $\hat{X} = 47°$. Through Y, draw a line such that $\hat{Y} = 104°$, letting this line meet the first line at Z as shown. Then $\triangle XYZ$ is the required triangle.

(b) Is $\hat{Z}$ equal to $\hat{C}$?

(c) Measure YZ and ZX.

Is each side of $\triangle XYZ$ $\frac{3}{2}$ times the corresponding side of $\triangle ABC$?

(d) Write down the ratio $\frac{XY}{AB}$, $\frac{YZ}{BC}$ and $\frac{ZX}{CA}$.

Is $\frac{XY}{AB} = \frac{YZ}{BC} = \frac{ZX}{CA} = \frac{3}{2}$ true?

(e) Do you agree with the statement below?
In $\triangle XYZ$ and $\triangle ABC$, if $\hat{X} = \hat{A}$ and $\hat{Y} = \hat{B}$, then $\triangle XYZ$ and $\triangle ABC$ are similar.

2. $\triangle ABC$ is a given triangle.

You can draw $\triangle XYZ$ such that $\frac{XY}{AB} = \frac{YZ}{BC} = \frac{ZX}{CA}$ by following the steps given below.

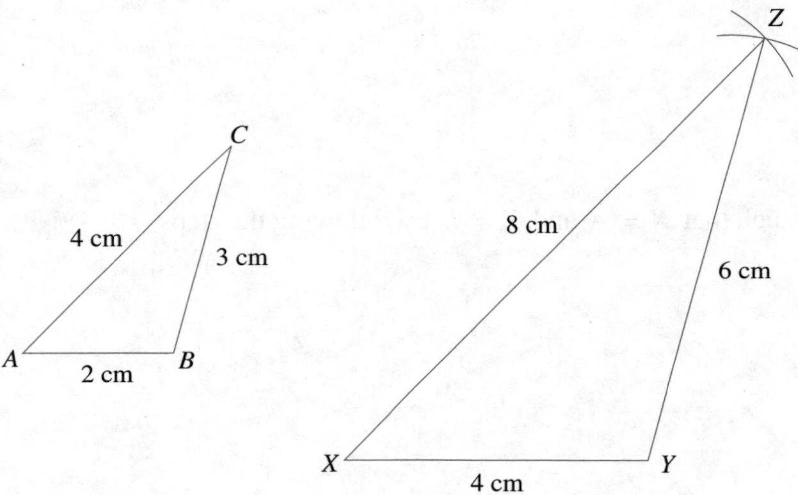

(a) Copy $\triangle ABC$.

To draw $\triangle XYZ$, any scale factor may be used. In this case, take $\frac{2}{1}$ as the scale factor. So $\frac{XY}{AB} = \frac{2}{1}$.
Therefore $XY = 2AB = 2 \times 2$ cm $= 4$ cm.
Similarly, $YZ = 2 \times 3$ cm $= 6$ cm and $ZX = 2 \times 4$ cm $= 8$ cm.
Now draw $\triangle XYZ$ as shown above on the right.
Then $\triangle XYZ$ is the required triangle.

(b) Make the necessary measurements to find out if the following statements are true.

$$\hat{X} = \hat{A},\ \hat{Y} = \hat{B} \text{ and } \hat{Z} = \hat{C}$$

(c) Do you agree with the statement below?

In $\triangle XYZ$ and $\triangle ABC$, if $\frac{XY}{AB} = \frac{YZ}{BC} = \frac{ZX}{CA}$, then $\triangle XYZ$ and $\triangle ABC$ are similar.

3. $\triangle ABC$ is a given triangle.

You can draw $\triangle XYZ$ such that $\hat{X} = \hat{A}$, $\frac{XY}{AB} = \frac{ZX}{CA}$ by following the steps given below.

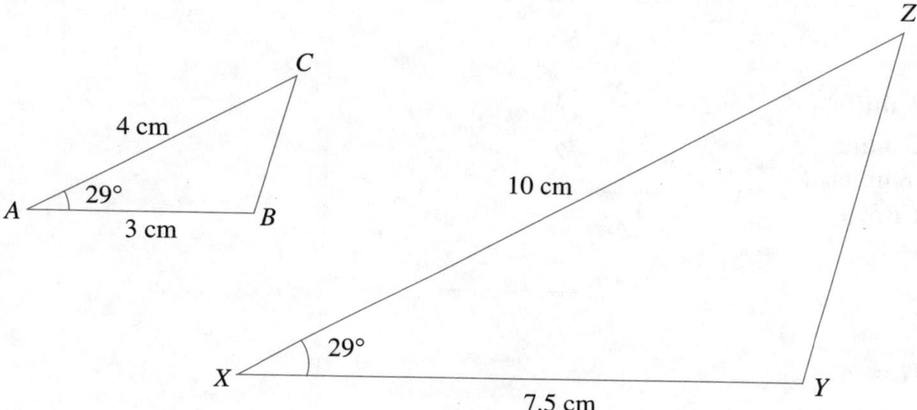

(a) Copy $\triangle ABC$.

To draw $\triangle XYZ$, any scale factor may be used. In this case, take $\frac{5}{2}$ as the scale factor. So $\frac{XY}{AB} = \frac{5}{2}$.

Therefore $XY = \frac{5}{2}AB = \frac{5}{2} \times 3$ cm = 7.5 cm.

Similarly, $ZX = \frac{5}{2} \times 4$ cm = 10 cm.

Now draw a line XY, 7.5 cm long.

Draw a line ZX, 10 cm long such that $\hat{X} = 29°$. Join YZ. Then $\triangle XYZ$ is the required triangle.

(b) Make the necessary measurements to find out if the following statements are true.

$$\hat{Y} = \hat{B},\ \hat{Z} = \hat{C} \text{ and } \frac{YZ}{BC} = \frac{5}{2}$$

(c) Do you agree with the statement below?

In $\triangle XYZ$ and $\triangle ABC$, if $\frac{XY}{AB} = \frac{ZX}{CA}$ and $\hat{X} = \hat{A}$, then $\triangle XYZ$ and $\triangle ABC$ are similar.

Remember these:

> **In $\triangle XYZ$ and $\triangle ABC$, if**
> **(a)** $\hat{X} = \hat{A}$ **and** $\hat{Y} = \hat{B}$ **or**
> **(b)** $\dfrac{XY}{AB} = \dfrac{YZ}{BC} = \dfrac{ZX}{CA}$ **or**
> **(c)** $\dfrac{XY}{AB} = \dfrac{ZX}{CA}$ **and** $\hat{X} = \hat{A}$,
> **then $\triangle XYZ$ and $\triangle ABC$ are similar.**

Worked Example 1

If $\hat{A} = \hat{D}$, $AB = 3$ units, $AC = 4$ units, $BC = 2$ units, $DE = 6$ units and $DF = 8$ units. Calculate the length of EF.

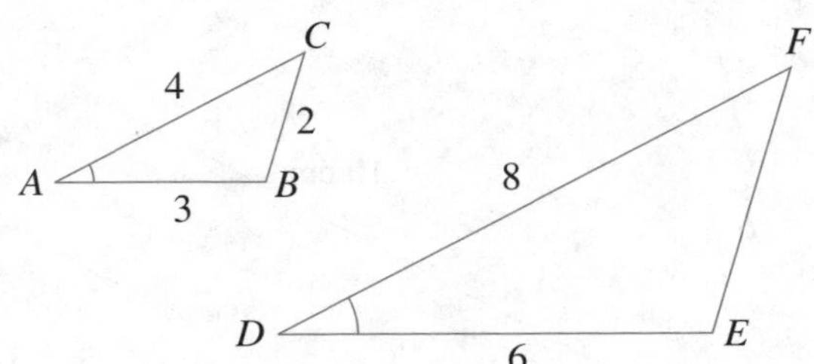

Solution:

$\dfrac{DE}{AB} = \dfrac{DF}{AC} = \dfrac{2}{1}$ and $\hat{D} = \hat{A}$

Therefore $\triangle DEF$ and $\triangle ABC$ are similar.

Then $\qquad \dfrac{EF}{BC} = \dfrac{2}{1}$

But $\qquad BC = 2$ units

$\therefore \qquad EF = 2 \times 2$ units

$\qquad = 4$ units

Worked Example 2

If $ED \mathbin{/\!/} AB$, $EC = 2$ units, $BC = 3$ units and $AB = 9$ units, find the length of DE.

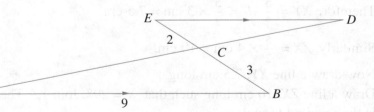

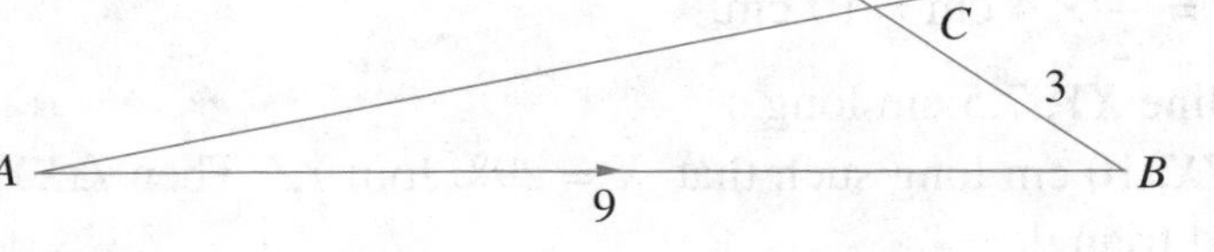

Solution:

$ED \mathbin{/\!/} AB$

Then $\hat{D} = \hat{A}$ and $\hat{E} = \hat{B}$.

Therefore $\triangle CDE$ and $\triangle CAB$ are similar.

Then $\qquad \dfrac{DE}{AB} = \dfrac{EC}{BC} = \dfrac{2}{3}$

But $\qquad AB = 9$ units

$\therefore \qquad DE = \dfrac{2}{3} \times 9$ units

$\qquad = 6$ units

Worked Example 3

In the given figure, if $AB \parallel DE$, $AB = 12$ units, $AD = 5$ units and $DC = 3$ units, find DE.

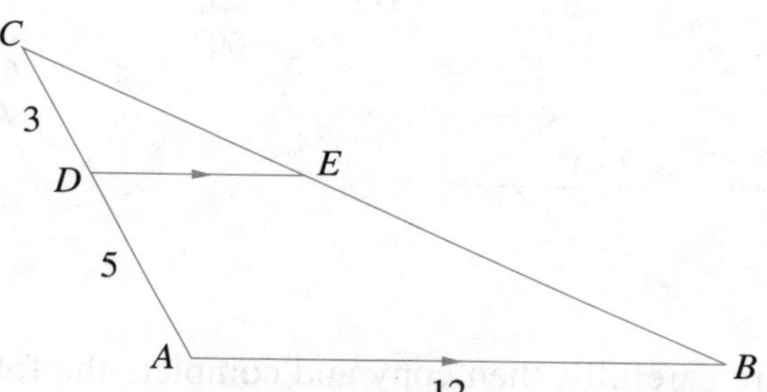

Solution:

$AB \parallel DE$

Then $D\hat{E}C = A\hat{B}C$ (corr. $\angle$s) and $\hat{C}$ is common to both triangles.

Therefore $\triangle CDE$ and $\triangle CAB$ are similar.

Then $\dfrac{DE}{AB} = \dfrac{CD}{CA} = \dfrac{3}{3+5} = \dfrac{3}{8}$

But $AB = 12$ units

$\therefore \quad DE = \dfrac{3}{8} \times 12$ units

$= \dfrac{9}{2}$ units

$= 4\dfrac{1}{2}$ units

Exercise 8.3

answers on p. 435

1. For each part, state whether the two triangles are similar.

(a)

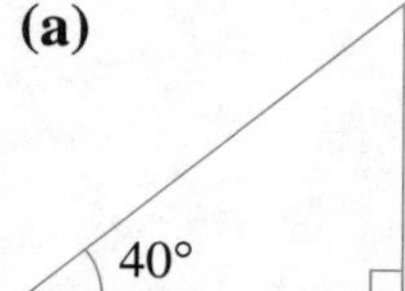

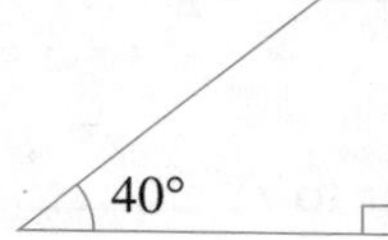

(b)

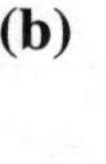

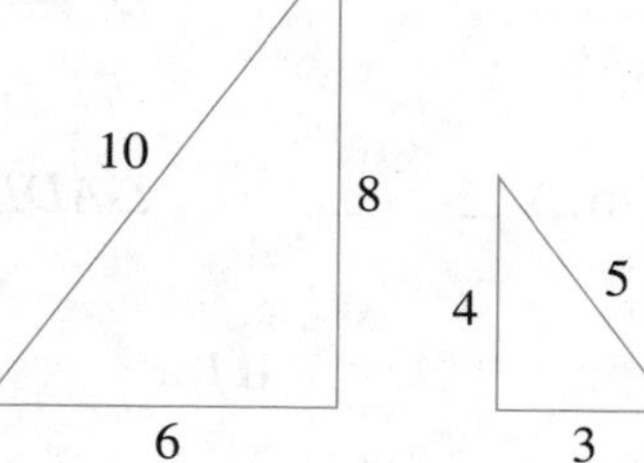

(c)

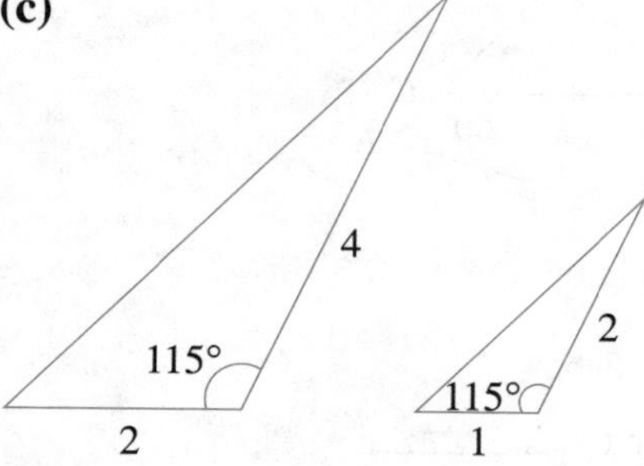

(d)

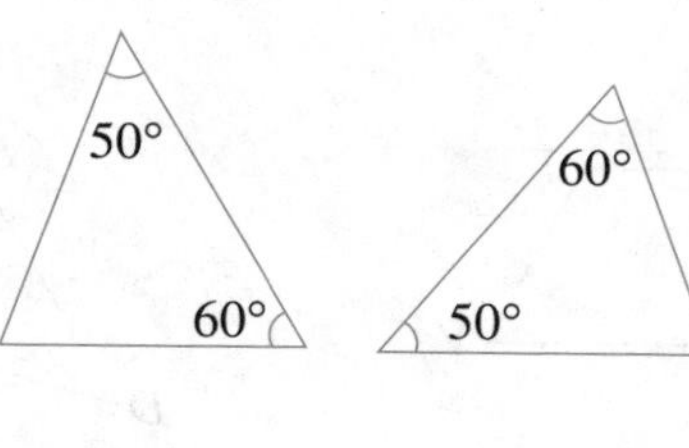

(e)

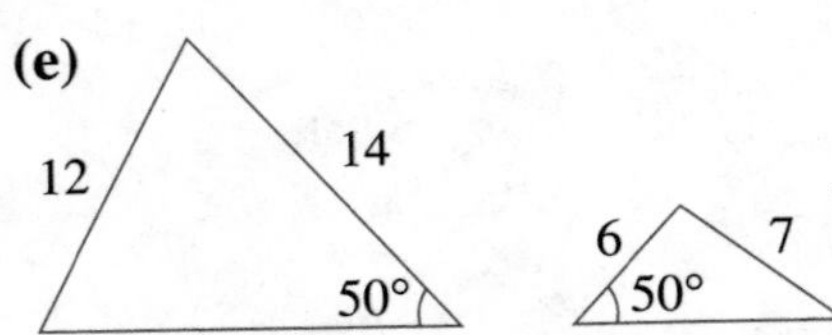

(f)

2. Study each figure carefully, then copy and complete the following.

(a)

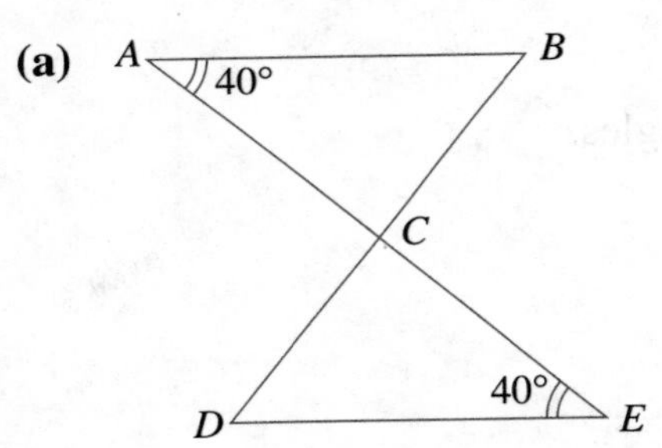

$\triangle ABC$ is similar to $\triangle$ ______.

(b)

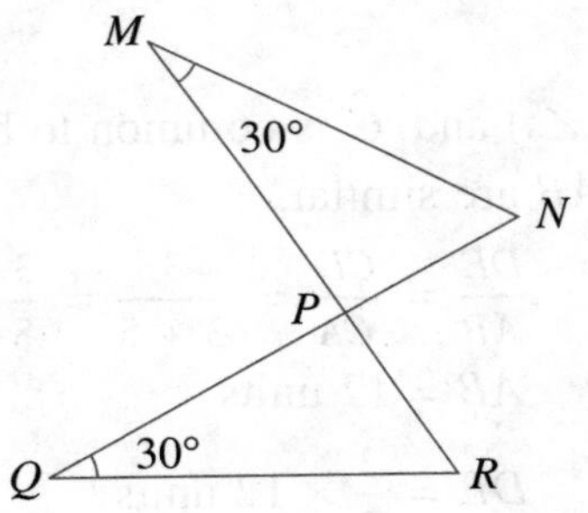

$\triangle PQR$ is similar to $\triangle$ ______.

(c)

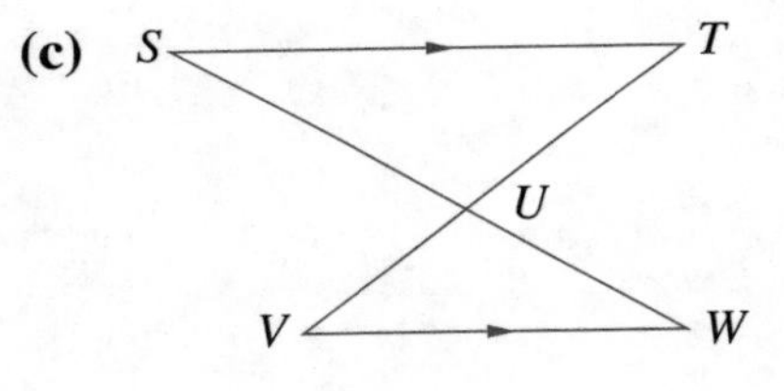

$\triangle STU$ is similar to $\triangle$ ______.

(d)

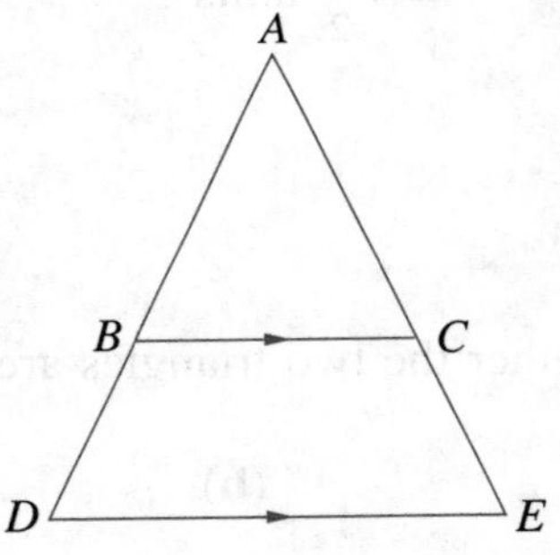

$\triangle ADE$ is similar to $\triangle$ ______.

(e)

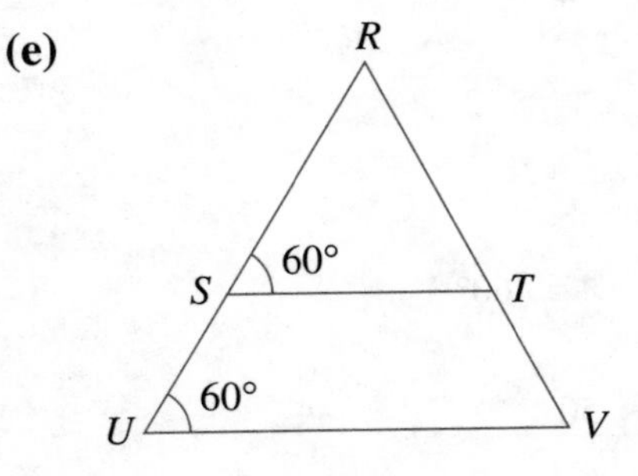

$\triangle RST$ is similar to $\triangle$ ______.

(f)

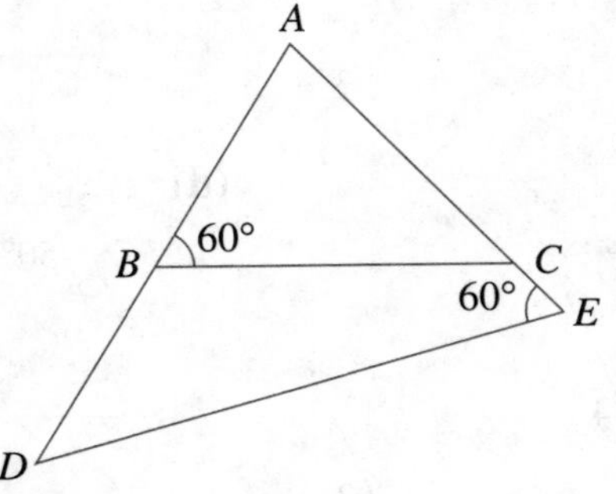

$\triangle ABC$ is similar to $\triangle$ ______.

(g)

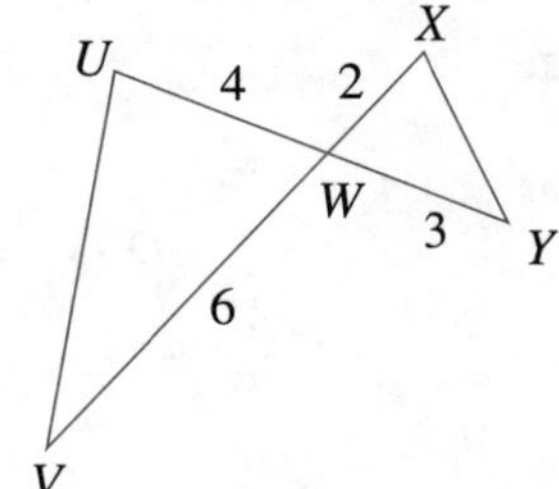

$\triangle UVW$ is similar to $\triangle$ ______.

(h)

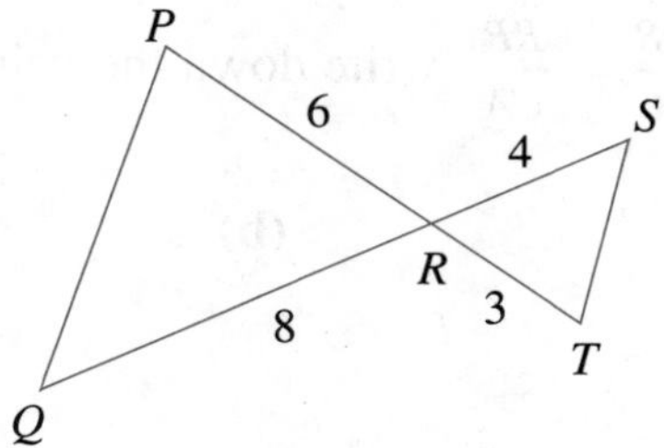

$\triangle RST$ is similar to $\triangle$ ______.

3. (a) Are the two triangles ($\triangle AED$ and $\triangle ABC$) in the figure on the right similar if $\frac{AE}{AB} = \frac{AD}{AC}$? If so, state why and name the pair of similar triangles in the correct order.

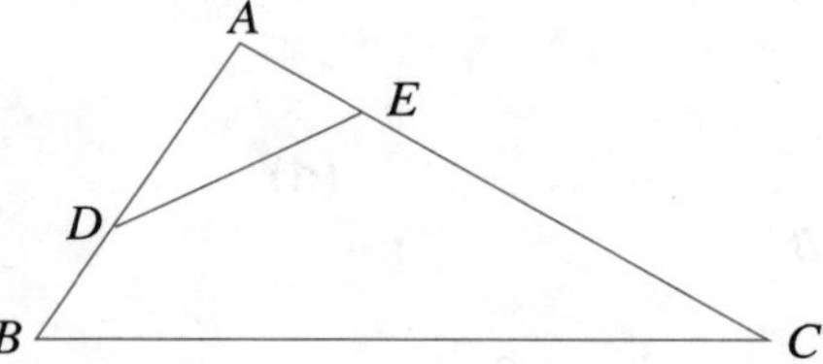

(b)

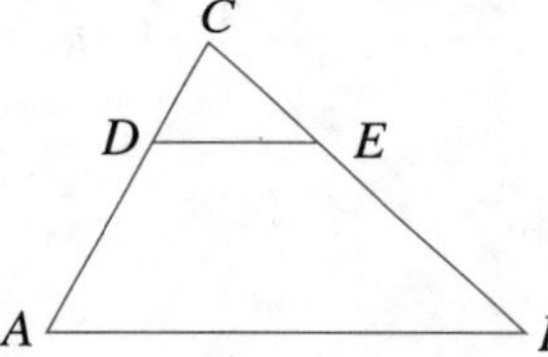

In the figure on the left, $AC = 18$ units, $BC = 24$ units, $DC = 6$ units and $EC = 8$ units. Are $\triangle CDE$ and $\triangle CAB$ similar?

4. (a) Are any two equilateral triangles similar?

(b) If two isosceles triangles have equal vertex angles, are the triangles similar?

(c) If two isosceles triangles have equal base angles, are the triangles similar?

5. In each case, name the pair of similar triangles, then copy and complete the statements.

(a) $\frac{PA}{BA} = \frac{\quad}{CA}$, $\frac{QP}{CB} = \frac{QA}{\quad}$, $\frac{QP}{PA} =$

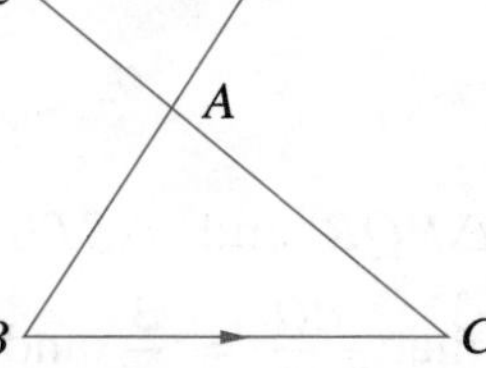

(b)

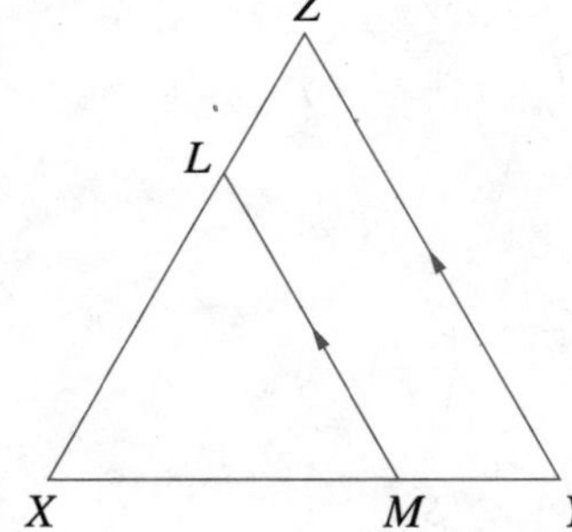

$\frac{XL}{XZ} = \frac{XM}{\quad}$, $\frac{YX}{MX} = \frac{\quad}{ML}$, $\frac{XM}{XL} = \frac{\quad}{XZ}$,

$\frac{XY}{XZ} = \frac{XM}{\quad}$, $\frac{ZX}{LX} = \frac{\quad}{MX}$, $\frac{ML}{YZ} = \frac{XL}{\quad}$.

6. Given that $\frac{PQ}{AB} = \frac{QR}{BC} = \frac{RP}{CA}$, write down the values of x, y and z.

(a)

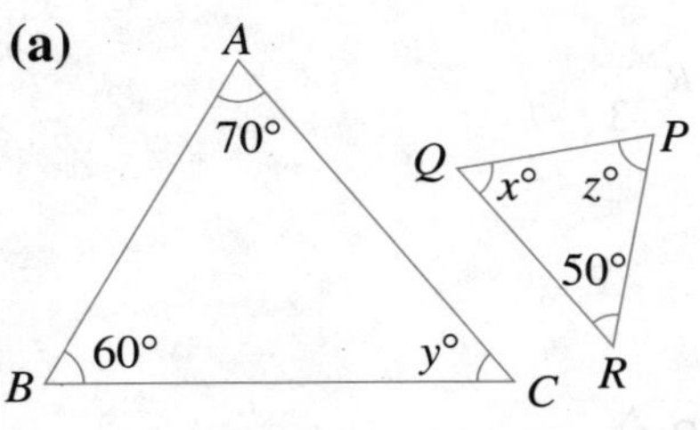

(b)

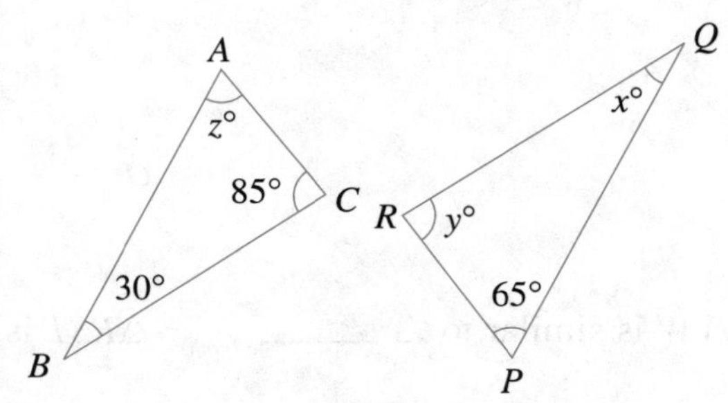

(c)

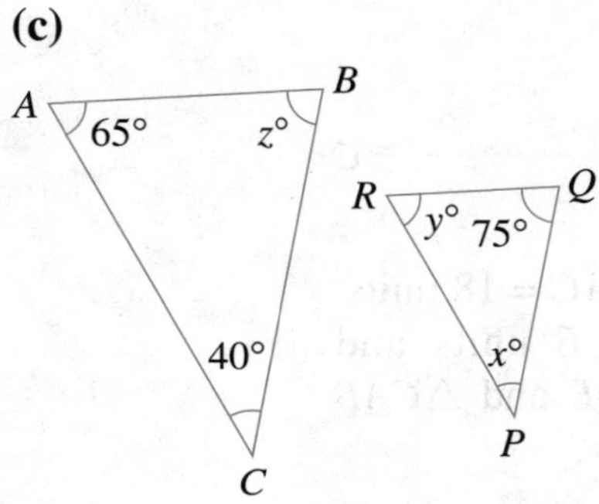

(d)

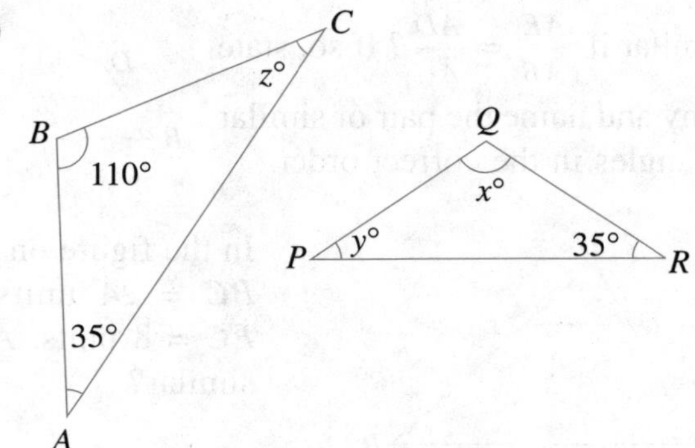

7. In the figures, if $\hat{A} = \hat{X}$, $AB = 6$ units, $AC = 8$ units, $BC = 4$ units, $XY = 12$ units and $XZ = 16$ units, calculate YZ.

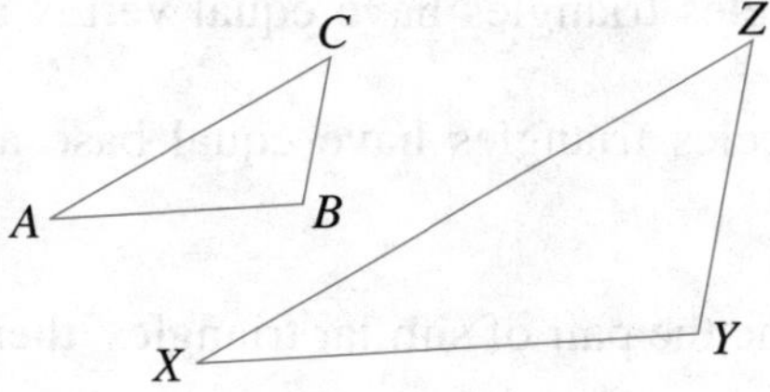

8. In the figures, $\triangle PQR$ and $\triangle STU$ are similar such that $\frac{RQ}{UT} = \frac{3}{2}$ and $PQ = 6$ units. Calculate ST.

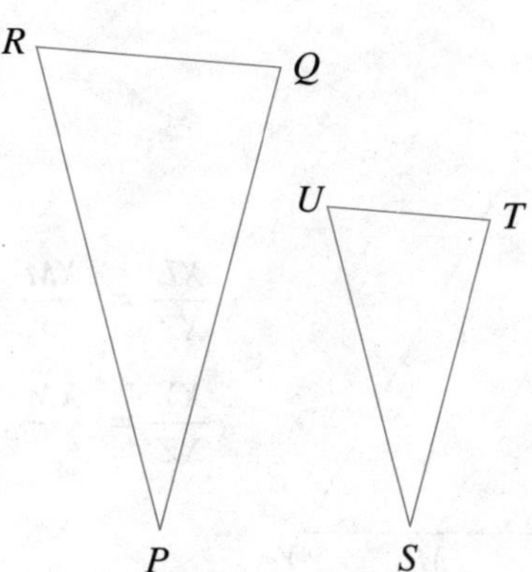

9. In the figure, if $AB \parallel PQ$, $AX = 5$ units, $QX = 2$ units and $AB = 6$ units, calculate QP.

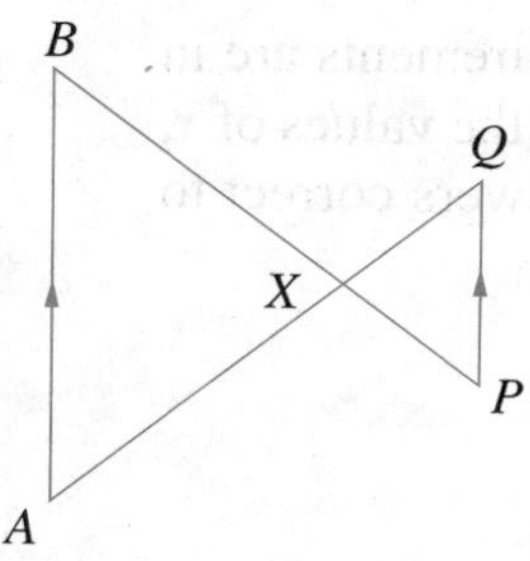

10. In the figure, if $XY \parallel MN$, $\frac{YZ}{MZ} = \frac{3}{4}$ and $XY = 5$ units, calculate NM.

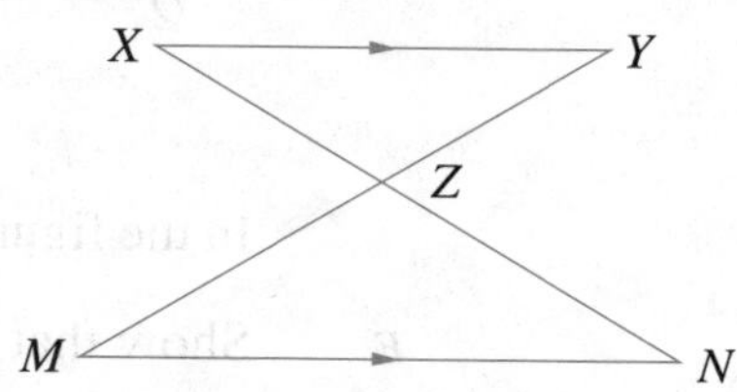

11. In the figure, $MN \parallel PQ$, $\frac{RM}{RP} = \frac{3}{8}$ and $PQ = 16$ units. Calculate MN.

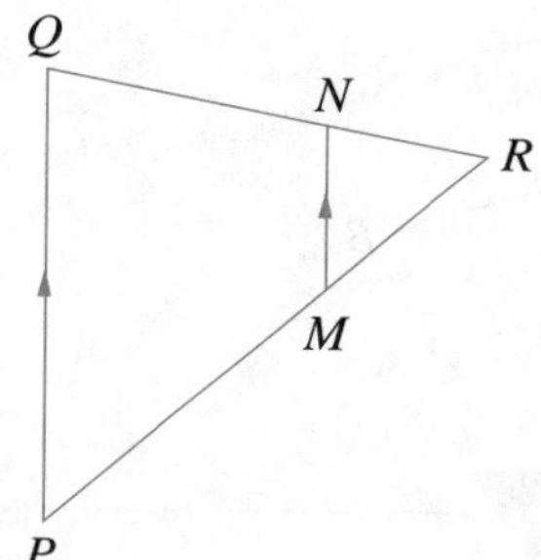

12. In the figure, if $XY \parallel BC$, $AX = 2$ units, $XB = 3$ units and $BC = 5$ units, calculate XY.

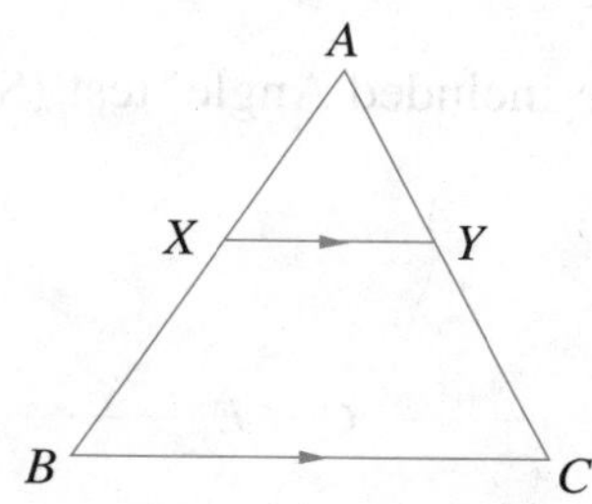

13. In the figure, all measurements are in centimetres.

(a) Explain why the figure contains two similar triangles.

(b) Write a correct statement of similarity and state the test used.

(c) Calculate AC, correct to 1 decimal place.

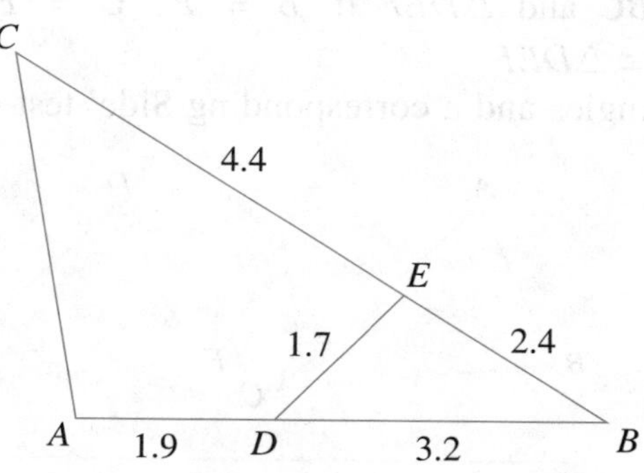

14. In the figure, all measurements are in centimetres. Calculate the values of x, y and z. Give your answers correct to 1 decimal place.

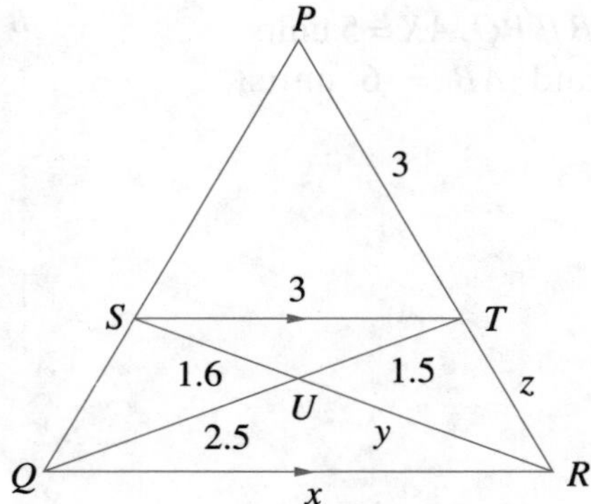

15. In the figure, $OE \parallel FB$ and $CD \parallel AB$.

Show that $\dfrac{ED}{FD} = \dfrac{OC}{AC}$.

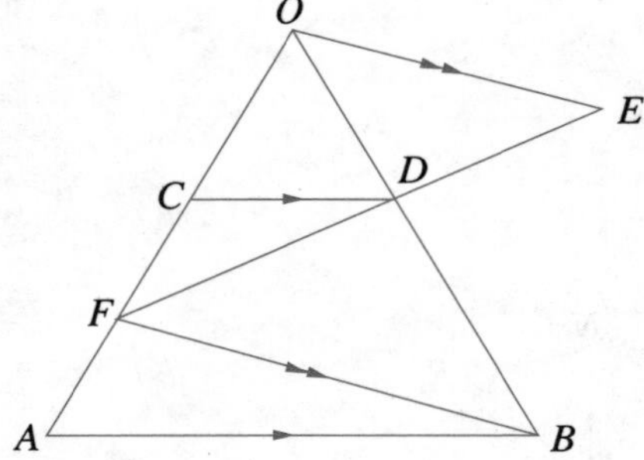

Chapter Review

1. In $\triangle ABC$ and $\triangle DEF$ if $AB = DE$, $\hat{B} = \hat{E}$ and $BC = EF$, then $\triangle ABC \equiv \triangle DEF$.
   'Two Sides and the included Angle' test (SAS)

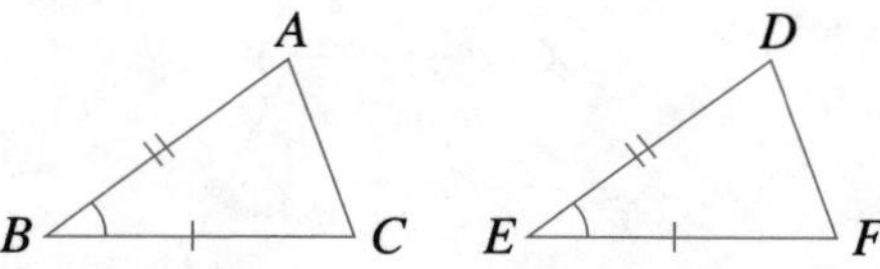

2. In $\triangle ABC$ and $\triangle DEF$ if $\hat{B} = \hat{E}$, $\hat{C} = \hat{F}$ and $BC = EF$, then $\triangle ABC \equiv \triangle DEF$.
   'Two Angles and a corresponding Side' test (AAS)

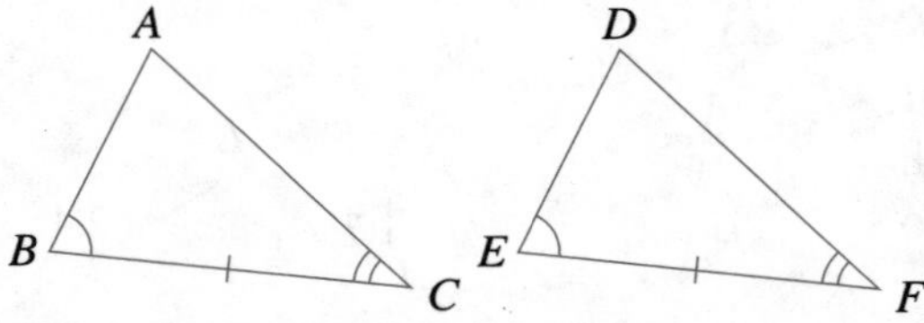

3. In $\triangle ABC$ and $\triangle DEF$ if $AB = DE$, $BC = EF$ and $CA = FD$, then $\triangle ABC \equiv \triangle DEF$.
'Side-Side-Side' test (SSS)

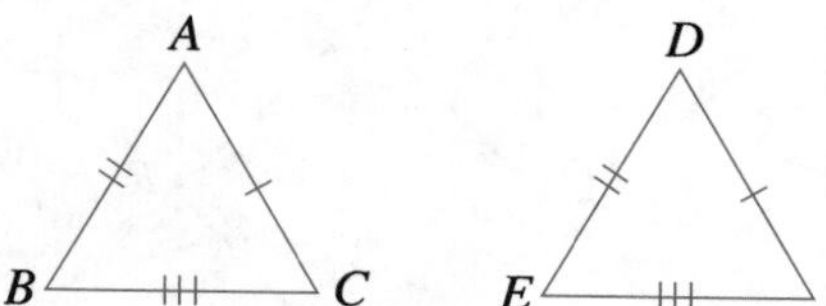

4. In $\triangle ABC$ and $\triangle DEF$ if $\hat{B} = \hat{E} = 90°$, $AB = DE$ and $AC = DF$, then $\triangle ABC \equiv \triangle DEF$.
'Right angle Hypotenuse and Side' test (RHS)

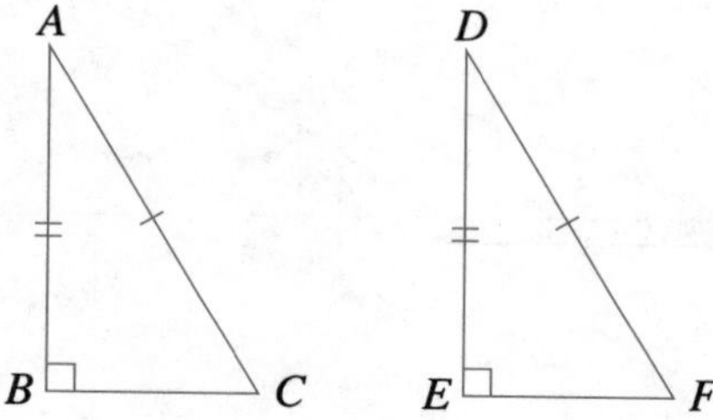

5. In $\triangle XYZ$ and $\triangle ABC$ if **(a)** $\hat{X} = \hat{A}$ and $\hat{Y} = \hat{B}$ or **(b)** $\frac{XY}{AB} = \frac{YZ}{BC} = \frac{ZX}{CA}$ or **(c)** $\frac{XY}{AB} = \frac{ZX}{CA}$ and $\hat{X} = \hat{A}$, then $\triangle XYZ$ and $\triangle ABC$ are similar.

Examples:

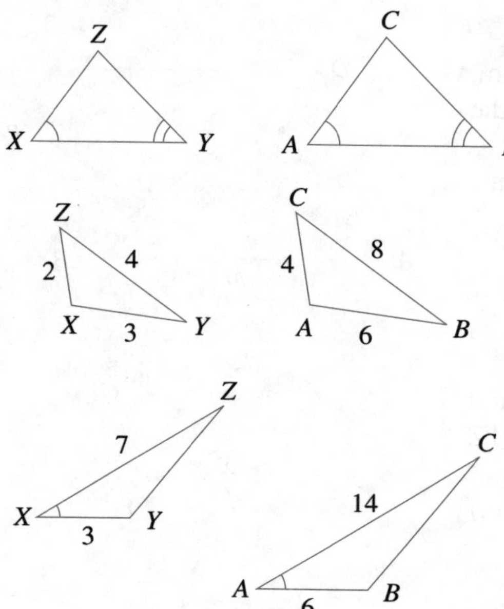

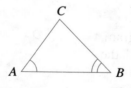

CHALLENGER 8

1. In the figure, $PRCQ$ is a parallelogram. Show that $AQ : QC = CR : RB$.

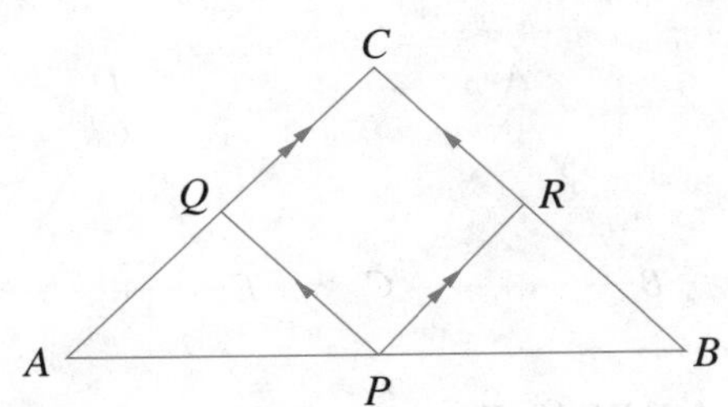

2. Find x in terms of y.

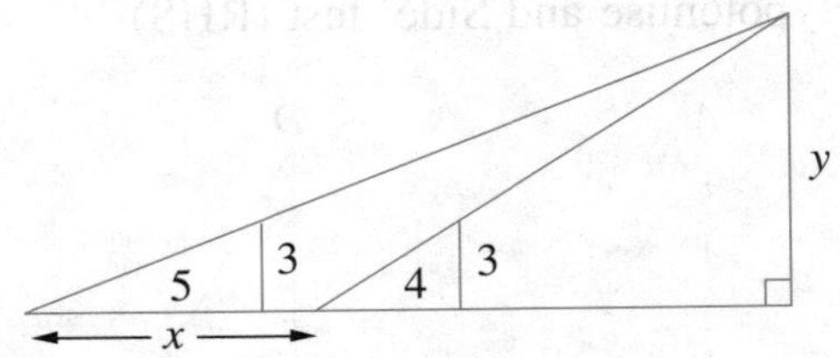

3. In the figure, $AM = MB$, $B\hat{C}N = A\hat{C}N$ and $A\hat{N}C = 90°$. Show that $BCNM$ is a trapezium.
(*Hint:* Make a suitable construction.)

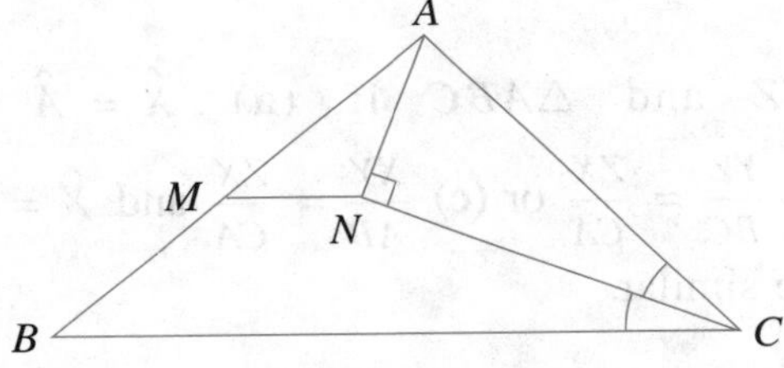

4. In the figure, $ABCD$ is a parallelogram. $AM = MB$ and $BP = 2PC$. Find the ratio $BQ : QD$.
(*Hint:* Make a suitable construction.)

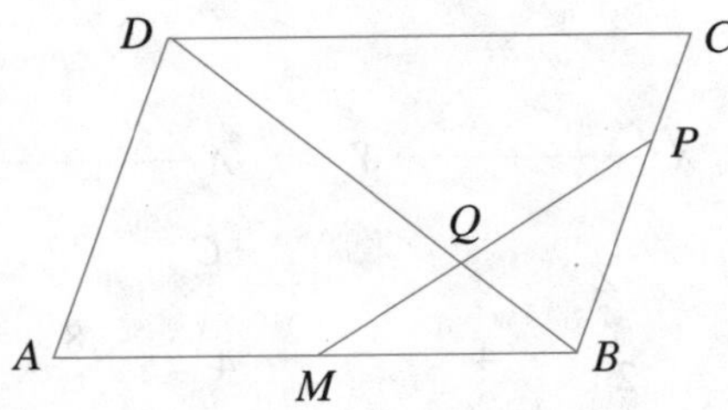

5. In the figure, XYZ is a straight line and $CX : XY = CA : AB$. Show that $\triangle BYZ$ is an isosceles triangle.
(*Hint:* Make a suitable construction.)

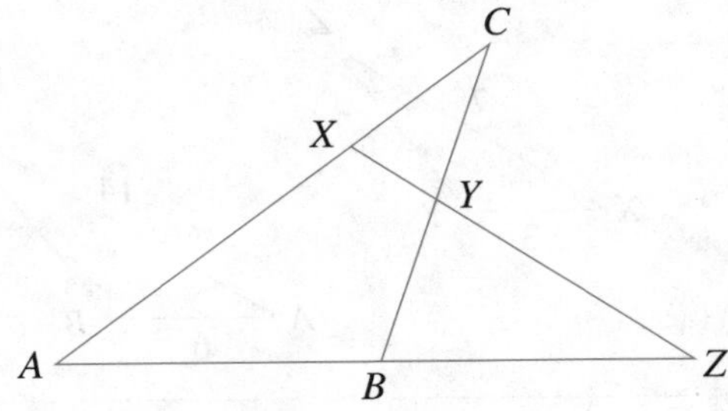

6. In the figure, $ABCD$ is a square. $E\hat{A}D = E\hat{D}A = 15°$. Show that $\triangle BCE$ is an equilateral triangle. (*Hint:* Consider the converse of the problem.)

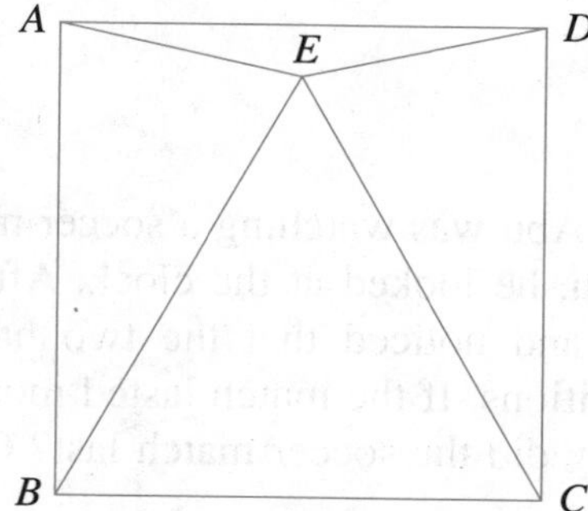

Problem Solving 8

Visiting the Supermarket

On his way to the supermarket shortly after 6.00 p.m., a boy observed that the hands of his watch formed an angle of 110°. On returning home before 7.00 p.m., he noted that the hands of his watch again formed an angle of 110°. For how long had he been away?

The strategies to use are **use a diagram** and **use an equation**.

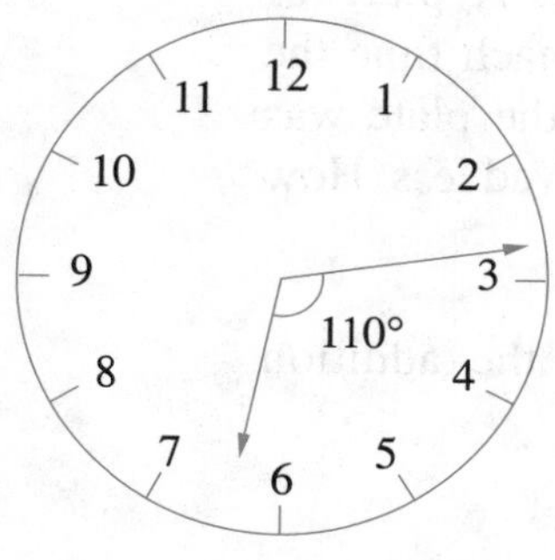

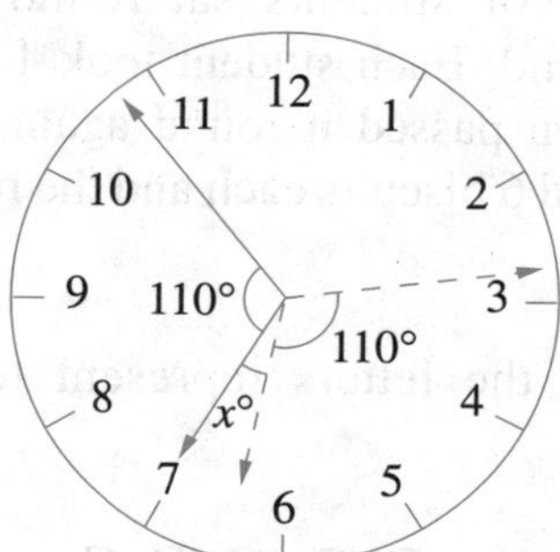

Suppose the hour hand turns $x°$.
Then the minute hand turns $110° + x° + 110°$ i.e. $220° + x°$.
But the minute hand turns 12 times as fast as the hour hand.

So $\dfrac{220 + x}{x} = \dfrac{12}{1}$

$\therefore x = 20$

The hour hand turns 30° in 1 h.
It turns 20° in 40 min.
So the boy had been away for 40 min.

1. **Watching TV** Abu was watching a soccer match on the TV. Before the start of the match, he looked at the clock. After the match, he looked at the clock again and noticed that the two hands on the clockface just interchanged positions. If the match lasted more than 1 hour but less than 2 hours, how long did the soccer match last? Give your answer correct to the nearest minute.

2. **Cubes and Squares**
   (a) Copy and complete the following two sets of calculations.

1	$=$	1^3	$=$
$1 + 2$	$=$	$1^3 + 2^3$	$=$
$1 + 2 + 3$	$=$	$1^3 + 2^3 + 3^3$	$=$
$1 + 2 + 3 + 4$	$=$	$1^3 + 2^3 + 3^3 + 4^3$	$=$

   (b) How are the two sets of results related?
   (c) Find the value of

$$1^3 + 2^3 + 3^3 + 4^3 + 5^3 + 6^3 + 7^3 + 8^3 + 9^3.$$

   (d) Given that the sum of the first 25 numbers, $1 + 2 + 3 + \ldots\ldots + 25$, is 325, find the value of

$$1^3 + 2^3 + 3^3 + \ldots\ldots + 25^3. \qquad (C)$$

3. **Round Table** A group of students sat round a table. A plate of 50 biscuits was passed round. Each student took 1 biscuit each time the plate came to him and then passed it round again. When the plate was empty, the majority received 6 biscuits each and the rest received less. How many students were there?

4. **Cross-roads** What do the letters represent to make the addition correct?

$$\begin{array}{r} CROSS \\ +\ ROADS \\ \hline DANGER \\ \hline \end{array}$$

Rule: The same letter represents the same digit. Different letters represent different digits.

REVISION EXERCISE 2

Revision 2A *(answers on p. 435)*

1. Solve the following equations.

   (a) $3x + 4y = 3$
   $x + 4y = 6$

   (b) $5x + 2y = 7$
   $15x + 6y = 8$

2. I think of two numbers. Twice the first number plus three times the second is 42. Three times the first minus twice the second is 24. Find the two numbers.

3. Solve the following inequalities.

   (a) $5 - 7x \leqslant -18$ **(b)** $3(x - 3) < 4(2x + 3)$

4. Use your geometrical instruments to copy the following figures and for each, construct a similar figure according to the given scale factor.

   (a)

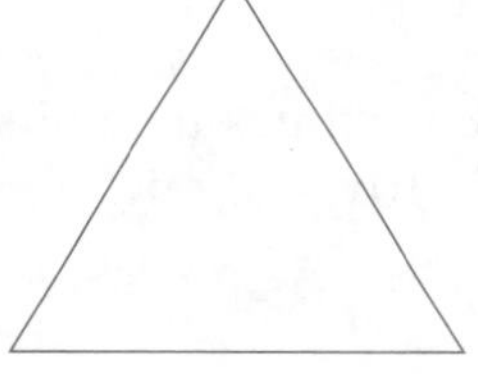

Scale factor 2

   (b)

Scale factor $\frac{5}{2}$

5. Ali bought a watch and 7 identical pens for \$200. The watch cost \$50 more than 5 pens. How much did he pay for the watch?

6. Using suitable scales, plot the graph of $y = 2x^2 + x - 5$.

   (a) Find y when $x = 1.5$. **(b)** Find x when $y = 11.5$.

7. A man bought some oranges at 20 cents each. He found that more than 15.6% were bad and he threw them away. He sold the remaining oranges at 35 cents each, thus making a profit of exactly \$19. How many oranges were bad?

8. In $\triangle ABC$, $DE \parallel BC$.

   (a) If $AB = 6$ cm, $AE = 2$ cm and $AC = 9$ cm, find AD.
   (b) If $AB = 12$ cm, $AD = 5$ cm and $DE = 4$ cm, find BC.
   (c) If $AC = 14$ cm, $AE = 5$ cm and $BC = 9$ cm, find DE.
   (d) If $AC = 15$ cm, $AE = 7$ cm and $AD = 6$ cm, find DB.
   (e) If $AB = 16$ cm, $DB = 6$ cm and $AC = 18$ cm, find AE.
   (f) If $AB = 18$ cm, $BC = 14$ cm and $DB = 4$ cm, find DE.

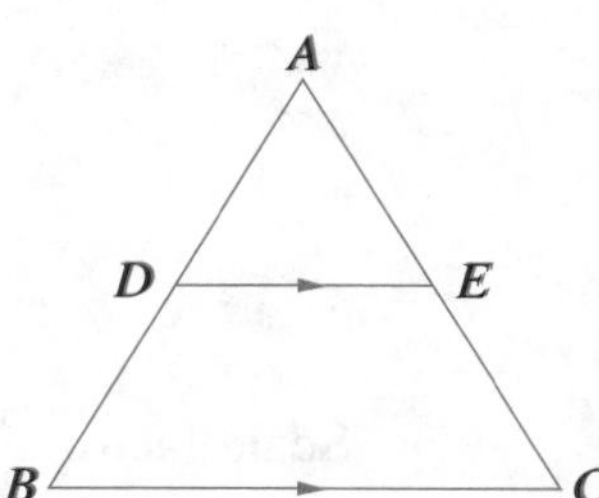

9. Draw the graph of each of the following equations using two ordered pairs of your choice. On your graphs,

(a) find the value of x in each case when $y = 8$,

(i) $y = \frac{3}{4}(1 - 5x)$ **(ii)** $4y - 7x - 25 = 0$

(b) find the ordered pair (x, y) satisfying both the equations in (a).

10. A packet of 120 g of tea contains about 26 teaspoonfuls. If Mary uses 5 teaspoonfuls a day for making tea for her family, for about how many days will a packet of 400 g of tea last?

Revision 2B *(answers on p. 435)*

1. Solve the following equations.

(a) $x + 2y = 12$
$2x + y = 16$

(b) $3x + 2y = 2$
$6x - 4y = 20$

2. In a two-digit number, the units digit is three times the tens digit. Four times the units digit is 3 less than the given number. Find the number. (*Hint:* The number is $10x + y$.)

3. If $\hat{A} = \hat{P}$, $AB = 3$ units, $AC = 4$ units, $BC = 2$ units, $PQ = 6$ units and $PR = 8$ units, calculate QR.

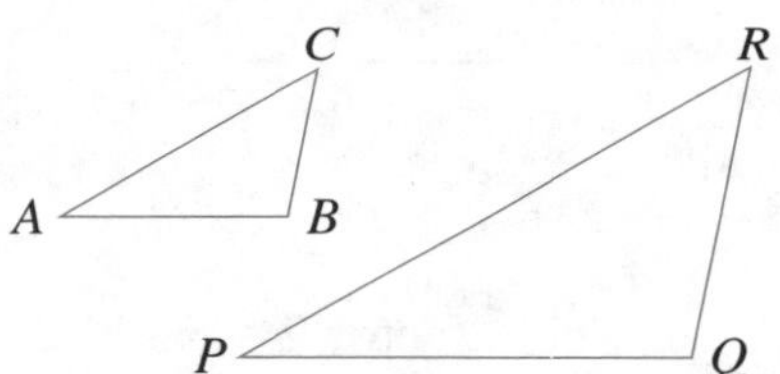

4. Solve the following inequalities.

(a) $x + \frac{11}{5} \geqslant \frac{22}{15}$ **(b)** $4x - 2 > 5 - 3x$

5. Use your geometrical instruments to copy the following figures and for each, construct a similar figure according to the given scale factor.

(a)

Scale factor $\frac{3}{2}$

(b)

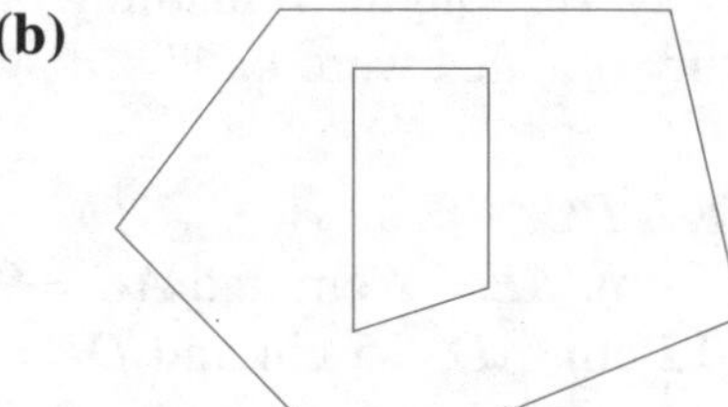

Scale factor $\frac{1}{2}$

6. Using suitable scales, plot the graph of $y = x^2 - 10x + 9$.
(a) Find y when $x = 1.5$.
(b) Find x when $y = 10.5$.

7. Three years ago, a man was 5 times as old as his son, but in 2 years time, he will be only 3 times as old as his son. How old is each of them?

8. A new machine costing \$8 000 depreciates (i.e. decreases) by 20% of its original value during the first year. During the second year, it depreciates by 15% of its value at the beginning of that year. Find the value of the machine at the end of the second year.

9. Mingfa bought 150 ballpoint pens for \$348 and he sold x of them at \$2.90 each and the rest at a discount of 50%. If he made a profit of $12\frac{1}{2}\%$ on the whole, find the value of x.

10. **(a)** Ali drives for x km at an average speed of 60 km/h. He returns by a different route, which is 5 km shorter, at an average speed of 50 km/h. The total time for both journeys is 1 hour 33 minutes.
(i) Form an equation in x and show that it reduces to $\frac{x}{6} + \frac{x-5}{5} = \frac{31}{2}$.
(ii) Solve the equation in part (a) to find the value of x.
(b) If $u + v = m$ and $\frac{1}{u} + \frac{1}{v} = \frac{1}{f}$, find a formula m in terms of u and f.

Revision 2C *(answers on p. 435)*

1. Solve graphically the following equations.
(a) $4x + 3y = 12$
$14x + 8y = 37$
(b) $4x + 5y = 6$
$12x + 5y = -2$

2. A two-digit number is four times the sum of its digits. If 27 is added to the number, the digits will be reversed. Find the number.

3. Figure $ABCD$ is a parallelogram.
Copy and complete the following.
(a) $\triangle ABD \equiv \triangle$ ______
(b) $\triangle AOB \equiv \triangle$ ______
(c) $\triangle ADC \equiv \triangle$ ______
(d) $\triangle AOD \equiv \triangle$ ______

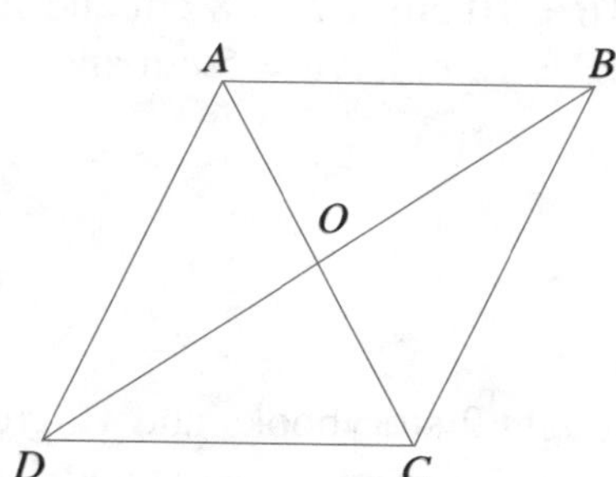

4. 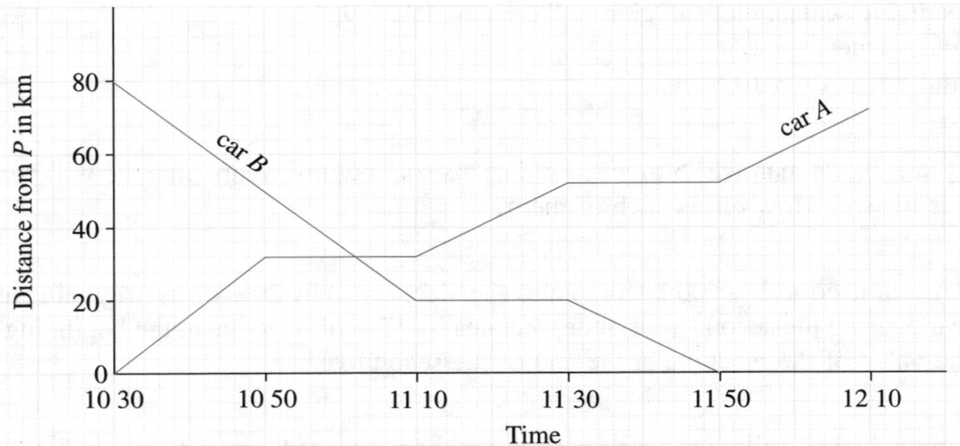

The graph shows car A travelling from point P to point Q. Car B travels from Q by the same route to P.

(a) What is the total distance travelled by car A?
(b) What is the average speed of car A for the whole journey?
(c) How long does car B take to complete its journey?
(d) What is the average speed of car B for the whole journey?
(e) When and where does car B stop and for how long?
(f) Where and when do the two cars pass each other?
(g) During which periods of time does car A travel at the same speed?

5. Solve the following inequalities.

(a) $10x + 12 \leqslant -13$ **(b)** $-\frac{1}{2}(2x - 3) \geqslant \frac{1}{3}(x + 2)$

6. Susan and her sister shared some money in the ratio $x : y$. Susan received \$45 more than her sister. If the amount to be shared was \$315, find the ratio $x : y$ in its simplest form.

7. In the figure, $EF \parallel AC$ and $FG \parallel BD$.
(a) If $AE = 3$ cm, $EB = 4$ cm and $CG = 5$ cm, find GD.
(b) If $AE = 5$ cm, $EB = 3$ cm and $GD = 5$ cm, find CG.
(c) If $AB = 10$ cm, $CD = 8$ cm and $EB = 3$ cm, find GD.
(d) If $AB = 12$ cm, $AE = 5$ cm and $CD = 16$ cm, find GD.

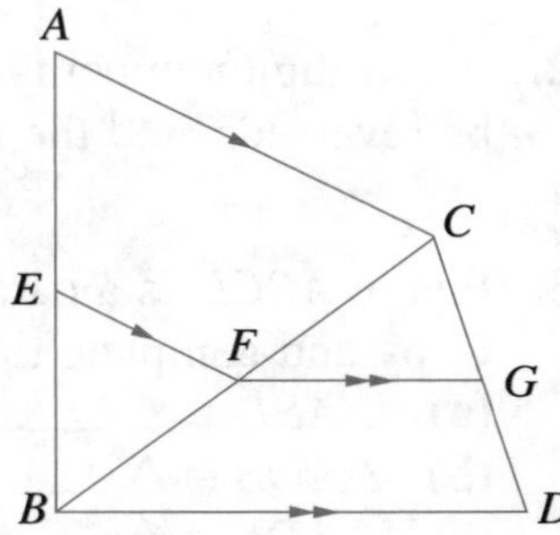

8. Henry bought 2 storybooks and 10 greeting cards for \$24. Paying the same price for each item, Peter bought 20 greeting cards and 1 storybook for \$27. Find the price for each item.

9. **(a)** Copy and complete the table of values for $y = x^2 - 2x$ given below.

x	1	2	3	4	5	6	7
y	−1		3	8	15		35

(b) Using 2 cm along the x-axis to represent 1 unit and 2 cm along the y-axis to represent 5 units, draw the graph of $y = x^2 - 2x$ and use it to answer the questions in (c) and (d).
(c) Find the value of y when $x = 5.2$.
(d) Find the value of x when $y = 31$.

10.

> **Health-Care Eating House**
>
> 10% off all vegetarian dishes
>
> Free rice and tea

GST at 3% is to be added after the discount (if applicable) has been deducted from the list price on the menu.
(a) How much must a customer pay if he has ordered 3 vegetarian dishes costing \$8 each and 2 non-vegetarian dishes costing \$12 each.
(b) If the GST is added by mistake before the discount is given, will the customer have to pay more or less? Give reason for your answer.

Revision 2D *(answers on p. 435)*

1. Solve the following equations.

(a) $7x + 3y = 40$
$5x + 6y = 26$

(b) $5y + 3x = -10$
$-5x + 2y = 9$

2. If the numerator and the denominator of a fraction are each increased by 2, the fraction becomes $\frac{5}{6}$ and if the numerator and the denominator are each decreased by 1, the fraction becomes $\frac{4}{5}$. Find the fraction.

3. In each of the following figures, AOD and BOC are straight lines. Name a pair of similar triangles, if any.

(a)

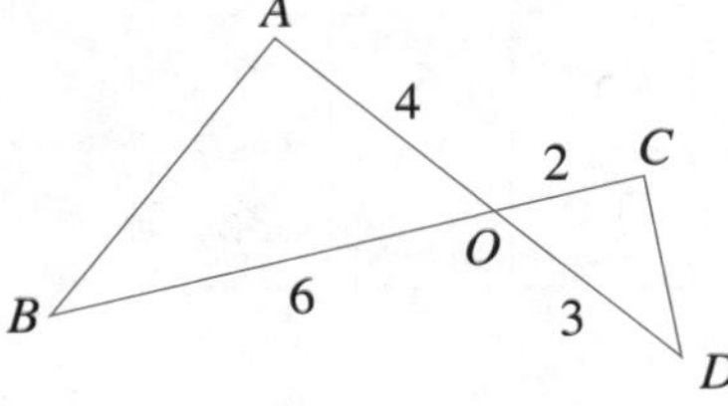

(b)

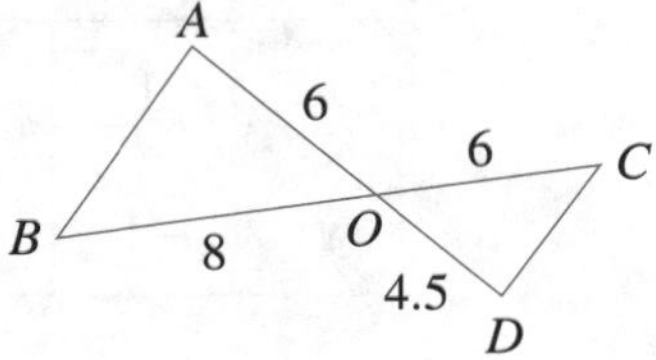

(c)

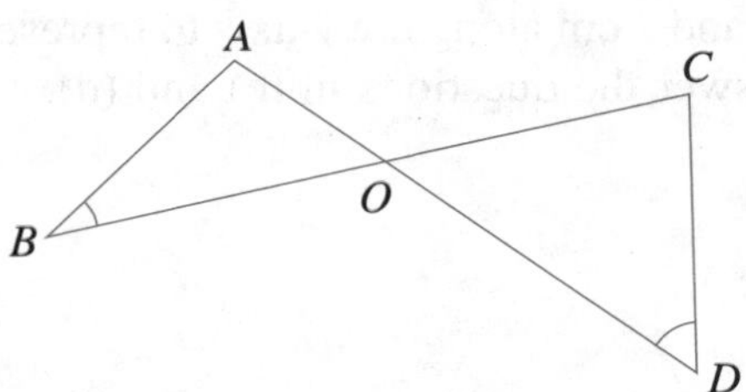

(d)

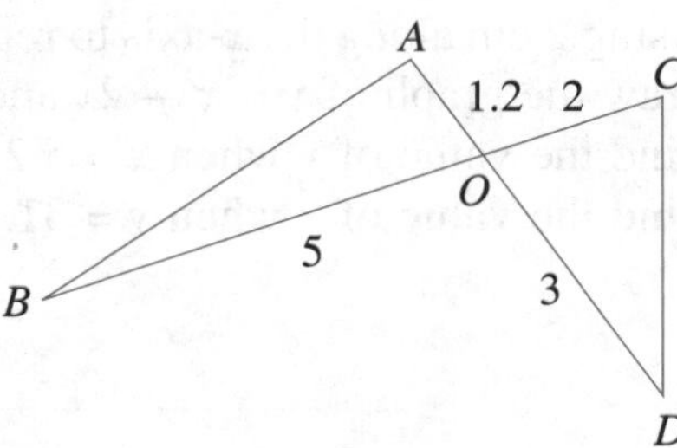

(e)

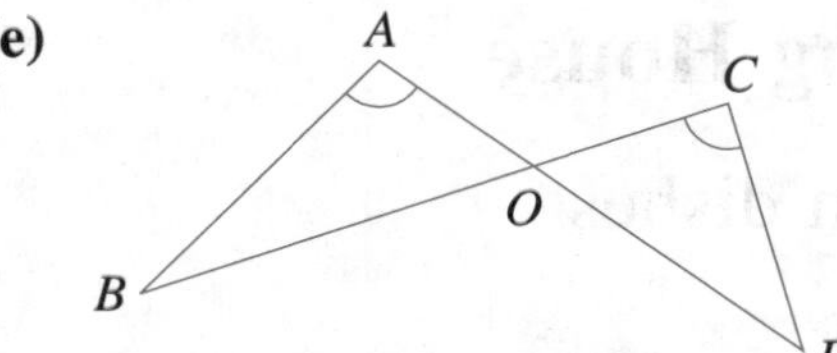

(f)

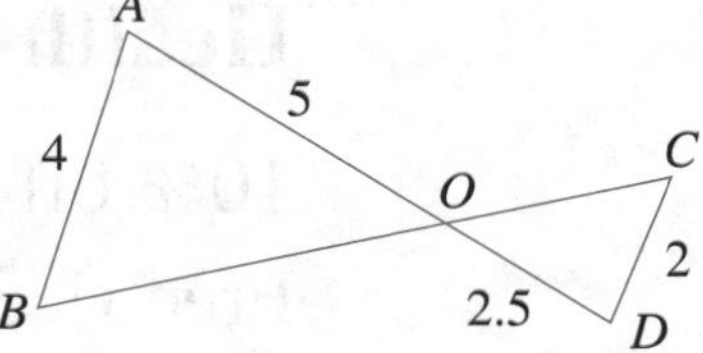

4. Solve the following inequalities.

(a) $x + \frac{3}{4} \leqslant \frac{7}{2}$ **(b)** $6x < -14$ **(c)** $5x - 2 > 6 - 3x$

5. Represent the set of values on a number line such that $x \geqslant -2$ and $x < 3$

(a) if x represents integers, **(b)** if x represents real numbers.

6. It takes $(20x + 17)$ minutes to cook x kg of green peas.

(a) Find the time it takes to cook 5 kg of such peas.

(b) If the peas are to be cooked by 13 30, find the time at which the cooking must start.

7.

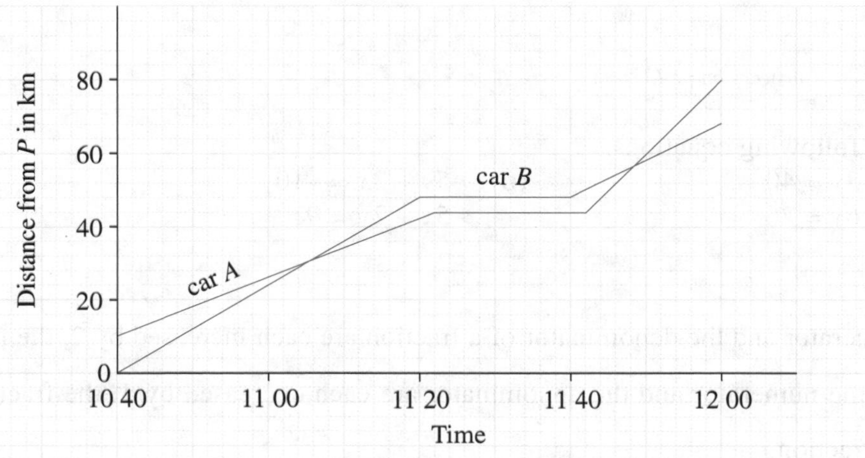

At 10 40, car B is at point P.

(a) What is the average speed of car A?
(b) What is the average speed of car B?
(c) When and where does car A overtake car B?
(d) When and where does car B overtake car A?

8. All 40 students in a class have at least 2 \$1 notes each, 29 students have at least 3 \$1 notes each, 21 students have at least 4 \$1 notes each and no student has more than 4 \$1 notes.

(a) How many students have exactly 3 \$1 notes each?
(b) How many \$1 notes are there among the 40 students?

9. It is given that 1 kg of sugar costs \$1.80.

(a) If x kg of sugar cost y dollars, write down the equation connecting x and y.
(b) Copy and complete the table:

x (kg)	0	
y (\$)		4.50

(c) Plot a straight line graph for the table with the following scale: 2 cm represents 1 kg along the x-axis and 1 cm represents \$1.00 along the y-axis. Use your graph to answer the questions in (d).
(d) Copy and complete. (Give your answers correct to the nearest 10 cents or 0.1 kg.)
(i) 2.6 kg of sugar cost \$ ______.
(ii) 7.2 kg of sugar cost \$ ______.
(iii) 5.8 kg of sugar cost \$ ______.
(iv) ______ kg of sugar cost \$10.10.
(v) ______ kg of sugar cost \$11.50.
(vi) ______ kg of sugar cost \$8.30.

10. A man is paid \$5.00 per hour for normal working hours. He is considered to have worked overtime if he works more than $7\frac{1}{2}$ hours on weekdays and more than $4\frac{1}{2}$ hours on Saturdays. The overtime rate is $1\frac{1}{2}$ times the normal rate. On Sundays, the man is paid double the normal rate. During a certain week, the man works the following number of hours:

Sun	Mon	Tue	Wed	Thur	Fri	Sat
4	10	10	9	10	$10\frac{1}{2}$	$7\frac{1}{2}$

If his deduction for CPF is 20% of his earnings, calculate his take-home pay for that week.

Revision 2E *(answers on p. 436)*

1. Solve the following equations.

(a) $3x + 4y = 4$
$6x + 8y = 9$

(b) $3x - 9y = -7$
$4y - x = 8$

2. Five years ago, Meiling was one-third as old as her mother. Ten years from now, her mother will be twice Meiling's age. How old are they now?

3. Solve the following inequalities.

(a) $x + \frac{1}{4} > -\frac{1}{3}$

(b) $4 - 4x \leqslant 5x + 6$

4. In $\triangle ABC$, $DE \parallel BC$.

(a) If $AE = 7$ cm, $EC = 4$ cm and $DB = 5$ cm, find AD.
(b) If $EC = 3$ cm, $AC = 9$ cm and $AD = 5$ cm, find DB.
(c) If $AD = 4$ cm, $DB = 5$ cm and $DE = 6$ cm, find BC.
(d) If $AD = 5$ cm, $DB = 4$ cm and $AC = 10$ cm, find EC.

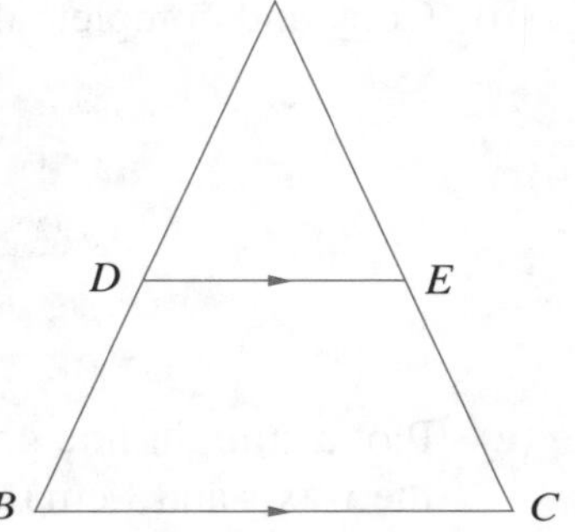

5. Cyclist X and cyclist Y are 50 km apart on the same stretch of road. They start their journey at the same time. If they travel in opposite directions, X will meet Y after 2 hours and if they travel in the same direction, X will catch up with Y after 5 hours. Find their speeds.

6. With \$7.00, I can buy either 15 ballpoint pens and 10 pencils or 50 pencils and 5 ballpoint pens. Find the price of each ballpoint pen and pencil.

7.

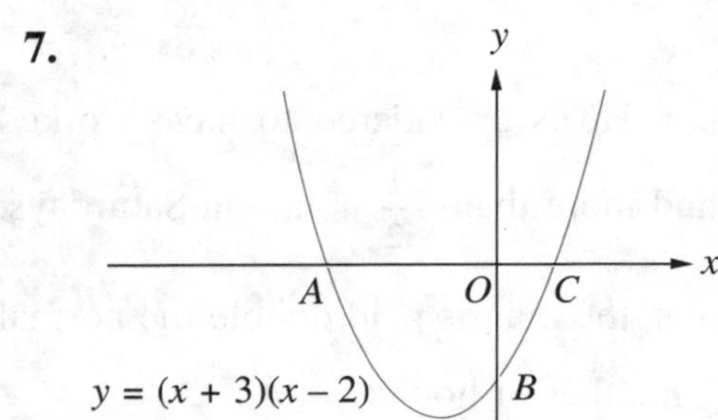

The curve $y = (x + 3)(x - 2)$ cuts the x-axis at the points A and C, and the y-axis at B.

(a) Write down the coordinates of the points A, B and C.
(b) Find the equation of the line of symmetry of the curve. *(C)*

8. **(a)** Copy and complete the table of values for $y = x^2 - 2x + 2$.

x	–3	–2	–1	0	1	2	3	4	5
y	17		5	2	1	2	5		17

(b) Using 2 cm along the x-axis to represent 1 unit and 1 cm along the y-axis to represent 1 unit, draw the graph of $y = x^2 - 2x + 2$.
(c) Find from your graph, the value of y when $x = 3.5$ and the value of x when $y = 12$.
(d) Does your graph have a line of symmetry?

9. A sales representative is given a choice of a basic monthly salary of \$500 plus 10% commission on sales, or \$1 000 plus 8% commission on sales.
(a) If he sells, on an average, \$20 000 worth of goods per month, calculate his monthly earnings under each scheme.
(b) If he sells x dollars per month, find the value of x for which his earnings under both schemes are the same.

10. A piece of elastic 12 cm long hangs from a nail N, as shown in diagram (i).
When a mass of m grams is attached to the lower end, the length of the elastic increases to L cm, as shown in diagram (ii).

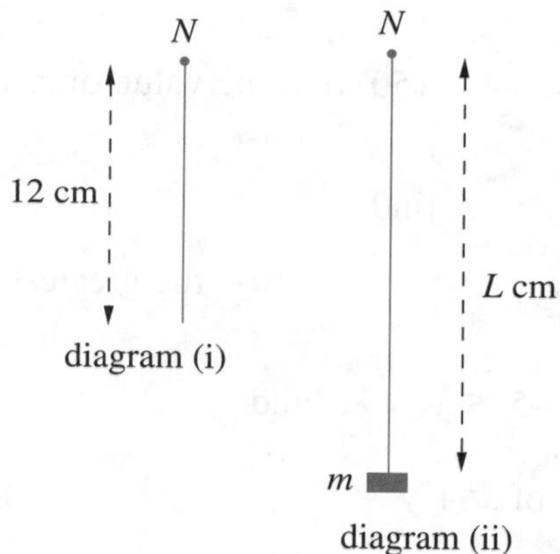

diagram (i)
diagram (ii)

For every 100 grams which is attached, the length of the elastic increases by 3 cm.
(a) Calculate the length of the piece of elastic when a mass of 700 grams is attached to it.
(b) If the length of the elastic is 48 cm, calculate the mass that is attached to it.
(c) Write down a formula connecting the length of the elastic, L cm, and the mass, m grams, which is attached to it.
(d) Use your formula to check your answers to parts (a) and (b). *(C)*

MISCELLANEOUS EXERCISE 2

(answers on p. 436)

1. State whether each of the following statements is true or false. Illustrate each answer with an example.

(a) If $x > 1$, then $x > x^2 > x^3 > x^4$.
(b) If $x < 1$, then $x < x^2 < x^3 < x^4$.
(c) If $x < 0$, then $x > x^2 > x^3 > x^4$.
(d) If $0 < x < 1$, then $x > x^2 > x^3 > x^4$.

2. **(a)** Express 0.72 as a fraction in its lowest terms.
(b) A number lies between 90 and 100. When it is divided by 7 there is a remainder of 5. What is the number?
(c) Find the largest prime number k for which $2k + 1 \leqslant 21$. *(C)*

3. If r is an integer such that $100 < \frac{r^3}{3} < 150$, find the value of r.

4. Given that $3 \leqslant x \leqslant 5$ and $5 \leqslant y \leqslant 7$, find

(a) the smallest value of $2x - y$, **(b)** the greatest value of $\frac{x}{y}$.

5. It is given that $3 \leqslant x \leqslant 11$ and $-5 \leqslant y \leqslant 8$. Find
(a) the largest possible value of $x - y$,
(b) the smallest possible value of $x^2 + y^2$.

6. A triangle ABC has sides of length

$$AB = 2x - 3y + 14,$$
$$BC = 5y - 4x,$$
$$CA = 4x - 6.$$

(a) In any triangle the sum of the lengths of any two sides is greater than the length of the third side. For example $AB + BC > CA$. Use this inequality to show that $3x - y - 10 < 0$.
(b) Deduce a second inequality involving x and y from the statement $CA + AB > BC$, simplifying your answer as far as possible.
(c) Using these inequalities, and given that $y = 5$, find the range of possible values of x. *(C)*

7. York is 110 km from Sheffield. A goods train leaves Sheffield at 10 00 and travels towards York at 40 km/h. After travelling 60 km the train stops for 45 minutes. The train completes the journey to York at 80 km/h.

(a) **(i)** Draw the distance-time graph for this journey. Use a scale of 4 cm to represent 1 hour for times from 10 00 to 14 00 on the horizontal axis. Use a scale of 2 cm to represent 10 km for distances from Sheffield from 0 km to 110 km on the vertical axis.
(ii) By adding another line to your graph find the time at which the train would have arrived in York if the whole journey had taken place at 40 km/h without stopping.

(b) A passenger train leaves York at 10 30 and travels at a constant speed to Sheffield, arriving at 12 15.

(i) On the same axes draw the distance-time graph for this journey.

(ii) Use your graph to find the distance from Sheffield at which the trains pass each other.

(C)

8. The diagram shows the graph of $y = x^2 - 4x$. The graph passes through the origin and crosses the x-axis again at the point A.

(a) Calculate the coordinates of A.

(b) **(i)** Write down the equation of the line of symmetry of the graph.

(ii) Find the coordinates of the lowest point on the graph.

(c) There is a point on the graph, other than the point (0, 0), where the x and y coordinates are equal. Find the coordinates of this other point.

(C)

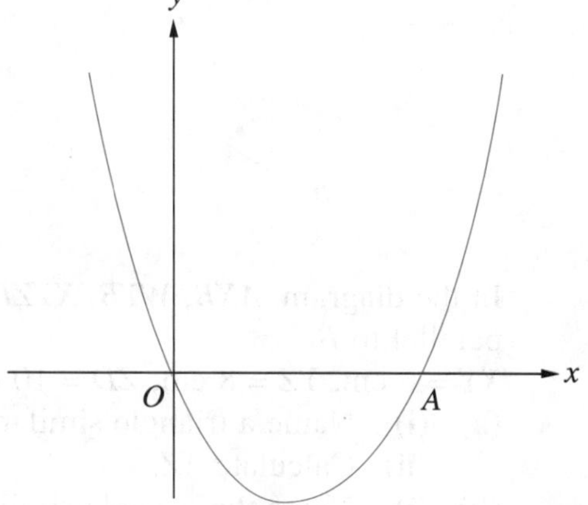

9. **(a)** Mary and Nancy went shopping together.

Apples	45¢ each
Oranges	50¢ each

(i) Mary bought some apples and oranges for \$6.70. This information can be expressed as

$$45x + 50y = 670.$$

What do the letters x and y stand for?

(ii) Nancy bought twice as many apples and half as many oranges as Mary for \$7.40. Write down an equation to represent this information.

(iii) Use the two equations in (a) and (b) to find the number of apples and the number of oranges bought by Mary.

(iv) Calculate the total number of fruits bought by Nancy.

(b) If $a = \dfrac{b-1}{b+2}$ and $b = \dfrac{2c+3}{3c-2}$, express a in terms of c and reduce the expression to its simplest form. (*Hint:* Express b in terms of a first.)

10. **(a)** John and his sister, Mary, are at the stadium to practise running. If John starts 2 seconds later than Mary, he will take 8 seconds to catch up with her. If John starts to run only when Mary is 8 metres ahead of him, he will take 5 seconds to catch up with her. If John's speed is x m/s and Mary's speed is y m/s, form two equations in x and y and solve them to find the value of x and of y.

(b) If each of p men is paid m dollars for x hours of work and each of q men is paid n dollars for y hours of work, find the average payment per man per hour, in terms of p, q, m, n, x and y.

11.

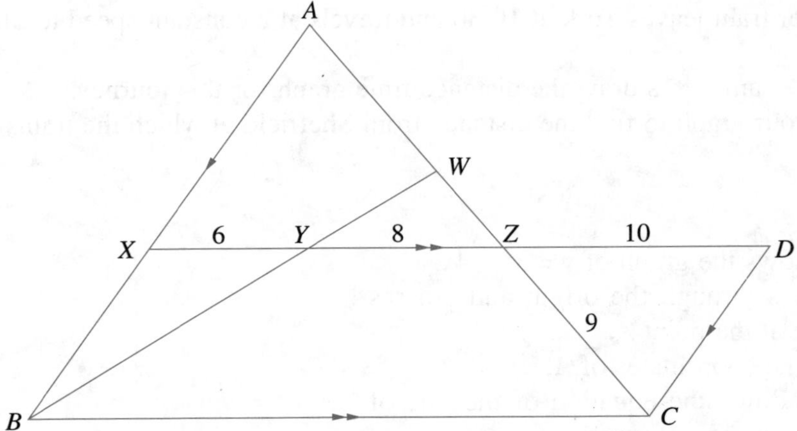

In the diagram, *AXB*, *WYB*, *XYZD* and *AWZC* are straight lines. *AB* is parallel to *DC* and *XD* is parallel to *BC*.
$XY = 6$ cm, $YZ = 8$ cm, $ZD = 10$ cm and $ZC = 9$ cm.

(a) **(i)** Name a triangle similar to triangle *ZDC*.
(ii) Calculate *AZ*.

(b) **(i)** Name the triangle similar to triangle *WYZ*.
(ii) Calculate *WZ*. (*C*)

12. In the figure, $\triangle ABC$ and $\triangle CDE$ are equilateral triangles. Explain why *AE* is equal to *BD*.

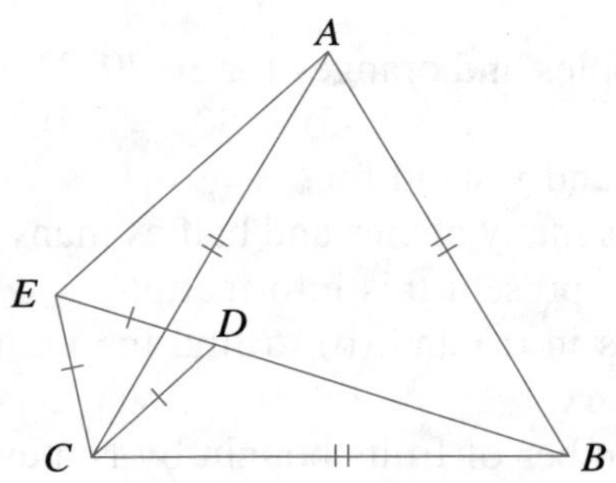

13. In the figure, $AB = AC$ and $AD = AE$. Explain why *BD* is equal to *CE*.

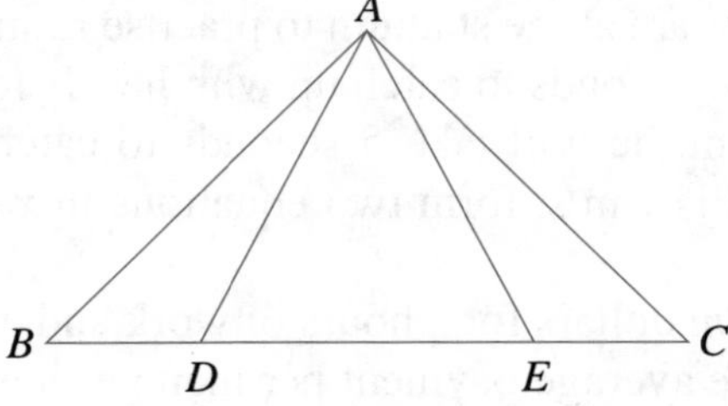

14. In the figure, $AD = BD$ and $A\hat{E}B = A\hat{D}B = 90°$. Show that $CD = HD$.

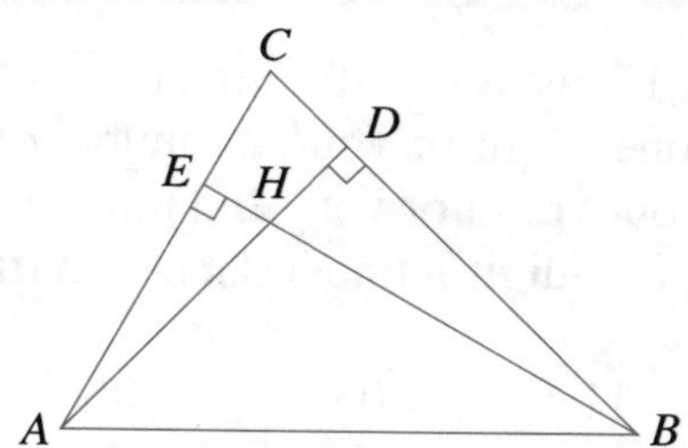

15. In the figure, $AQ = BQ$, $A\hat{N}B = A\hat{R}P = 90°$. Show that $SN = SR$.

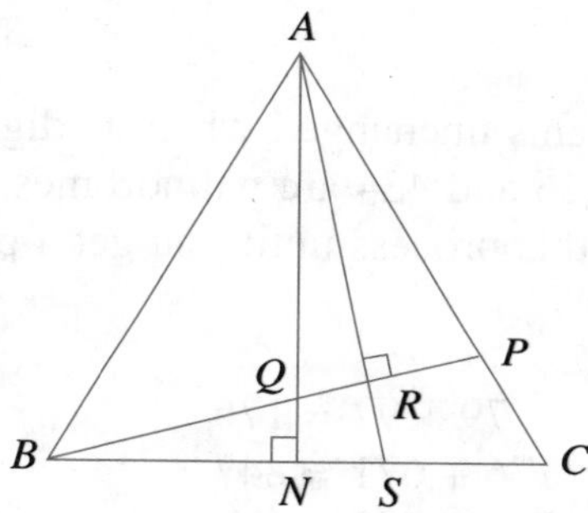

INVESTIGATION 2

1. Take any two-digit number, say 17, as your 1st number.
Add the tens digit to twice the ones digit of your 1st number to get your 2nd number.
Add the 'tens digit' to twice the ones digit of your 2nd number to get your 3rd number and so on.
When the resulting number is a one-digit number such as 3, treat it as 03, etc.

For example, 17, 15 , 11 , 03 , 06 , ...

	15	11	03	06
	↑	↑	↑	↑
	1 + 2(7)	1 + 2(5)	1 + 2(1)	0 + 2(3)

Investigate using other numbers and describe your observations.

2. A number is a palindrome if it remains unchanged when its digits are arranged in the reversed order, for example: 1 247 421, 62 826 and 434 are palindromes. Take a 2-digit number, say 79. Reverse the digits and add. Repeat this process until you get a palindrome.

Example:

79 + 97 = 176
176 + 671 = 847
847 + 748 = 1 595
1 595 + 5 951 = 7 546
7 546 + 6 457 = 14 003
14 003 + 30 041 = 44 044 (stop)

(a) Take another 2-digit number, say 78.
Reverse the digits and add. Repeat the process.
Do you get a palindrome?
If so, what is the palindrome you get?
(b) Investigate for other 2-digit numbers.
(c) If you start with 98, will you get a palindrome? If so, what is it?

3. Start with a list of the first ten prime numbers and form a second list by taking the difference between each pair of adjacent numbers listed. Repeat this to form the third list and so on.

2 3 5 7 11 13 17 19 23 29
1 2 2 4 2 4 2 4 6
1 0 2 2 2 2 2 2

(a) Complete the triangular pattern. What number does the pattern end with?
(b) Repeat (a) by starting with a list of the first fifteen prime numbers. Describe your observation.
(c) Will you get the same result if you start with the first twenty prime numbers? Investigate.

4. Lines joining pairs of points which are not adjacent to each other are called diagonals of a polygon. For example, AC, AD, BE, BD and CE are diagonals of the polygon $ABCDE$.

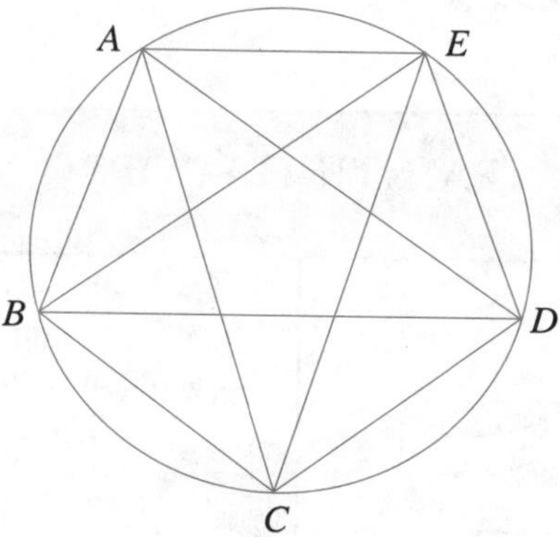

(a) Copy and complete the table below.

No. of points on the circle	No. of sides of a polygon	No. of diagonals
5	5	5
6		
7		
8		
9		
10		

(b) What pattern do you observe?

(c) Is there a relationship between the number of diagonals and the number of sides of a polygon? Write down an expression for the number of diagonals of a polygon with n sides?

Chapter 9

Mensuration

Chapter Highlights

- Expressing arc length as fraction of circumference, including finding arc length
- Expressing sector area as fraction of area of circle, including finding sector area
- Solving problems involving arc length and sector area
- Recognising that volume of a cone or pyramid is one-third the product of base area and height
- Finding the volume and surface area of a pyramid or cone
- Solving problems involving volume and surface area of a pyramid and cone
- Finding the volume and surface area of a sphere
- Solving problems involving volume and surface area of a sphere and cone
- Using the relationships between areas of similar figures
- Using the relationships between volumes of similar solids

9.1 SECTORS

Fig. 9.1 shows a circle with centre O. The shaded region is called a **sector** of the circle. It is bounded by the **minor arc** APB and the radii OA and OB. We refer to this as a **minor sector** of the circle. The unshaded region bounded by the **major arc** AQB and the radii OA and OB is referred to as a **major sector** of the circle.

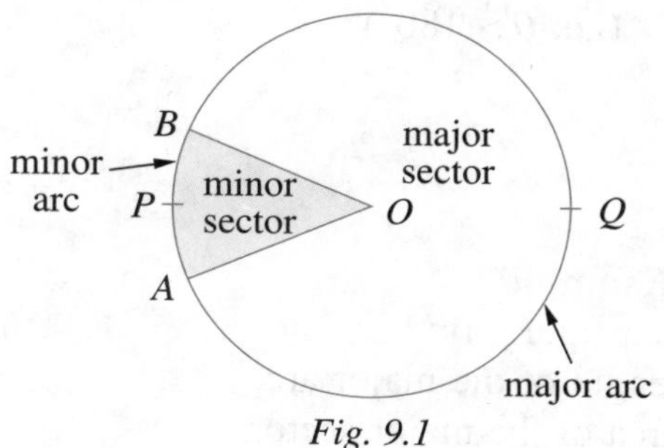

Fig. 9.1

Examples

(a) Consider the sector $OAPB$ in Fig. 9.2.

The area of sector $OAPB = \frac{1}{6}$ the area of the circle.

The length of arc $APB = \frac{1}{6}$ of the circumference.

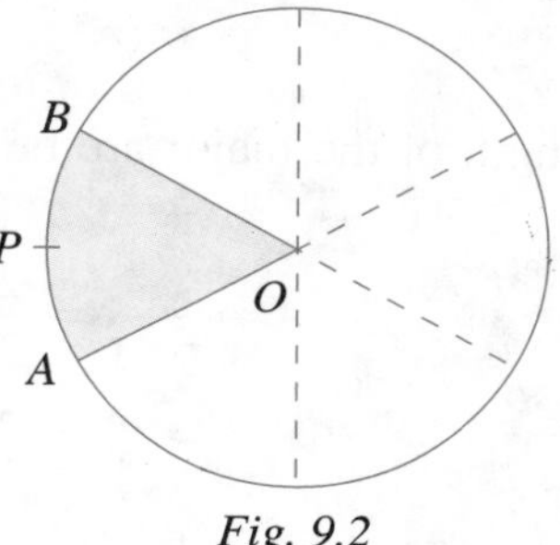

Fig. 9.2

(b) Consider the sector $OAPB$ in Fig. 9.3. The arc APB **subtends** an angle of 37° at the centre of the circle. The length of the arc is 37 of 360 equal parts of the circumference.

Thus length of arc $APB = \frac{37}{360} \times$ circumference

or $\frac{\text{length of arc } APB}{\text{circumference}} = \frac{37}{360}$.

Also area of sector $OAPB = \frac{37}{360} \times$ area of circle

or $\frac{\text{area of sector}}{\text{area of circle}} = \frac{37}{360}$.

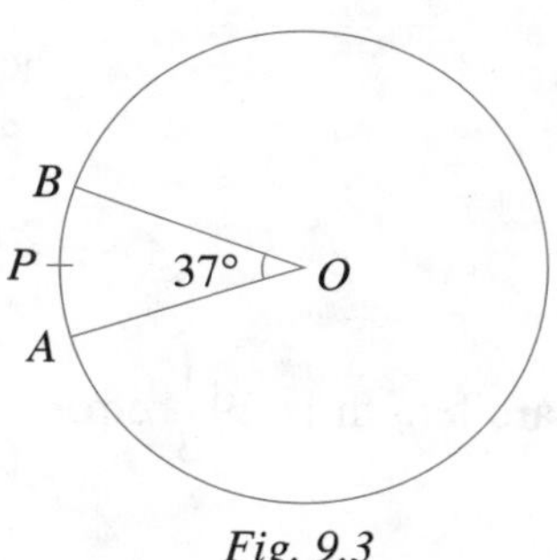

Fig. 9.3

In general, we have:

- $\dfrac{\textbf{Length of Arc}}{2\pi r} = \dfrac{\theta}{360}$
- $\dfrac{\textbf{Area of Sector}}{\pi r^2} = \dfrac{\theta}{360}$

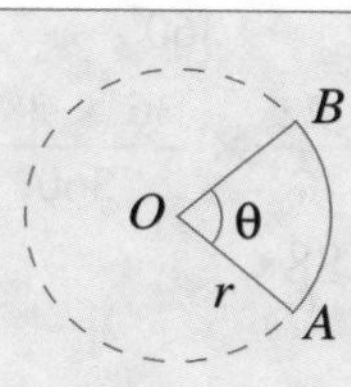

Note: 1. The Greek letter θ is read as theta.
2. We can also use these formulae if OAB is a major sector (i.e. $\theta > 180°$).

Worked Example 1

In the given figure, find

(a) the length of the major arc,

(b) the area of the major sector.

$\left(\text{Take } \pi = \frac{22}{7}.\right)$

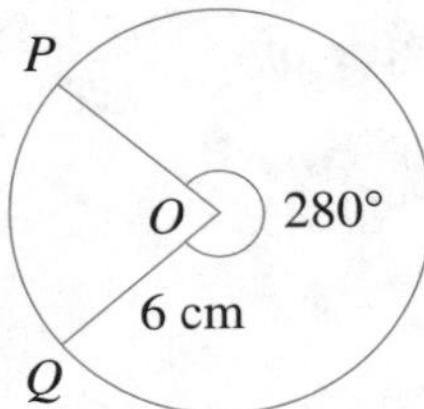

Solution:

(a) Let the length of the major arc be x cm.

You may take $\pi \approx 3$ to estimate x first. So $x \approx \frac{2 \times 3 \times 6 \times 280}{360} = 28$

$$\frac{x}{2\pi(6)} = \frac{280}{360}$$

$$\therefore x = \frac{2\pi(6) \times 280}{360}$$

$$= 2 \times \frac{22}{7} \times \frac{6 \times 280}{360}$$

$$= \frac{88}{3}$$

$$= 29\frac{1}{3}$$

Thus the arc length is $29\frac{1}{3}$ cm.

(b) Let the area of the major sector be y cm^2.

Can you find y mentally?

$$\frac{y}{\pi(6)^2} = \frac{280}{360}$$

$$\therefore y = \frac{\pi(6)^2 \times 280}{360}$$

$$= \frac{22}{7} \times \frac{36 \times 280}{360}$$

$$= 88$$

Thus the area is 88 cm^2.

Worked Example 2

In the figure, $A\hat{O}B = 75°$. Find

(a) the perimeter of the minor sector if the radius OA is 3 cm,

(b) the radius if the area of the minor sector is 24 cm^2.

Take π to be $\frac{22}{7}$ and give your answers correct to the nearest centimetre.

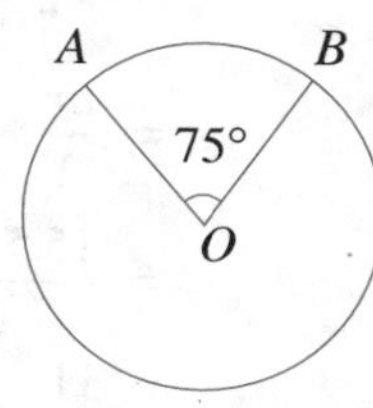

Solution:

(a) Let the length of the minor arc AB be x cm.

$$\frac{x}{2\pi(3)} = \frac{75}{360}$$

$$\therefore x = \frac{75}{360} \times 2\pi(3)$$

$$= \frac{5}{4}\pi$$

Thus the perimeter $= \left(\frac{5}{4}\pi + 3 + 3\right)$ cm

$= \left(\frac{5}{4}\pi + 6\right)$ cm or 10 cm, correct to the nearest cm.

(b) Let the radius be r cm.

$$\frac{\pi r^2}{24} = \frac{360}{75}$$

$$r^2 = \frac{24 \times 360}{75\pi}$$

$$\therefore r \approx 6.05$$

Thus the radius is 6 cm, correct to the nearest cm.

Worked Example 3

The figure shows a sector of a circle with arc length a cm and radius r cm. Find the area of the sector of the circle if $a = 15.5$ and $r = 4$.

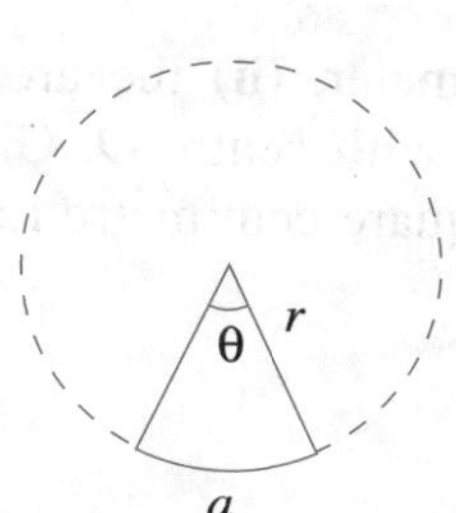

Solution:

Let the area be A cm^2.

We have $$\frac{a}{2\pi r} = \frac{\theta}{360}$$

$$\frac{A}{\pi r^2} = \frac{\theta}{360}$$

Then $$\frac{a}{2\pi r} = \frac{A}{\pi r^2}$$

$$\therefore \qquad A = \frac{a}{2\pi r} \times \pi r^2$$
$$= \frac{ar}{2}$$
$$= \frac{15.5 \times 4}{2}$$
$$= 31$$

Thus the area is 31 cm^2.

Notice that the relationship between the area of a sector A, its arc length a and its radius r is given by:

$$A = \frac{ar}{2}$$

Exercise 9.1 

answers on p. 436

1. It is given that the circumference of a circle is 176 cm. Calculate, giving each answer correct to the nearest centimetre, the length of the arc which subtends an angle θ at the centre when θ is:
   (a) 45° **(b)** 152° **(c)** 310°
   (d) 76° **(e)** 184° **(f)** 320°

2. It is given that the area of a circle is 616 cm^2. Calculate, giving each answer correct to the nearest square centimetre, the area of the sector of which the arc subtends an angle of θ at the centre when θ is:
   (a) 84° **(b)** 210° **(c)** 315°
   (d) 110° **(e)** 270° **(f)** 280°

3. Find **(i)** the perimeter, **(ii)** the area of the minor sector of each of the following circles with centre O. Give each answer correct to the nearest centimetre and square centimetre respectively. (Take $\pi = 3.14$.)

(a)

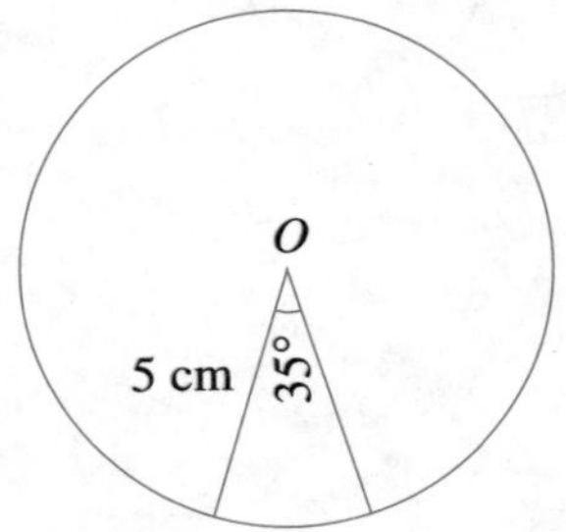

(b)

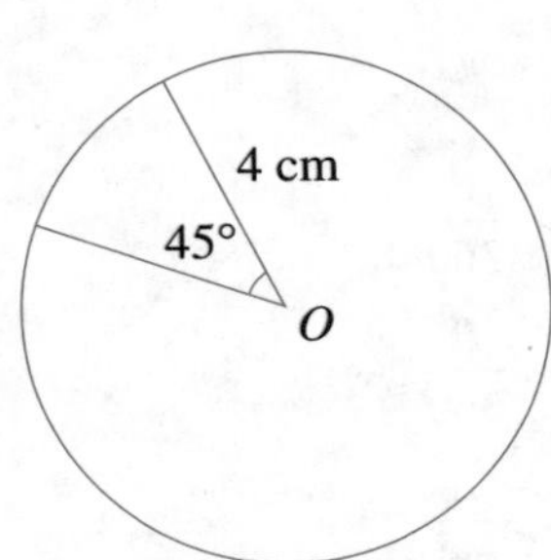

4. Find **(i)** the perimeter, **(ii)** the area of the major sector of each of the following circles with centre O. Give each answer correct to the nearest centimetre and square centimetre respectively. $\left(\text{Take } \pi = \frac{22}{7}.\right)$

(a)

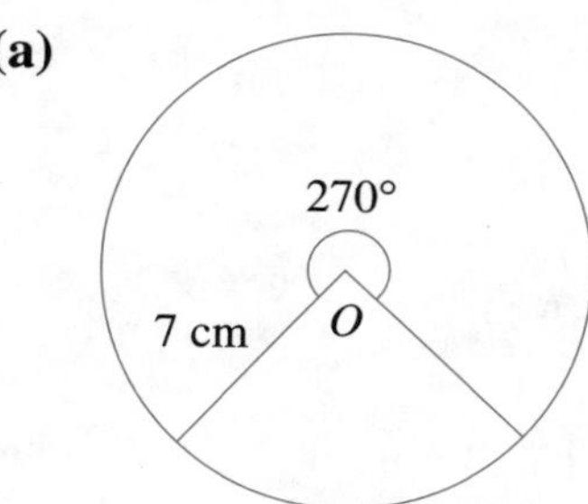

(b)

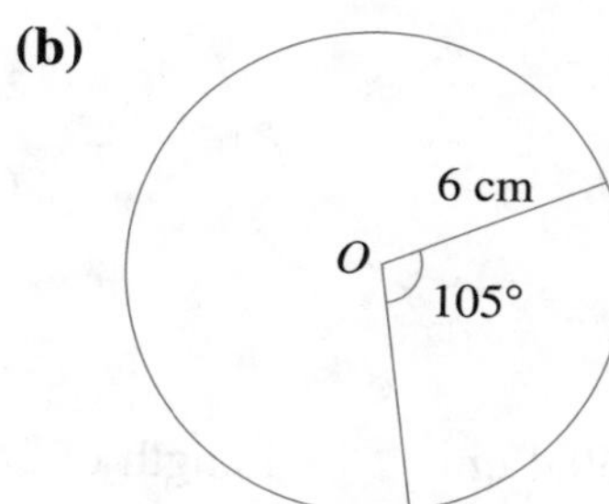

5. If the radius of a circle is 21 cm, find the central angle subtended by each of the arcs whose lengths are given below. Give each answer correct to the nearest degree.
(a) 6 cm **(b)** 5.5 cm **(c)** 8.2 cm
(d) 15.6 cm **(e)** 120 cm **(f)** 110 cm

6. The radius of a circle is 6 cm. Find the central angle subtended by the arc of each of the sectors whose areas are given below. Give each answer correct to the nearest degree.
(a) 20.5 cm^2 **(b)** 67.3 cm^2 **(c)** 58.6 cm^2
(d) 100.4 cm^2 **(e)** 5.6 cm^2 **(f)** 7.5 cm^2

7. Find the radius of each of the following circles with centre O. Give each answer correct to the nearest centimetre.

(a)

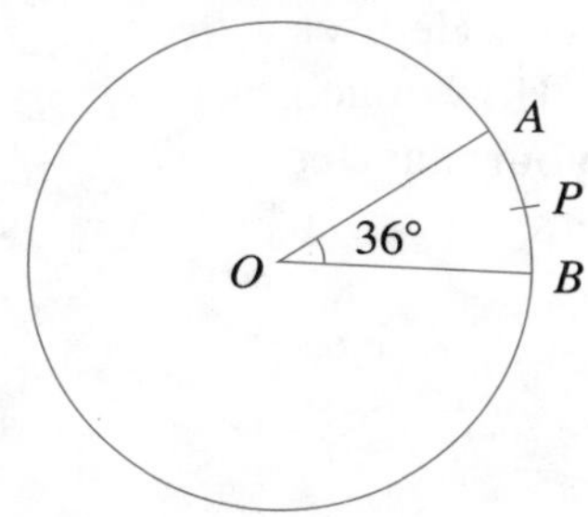

Area of $OAPB$ = 66.6 cm^2

(b)

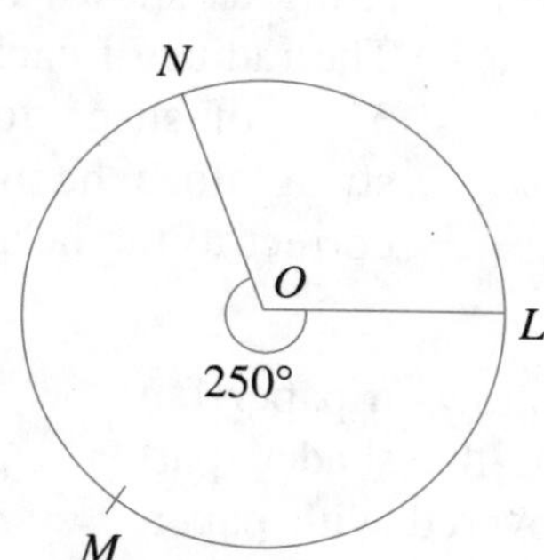

Area of $OLMN$ = 325.5 cm^2

8. Find the radius of each of the following circles with centre O. Give each answer correct to the nearest centimetre.

(a)

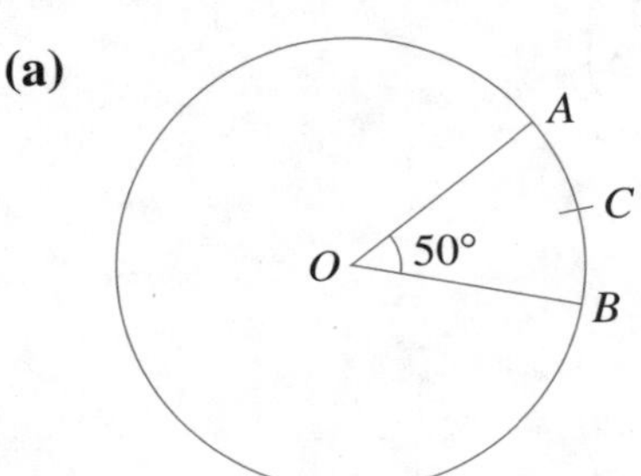

Length of arc ACB = 59.4 cm

(b)

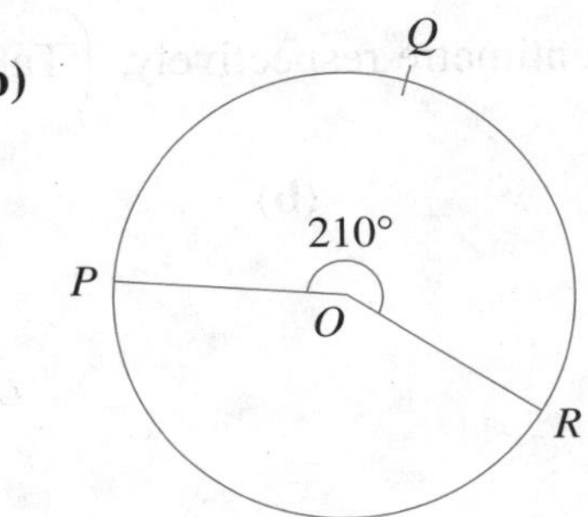

Length of arc PQR = 132.3 cm

9. The figure on the right shows a sector of a circle with arc length a cm and radius r cm. Calculate, giving each answer correct to the nearest square centimetre, the area of the sector when:

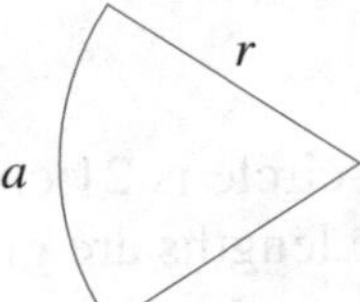

(a) $a = 10$, $r = 5$ **(b)** $a = 6$, $r = 7$
(c) $a = 12.2$, $r = 8.1$ **(d)** $a = 28.5$, $r = 9.9$
(e) $a = 100$, $r = 9$ **(f)** $a = 50$, $r = 6.5$

10. A circular saw is used to saw timber. A portion of the saw is illustrated in the figure. Every time the saw turns through an angle θ, the next tooth is in position. If there are 40 teeth on the saw, find the value of θ.

11. **(a)** A circular pizza weighs 1 kg. A wedge-shaped piece with a central angle of 90° is cut out. How much does this wedge weigh?

(b) If a slim wedge with a central angle of 20° is cut out, how much does this piece weigh?

12. Ahmad ties 4 circular tins with a piece of string as shown in the figure on the left. The radius of each tin is 5.5 cm. He uses 3 cm of string for the knot. How much string does he use? Give your answer correct to the nearest centimetre.

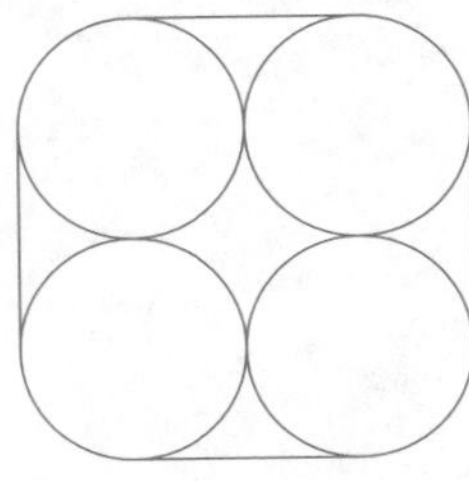

13. The figure on the right shows a paper fan which is fully opened. If the shaded part represents the portion covered with paper, find the area of paper used, correct to the nearest cm^2.

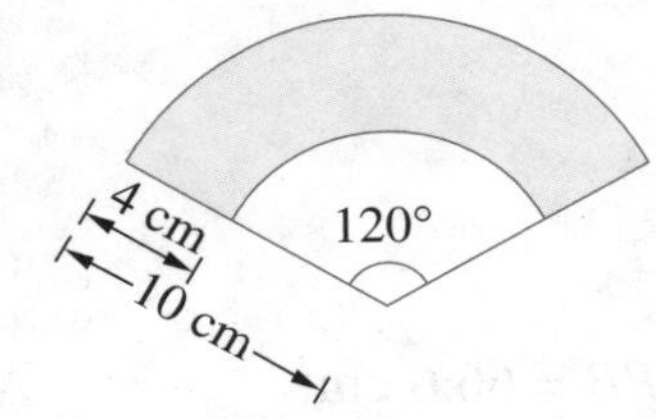

14. **(a)** How many minutes does it take for the minute hand of a clock to turn through 216°?

(b) The tip of a minute hand moves in a circle of radius 14 cm. Taking π to be $\frac{22}{7}$, calculate the distance moved by the tip of the hand in 15 minutes. *(C)*

9.2 CONES AND PYRAMIDS

Volume

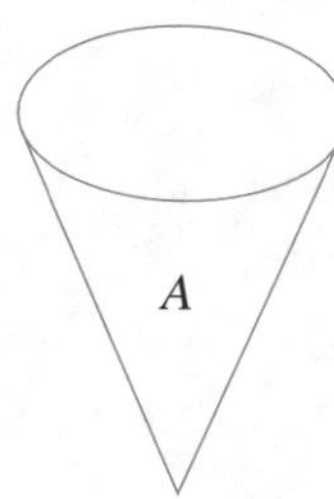

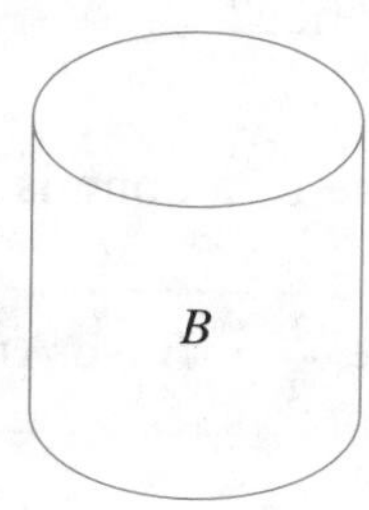

Fig. 9.4

A cone has a circular base, a curved surface and a vertex.

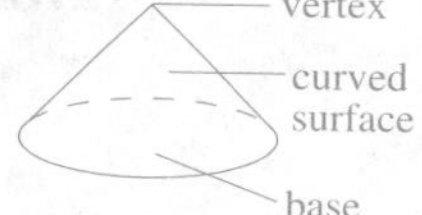

Fig. 9.4 shows two containers *A* and *B*. Container *A* has the shape of a cone and container *B* has the shape of a cylinder. Notice that a cylinder has uniform cross-section while the cone does not have. It is given that both containers have the same height and same base area.

If you fill the containers with sand to compare the volumes, you will discover how the volumes are related.

Class Activity

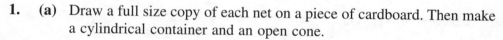

1. **(a)** Draw a full size copy of each net on a piece of cardboard. Then make a cylindrical container and an open cone.

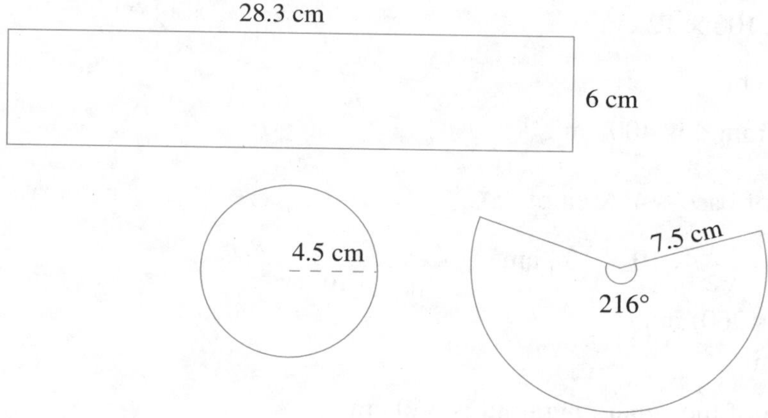

(b) Compare the heights of your cylinder and cone. Are they equal?
(c) Compare the base areas of your cylinder and cone. Are they equal?
(d) Use sand or rice grains to compare the volumes of your cylinder and cone. What do you notice?

2. **(a)** Use cardboard to make an open cone of a size of your choice.
(b) Measure the height of the cone and the diameter of the base of your cone.
(c) Make a cylindrical container with the same height and same base area as your cone.
(d) Use sand or rice grains to compare the volumes of your cone and cylinder. What do you notice?

The above suggests that the volume of a cone is given by the following rule.

$$\textbf{Volume of Cone} = \frac{1}{3} \times \textbf{Base Area} \times \textbf{Height}$$

Similarly, it can be shown that the volume of a pyramid is:

$$\textbf{Volume of Pyramid} = \frac{1}{3} \times \textbf{Base Area} \times \textbf{Height}$$

Worked Example 1

Find the volume and the total surface area of a square pyramid given that an edge of the base is 10 cm, the slant height of a triangular face is 13 cm and the height is 12 cm.

A pyramid is a solid whose base can be any polygon but all other faces are triangles.

Solution:

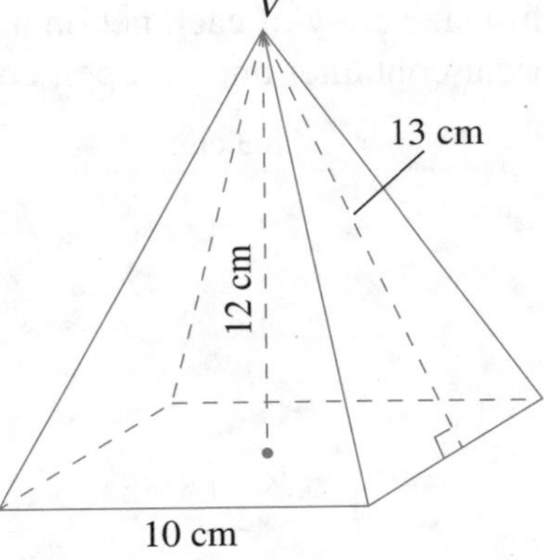

$$\text{Volume of pyramid} = \frac{1}{3} \times \text{Base area} \times \text{Height}$$
$$= \frac{1}{3} \times 100 \times 12 \text{ cm}^3$$
$$= 400 \text{ cm}^3$$

Thus the volume of the pyramid is 400 cm^3.

$$\text{Total surface area} = \text{Area of base} + 4(\text{Area of } \triangle)$$
$$= 100 + 4\left(\frac{1}{2} \times 10 \times 13\right) \text{ cm}^2$$
$$= (100 + 260) \text{ cm}^2$$
$$= 360 \text{ cm}^2$$

Thus the total surface area of the square pyramid is 360 cm^2.

Surface Area of a Cone

The surface area of a solid cone is the sum of the area of the lateral (or curved) surface and the area of the base.

Example

Let us find the lateral surface area of a cone. Consider the cone shown in Fig. 9.5. Imagine the lateral surface of the cone is opened as shown in Fig. 9.6.

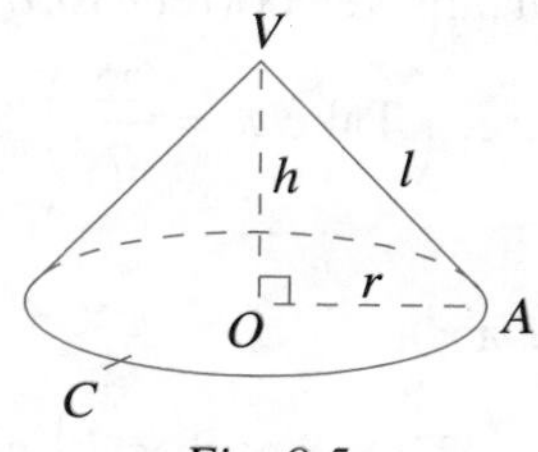

Fig. 9.5

Then the arc ACA' is equal to the circumference of the base of the cone which is $2\pi r$.

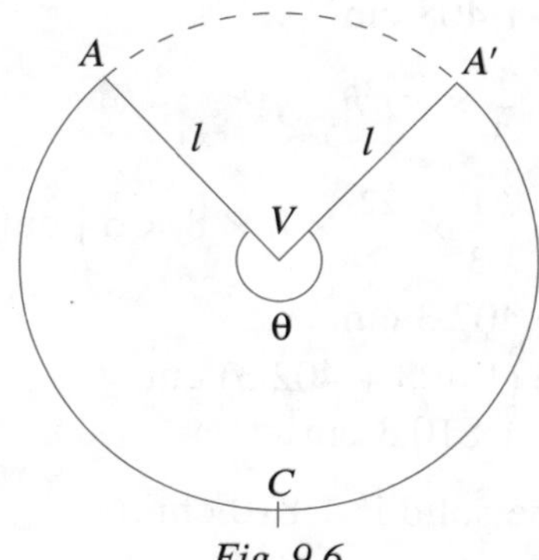

Fig. 9.6

Now $\qquad \dfrac{\text{arc length}}{\text{circumference}} = \dfrac{\theta}{360}$

$$\frac{2\pi r}{2\pi l} = \frac{\theta}{360} \quad \text{......................... (1)}$$

Also $\qquad \dfrac{\text{area of sector}}{\text{area of circle}} = \dfrac{\theta}{360}$

$$\frac{\text{area of sector}}{\pi l^2} = \frac{\theta}{360} \quad \text{......................... (2)}$$

Equating (1) and (2), we have

$$\frac{\text{area of sector}}{\pi l^2} = \frac{2\pi r}{2\pi l}$$

Thus $\qquad \text{area of sector} = \dfrac{2\pi r \times \pi l^2}{2\pi l}$

$$= \pi r l$$

We see that the lateral surface area A of a cone of radius r and slant height l is given by the rule:

$$\mathbf{A = \pi r l}$$

Worked Example 2

The figure on the right shows a solid made up of a cone and a cylinder. The radius of the cylinder is 8 cm and its height is 7 cm. The height of the solid is 13 cm. Find the volume of the solid. Give your answer correct to the nearest cubic centimetre. $\left(\text{Take } \pi = \frac{22}{7}.\right)$

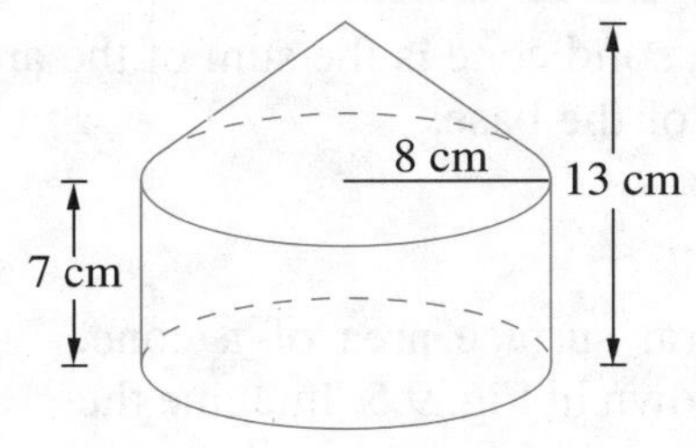

Solution:

Volume of cylinder $= \pi r^2 h$

$= \left(\frac{22}{7} \times 8 \times 8 \times 7\right) \text{ cm}^3$

$= 1\ 408 \text{ cm}^3$

Volume of the cone $= \frac{1}{3} \times \pi r^2 h$

$= \left(\frac{1}{3} \times \frac{22}{7} \times 8 \times 8 \times 6\right) \text{ cm}^3$

$= 402.3 \text{ cm}^3$

Volume of the solid $= (1\ 408 + 402.3) \text{ cm}^3$

$= 1\ 810.3 \text{ cm}^3$

Thus the volume of the solid is 1 810 cm^3.

Worked Example 3

Find the lateral surface area and the total surface area of a right circular cone whose slant height is 13 cm and radius of the base is 5 cm. Give each answer correct to the nearest square centimetre. $\left(\text{Take } \pi = \frac{22}{7}.\right)$

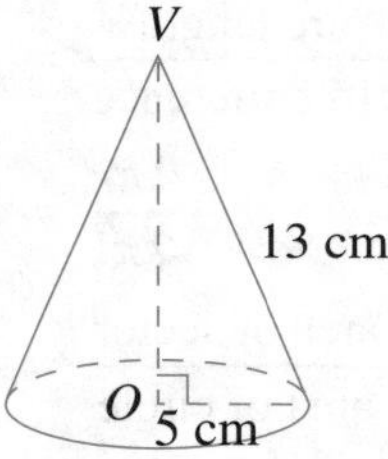

Solution:

Area of lateral surface $= \pi rl$

$= \left(\frac{22}{7} \times 5 \times 13\right) \text{ cm}^2$

$= 204.29 \text{ cm}^2$

Thus the lateral surface area of the cone is 204 cm^2.

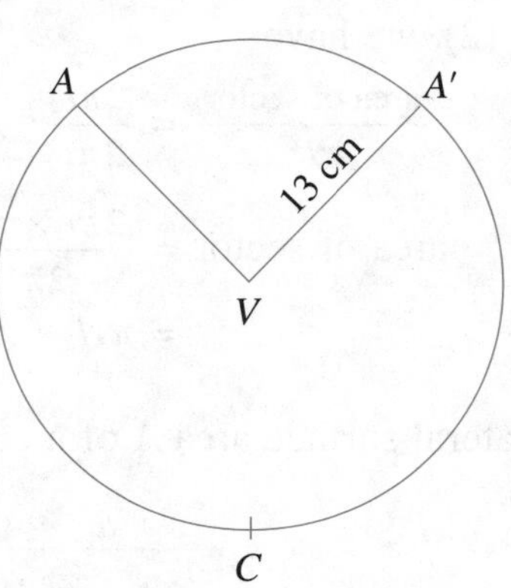

Area of base of cone $= \pi r^2$

$= \left(\frac{22}{7} \times 25\right) \text{ cm}^2$

$= 78.57 \text{ cm}^2$

$\therefore$ total surface area of cone $= (204.29 + 78.57) \text{ cm}^2$

$= 282.86 \text{ cm}^2$

Thus the total surface area of the cone is 283 cm^2.

Worked Example 4

A solid stands on a rectangular base as shown. EG and FH are perpendicular to the base. If $AB = 16$ cm, $BC = 12$ cm, $EG = FH = 11$ cm and $EF = 10$ cm, find the volume of the solid.

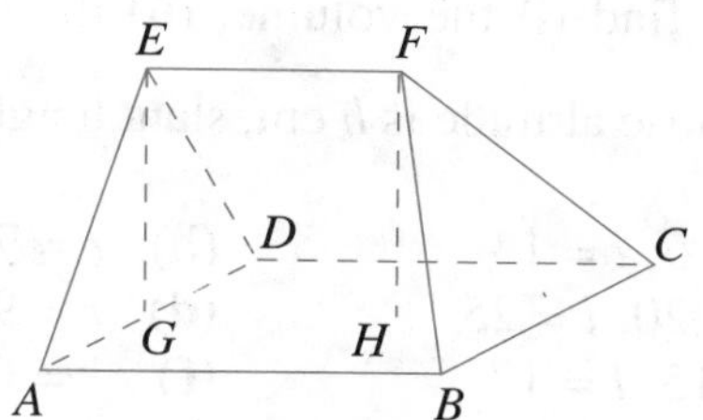

Solution:

Take two points X and Y on the base as shown. Divide the solid into a triangular prism $EADFYX$ and a pyramid $FBCXY$ by cutting through the points F, X and Y.

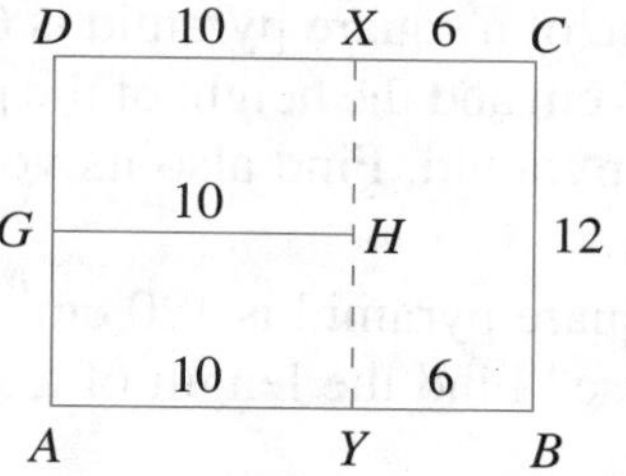

Now volume of the solid = volume of triangular prism + volume of pyramid

$$= \left[\frac{1}{2} \times 12 \times 11 \times 10 + \frac{1}{3}(6 \times 12) \times 11\right] \text{ cm}^3$$

$$= (660 + 264) \text{ cm}^3$$

$$= 924 \text{ cm}^3$$

Recall:
Volume of prism is base area × height, that is, area of $\triangle ADE \times EF$.

Note: The strategies used are **to draw a diagram** and **to use spatial visualisation.**

Exercise 9.2

answers on p. 436

1. Calculate the volume of each of the following solids. $\left(\text{Take } \pi = \frac{22}{7}.\right)$

(a)

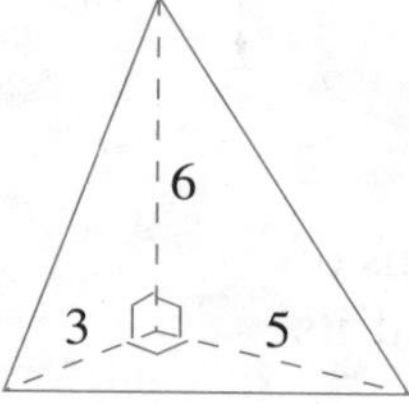

(b)

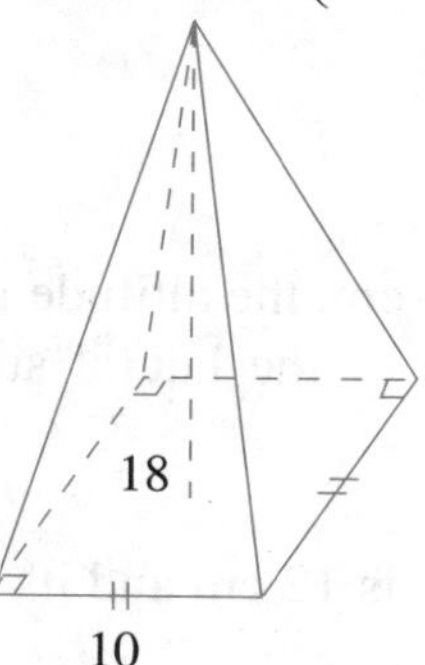

(c)

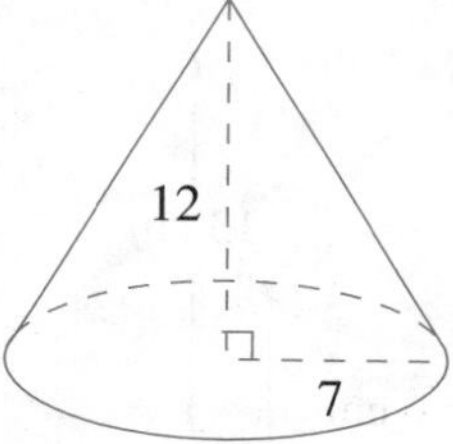

(d)

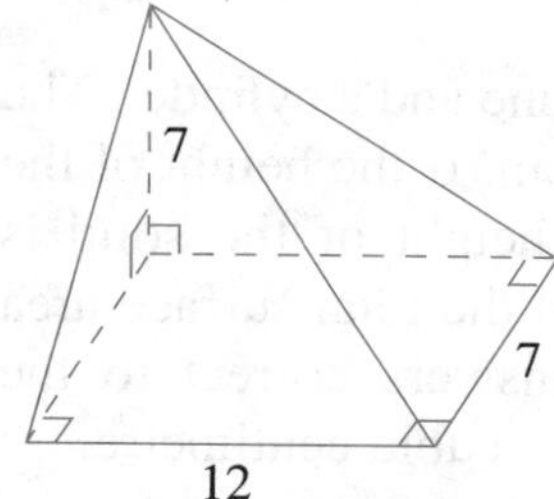

2. Taking $\pi = \frac{22}{7}$, find **(i)** the volume, **(ii)** the total surface area of a right circular cone whose altitude is h cm, slant height l cm and base radius r cm if:

(a) $r = 12, h = 5, l = 13$
(b) $r = 7, h = 24, l = 25$
(c) $r = 15, h = 20, l = 25$
(d) $r = 9, h = 12, l = 15$
(e) $r = 8, h = 15, l = 17$
(f) $r = 6, h = 8, l = 10$

3. One edge of the base of a square pyramid is 6 cm long. The slant height of a triangular face is 5 cm and the height of the pyramid is 4 cm. Find the total surface area of the pyramid. Find also its volume.

4. The volume of a square pyramid is 120 cm^3 and its altitude is 5 cm. What is the area of its base? Find the length of a side of the base.

5. A triangular pyramid $ABCD$ is cut from the corner of a cube. Given that $AB = AC = AD = 6$ cm, find the volume of the pyramid.

$\left(\text{Volume of a pyramid} = \frac{1}{3}\text{ area of base} \times \text{height}\right)$

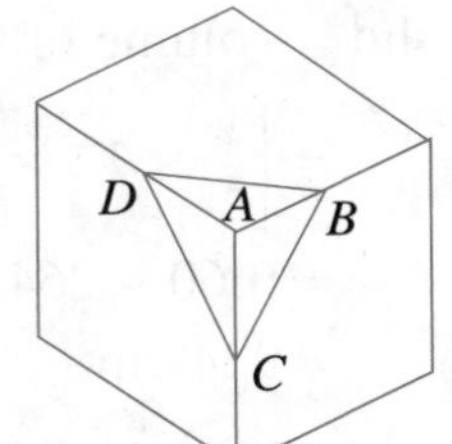

6. A cone is contained in a cylinder so that their bases and heights are the same, as shown in the figure on the right. Calculate the volume of the space lying in between the cylinder and the cone (that is, inside the cylinder but outside the cone).

$\left(\text{Take } \pi = \frac{22}{7}.\right)$

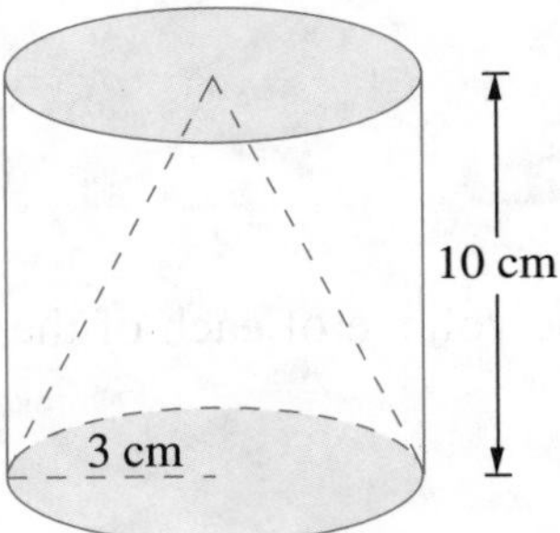

7. The slant height of a cone is 8.5 cm, the altitude is 7.5 cm and the radius of its base is 4 cm. Find the area of the lateral surface of the cone and its volume in terms of π.

8. The radius of the base of a cone is 12 cm and its volume is 720π cm^3. Find its height.

9. The solid is made up of a cone and a cylinder. The radius of the cylinder is 6 cm. If the height of the cylinder is 5 cm and the height of the solid is 13 cm, find the volume and the total surface area of the solid. Give your answers correct to the nearest square centimetre or cubic centimetre.

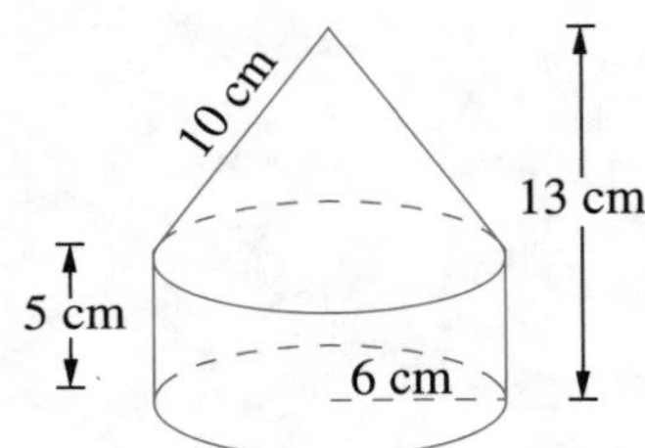

10.

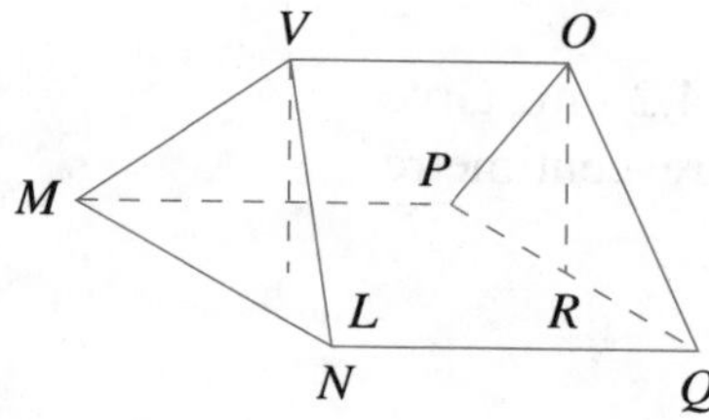

The solid is made up of a triangular prism and a pyramid. VL and OR are perpendicular to the base. If NQ = 20 cm, MN = 16 cm, VO = 15 cm and $VL = OR$ = 12 cm, find the volume of the solid.

***11.** The figure on the right is made up of a prism, whose base is a right-angled triangle and a pyramid. Find the volume if VP = 16 cm, MN = 10 cm, ON = 6 cm, NP = 8 cm and OP = 10 cm.

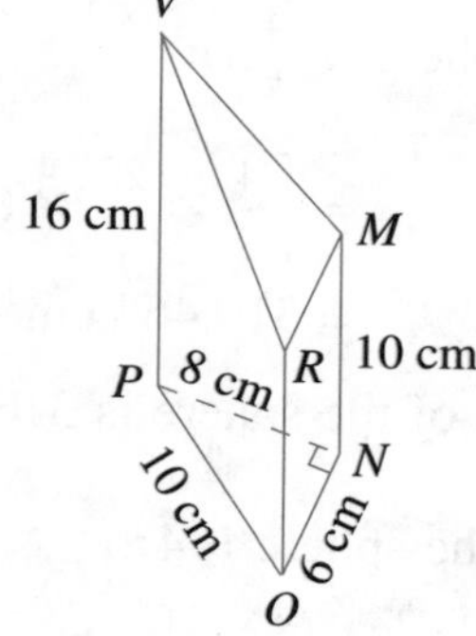

***12.** A right circular, conical vessel of altitude 21 cm and base radius 11 cm is kept with its vertex downwards. If 2 litres of water is poured into it, how high above the vertex will the level of the water be?

***13.**

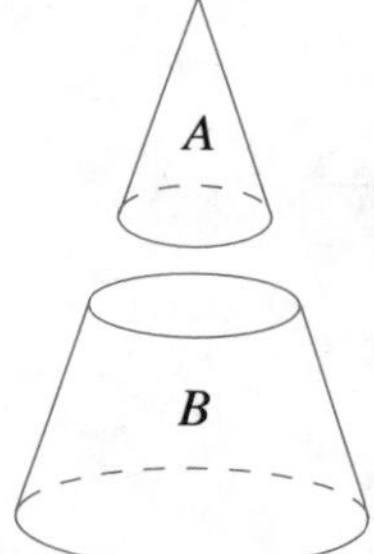

A cone is divided into parts A and B. The vertical heights of A and B are equal. The volume of cone A is x cm^3.

(a) Express the volume of the whole cone in terms of x.

(b) If the volume of part B is 3 500 cm^3, calculate the volume of cone A.

9.3 SPHERE

The volume V and surface area S of a sphere of radius r are given by the formulae:

A sphere is a round solid shape like a ball.

$$V = \frac{4}{3}\pi r^3$$

$$S = 4\pi r^2$$

There is no easy way of establishing the above rules at the elementary stage. One way to prove these is to use *calculus*, which is a branch of advanced mathematics.

Worked Example 1

Find **(a)** the volume, **(b)** the surface area of a sphere of radius 4.2 cm. Give your answers correct to the nearest cubic centimetre and square centimetre respectively. $\left(\text{Take } \pi = \frac{22}{7}.\right)$

Solution:

(a) Volume of the sphere $= \frac{4}{3}\pi r^3$

$$= \left[\frac{4}{3} \times \frac{22}{7} \times (4.2)^3\right] \text{ cm}^3$$

$$= 310.464 \text{ cm}^3$$

Thus the volume of the sphere is 310 cm^3.

(b) Surface area of the sphere $= 4\pi r^2$

$$= \left[4 \times \frac{22}{7} \times (4.2)^2\right] \text{ cm}^2$$

$$= 221.76 \text{ cm}^2$$

Thus the surface area of the sphere is 222 cm^2.

Worked Example 2

A thin hemispherical bowl which has a radius of 6 cm is filled to the brim with water. Find **(a)** the volume of water, **(b)** the outer surface area of the bowl. Give your answers correct to the nearest cubic centimetre and square centimetre respectively. (Take $\pi = 3.14$.)

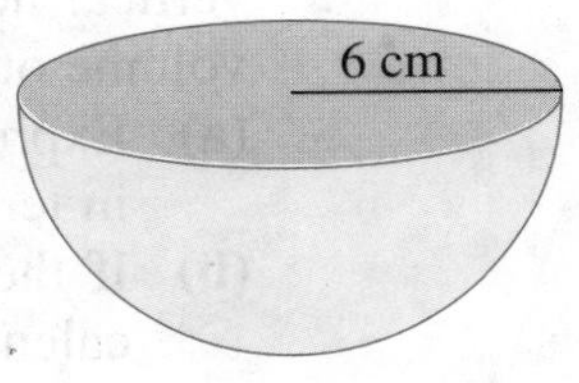

Solution:

(a) Volume of water $= \frac{1}{2}\left(\frac{4}{3}\pi r^3\right)$

$$= \left(\frac{1}{2} \times \frac{4}{3} \times 3.14 \times 6 \times 6 \times 6\right) \text{ cm}^3$$

$$= 452.16 \text{ cm}^3$$

Thus the volume of water is 452 cm^3.

(b) Outer surface area of the bowl $= \frac{1}{2}(4\pi r^2)$

$$= \left(\frac{1}{2} \times 4 \times 3.14 \times 6 \times 6\right) \text{ cm}^2$$

$$= 226.08 \text{ cm}^2$$

Thus the outer surface area of the bowl is 226 cm^2.

Worked Example 3

The solid is made up of a cone and a hemisphere as shown. Find its volume.

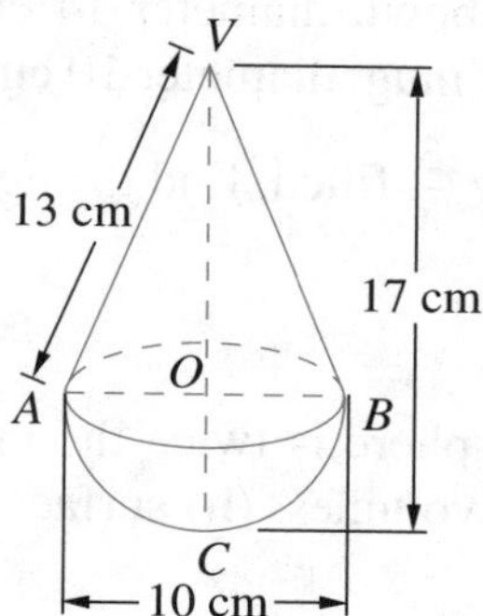

Solution:

$OB = 5$ cm, $VO = (17 - 5)$ cm $= 12$ cm.

Volume of the solid = volume of cone VAB + volume of hemisphere ACB

$$= \frac{1}{3}\pi r^2 h + \frac{1}{2}\left(\frac{4}{3}\pi r^3\right)$$

$$= \frac{1}{3}\pi(5)^2(12) + \frac{1}{2}\left[\frac{4}{3}\pi(5^3)\right]$$

$$= 100\pi + \frac{250\pi}{3}$$

$$= \frac{550}{3}\pi \text{ cm}^3 \text{ or } 576 \text{ cm}^3$$

Thus the volume of the solid is 576 cm^3.

Exercise 9.3

answers on p. 437

1. Find the volume and surface area of a sphere of radius r cm when r is:
   (a) 4.6 **(b)** 8.7 **(c)** 16.8
   (d) 9.5 **(e)** 11.8 **(f)** 15.2
   Give your answer correct to the nearest cubic centimetre or square centimetre. (Take $\pi = 3.14$.)

2. Find the radius and volume of each of the spheres whose surface areas are given below. $\left(\text{Take } \pi = \frac{22}{7}.\right)$
   (a) 616 cm^2 **(b)** $50\frac{2}{7}$ cm^2 **(c)** $113\frac{1}{7}$ cm^2
   (d) 5 544 cm^2 **(e)** 2 464 cm^2 **(f)** $201\frac{1}{7}$ cm^2

3. A spherical tank has a radius of 3 m. How many litres of water can it contain?

4. A hemispherical bowl, diameter 14 cm, full of water, is emptied into an empty cylindrical mug, diameter 10 cm, both measurements being internal. If the mug is now $\frac{3}{4}$ filled, find the depth of the mug, correct to 1 decimal place.

5. The radius of a sphere is twice the radius of another sphere. What is the ratio of their **(a)** volumes, **(b)** surface areas?

6. The earth's radius is approximately four times the radius of the moon. Compare **(a)** the volumes, **(b)** the surface areas of the moon and the earth.

7. About a quarter of the earth's surface is land. How many millions of square kilometres of the earth's surface are covered by water? (Use 6 300 km as an approximation for the earth's radius and $\frac{22}{7}$ for π.)

8. In a hemispherical solid, a conical part is removed as shown. Find the volume of the resulting solid.

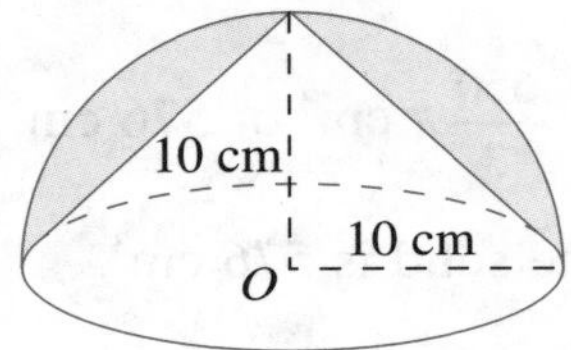

9. If the radius of a sphere is doubled, what effect does this have on its volume and its surface area?

10. If the diameter of a sphere is halved, what effect does this have on its volume and its surface area?

11. The paint used to cover the outer surface of a ball of radius 10 cm costs 2 cents. What is the cost of the paint used to cover the outer surface of a spherical storage tank of radius 10 m?

12. The figure below shows a spherical shell. Find the volume and surface area of the solid.

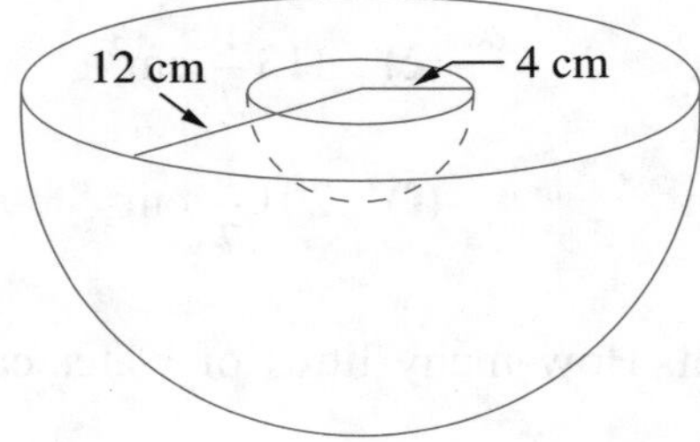

13. The solid is made up of a hemisphere and a cone. Find its surface area and its volume.

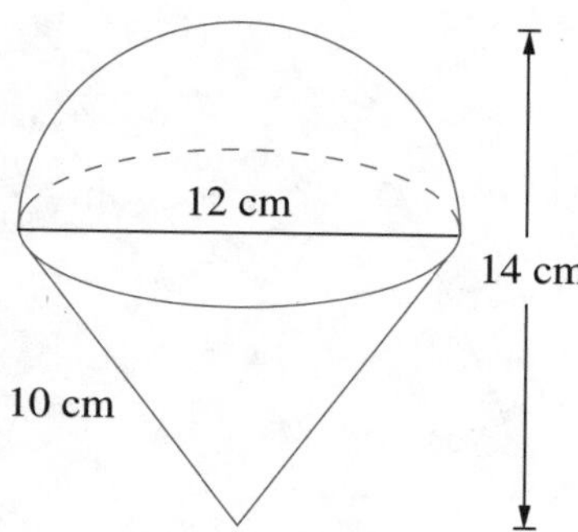

14. In this question, take π to be 3.142. The volume of a sphere of radius r is $\frac{4}{3}\pi r^3$. The volume of a cone is $\frac{1}{3}$base area $\times$ height. A child's toy is formed by joining the plane face of a solid hemisphere of radius 6 cm to the base of a solid cone of radius 6 cm, as shown in the diagram.

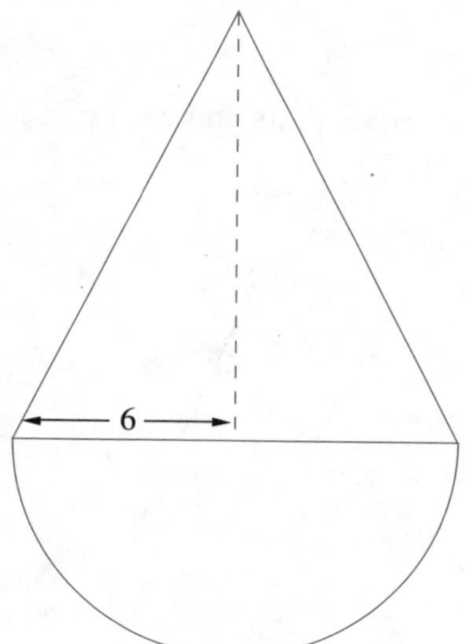

(a) Find the volume of the hemisphere.
(b) The volume of the cone is 408 cm^3. Find its height.
(c) The hemisphere is made of a metal alloy, and 1 cm^3 of the alloy weighs 1.1 g. The cone is made of wood, and 1 cm^3 of the wood weighs 0.8 g. Find the total mass of the toy.
(d) The hemispherical bases of a number of these toys are formed by melting down a solid cylinder of the alloy, of radius 8 cm and length 24 cm. Find the number of complete hemispheres that can be made from the cylinder.

9.4 AREAS OF SIMILAR FIGURES

Examples

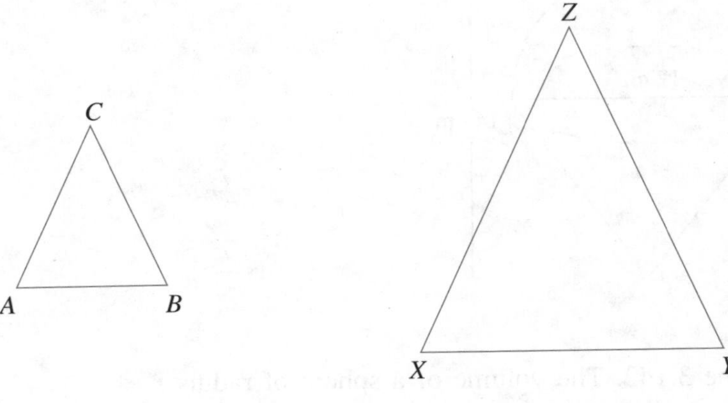

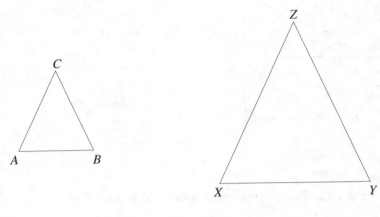

Fig. 9.7

Fig. 9.7 shows that $\triangle XYZ$ and $\triangle ABC$ are similar such that $\frac{XY}{AB} = \frac{2}{1}$. What is $\frac{\text{area of } \triangle XYZ}{\text{area of } \triangle ABC}$?

Fig. 9.8 shows that $\triangle XYZ$ is divided into four equal parts and each part has the same area as $\triangle ABC$.

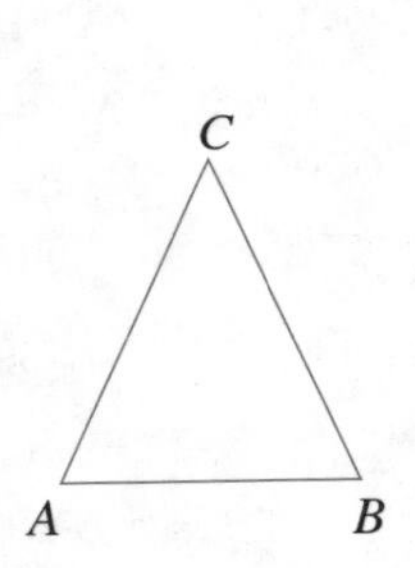

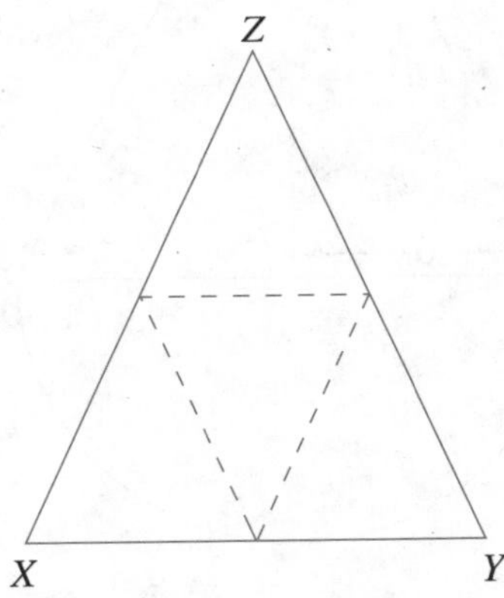

Fig. 9.8

Thus $\frac{\text{area of } \triangle XYZ}{\text{area of } \triangle ABC} = \frac{4}{1}$.

Notice that $\frac{4}{1}$ can be written as $\left(\frac{2}{1}\right)^2$.

So we see that $\frac{\text{area of } \triangle XYZ}{\text{area of } \triangle ABC} = \left(\frac{XY}{AB}\right)^2$.

Again, Fig. 9.9 shows that $\triangle STU$ and $\triangle PQR$ are similar such that $\frac{ST}{PQ} = \frac{3}{2}$.

Thus $\frac{\text{area of } \triangle STU}{\text{area of } \triangle PQR} = \frac{9}{4} = \left(\frac{3}{2}\right)^2$.

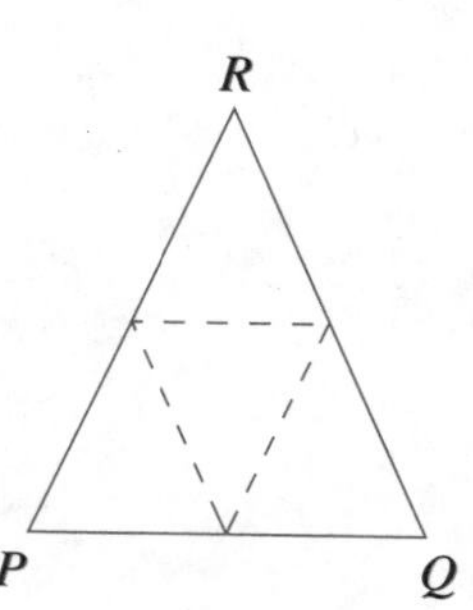

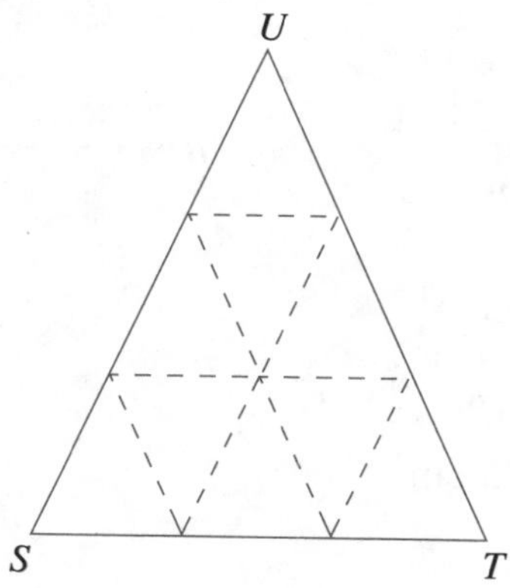

Fig. 9.9

So we see that $\frac{\text{area of } \triangle STU}{\text{area of } \triangle PQR} = \left(\frac{ST}{PQ}\right)^2$.

This relationship applies to any pair of similar figures.

> **If the ratio of the corresponding lengths of two similar figures is $\frac{a}{b}$, then the ratio of their areas is $\left(\frac{a}{b}\right)^2$.**

Worked Example 1

A and *B* are two similar figures. One side of *A* is 2 units long and the corresponding side of *B* is 3 units long. Find the ratio of the area of *A* to that of *B*.

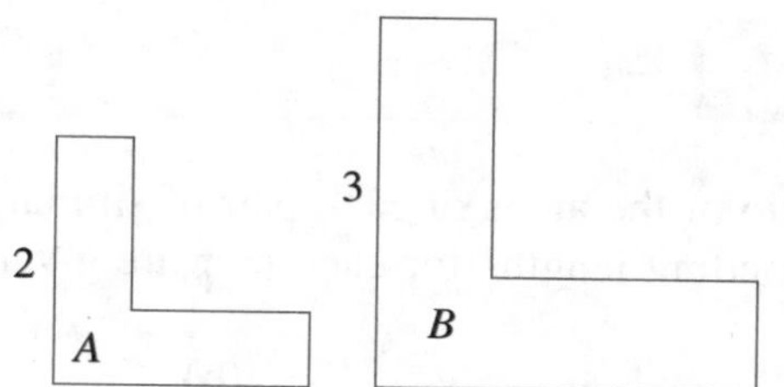

Solution:

$$\frac{\text{Area of } A}{\text{Area of } B} = \left(\frac{2}{3}\right)^2$$

$$= \frac{4}{9}$$

Worked Example 2

If $\dfrac{CE}{AE} = \dfrac{5}{3}$ and area of $\triangle AED = 9\text{ cm}^2$, find the area of $\triangle CEB$.

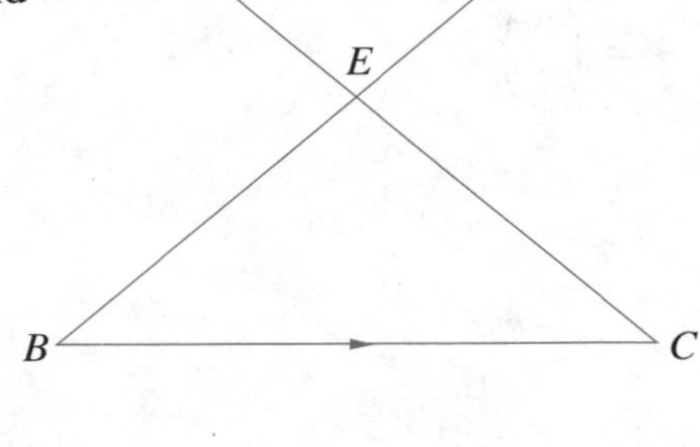

Solution:

$$\frac{\text{Area of } \triangle CEB}{\text{Area of } \triangle AED} = \left(\frac{5}{3}\right)^2 = \frac{25}{9}$$

But area of $\triangle AED = 9\text{ cm}^2$

$\therefore$ area of $\triangle CEB = \dfrac{25}{9} \times 9\text{ cm}^2 = 25\text{ cm}^2$

Worked Example 3

The scale of a map is 3 cm to 1 km. Find the area of a piece of land represented by an area of $4\frac{1}{2}\text{ cm}^2$ on the map.

Solution:

3^2 cm^2 on a map represents 1^2 km^2 on the ground, i.e. 9 cm^2 represents 1 km^2.

$\therefore 4\frac{1}{2}\text{ cm}^2$ on the map represents $\dfrac{4\frac{1}{2}}{9} \times 1\text{ km}^2 = \dfrac{9}{2} \times \dfrac{1}{9}\text{ km}^2 = \dfrac{1}{2}\text{ km}^2$

Exercise 9.4 

answers on p. 437

1. Find the ratio of the areas of each pair of similar figures. The measures of the corresponding lengths for each pair are given.

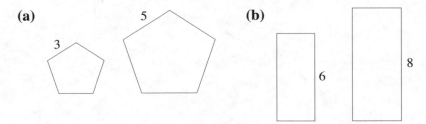

(a)

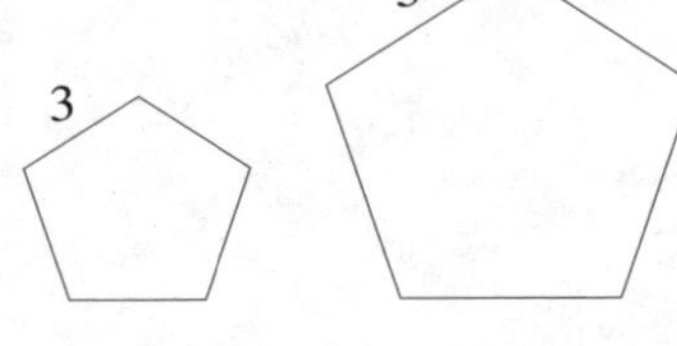

(b)

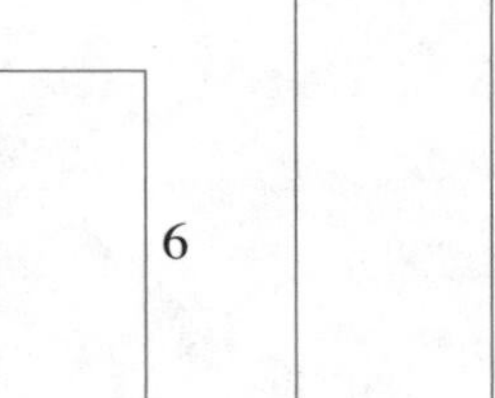

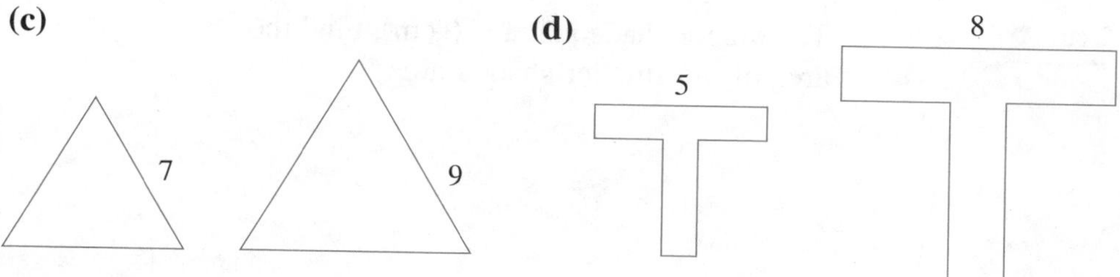

2. Two triangles are similar. The side of one is 2 units long. The corresponding side of the other is 5 units long. What is the ratio of their areas?

3. Two triangles are similar. The sides of one are three times as long as the sides of the other. What is the ratio of their areas?

4. The ratio of the areas of two similar triangles is 25 : 1. What is the ratio of the lengths of their corresponding sides?

5. Two polygons are similar. A side of one is 3 cm long. The corresponding side of the other is 7 cm. The area of the first polygon is 25 cm^2. What is the area of the other?

6. A side of one of two similar polygons is 3 cm long. The corresponding side of the other is 5 cm long. The area of the first polygon is 2 cm^2. What is the area of the other?

7. Two polygons are similar. A side of one is 2 cm long. The corresponding side of the other is 3 cm long. The area of the first polygon is 15 cm^2. What is the area of the other?

8. A piece of land has an area of $5\frac{1}{2}$ km^2. Find the area of this land on a map whose scale is 1 cm to 1 km.

9. On a plan, a piece of land is represented by an area of dimensions $4\frac{1}{2}$ cm $\times$ 3 cm. If the scale is 2 cm to 100 m, what is the actual area of the land?

10. In the diagram, the points D and E are such that $\frac{AD}{AB} = \frac{AE}{AC} = \frac{1}{3}$. Given that the area of triangle ABC is 36 cm^2, find the area of $\triangle ADE$.

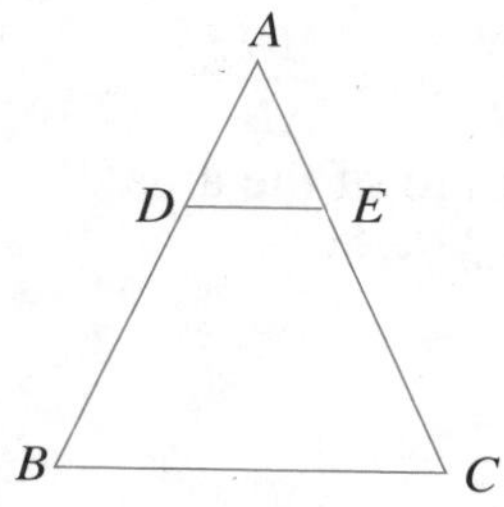

11. 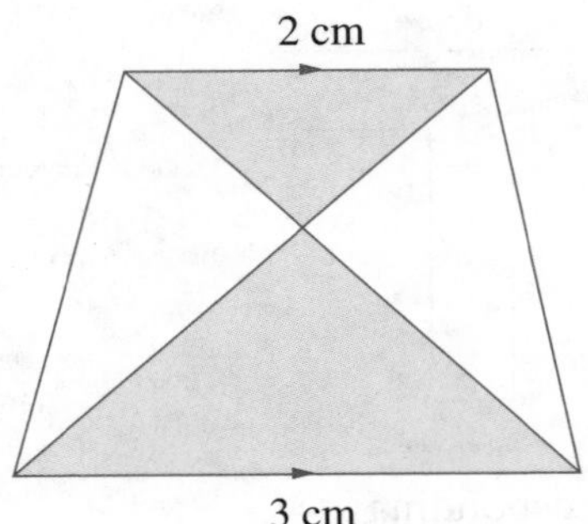

The bigger shaded area is 6 cm^2. Find the area of the smaller shaded area.

12. If $\frac{AE}{CE} = \frac{2}{3}$ and the area of $\triangle DEC = 27$ cm^2, find the area of $\triangle AEB$.

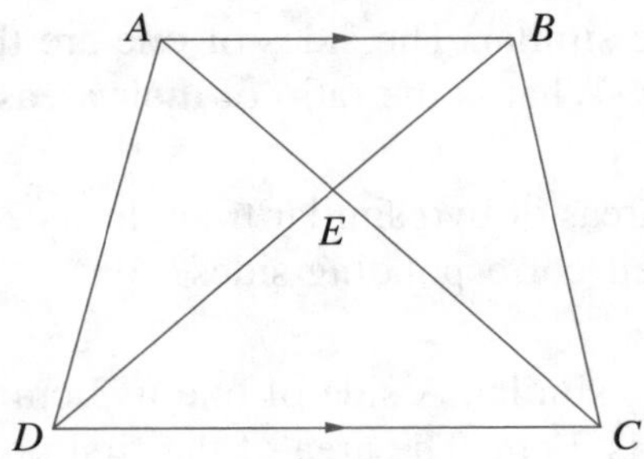

***13.** A rectangle has length 12 cm and breadth 8 cm. A second rectangle, geometrically similar to the first, has adjacent sides 4 cm and x cm long. Calculate the two possible values of x.

***14.** 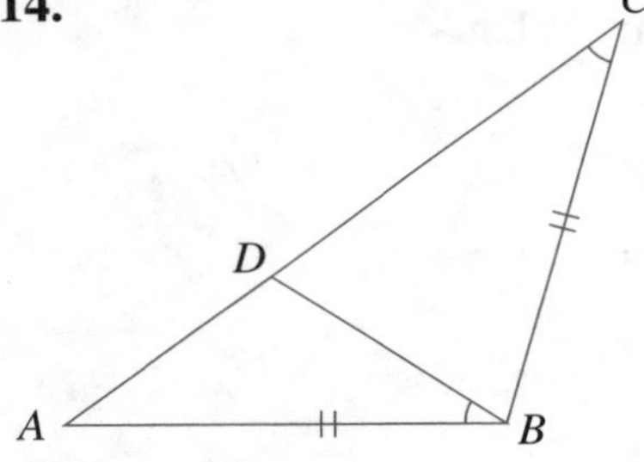

In the diagram, which is not drawn to scale, $A\hat{B}D = A\hat{C}B$ and $AB = BC$.

(a) Explain why $AD = BD$.

(b) Copy and complete the two statements:

(i) $\frac{AC}{AB} = \frac{}{AD}$

(ii) $\frac{\text{Area of } \triangle ABD}{\text{Area of } \triangle ACB} = \frac{AB^2}{}$

***15.** In the figure, $MN \mathbin{/\!/} AB$ and the measurements are in cm.

(a) Calculate $\frac{ON}{NB}$ and $\frac{MN}{AB}$.

(b) What is the ratio of the area of $\triangle OMN$ to quadrilateral $MNBA$?

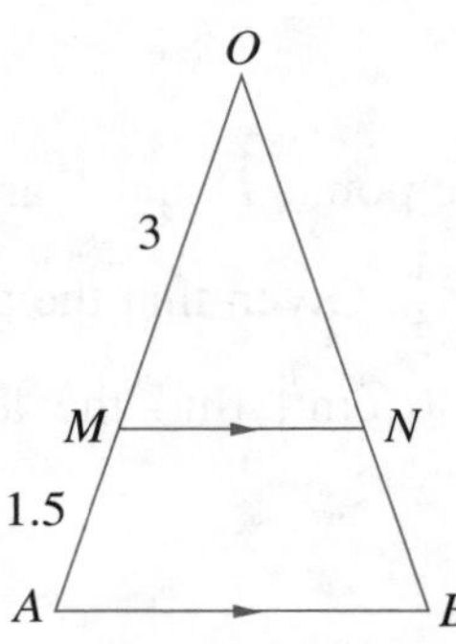

*16. In the diagram, P is the point on AC such that $AP = 2PC$, R is the point on BP such that $BR = 3RP$ and QR is parallel to AC. Given that the area of $\triangle BPA$ is 32 cm², calculate the area of
(a) $\triangle BPC$,
(b) $\triangle BRQ$. (*C*)

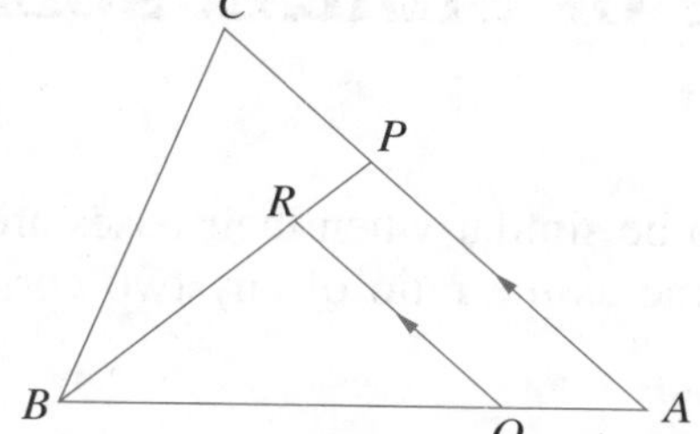

17. The size of an ordinance survey map is 30 cm by 25 cm and has a scale of 1 : 10 000. Find, in square kilometres, the actual area this map represents.

18. It costs \$5.00 to mow a rectangular field 40 m long and 25 m wide. How much will it cost to mow a similar field $67\frac{1}{2}$ m wide at the same rate?

19. A map is drawn to a scale of 1 : 20 000.
(a) On the map, the perimeter of a reservoir is represented by a length of 185 cm. Calculate the actual perimeter of the reservoir, giving your answer in kilometres.
(b) The actual area of a plantation is 3.2 km². Calculate the area on the map which represents the plantation, giving your answer in square centimetres. (*C*)

20. As a homework exercise, a boy has to draw a plan of his bedroom using a scale of 1 cm to represent 20 cm.
(a) His bed is 92 cm wide. What will be the width of the bed on his plan?
(b) On the plan the area represented by his room is 140 cm². What is the actual area of his room? Give your answer in square metres. (*C*)

21. All the lengths on a scale drawing are one sixth of their true length.
(a) Calculate the actual length of a line represented on the scale drawing by a length of 15.5 cm.
(b) Calculate the area on the scale drawing which represents an actual area of 522 cm². (*C*)

22. Two photographs, of different sizes, show exactly the same picture. The smaller photograph measures 10 cm by 14 cm and the larger photograph measures 15 cm by 21 cm.
(a) Given that the height of a tree in the larger photograph is 12 cm, find the height of the same tree in the smaller photograph.
(b) Given that a wall covers an area of 8 cm² in the smaller photograph, find the area the same wall covers in the larger photograph. (*C*)

9.5 VOLUMES OF SIMILAR SOLIDS

Example

Two prisms are said to be similar when their bases are similar and the ratio of their heights is the same as the ratio of any two corresponding sides of their bases.

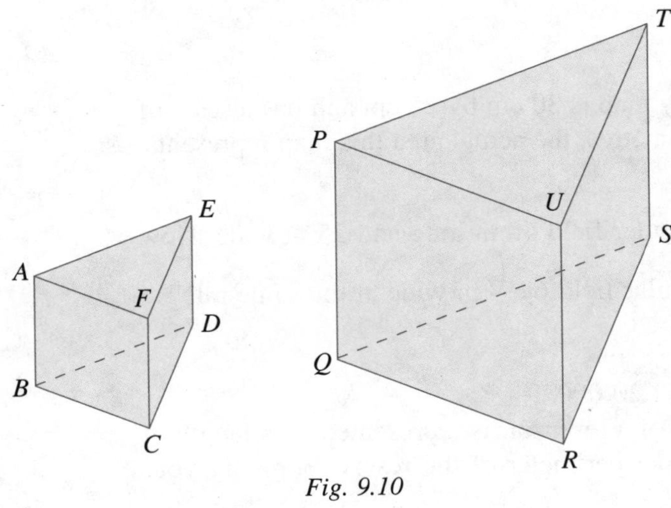

Fig. 9.10

Fig. 9.10 shows that the prism *PQRSTU* and the prism *ABCDEF* are similar such that $\frac{PQ}{AB} = \frac{2}{1}$.

What is $\frac{\text{volume of } PQRSTU}{\text{volume of } ABCDEF}$?

Fig. 9.11 shows how the prism *PQRSTU* is divided into eight equal parts and each part has the same volume as the prism *ABCDEF*.

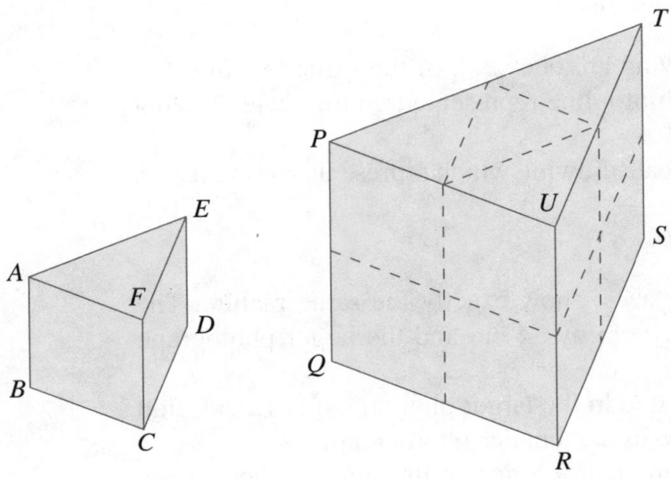

Fig. 9.11

Thus $\dfrac{\text{volume of } PQRSTU}{\text{volume of } ABCDEF} = \dfrac{8}{1}$.

Notice that $\dfrac{8}{1}$ can be written as $\left(\dfrac{2}{1}\right)^3$.

So we see that $\dfrac{\text{volume of prism } PQRSTU}{\text{volume of prism } ABCDEF} = \left(\dfrac{PQ}{AB}\right)^3$.

We also observe that each face of the bigger prism has an area four times as large as the corresponding face of the smaller prism.

It follows that $\dfrac{\text{total surface area of } PQRSTU}{\text{total surface area of } ABCDEF} = \left(\dfrac{PQ}{AB}\right)^2$.

These relationships apply to any pair of similar solid figures.

If the ratio of the corresponding lengths of two similar solids is $\frac{a}{b}$, then

- **the ratio of their volumes is $\left(\frac{a}{b}\right)^3$,**
- **the ratio of their total surface areas is $\left(\frac{a}{b}\right)^2$.**

Worked Example 1

X and Y are two similar cylinders. The radius of X is 3 units and the corresponding radius of Y is 4 units. Find the ratio of the volume of cylinder X to that of cylinder Y.

Solution:

$$\frac{\text{Volume of cylinder } X}{\text{Volume of cylinder } Y} = \left(\frac{3}{4}\right)^3$$
$$= \frac{27}{64}$$

Worked Example 2

A model water tank is made to a scale of 1 : 20. The actual water tank has a volume of 1 000 m^3. Calculate the volume of the model.

Solution:

$$\frac{\text{Volume of the model tank}}{\text{Volume of the actual tank}} = \left(\frac{1}{20}\right)^3$$
$$= \frac{1}{8\,000}$$

But volume of the actual tank = 1 000 m^3

$\therefore$ volume of the model tank $= \left(\frac{1}{8\ 000} \times 1\ 000\right)\ m^3$

$= 0.125\ m^3$

Worked Example 3

If the base areas of two similar cones *A* and *B* are in the ratio 4 : 9, find the ratio of their volumes.

Solution:

Let the radii of cones *A* and *B* be r_1 and r_2.

We have
$$\left(\frac{r_1}{r_2}\right)^2 = \frac{4}{9}$$
$$\frac{r_1}{r_2} = \frac{2}{3}$$
$$\left(\frac{r_1}{r_2}\right)^3 = \left(\frac{2}{3}\right)^3$$
$$= \frac{8}{27}$$

Thus
$$\frac{\text{volume of cone } A}{\text{volume of cone } B} = \frac{8}{27}$$

Exercise 9.5

answers on p. 437

1. Find the ratio of the volumes of each pair of similar solids. The measures of the corresponding lengths for each pair are given.

(a)

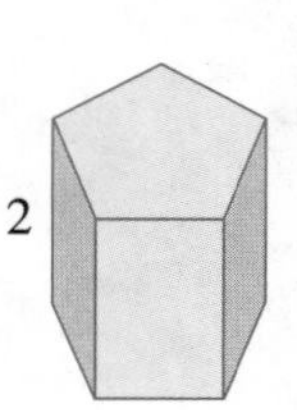

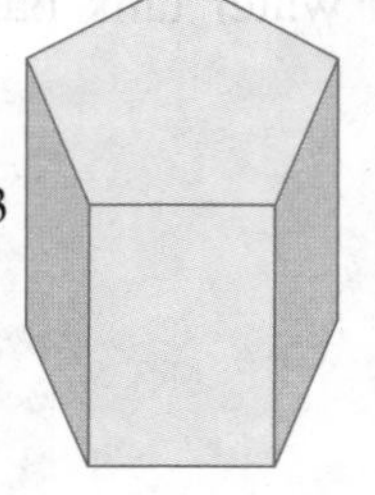

(b)

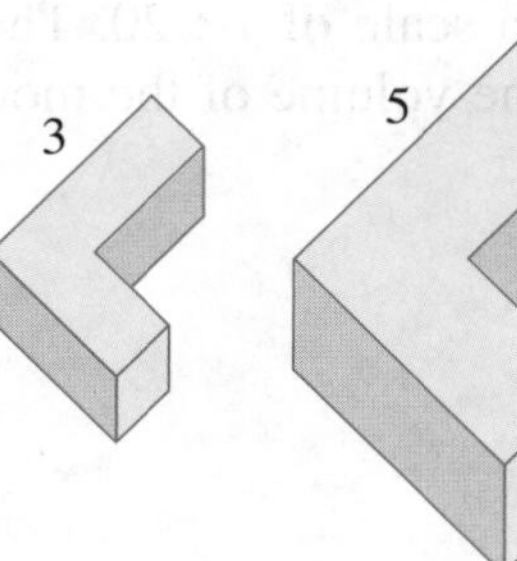

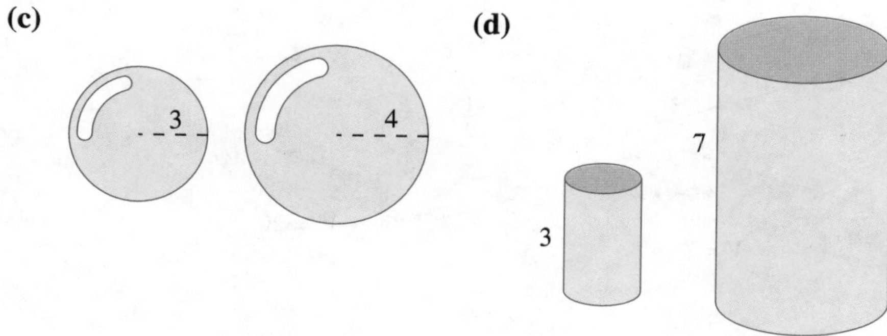

2. Each pair of the following figures are similar. Find the desired volume.

(a)

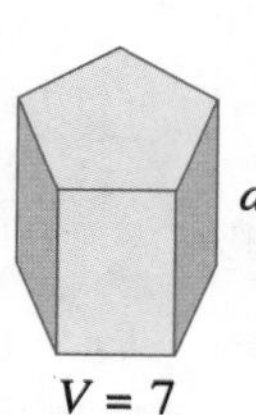

$V = 7$

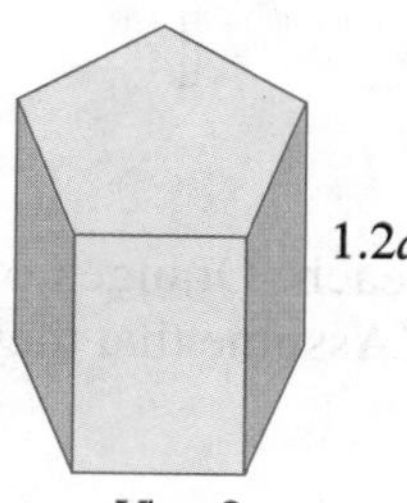

$V' = ?$

(b)

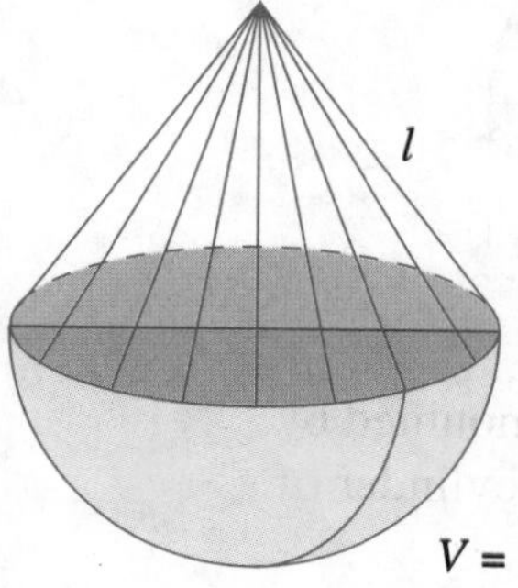

$V = 10$

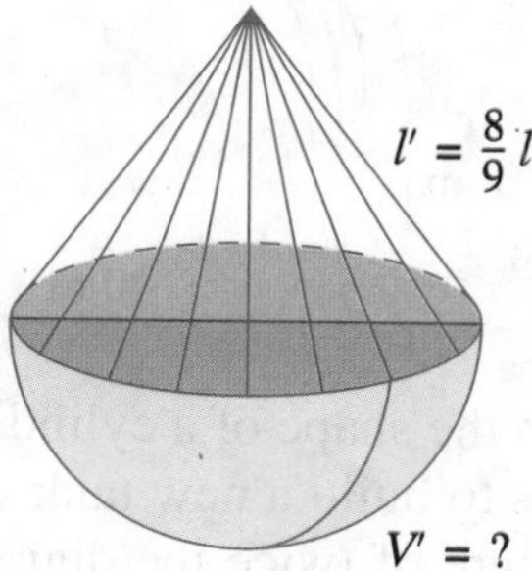

$V' = ?$

(c)

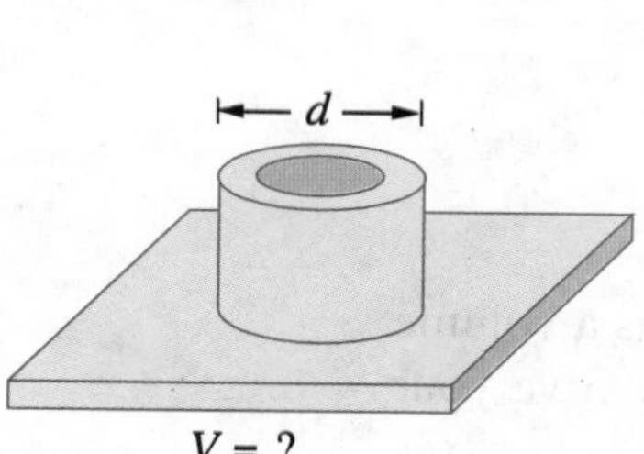

$V = ?$

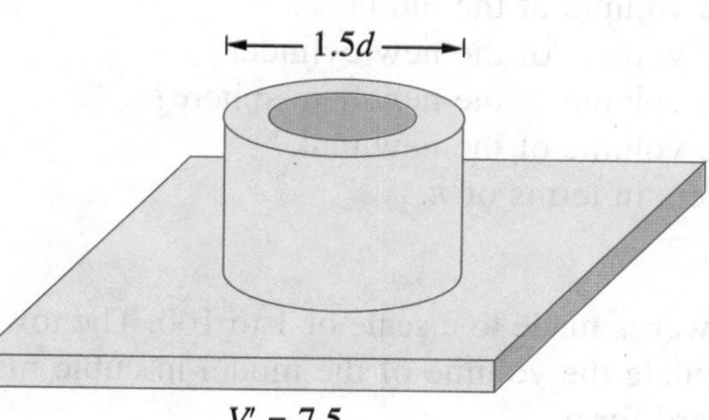

$V' = 7.5$

(d)

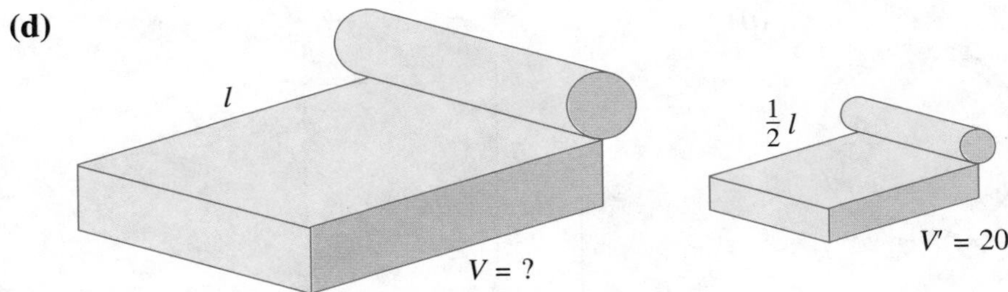

3. Two steel keys have the same shape. One is 4 cm long and the other 6 cm long. If the smaller key weighs 30 g, how much does the larger key weigh?

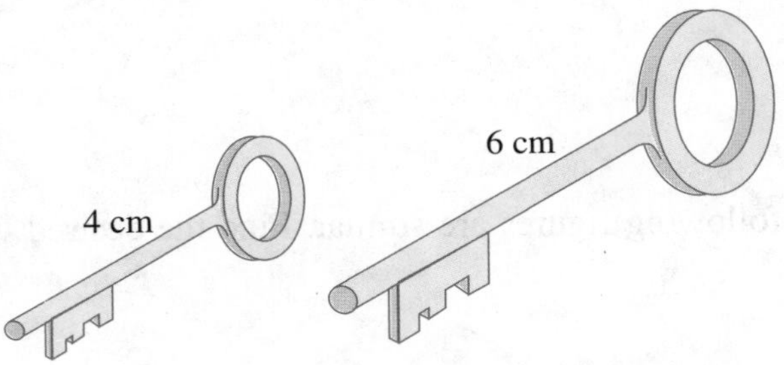

4. Oranges of diameter 6 cm cost 15 cents each. Oranges of diameter 8 cm cost 30 cents each. Which is a better buy? (Assume that they are of the same variety.)

5.

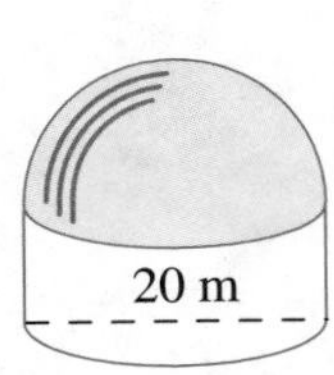

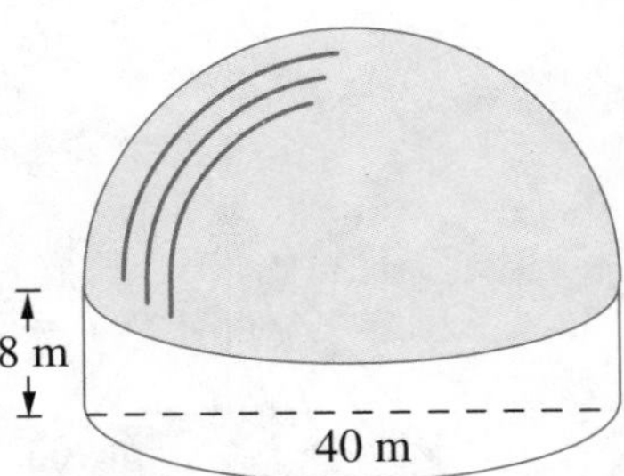

A gas company has a storage tank in the shape of a cylinder surmounted by a hemisphere. The company decides to build a new tank with a cylinder of the same height but with a hemisphere of twice the diameter.

(a) What is the volume of the old cylinder?
(b) What is the volume of the old hemisphere?
(c) What is the volume of the old tank?
(d) What is the volume of the new cylinder?
(e) What is the volume of the new hemisphere?
(f) What is the volume of the new tank?

Give your answers in terms of π.

6. A model of a tower is made to a scale of 1 to 100. The tower has a volume of 900 m^3. Calculate the volume of the model in cubic metres. Give your answer in standard form. *(C)*

7. Find **(i)** the ratio of the surface areas, **(ii)** the ratio of the volumes of the following.
   (a) Two similar spheres of radii 3 cm and 5 cm.
   (b) Two similar solid cones of heights 6 cm and 8 cm.
   (c) Two similar solid cylinders with base radii 2 cm and 6 cm.

8. The base areas of two similar cones are in the ratio 4 : 9.
   (a) Find the ratio of their heights.
   (b) If the volume of the smaller cone is 200 cm^3, find the volume of the larger cone.

9. The volumes of two similar glasses are in the ratio 8 : 27.
   (a) Find the ratio of their base radii.
   (b) If the smaller glass has a base area of 36 cm^2, what is the base area of the bigger glass?

10. A solid cube whose edge is 4 cm long weighs 192 g. How heavy will a similar cube be if its edge measures 9 cm?

11. The surface area of a sphere is 50 cm^2. Its volume is $\frac{1}{8}$ of that of another sphere. What is the surface area of the bigger sphere?

12. The area of the wind screen of a model of a car is $\frac{1}{900}$ that of the car. Find the ratio of the volume of the model to the volume of the car.

13. Two toy boats are geometrically similar and one is $2\frac{1}{2}$ times as long as the other.
    (a) Given that the height of the mast of the smaller boat is 14 cm, calculate the height of the mast of the larger boat.
    (b) Write down the ratio of the surface area of the smaller boat to that of the larger boat, expressing your answer as a fraction. (*C*)

14. A woman buys two cylinder tins of beans in her local supermarket. The tins are geometrically similar to each other. The height of one tin is 8 cm and the height of the other tin is 12 cm.

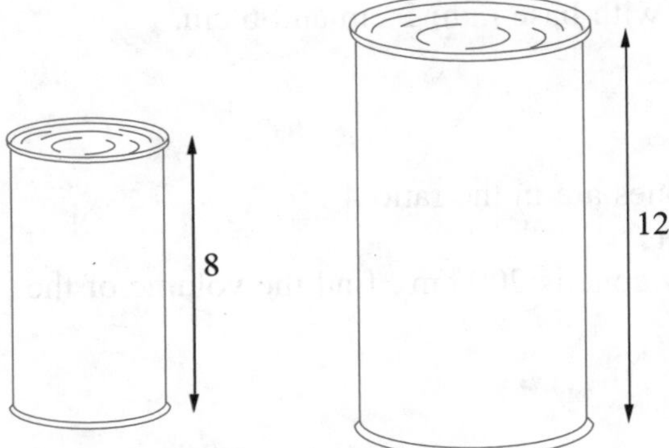

(a) The radius of the small tin is 5 cm. Calculate the radius of the large tin.
(b) Calculate the ratio volume of small tin : volume of large tin, giving your answer in its simplest terms.
(c) The cost of a small tin of beans is 80 cents. Calculate the cost of a large tin of beans, assuming there is no reduction for buying the larger tin.

(C)

Chapter Review

1. Sector of a Circle

- $\dfrac{\text{Length of arc}}{2\pi r} = \dfrac{\theta}{360}$
- $\dfrac{\text{Area of sector}}{\pi r^2} = \dfrac{\theta}{360}$

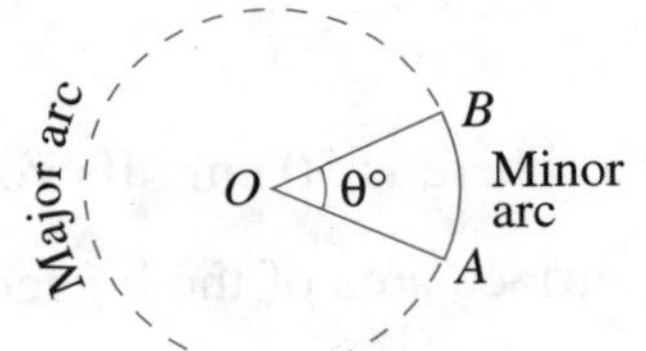

- Area of the sector of circle

$$A = \frac{ar}{2}$$

where A is the area of the sector, a is the length of the arc and r is the radius of the circle.

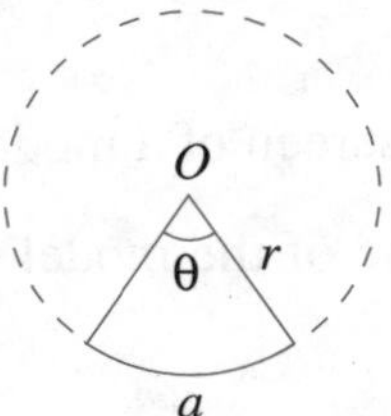

2. Cone

Volume of a cone $= \dfrac{1}{3} \times$ Base Area $\times$ Height

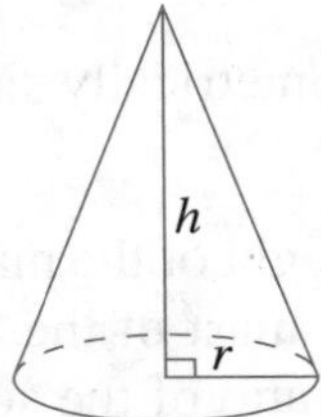

3. Pyramid

Volume of a pyramid = $\frac{1}{3}$ × Base Area × Height

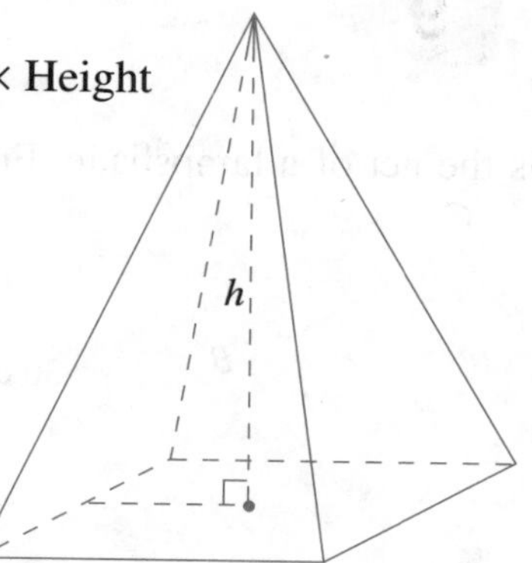

4. Surface Area of a Cone

$A = \pi rl$, where A is the lateral surface area of the cone of radius r and slant height l.

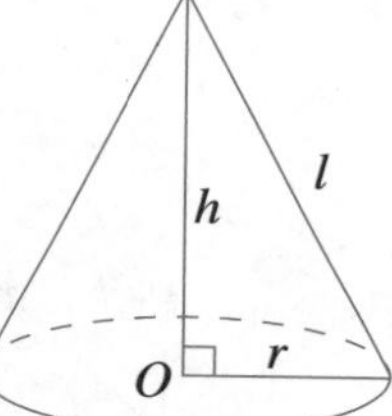

5. Sphere

The volume, V, and surface area, S, of a sphere of radius r are given by the formulae

$$V = \frac{4}{3}\pi r^3$$
$$S = 4\pi r^2$$

6. Areas of Similar Figures

If the ratio of the corresponding lengths of two similar figures is $\frac{a}{b}$,

then the ratio of their areas is $\left(\frac{a}{b}\right)^2$.

7. Volumes of Similar Solids

If the ratio of the corresponding lengths of two similar solids is $\frac{a}{b}$, then

(a) the ratio of their volumes is $\left(\frac{a}{b}\right)^3$,

(b) the ratio of their total surface area is $\left(\frac{a}{b}\right)^2$.

CHALLENGER 9

1. The figure *ABCD* is the net of a lampshade. Find the width *AB*.

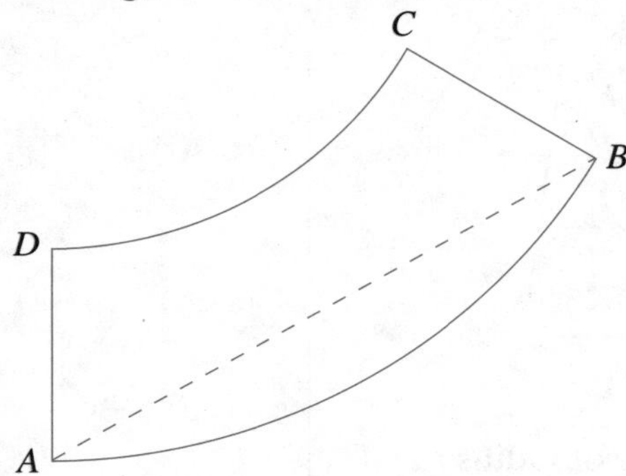

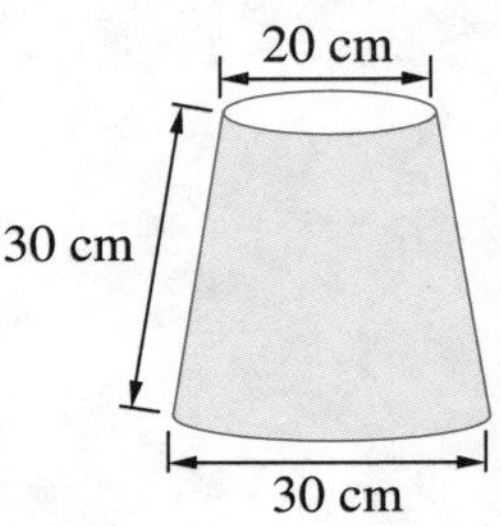

2. The figure shows a sealed plastic container which is $\frac{3}{4}$ filled with water. Its shape is a triangular prism. If $A\hat{B}C = 90°$, $AB = 30$ cm, $BC = 40$ cm and $AC = 50$ cm, find the height of the water level

(a) if the container stands on the face *ABED*,

(b) if the container stands on the face *ACFD*.

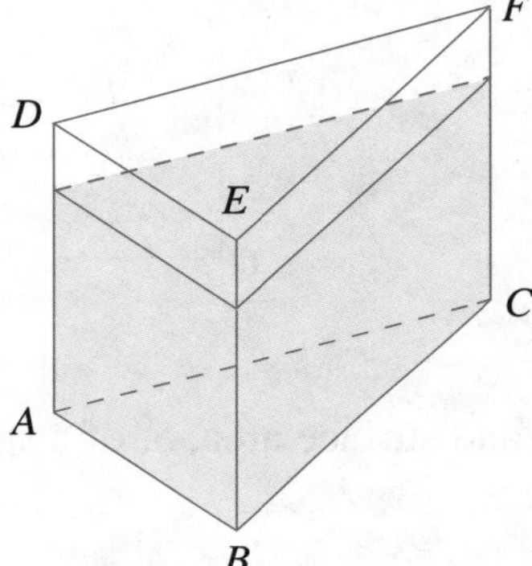

3. Two circles have a common centre *O* and radii *a* and *b* ($a < b$). If the total area of the shaded part is $\frac{1}{2}$ of the area of the bigger circle, find the ratio a^2 to b^2.

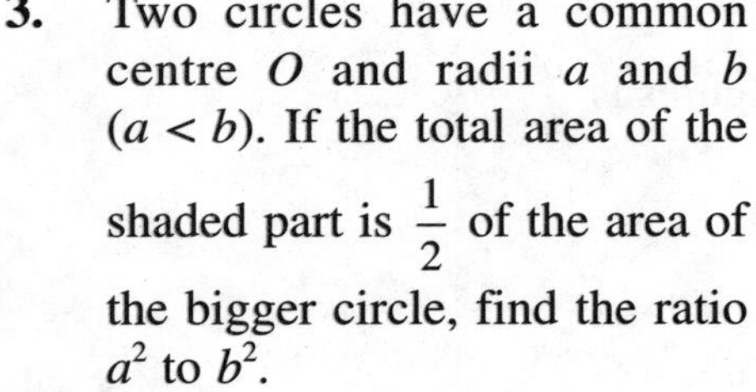

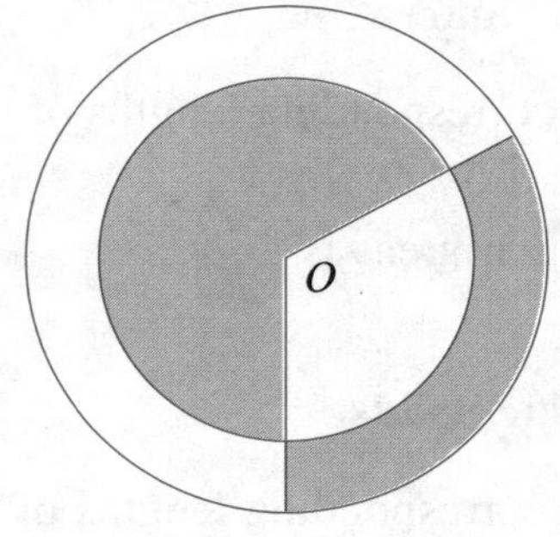

4. An insect wishes to get from *A* to *B* along the curved surface of a solid circular cone of diameter 20 cm. Find the shortest distance of its path.

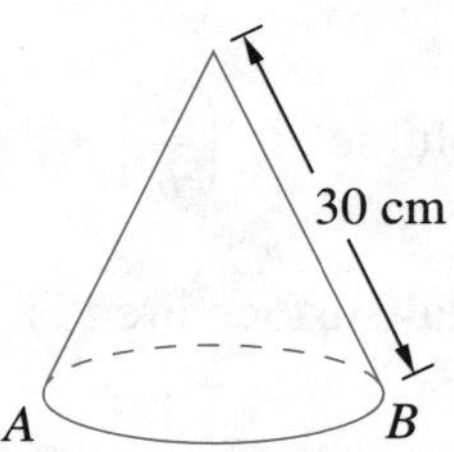

5. In the figure, sector AOB is a quadrant. $\overset{\frown}{AP} = \overset{\frown}{PQ} = \overset{\frown}{QB}$ and $PR \parallel QS \parallel BO$. What fraction of the circle is shaded?
(*Note:* $\overset{\frown}{AP}$ means arc AP.)

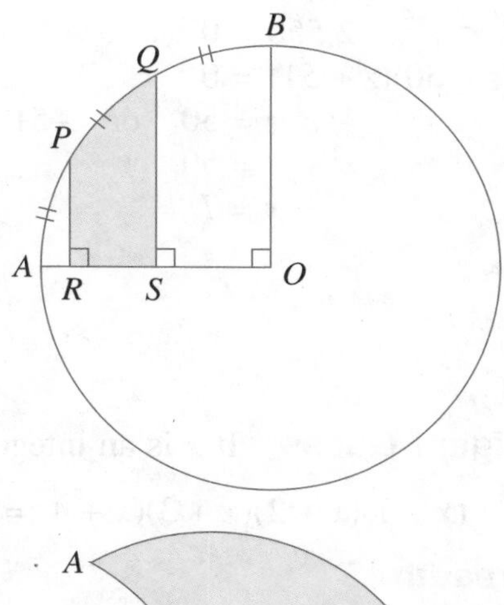

6. The shaded region is bounded by two arcs of the same radius 7 cm. Find the perimeter of the shaded region. $\left(\text{Take } \pi = \frac{22}{7}.\right)$

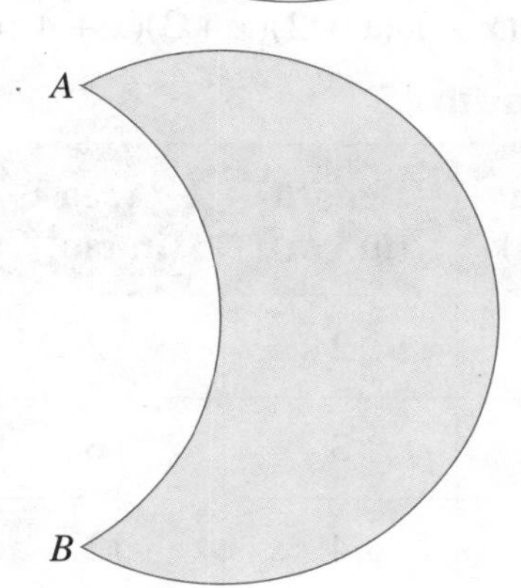

Problem Solving 9

Hidden Clue

If x is a positive integer, find a value of x for which $(x^2 + 2)(x^2 + 1) = 2\ 550$.

An obvious strategy to use is **guess and check**. So we can try $x = 1, 2, 3, \ldots$. However if the solution is a large number, we may have to make many trials. Let us study the equation again to look for hidden clue. We observe that the two factors on the left side are consecutive integers. This suggests we should try values close to the square root of 2 550 for the factors $(x^2 + 2)$ and $(x^2 + 1)$. As $\sqrt{2\ 550} \approx 50.5$ (by calculator) and 51×50 is indeed 2 550, we write

$$(x^2 + 2)(x^2 + 1) = 51 \times 50$$
$$x^2 + 2 = 51$$
$$\therefore x = 7 \quad (x \text{ is positive})$$

What if the condition that x is a positive integer is removed?

We observe that the given equation is of the form $(y + 2)(y + 1) = 2\ 550$ where $y = x^2$. So, we can solve for y first and then find x. If we let $z = x^2 + 1$, we can also solve the equation $(z + 1)(z) = 2\ 550$ for z and then find x.

So
$$z^2 + z - 2\,550 = 0$$
$$(z - 50)(z + 51) = 0$$
$$z = 50 \quad \text{or} \quad -51 \text{ (rejected)}$$
$$x^2 + 1 = 50$$
$$x = 7$$

1. **Make an Intelligent Guess** If x is an integer, solve the equation:

$$(x + 1)(x + 2)(x + 3)(x + 4) = 3\,024$$

2. **Length and Breadth**

Width (in cm)	Length (in cm)	Area (in cm^2)	Perimeter (in cm)
1	2	2	6
2	3	6	10
3	4	12	14
4	5	20	18

A sequence of rectangles was drawn. In each case the length and the width were exact numbers of centimetres and the length was always one centimetre more than the width. The area and the perimeter of each of the first four rectangles were calculated and the results were recorded in the table as shown.

(a) Calculate the width and length of a rectangle in the sequence which has an area of 132 cm^2.

(b) Calculate the width and length of a rectangle in the sequence which has a perimeter of 50 cm. *(C)*

3. **Age Problem** When Abu's age is equal to Bala's present age, Bala will be twice as old as Caihui. Find the ratio of Caihui's age to Abu's age now.

4. **Famous Men** What do the letters represent to make the addition correct?

$$\begin{array}{r} NEWTON \\ +\quad KLEIN \\ \hline KEPLER \\ \hline \end{array}$$

Rule: The same letter represents the same digit. Different letters represent different digits.

Chapter 10

Pythagoras' Theorem and Trigonometry

Chapter Highlights

- Demonstrating an understanding of the Pythagoras' Theorem, including stating the theorem
- Recognising the hypothenuse
- Determining whether a triangle with given sides is a right-angled triangle, including identifying the right angle
- Applying the Pythagoras' Theorem to find a side of a right-angled triangle
- Solving problems using the Pythagoras' Theorem
- Solving problems involving heights and distances by scale drawing, including using the terms angle of elevation and angle of depression
- Recognising that the sine, cosine or tangent ratio for a given angle depends on the angle irrespective of the size of the triangle
- Recognising the hypothenuse, side opposite and side adjacent to a given angle
- Stating the sine, cosine and tangent ratios in terms of the sides of a right-angled triangle
- Using a calculator to find the sine, cosine or tangent ratio of a given angle
- Using a calculator to find the angle given the sine, cosine or tangent ratio for an unknown angle
- Using the sine, cosine or tangent ratio to find a side or an angle of a right-angled triangle or a related figure
- Solving simple trigonometrical problems in two dimensions

10.1 PYTHAGORAS' THEOREM

Ancient Egyptian surveyors knew that a triangle with sides 3, 4 and 5 units contains a right angle. They used this fact to mark out right angles on farm lands.

Pythagoras' theorem is a rule that describes the relationship between the lengths of the sides of any right-angled triangle.

The following class activity will help you discover the relationship between the sides of a right-angled triangle.

Class Activity 1

1. *ABC* is a right-angled triangle drawn on a grid of 1 cm. The longest side *AB* of the right-angled triangle is called the **hypotenuse**.

Study the figure below and answer the questions that follow.

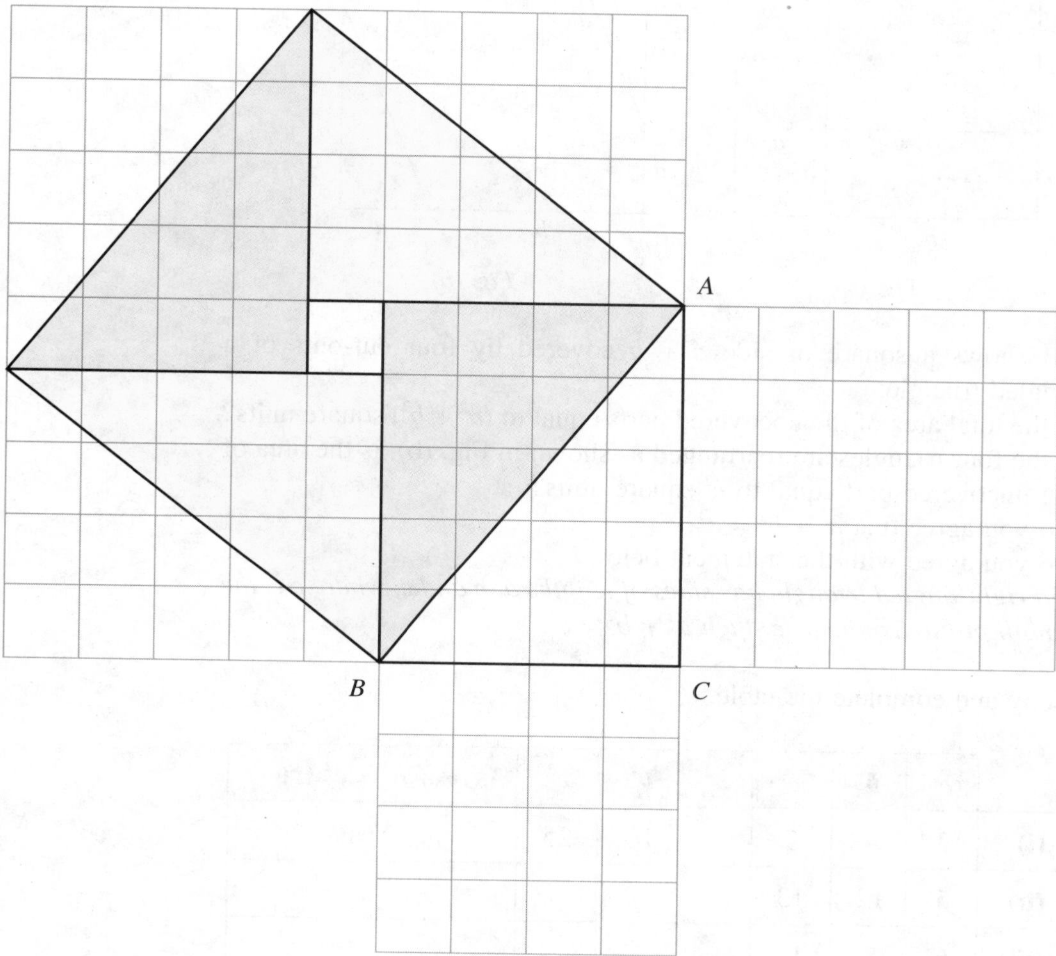

(a) Notice that the square on the hypotenuse AB is divided into four triangular parts and a square part.

(i) Is the area of each triangular part equal to $\frac{1}{2} \times 4 \times 5$ cm^2?

(ii) Is the area of the square part equal to 1×1 cm^2?

(iii) Is the total area of these parts equal to

$$\left[4\left(\frac{1}{2} \times 4 \times 5\right) + 1 \times 1\right] \text{ cm}^2?$$

(iv) Is the area of the square on AB equal to 41 cm^2?

(b) **(i)** Is the area of the square on BC equal to 4×4 or 16 cm^2?

(ii) Is the area of the square on AC equal to 5×5 or 25 cm^2?

(iii) Is the sum of their areas equal to 41 cm^2?

(c) Is $AC^2 + BC^2 = AB^2$?

2.

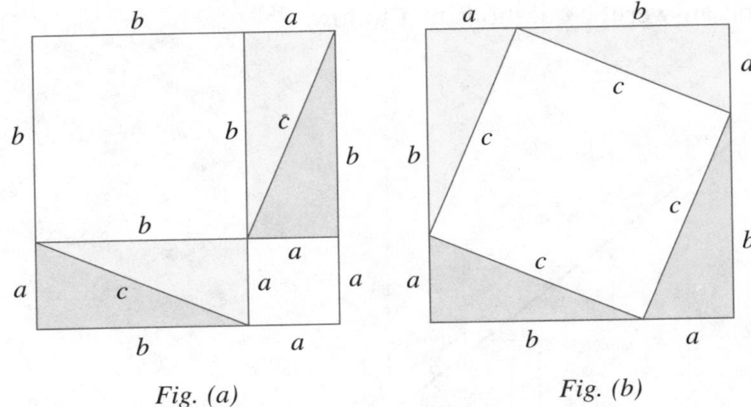

Fig. (a) *Fig. (b)*

Fig. (a) shows a square of side $a + b$ covered by four cut-outs of a right-angled triangle.

(a) Is the total area of the uncovered parts equal to $(a^2 + b^2)$ square units?

(b) If the four triangles are rearranged as shown in Fig. (b), is the area of the uncovered part equal to c^2 square units?

(c) Do you agree that $a^2 + b^2 = c^2$?

(d) Do you agree with the statement below?
If a right-angled triangle has sides of lengths a, b and c, where c is the length of the hypotenuse, then $a^2 + b^2 = c^2$.

3. **(a)** Copy and complete the table.

	a	b	c	a^2	b^2	c^2	Is $a^2 + b^2 = c^2$ true?
(i)	3	4	5	9	16	25	Yes
(ii)	5	12	13				
(iii)	6	8	11				
(iv)	8	15	17				
(v)	4	9	10				
(vi)	7	24	25				

(b) Using the values of a, b and c as lengths in each case, draw a triangle. You may use 1 cm as a unit or 5 mm as a unit where appropriate. State whether each of the triangles is a right-angled triangle.

(c) Do you agree that in $\triangle ABC$ if $a^2 + b^2 = c^2$, then the angle opposite the side c is a right angle?

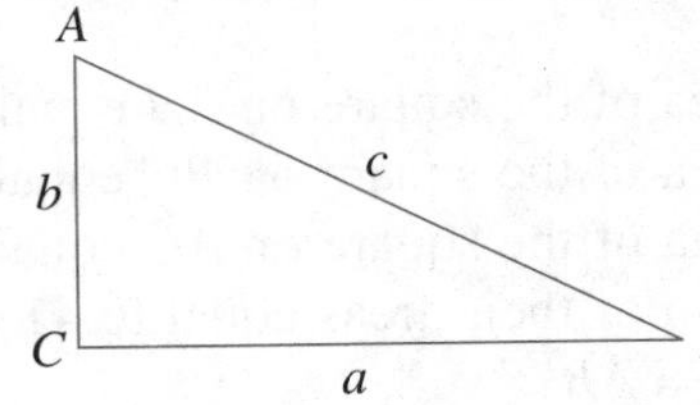

Remember this:

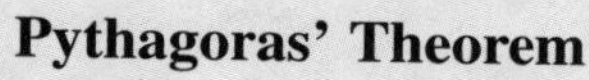

Pythagoras' Theorem

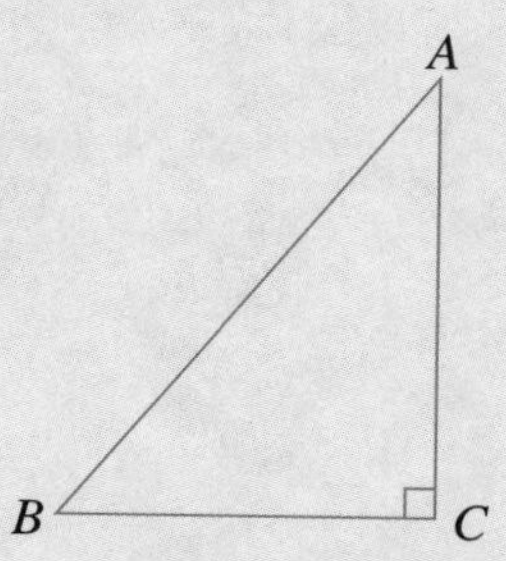

In $\triangle ABC$ if $\hat{C} = 90°$, then $AC^2 + BC^2 = AB^2$.

In $\triangle ABC$ if $AC^2 + BC^2 = AB^2$, then $\hat{C} = 90°$.

Worked Example 1

In $\triangle ABC$, $\hat{C} = 90°$. Find

(a) c if $a = 9$ and $b = 12$,

(b) b if $a = 4$ and $c = 8.5$.

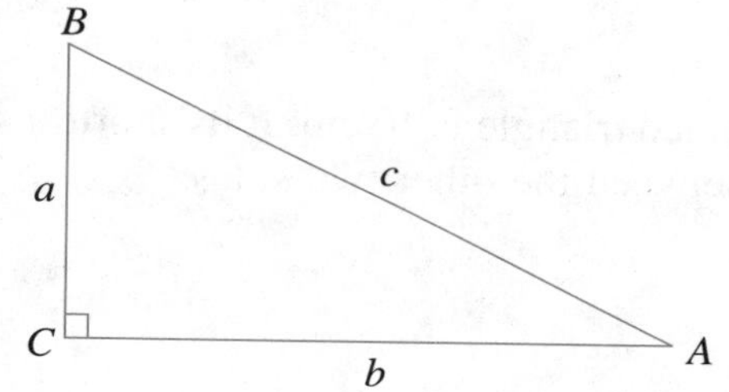

Solution:

(a)
$$\begin{aligned} c^2 &= a^2 + b^2 \\ &= 9^2 + 12^2 \\ &= 81 + 144 \\ &= 225 \\ \therefore c &= \sqrt{225} \\ &= 15 \end{aligned}$$

(b)
$$\begin{aligned} a^2 + b^2 &= c^2 \\ b^2 &= c^2 - a^2 \\ &= 8.5^2 - 4^2 \\ &= 72.25 - 16 \\ &= 56.25 \\ \therefore b &= \sqrt{56.25} \\ &= 7.5 \end{aligned}$$

Worked Example 2

Find x and y in the figure.

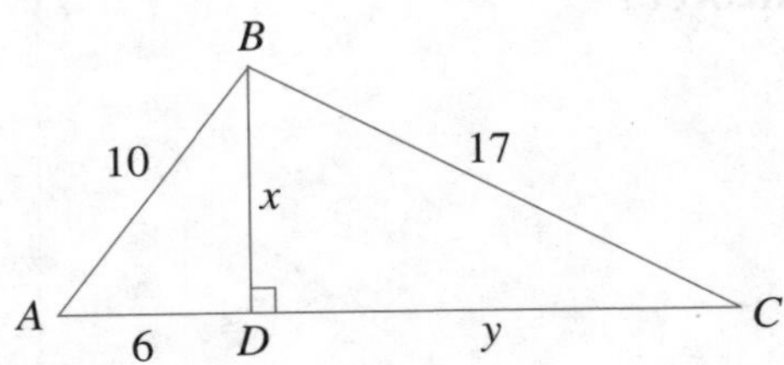

Solution:

In $\triangle ABD$, $10^2 = 6^2 + x^2$

$$\therefore x^2 = 10^2 - 6^2 = (10 + 6)(10 - 6) = (16)(4) = 64$$

$$\therefore x = \sqrt{64} = 8$$

In $\triangle BDC$, $17^2 = x^2 + y^2$

$$\therefore y^2 = 17^2 - x^2 = 289 - 64 = 225$$

$$\therefore y = \sqrt{225} = 15$$

Worked Example 3

The perimeter of a right-angled triangle is 40 cm. If its shortest side is 8 cm, find the difference in lengths between the other two sides.

Solution:

We have:

$$x + y + 8 = 40$$

$$x + y = 32$$

Also $\quad x^2 - y^2 = 8^2$

$$(x + y)(x - y) = 64$$

$$x - y = \frac{64}{32} = 2$$

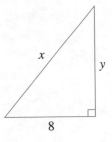

The difference between the other two sides is 2 cm.

Note: The strategy used is **to think of a related problem**:

$$a^2 - b^2 = (a + b)(a - b)$$

If $a^2 - b^2$ and $a + b$ are knowns, the unknown $a - b$ can be found.

Exercise 10.1 

answers on p. 437

1. In each of the following triangles, name the hypotenuse.

(a) 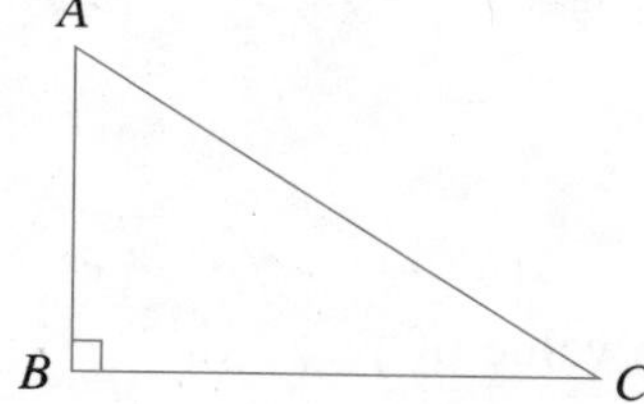

(b) 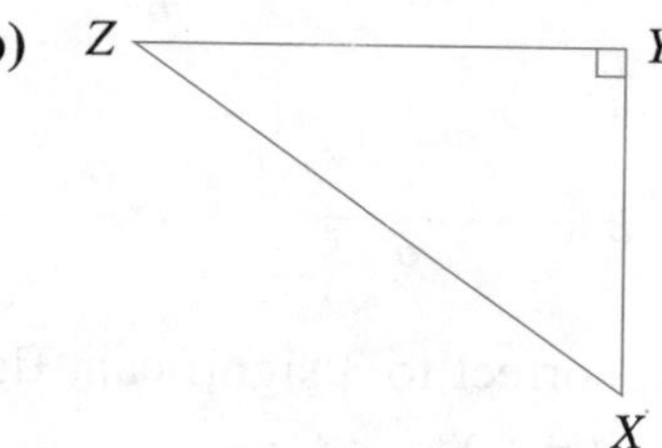

2. In $\triangle XYZ$, $\hat{Y} = 90°$. Find
(a) y if $z = 6$ and $x = 8$,
(b) z if $y = 20$ and $x = 16$,
(c) x if $z = 10$ and $y = 26$.

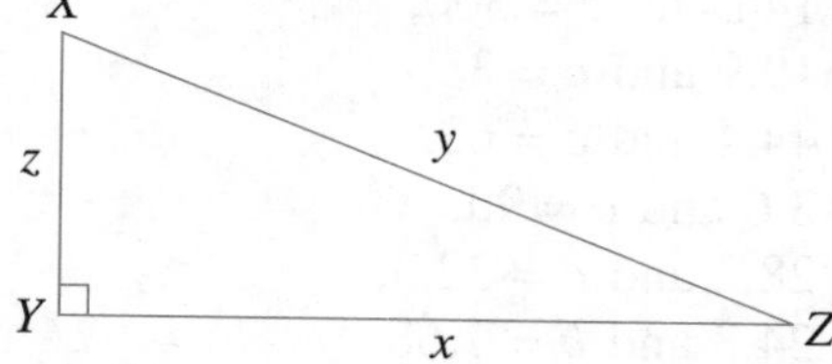

3. In $\triangle PQR$, $\hat{Q} = 90°$. Find
(a) p if $q = 25$ and $r = 7$,
(b) q if $p = 8$ and $r = 15$,
(c) r if $q = 65$ and $p = 16$.

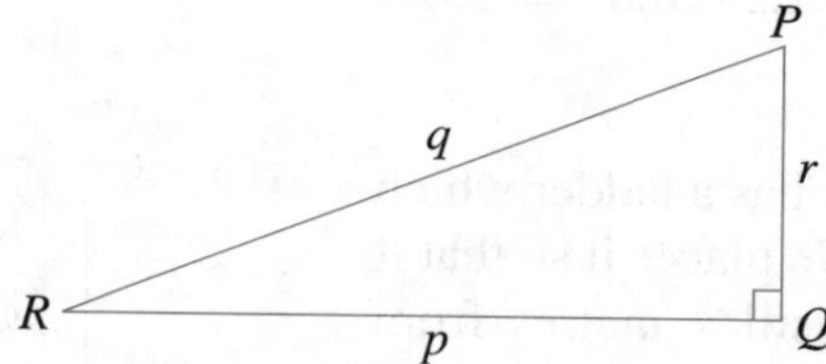

4. In $\triangle TUV$, $\hat{V} = 90°$. Find
(a) t if $u = 35$ and $v = 37$,
(b) u if $v = 41$ and $t = 40$,
(c) v if $t = 5$ and $u = 12$.

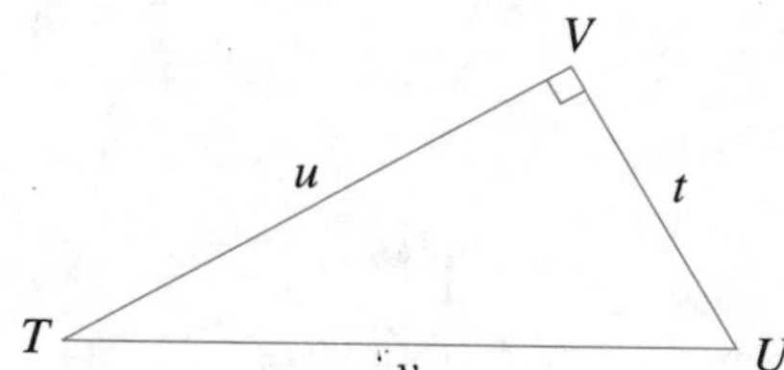

5. Determine which of the following triangles are right-angled and state the right angle.
(a) In $\triangle ABC$, $AB = 8$ cm, $BC = 9$ cm and $AC = 7$ cm.
(b) In $\triangle PQR$, $PQ = 15$ cm, $QR = 25$ cm and $PR = 20$ cm.
(c) In $\triangle XYZ$, $XY = 36$ cm, $YZ = 39$ cm and $XZ = 15$ cm.
(d) In $\triangle STU$, $ST = 9$ cm, $TU = 15$ cm and $SU = 20$ cm.
(e) In $\triangle CDE$, $CD = 8$ cm, $DE = 15$ cm and $CE = 17$ cm.
(f) In $\triangle LMN$, $LM = 20$ cm, $MN = 21$ cm and $NL = 29$ cm.

6.

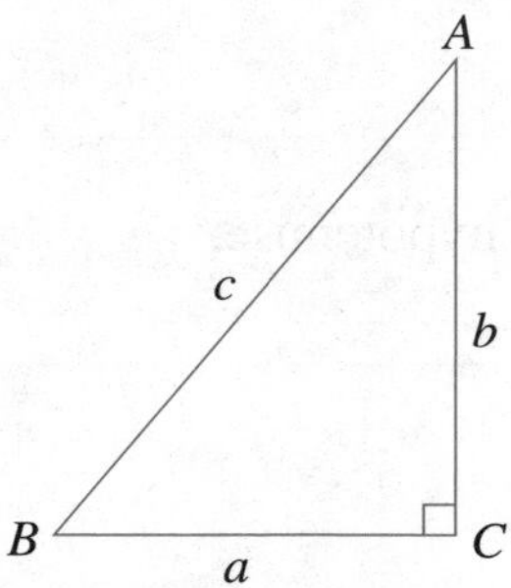

In $\triangle ABC$, $\hat{C} = 90°$. Find, correct to 3 significant figures, the value of

(a) a if **(i)** $b = 3.3$ and $c = 8.8$,
(ii) $b = 19.6$ and $c = 32.3$,
(iii) $b = 1.2$ and $c = 10.8$,
(iv) $b = 144$ and $c = 300$,

(b) b if **(i)** $a = 19.9$ and $c = 38$,
(ii) $a = 44.4$ and $c = 62$,
(iii) $a = 3.6$ and $c = 9.1$,
(iv) $a = 28.2$ and $c = 32.3$,

(c) c if **(i)** $a = 24.8$ and $b = 7.68$,
(ii) $a = 59.9$ and $b = 31.9$,
(iii) $a = 100$ and $b = 40$,
(iv) $a = 1.24$ and $b = 3.82$.

7. A window-cleaner has a ladder which is 5 metres long. He places it so that it reaches a windowsill 4 metres from the ground. How far from the wall is the foot of the ladder?

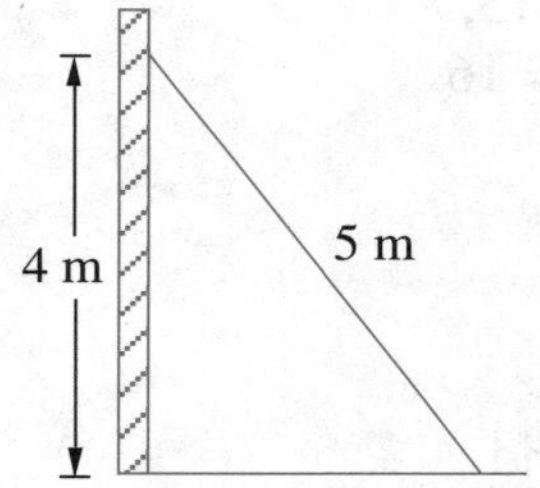

8.

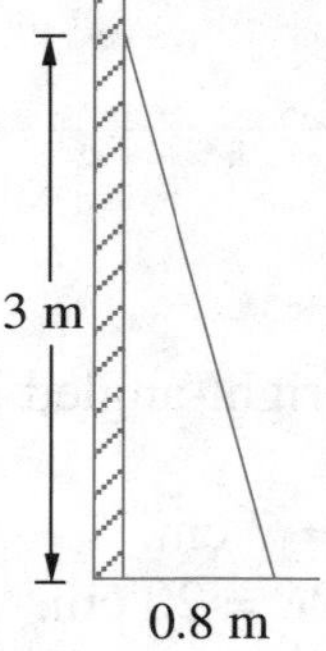

A ladder leans against the wall and reaches a height of 3 m. If the foot of the ladder is 0.8 m from the wall, find, in metres, the length of the ladder. Give your answer correct to 1 decimal place.

9. P and Q are on the opposite sides of a pond. M is a point such that PM and QM can be measured. It is found that PM = 24 m, QM = 26 m and $Q\hat{P}M = 90°$. Calculate the distance between P and Q.

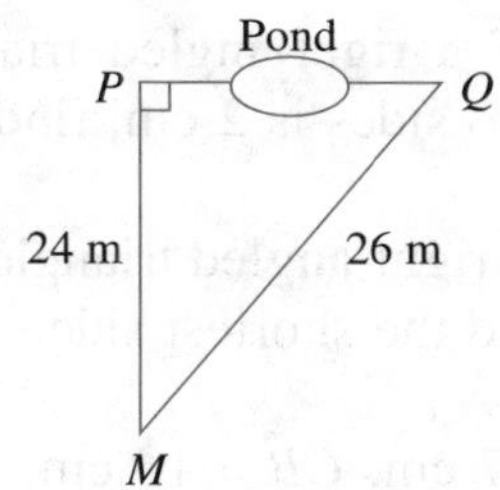

10. In the figure on the right, find h and a.

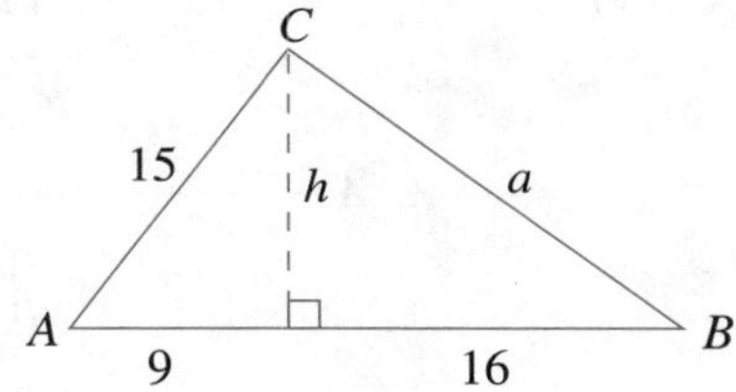

11. In the figure on the left, find x and a.

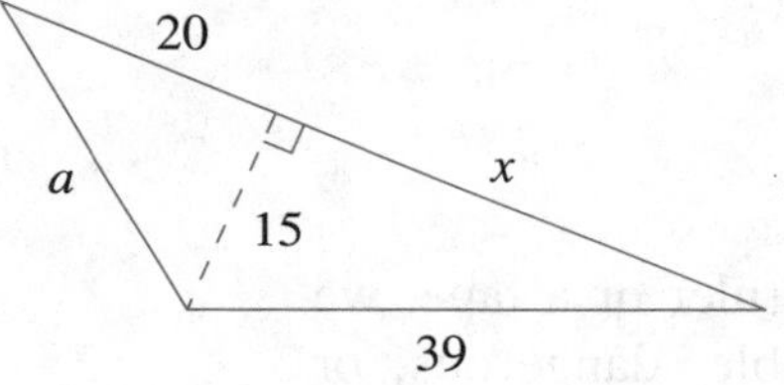

12. Calculate the length of QR in $\triangle PQR$.

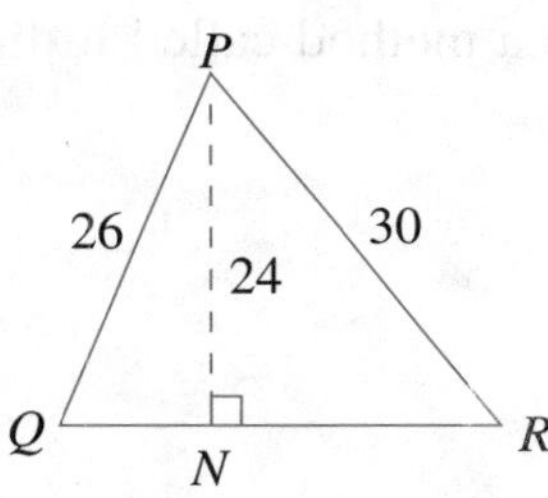

13. A bridge AB with supports MC and MD is built across a river. If AB = 15 m, AC = 4 m and $AM = MB$, find the length of the support MC.

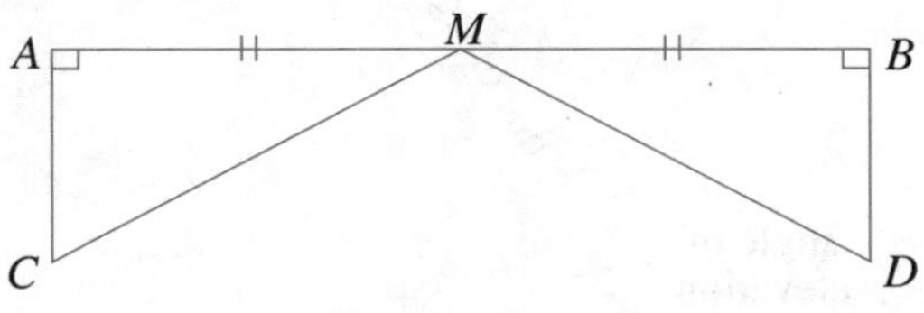

14. The rectangular solid on the right has edges with measurements indicated.

(a) Which angle of $\triangle HFB$ is a right angle?

(b) Calculate the length of diagonal BH. (*Hint:* Calculate the length of HF first.)

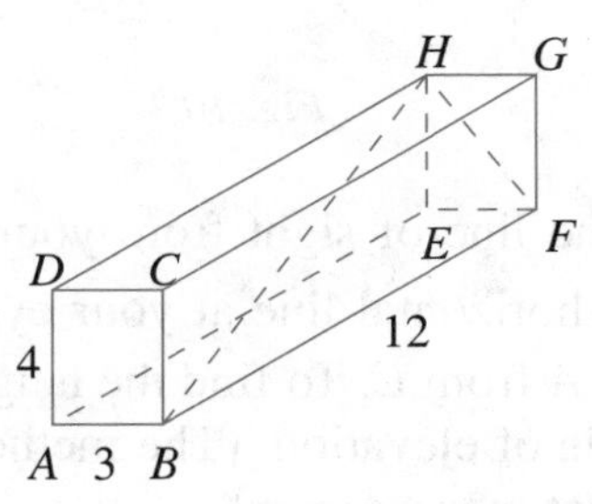

15. The shortest side of a right-angled triangle is 6 cm. If the difference between the other two sides is 2 cm, find the perimeter of the triangle.

16. The longest side of a right-angled triangle is 13 cm. If the perimeter of the triangle is 30 cm, find the shortest side.

17. In $\triangle ABC$, if $AC = 17$ cm, $CB = 10$ cm, $AD = x$ cm, $DB = y$ cm and $AB = 21$ cm, find the value of $(x - y)$.

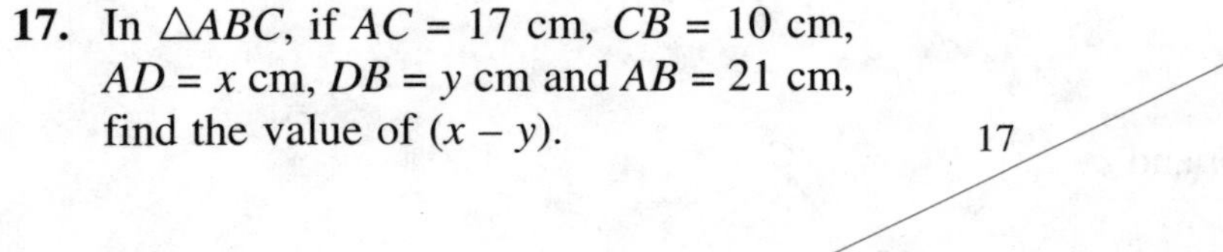

10.2 INDIRECT MEASURE

When we measure the width of a table or a room with a ruler or a tape, we call this **direct measurement**. Sometimes, it is impossible, dangerous, or inconvenient to make direct measurement, for example, in finding the height of a building. Then we use a method called **indirect measurement**.

Examples

(a)

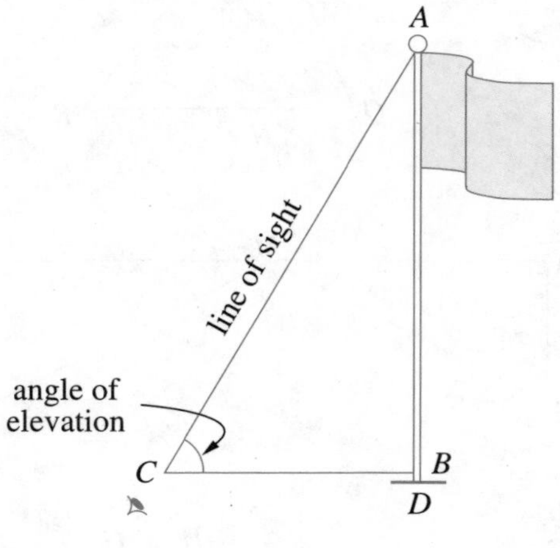

Fig. 10.1

In Fig. 10.1, *CA* is the line of sight from your eye to the point *A* of the flagpole and *CB* is a horizontal line at your eye level. $A\hat{C}B$ is called the **angle of elevation** of *A* from *C*. To find the height of the flagpole *AD*, you first measure the angle of elevation. (The method will be explained later.) Then find *CB* by direct measurement.

Suppose $A\hat{C}B = 60°$ and $CB = 4$ m. You then make a scale drawing, using 1 cm to represent 1 m, to construct a similar right-angled $\triangle A'B'C'$. Measure $A'B'$ which is about 6.9 cm. Thus the height of the flagpole is 6.9 m plus the distance of your eye level from the ground.

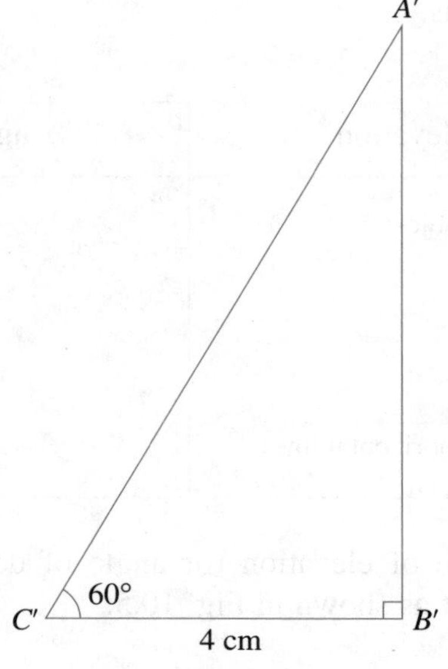

Fig. 10.2

Note: To make calculations simpler, the distance between the eye level and the ground level is often ignored; thus sentences such as '. . . the angle of elevation of the top of a tree from a point on the ground is . . .' or '. . . the angle of elevation of a flagpole is . . .' are often seen in textbook problems.

(b) Let us study Fig. 10.3.

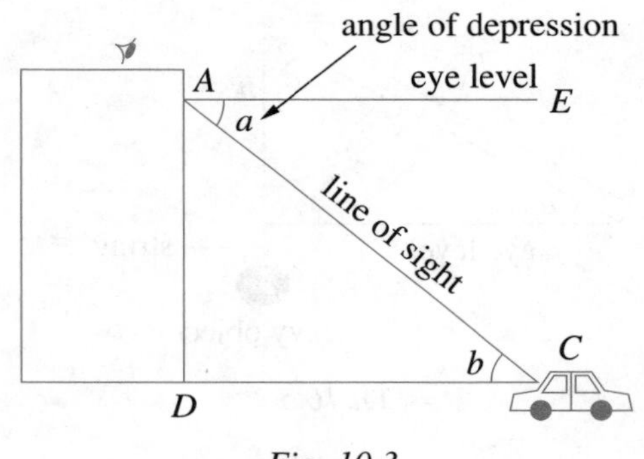

Fig. 10.3

If your eye level is at a known height AD and you wish to find the distance DC, you measure angle a, which is called the **angle of depression** of C from A.

Since AE is parallel to DC, we have $\hat{a} = \hat{b}$. You can find CD by drawing a triangle similar to $\triangle ACD$ with a scale of your choice.

Suppose $\hat{a} = 40°$ and $AD = 30$ m. You then use a scale 1 cm to 5 m and draw $\triangle A'C'D'$ as shown. By measurement, $C'D'$ is about 7.2 cm. Thus the distance CD is about 5×7.2 m or 36 m.

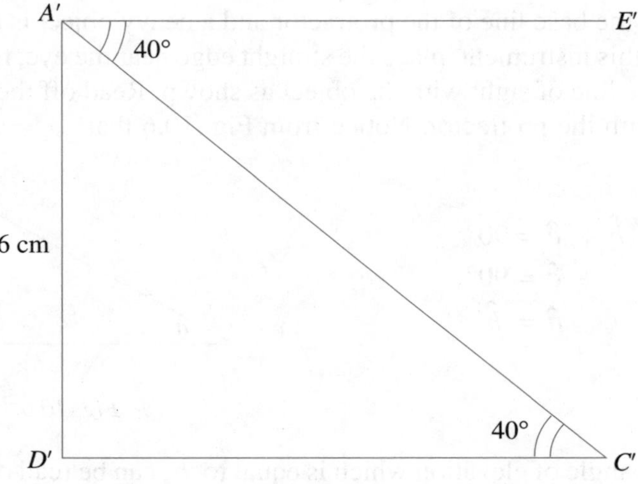

Fig. 10.4

Remember these terms.

Angle of Elevation	Angle of Depression
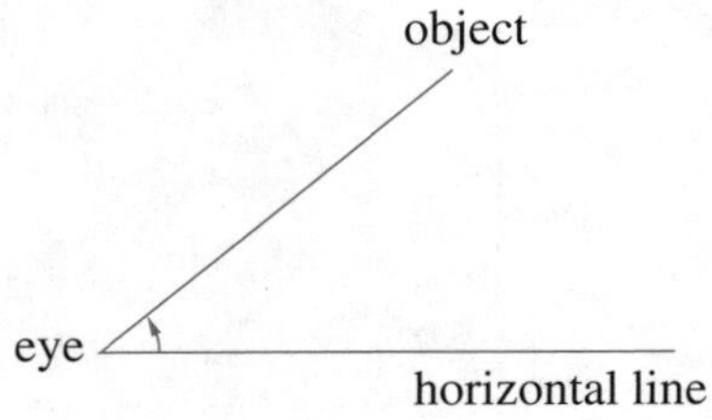 object eye horizontal line	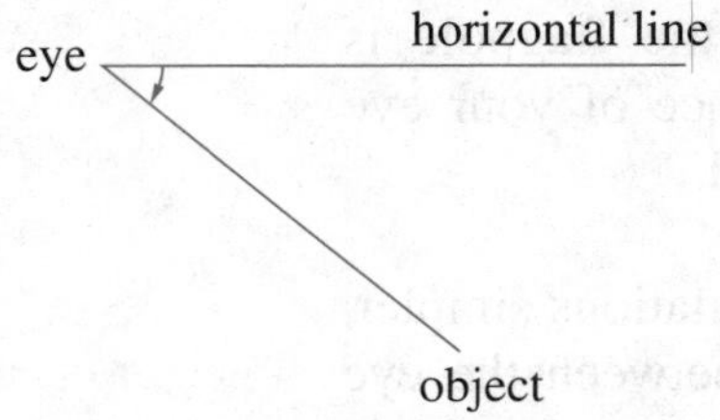 eye horizontal line object

To measure the angle of elevation (or angle of depression), you can use a homemade instrument as shown in Fig. 10.5.

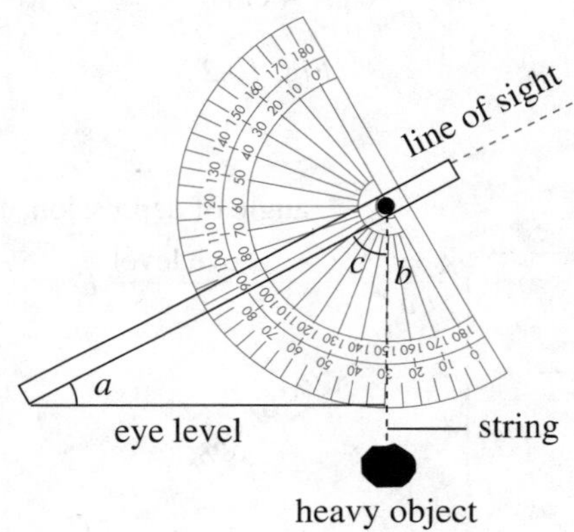

Fig. 10.5

This instrument consists of a protractor fixed to a straight edge which is perpendicular to the base line of the protractor. One end of a string is fixed to the midpoint of the base line of the protractor and a heavy object is tied to the other end. To use this instrument, place the straight edge near the eye, making sure that it falls on the line of sight with the object as shown. Read off the angle made by the string with the protractor. Notice from Fig. 10.6 that:

$$\hat{b} + \hat{c} = 90°$$
$$\hat{a} + \hat{c} = 90°$$
$$\hat{a} = \hat{b}$$

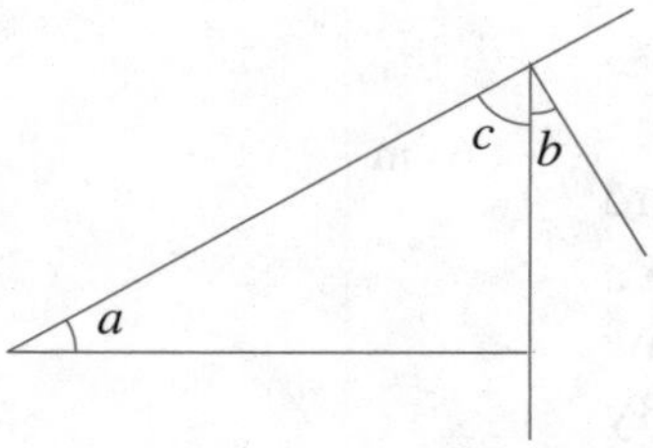

Fig. 10.6

Thus $\hat{a}$, the angle of elevation which is equal to $\hat{b}$, can be read off directly from the protractor.

Exercise 10.2

answers on p. 438

By means of scale drawings, solve the following problems. Give each answer in the appropriate unit correct to the nearest whole number unless otherwise stated. (You may choose your own scale.)

For questions 1 to 3; you may first use the given diagrams to estimate the answers. Then draw appropriate diagrams to find more accurate answers.

1. A ladder, 5 m long, leans against a wall and makes an angle of 70° with the ground. How high up the wall does the ladder reach? How far from the wall is the foot of the ladder? Give your answers correct to 1 decimal place.

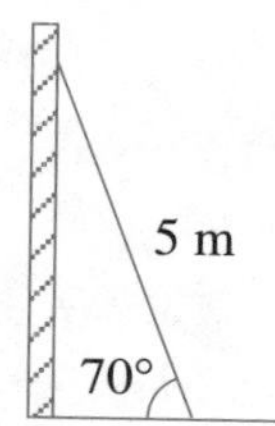

2. A man starts at O and wishes to reach a point P, 500 metres northeast of O. If he gets to P by first walking due north and then due east, how far will he have to walk in each direction?

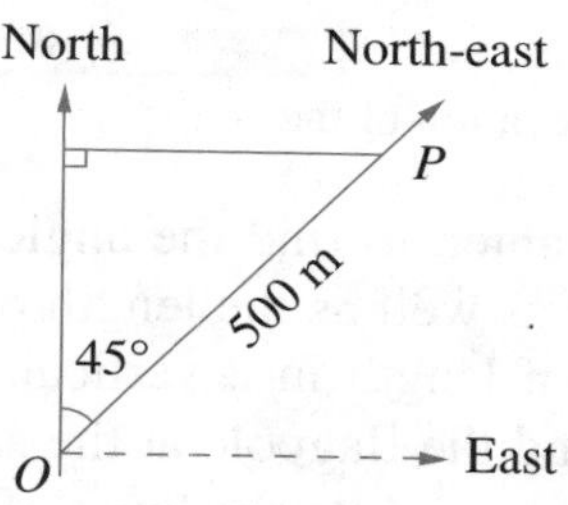

3. From the top of a building 30 m high, a man watches people walking along the street. If the angle of depression of the foot of a pedestrian is 50°, how far is the pedestrian from the foot of the building?

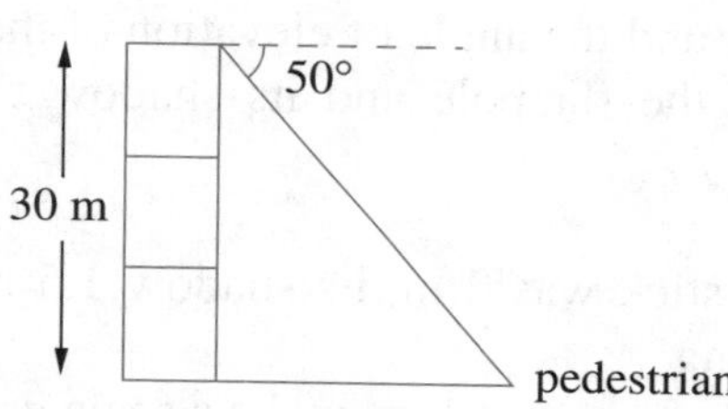

4. Find the height of a tower if the angle of elevation of the top is 40° at a point 50 metres from its foot.

5. Use a homemade instrument for measuring angle and a measuring tape to estimate the height of

(a) the school building,

(b) the flagpole,

(c) the school hall.

10.3 TRIGONOMETRICAL RATIOS

We have seen in the earlier sections how we can apply the useful property of similar right-angled triangles in practical situations. This leads us to the study of a branch of mathematics called **Trigonometry**. The word *trigonometry* comes from the two Greek words *Trigonon*, meaning triangle, and *metron*, meaning measure.

Trigonometry is mathematics that is concerned with the measurement of triangles.

Class Activity 2

1.

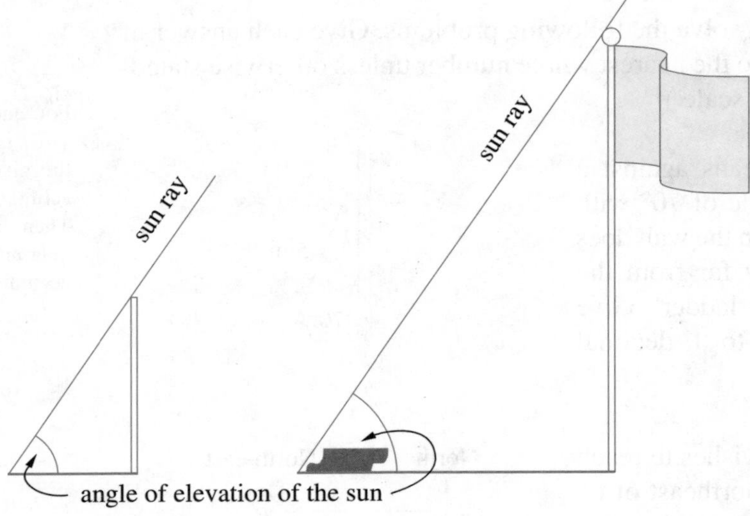

A group of students wanted to find the angle of elevation of the sun at a certain time of the day as well as the length of a vertical flagpole. Having set up a stick of known length in a vertical position, they measured the shadows of the stick and the flagpole at the same time. Then they made a scale drawing of the stick and its shadow to find the angle of elevation of the sun. Having found the angle of elevation of the sun, they made another scale drawing of the flagpole and its shadow to find the length of the flagpole.

Suppose that the stick was 2 m, its shadow 1.5 m and the shadow of the flagpole 4.5 m long.

(a) Using 2 cm to represent 1 m, make a scale drawing of the stick and its shadow to find the angle of elevation of the sun.

(b) With the same scale and the same angle of elevation as in (a), make a scale drawing to find the length of the flagpole.

2. Study $\triangle ABC$ and $\triangle XYZ$. (They are not drawn to scale.) Then answer the following questions.

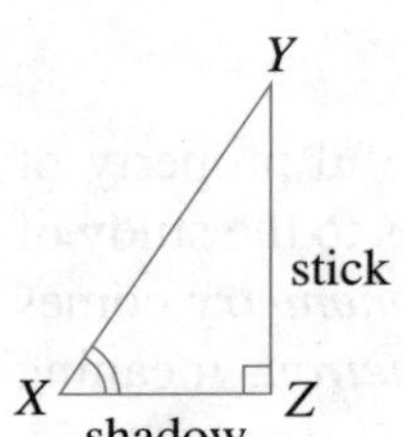

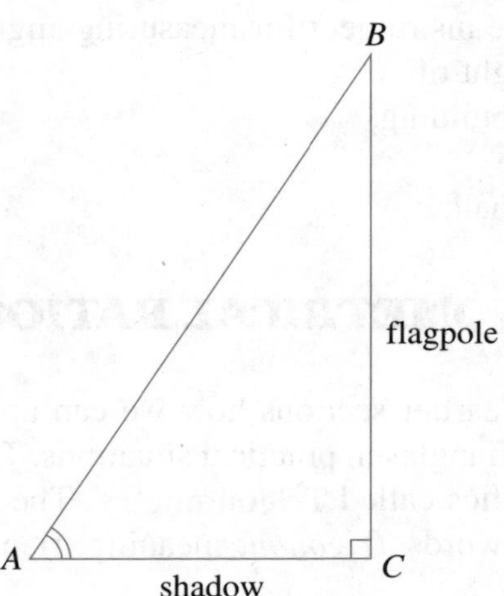

(a) It is given that $\hat{A} = \hat{X}$.

(i) Are $\triangle ABC$ and $\triangle XYZ$ similar?

(ii) Are the following true?

$$\frac{BC}{YZ} = \frac{AC}{XZ}$$

$$\frac{BC}{AC} = \frac{YZ}{XZ}$$

(b) Refer to question 1 and find the length of the flagpole by calculation, using the relation $\frac{BC}{AC} = \frac{YZ}{XZ}$.

(c) If the shadow of the flagpole was not measured at the same time as the shadow of the stick, would you still be able to calculate the length of the flagpole this way? Do you agree that, for any vertical pole, the ratio $\frac{\text{length of pole}}{\text{length of shadow}}$ depends on the angle of elevation of the sun?

(d) In any triangle ABC with a right angle at C, we refer to AC as the side adjacent to $\hat{A}$, BC as the side opposite $\hat{A}$ and AB as the hypotenuse. Do you agree that each of the ratios

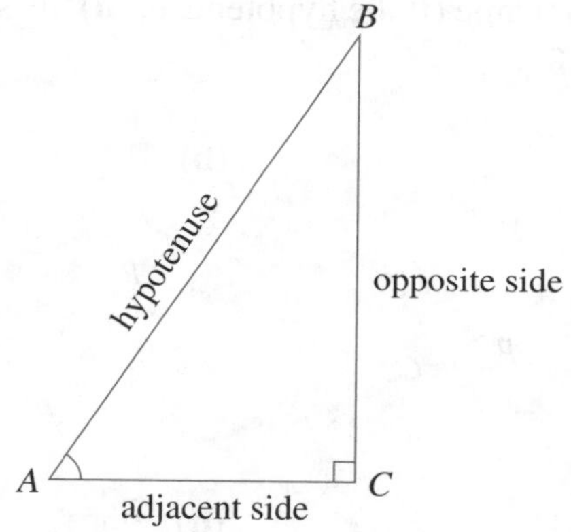

$$\frac{\text{side opposite } \hat{A}}{\text{side adjacent to } \hat{A}},$$

$$\frac{\text{side opposite } \hat{A}}{\text{hypotenuse}} \text{ and}$$

$$\frac{\text{side adjacent to } \hat{A}}{\text{hypotenuse}}$$

depends on $\hat{A}$?

In any triangle ABC where $\hat{C} = 90°$, we define

(i) the ratio $\frac{\text{side opposite } \hat{A}}{\text{hypotenuse}}$ as the **sine** of $\hat{A}$, written as $\sin \hat{A}$,

(ii) the ratio $\frac{\text{side adjacent to } \hat{A}}{\text{hypotenuse}}$ as the **cosine** of $\hat{A}$, written as $\cos \hat{A}$,

(iii) the ratio $\frac{\text{side opposite } \hat{A}}{\text{side adjacent to } \hat{A}}$ as the **tangent** of $\hat{A}$, written as $\tan \hat{A}$.

MATHSTORY

Although the word trigonometry is from the Greek word trigonon (triangle) and me'tron (measure), it was first used by European mathematicians around 1590. The term sine originated with the Hindus who referred to it as jya, meaning chord. Newton first used the term cosine in 1658.

These three ratios, sine, cosine and tangent of a given angle, are called **trigonometrical ratios**. Trigonometry is the study of the relationships between the measures of sides and angles in triangles.

Remember these:

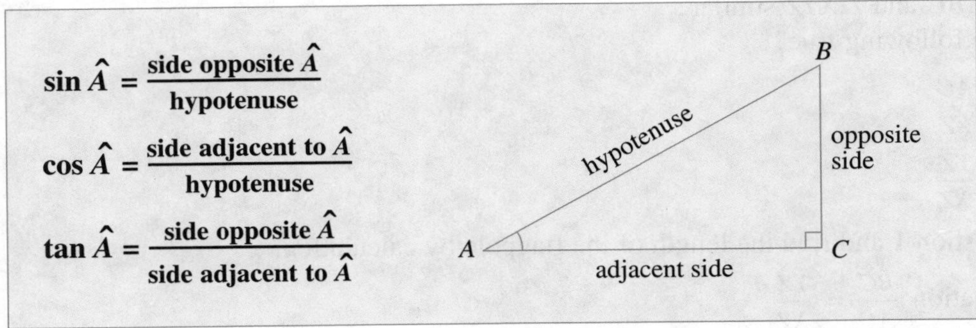

Exercise 10.3

answers on p. 438

1. For each diagram, name **(i)** the hypotenuse, **(ii)** the side opposite $\hat{p}$, **(iii)** the side adjacent to $\hat{p}$.

(a)

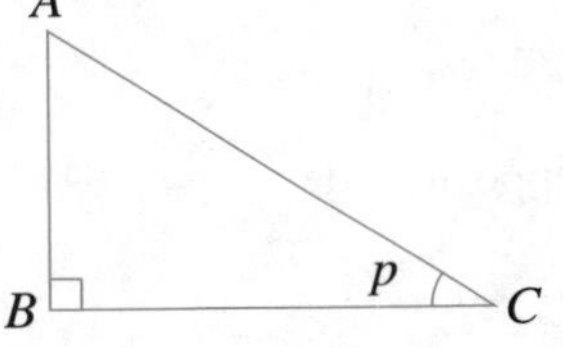

(b)

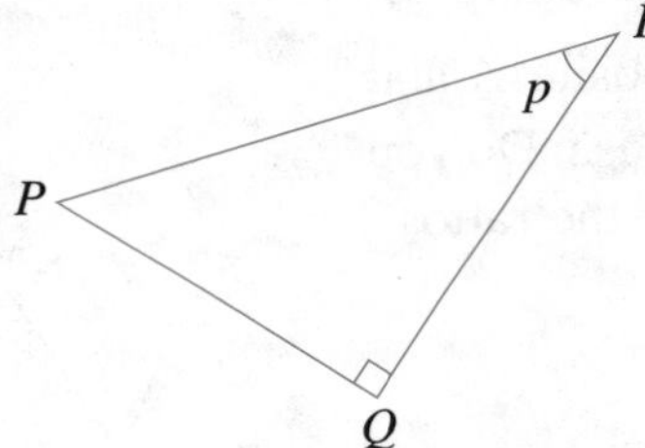

(c)

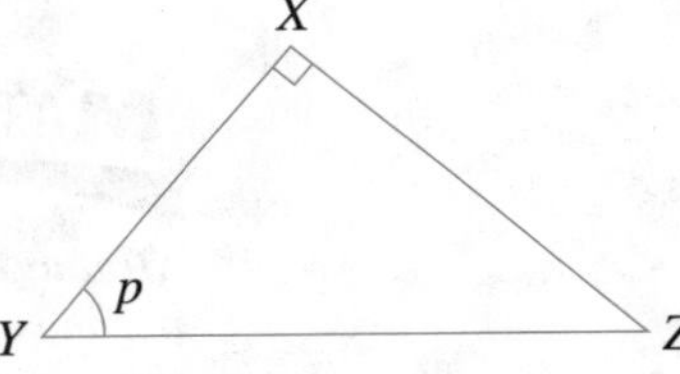

(d)

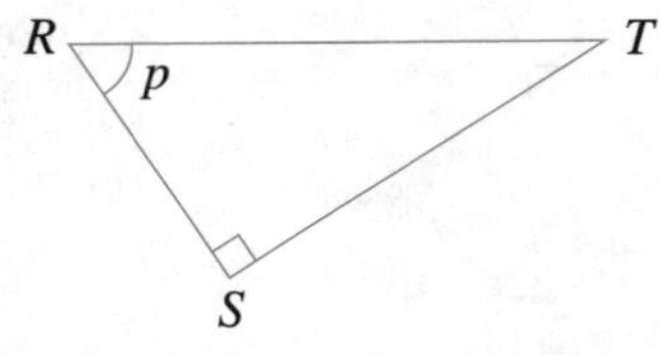

2. In $\triangle XYZ$, $\hat{X}$ is a right angle.

(a) In terms of XY, YZ and ZX, find $\sin \hat{Y}$, $\cos \hat{Y}$ and $\tan \hat{Y}$.

(b) In terms of XY, YZ and ZX, find $\sin \hat{Z}$, $\cos \hat{Z}$ and $\tan \hat{Z}$.

3. Find $\sin \hat{A}$, $\cos \hat{A}$ and $\tan \hat{A}$ in terms of p, q and m in each case.

(a)

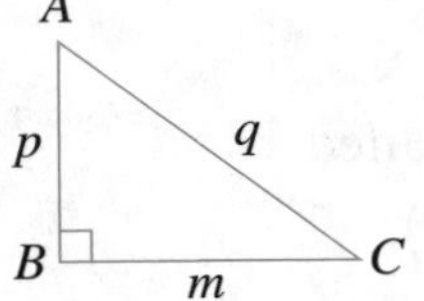

(b)

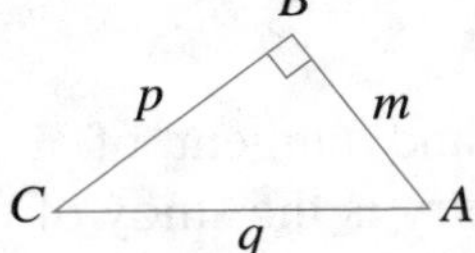

(c)

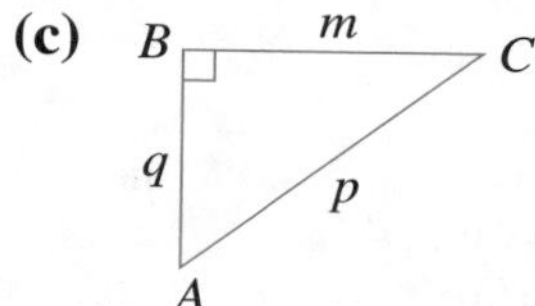

(d)

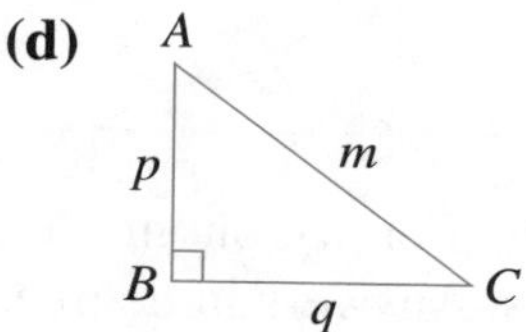

10.4 TRIGONOMETRICAL RATIOS BY USING A CALCULATOR

Example

Let us determine the trigonometrical ratios for an angle of 25°. We can draw, using any length of your choice as the base, an accurate diagram of a right-angled triangle in which one of the angles is 25° as shown below. We can then measure the sides of the triangle and find the trigonometrical ratios as follows:

$$\sin 25° = \frac{AC}{AB} = \frac{2.8}{6.6} = 0.42$$

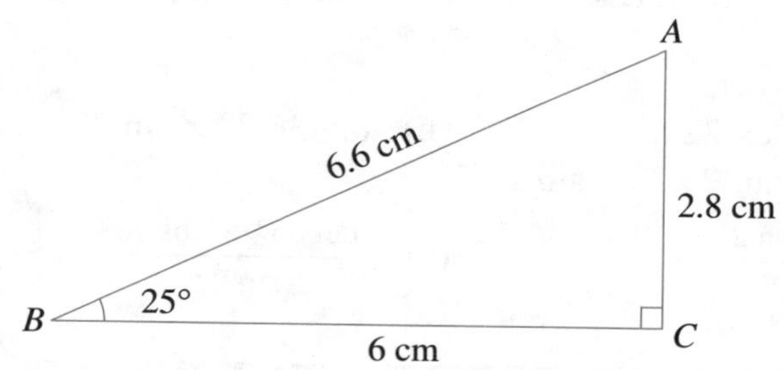

$$\cos 25° = \frac{BC}{AB} = \frac{6}{6.6} = 0.91$$

$$\tan 25° = \frac{AC}{BC} = \frac{2.8}{6} = 0.47$$

You can also find the values of trigonometrical ratios by using a calculator. (Refer to the instructions in the booklet that comes with your calculator.)

Thus

$\sin 25° = 0.422\,6$ (4 sig. fig.)
$\cos 25° = 0.906\,3$ (4 sig. fig.)
$\tan 25° = 0.466\,3$ (4 sig. fig.)

Exercise 10.4

answers on p. 438

Use a calculator to do the following. For trigonometrical ratios, give your answers correct to 4 significant figures. Answers in degrees should be given to 1 decimal place.

1. Find the following trigonometrical ratios.

(a) $\sin 20°$ **(b)** $\sin 25.3°$ **(c)** $\sin 42.7°$
(d) $\cos 20°$ **(e)** $\cos 20.4°$ **(f)** $\cos 28.4°$
(g) $\tan 45°$ **(h)** $\tan 64.4°$ **(i)** $\tan 50.5°$
(j) $\sin 46°$ **(k)** $\tan 35°$ **(l)** $\cos 28°$
(m) $\sin 24.5°$ **(n)** $\tan 43.4°$ **(o)** $\cos 54.8°$
(p) $\sin 4.2°$ **(q)** $\tan 3.1°$ **(r)** $\cos 86.1°$
(s) $\sin 23° \times \cos 43°$ **(t)** $\tan 42° \times \sin 57°$ **(u)** $\cos 44° \times \tan 26°$

2. Find $\hat{a}$ if:

(a) $\sin \hat{a} = 0.010\,5$ **(b)** $\sin \hat{a} = 0.245$ **(c)** $\sin \hat{a} = 0.353$
(d) $\cos \hat{a} = 0.996$ **(e)** $\cos \hat{a} = 0.956$ **(f)** $\cos \hat{a} = 0.013\,7$
(g) $\tan \hat{a} = 0.019$ **(h)** $\tan \hat{a} = 0.997$ **(i)** $\tan \hat{a} = 1.23$

3. Find $\hat{a}$ if:

(a) $\cos \hat{a} = \sin 52.1° \times \tan 22.4°$ **(b)** $\sin \hat{a} = \tan 46.2° \times \cos 47.1°$
(c) $\tan \hat{a} = \sin 36.5° \times \cos 53.5°$ **(d)** $\cos \hat{a} = \tan 35.4° \times \sin 23.6°$

4. Calculate the following.

(a) $\sin 25.4° \times \cos 22.6°$ **(b)** $\tan 36.7° \times \sin 42° \times \cos 10.2°$
(c) $\cos 41.2° \times \tan 24.2° \times \sin 29.2°$
(d) $\dfrac{\sin 42.5° \times \tan 27.9°}{\cos 45.8°}$ **(e)** $\dfrac{\tan 66° \times \cos 73°}{\sin 82°}$

10.5 SOLUTION OF RIGHT-ANGLED TRIANGLES

Worked Example 1

The right-angled triangle *DEF* has hypotenuse *DE*, 35 cm long, and $\hat{D} = 40°$. Find *EF* and *FD*. Give your answers correct to 2 significant figures.

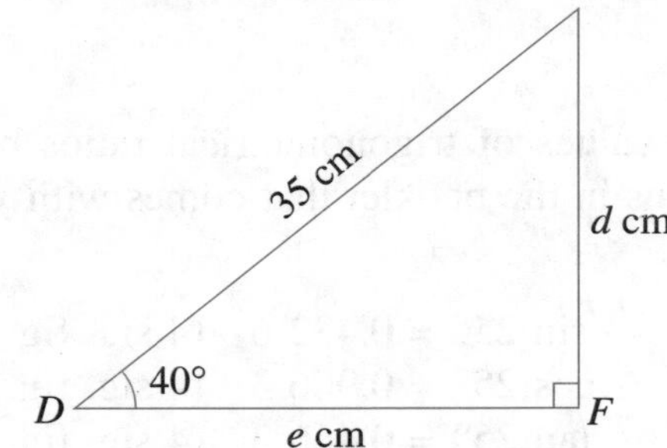

Solution:

We have $\sin 40° = \dfrac{EF}{DE}$

$= \dfrac{d}{35}$

Then $\quad 0.642\ 8 = \dfrac{d}{35}$

$$d = 35 \times 0.642\ 8$$
$$= 22.498$$
$$= 22 \quad \text{(2 sig. fig.)}$$

Similarly, $\quad \cos 40° = \dfrac{e}{35}$

$$e = 35 \cos 40°$$
$$= 35 \times 0.766$$
$$= 26.81$$
$$= 27 \quad \text{(2 sig. fig.)}$$

Worked Example 2

Find the angles and sides indicated by the letters in the following diagrams. Give your answers correct to 2 significant figures or the nearest degree.

(a)

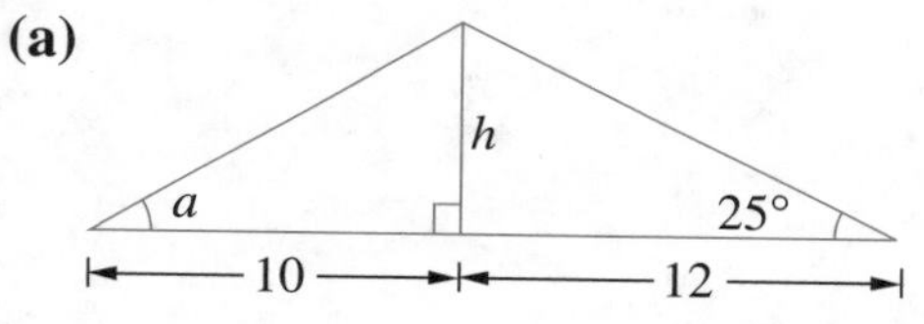

(b)

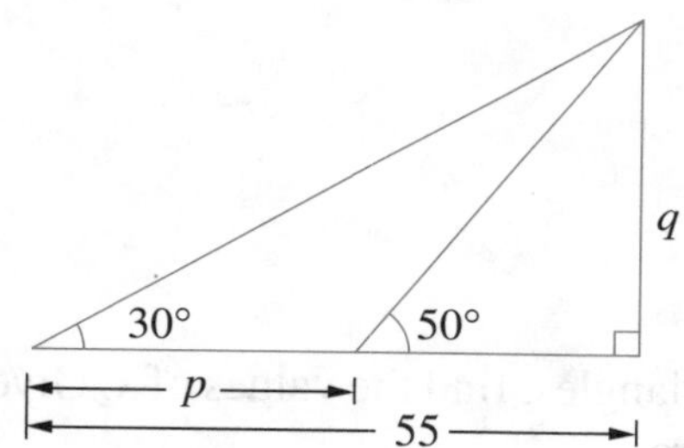

Solution:

(a) $h = 12 \tan 25°$
$= 12 \times 0.466\ 3$
$= 5.595\ 6$
$= 5.6 \quad$ (2 sig. fig.)

$\tan \hat{a} = \dfrac{h}{10}$ $\left(\begin{array}{l} h \text{ must be taken as } 5.595\ 6 \text{ and} \\ \text{not } 5.6 \text{ or accuracy may be lost.} \end{array}\right)$

$= \dfrac{5.595\ 6}{10}$

$= 0.559\ 6$

$\therefore \hat{a} = 29° \quad$ (nearest degree)

(b) $q = 55 \tan 30°$
$= 55 \times 0.577\ 4$
$= 31.76$
$= 32 \quad$ (2 sig. fig.)

$55 - p = \dfrac{q}{\tan 50°}$

$= \dfrac{31.76}{1.192}$

$= 26.64$

$\therefore p = 55 - 26.64$

$= 28.36$

$= 28 \quad$ (2 sig. fig.)

Exercise 10.5

answers on p. 438

1. In the given right-angled triangles, find the values of x. Give your answers correct to 2 significant figures.

(a)

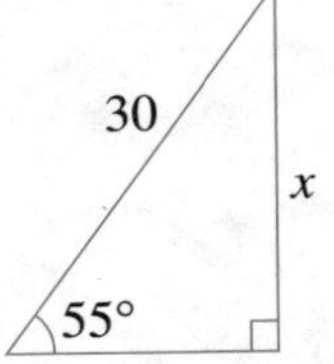

(b)

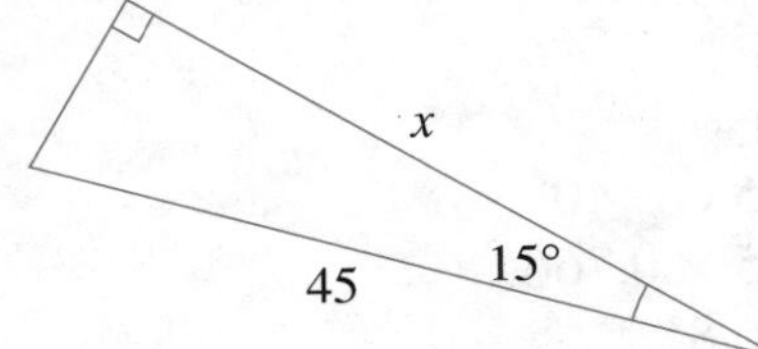

(c)

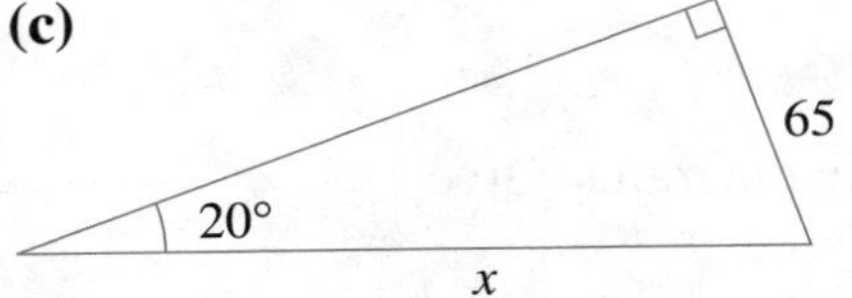

(d)

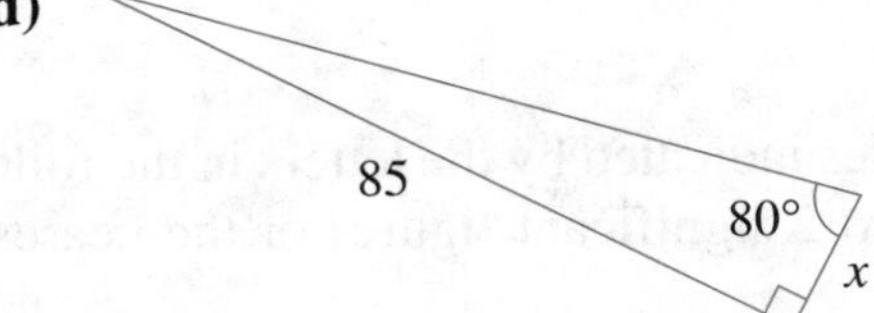

2. In the right-angled triangles, find the values of x. Give your answers correct to 4 significant figures.

(a)

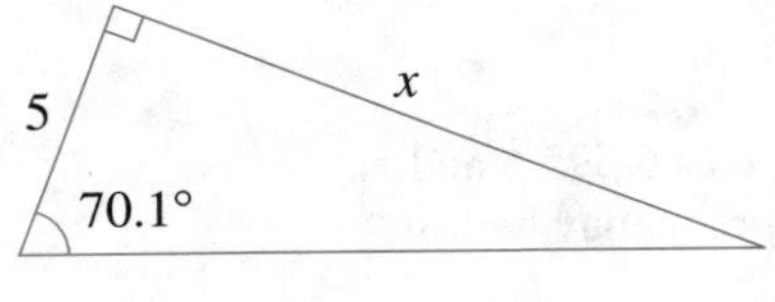

(b)

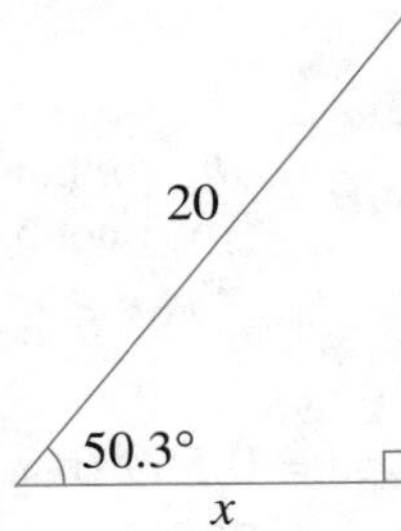

(c)

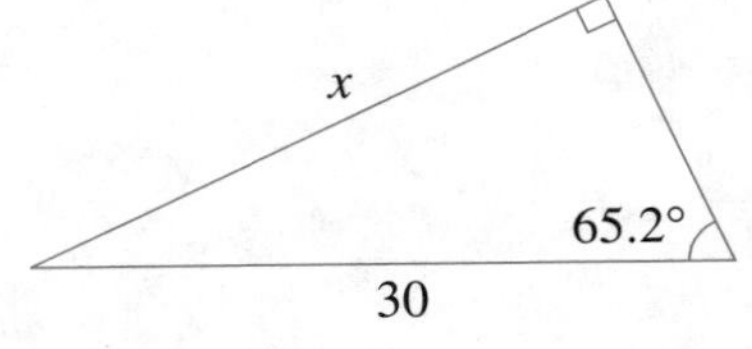

(d)

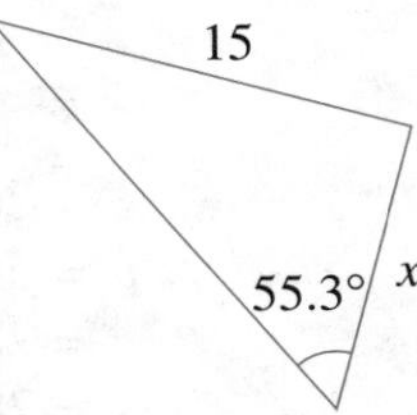

3. Find $\hat{a}$. Give each answer correct to the nearest degree.

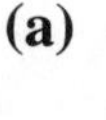

(a)

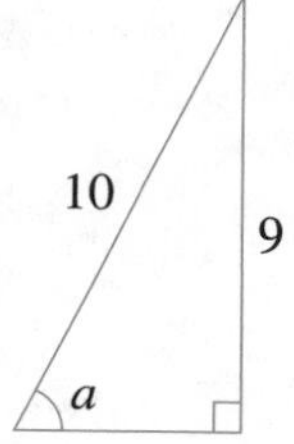

(b)

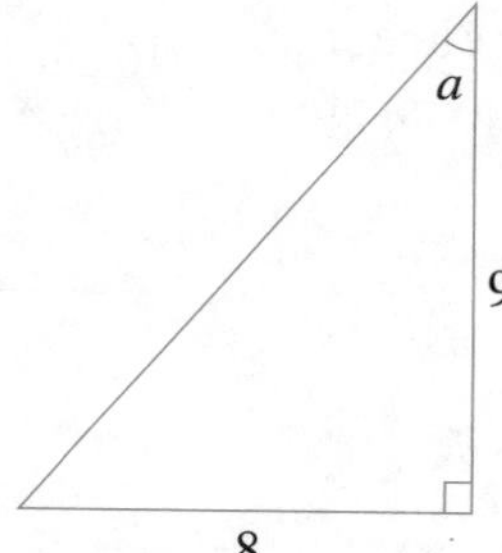

(c)

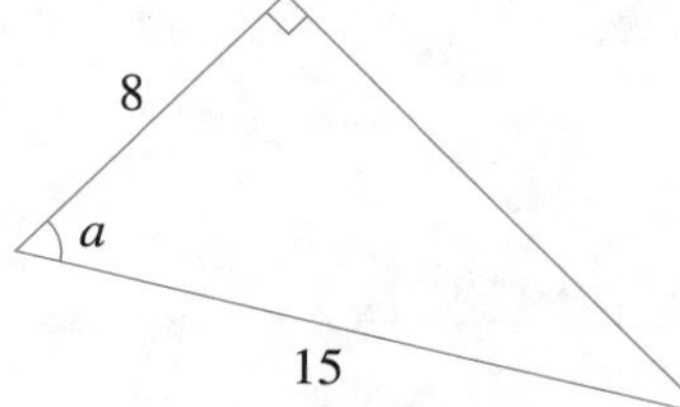

(d)

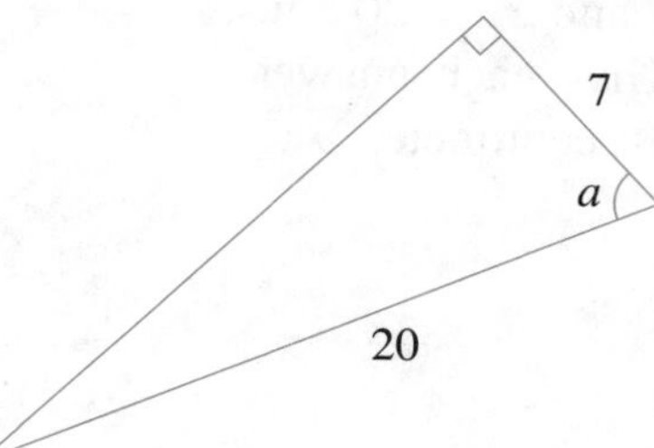

4. Find $\hat{p}$. Give each answer in degrees, correct to 1 decimal place.

(a)

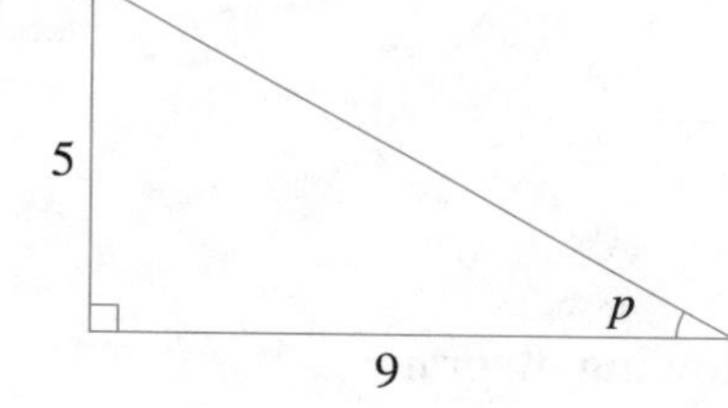

(b)

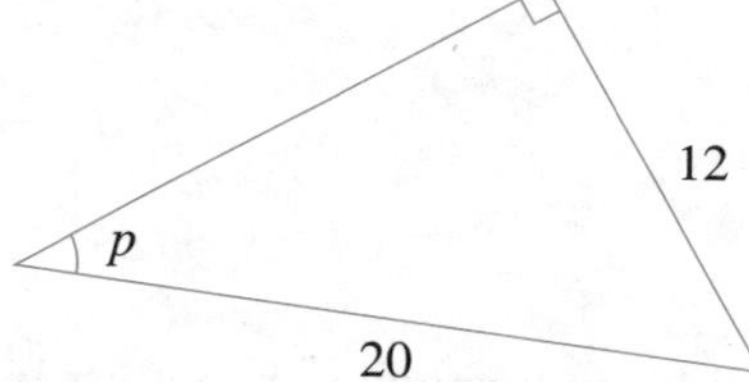

(c)

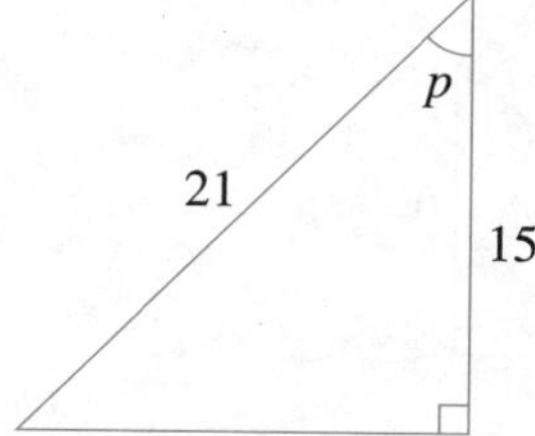

(d)

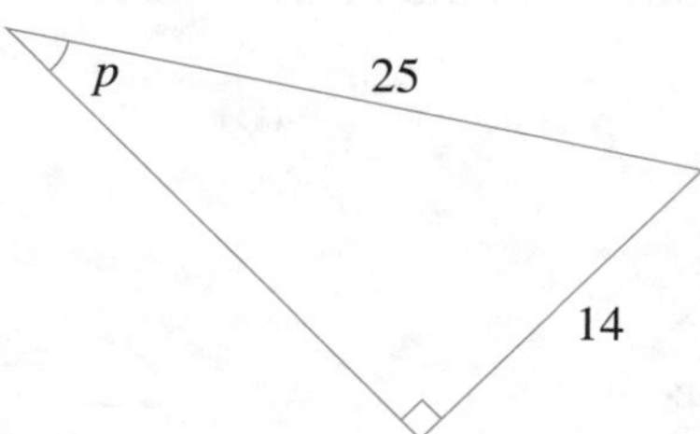

5. A diagonal of a rectangle is 10 cm long and makes an angle of 60° with one of the sides. Find the lengths of the sides of the rectangle. Give each answer correct to the nearest centimetre.

6. A diagonal of a rectangle makes an angle of 39° with its longer side. Find the width of the rectangle if its length is 50 cm. Give your answer correct to the nearest centimetre.

7. Triangle ABC has $AB = AC = 10$ cm, and $B\hat{A}C = 82°$. Find BC. Give your answer correct to the nearest centimetre. (*Hint:* AN is the axis of symmetry.)

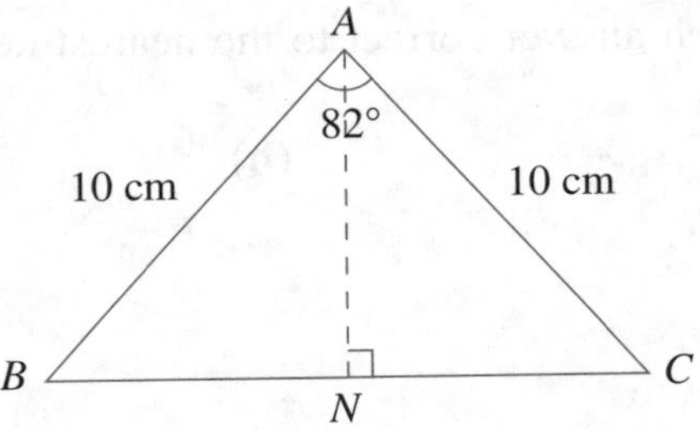

8. In triangle XYZ, $\hat{Y} = \hat{Z} = 50°$, XN is perpendicular to YZ and $YZ = 20$ cm. Find XY and XN. Give each answer correct to the nearest centimetre.

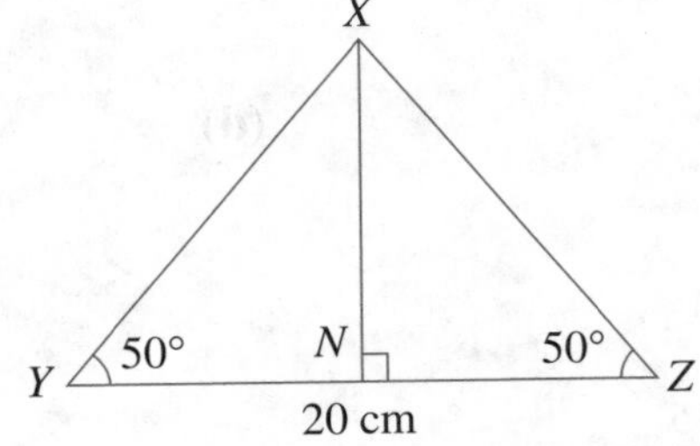

9. The sides of the triangle are 6, 6 and 8 units long. Find the angles of the triangle. Give each answer correct to the nearest degree.

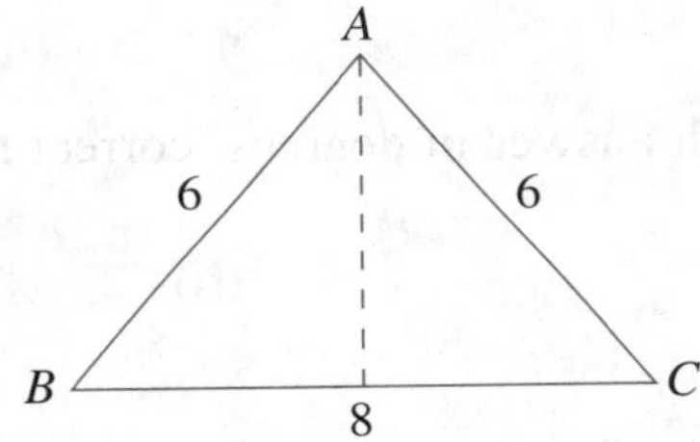

10. Find the angles and sides indicated by the letters in the following diagrams. Give each answer correct to the nearest whole number or degree.

(a)

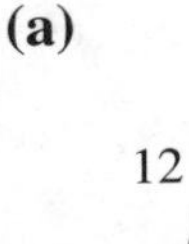

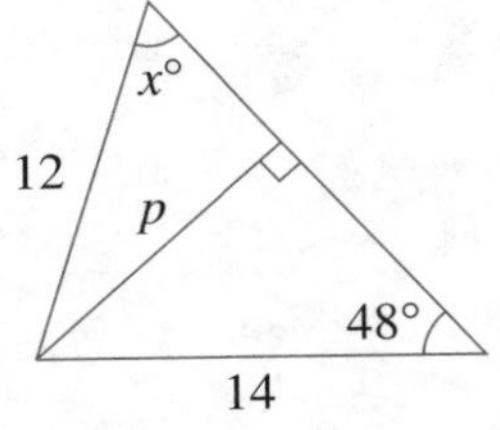

(b)

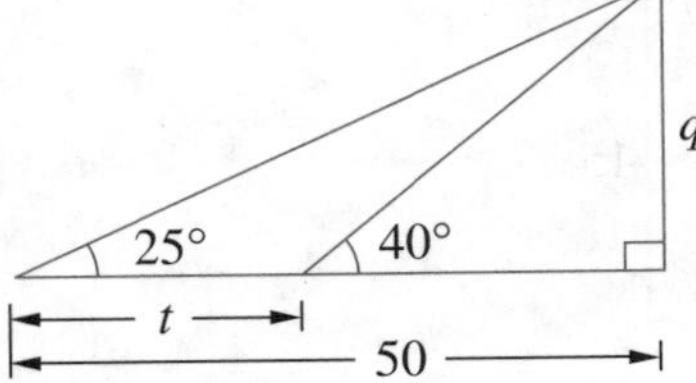

(c)

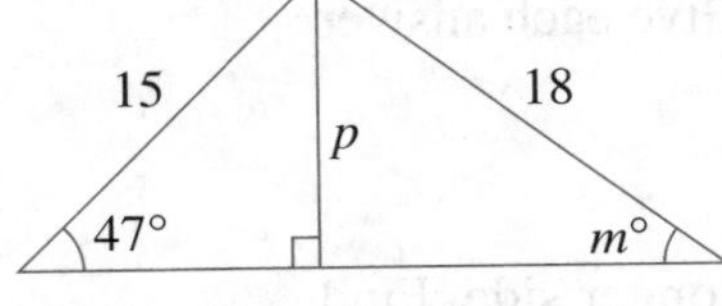

(d)

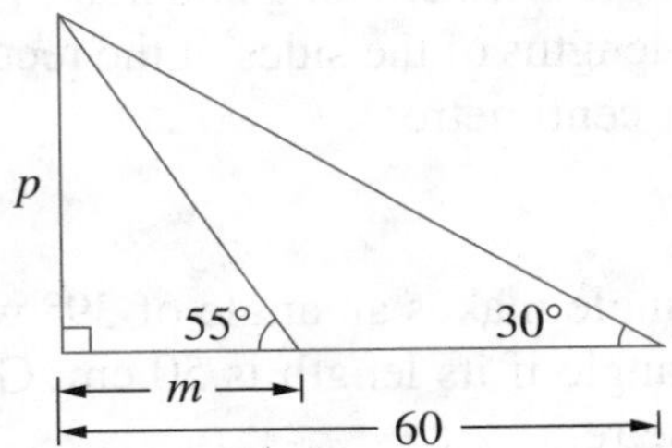

(e)

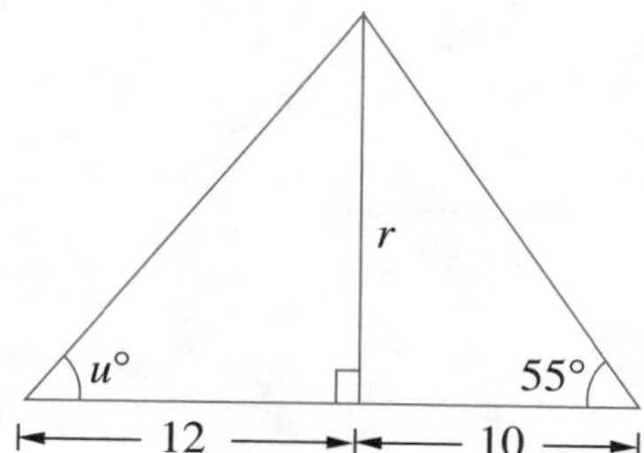

(f)

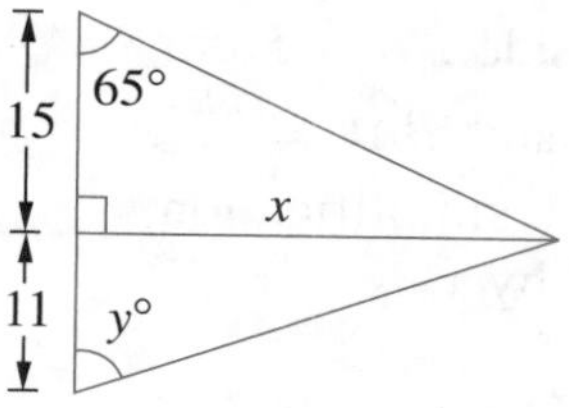

11. In triangle KLM, KL, KM and $\hat{K}$ are given. By considering the right-angled triangle KPM, find MP and the area of the triangle KLM. Give each answer correct to the nearest whole number.

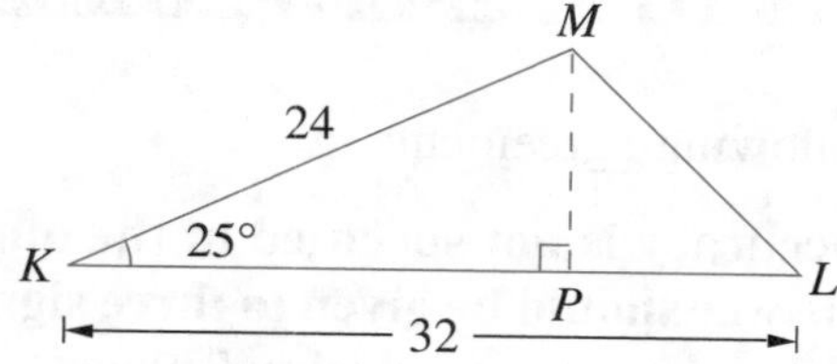

12. ABC is a triangle in which $B\hat{A}C = 90°$, $AC = 40$ cm and $BC = 41$ cm. AB is produced to P and AC is produced to Q.

(a) Showing your working clearly, explain why $AB = 9$ cm.

(b) Calculate

(i) $\tan B\hat{C}A$,

(ii) $P\hat{B}C$,

(iii) $B\hat{C}Q$.

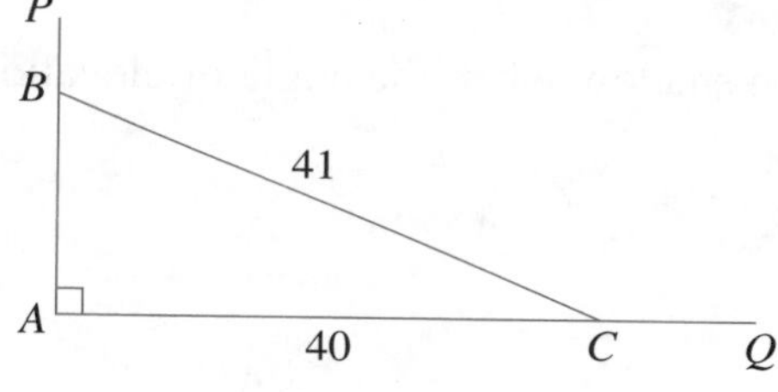

***13.** In the figure, AD is perpendicular to BC and DE is perpendicular to AC. The angle ABD is 70° and $AB = DC = 1$ m. Calculate the value of x. Hence, calculate the length of CE.

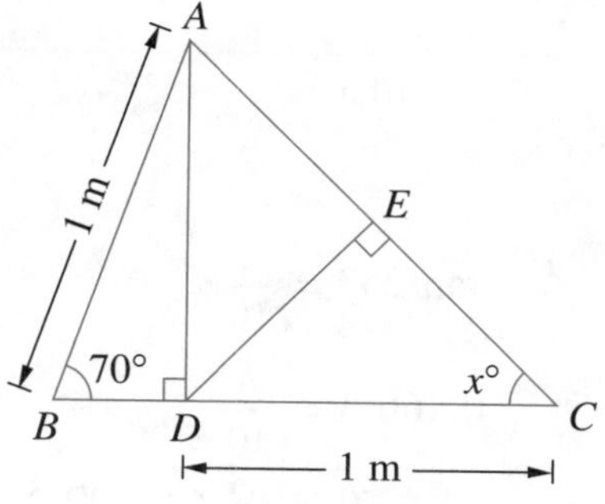

***14.** **(a)** Calculate CN.

(b) Calculate the area of $\triangle ABC$.

(c) If D is the midpoint of BC and E is the midpoint of AC, state the area of quadrilateral $ABDE$.

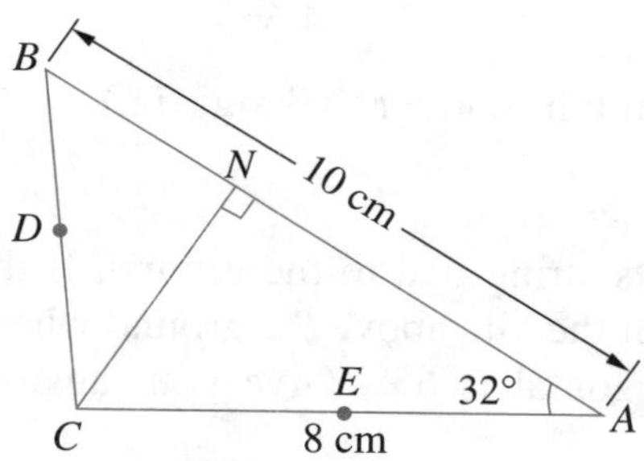

***15.** In the triangle ABC, the side $AB = 5$ cm, $AC = 10$ cm, $BC = 3x$ cm and $B\hat{A}C = 27°$.

(a) Write down, without simplification, the equation satisfied by x.

(b) Find x.

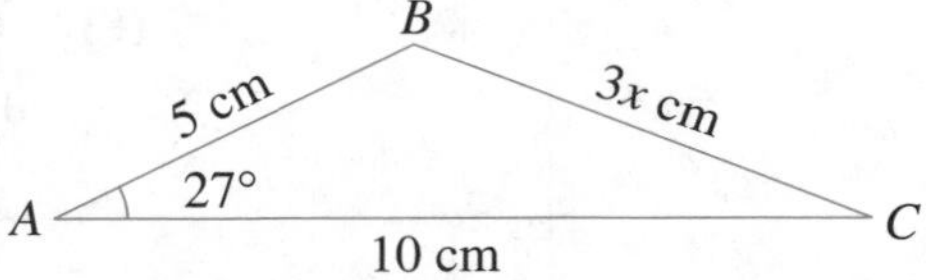

10.6 APPLICATIONS OF TRIGONOMETRICAL RATIOS TO SIMPLE PROBLEMS

Let us have the following agreement:

If the degree of accuracy is not specified in the question and if the answer is not exact, the answer should be given to three significant figures. Answers in degrees should be given to one decimal place.

Worked Example 1

A tree casts a 10 m shadow when the angle of elevation of the sun is 25°. How tall is the tree?

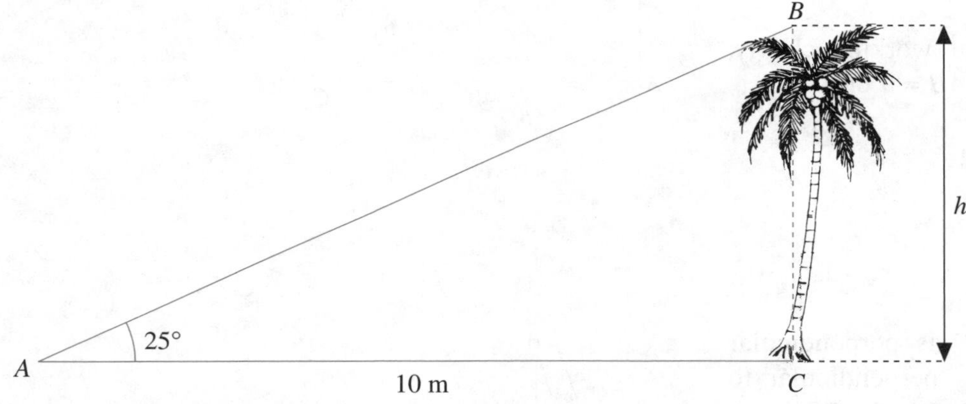

Solution:

We have

$$\tan 25° = \frac{h}{10}$$

$$0.466\ 3 = \frac{h}{10}$$

$$h = 10 \times 0.466\ 3$$

$$= 4.663$$

Thus the tree is 4.66 m tall (correct to 3 sig. fig.).

Worked Example 2

A kite in the air has its string tied to the ground. If the length of the string is 58 m, find the height of the kite above the ground when the string is taut and its inclination to the horizontal is 65°. Give your answer correct to the nearest metre.

Solution:

In the diagram, K represents the kite, which is h m above the ground level HG. KG is perpendicular to HG. Consider the right-angled triangle HGK.

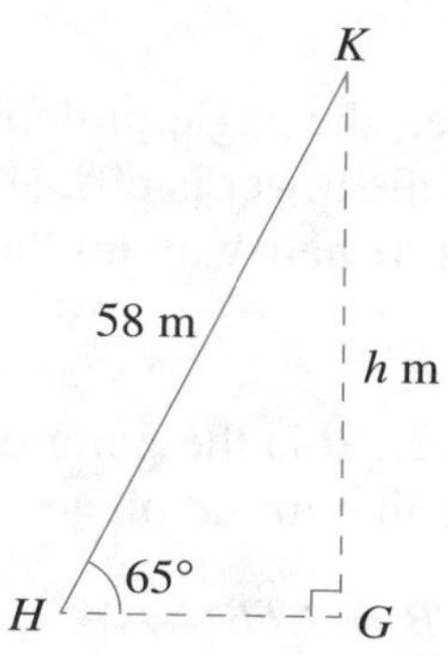

$$\sin 65° = \frac{h}{58}$$

$$\therefore h = 58 \sin 65°$$
$$= 58 \times 0.906\,3$$
$$= 52.565$$

Thus the kite is 53 m high (correct to the nearest metre).

Worked Example 3

A ladder 3 m long rests against a vertical wall so that the distance between the foot of the ladder and the wall is 0.75 m.

(a) Find the angle the ladder makes with the wall.

(b) Find the height above the ground at which the upper end of the ladder touches the wall.

Solution:

Let AB represent the ladder, AC the horizontal ground and BC the vertical wall.

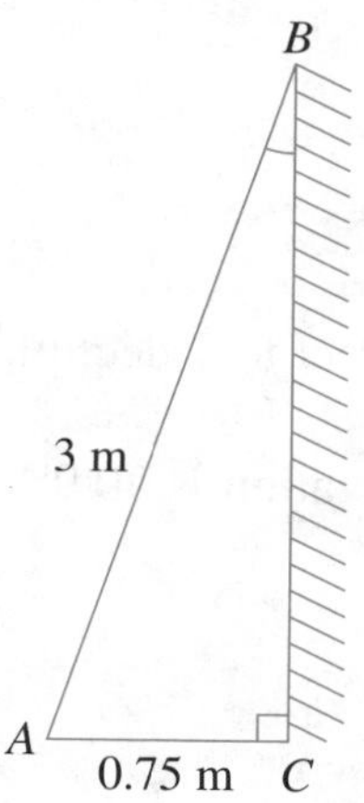

(a) $\sin \hat{B} = \dfrac{AC}{AB}$

$= \dfrac{0.75}{3}$

$= 0.25$

$\therefore \hat{B} = 14.5°$ (correct to 1 dec. pl.)

Thus the ladder makes an angle of 14.5° with the wall.

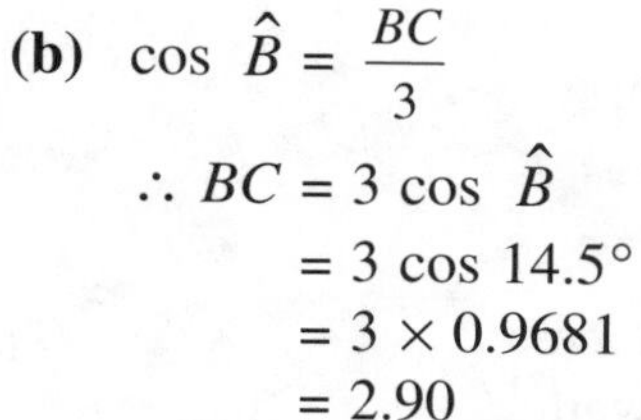

(b) $\cos \hat{B} = \dfrac{BC}{3}$

$\therefore BC = 3 \cos \hat{B}$

$= 3 \cos 14.5°$

$= 3 \times 0.9681$

$= 2.90$

Thus the ladder reaches 2.90 m (correct to 3 sig. fig.) up the wall.

(An alternative way to find BC is to use Pythagoras' Theorem. Do this and compare your answer with the one we found by trigonometry.)

Worked Example 4

From the top of a tower, the angle of depression of a point on the ground 10 m away from the base of the tower is 60°. How tall is the tower? What is the angle of elevation of a point M half-way up the tower?

Solution:

T is the top of the tower, B is the point on the ground and TL is a horizontal line in the plane of $\triangle TGB$.

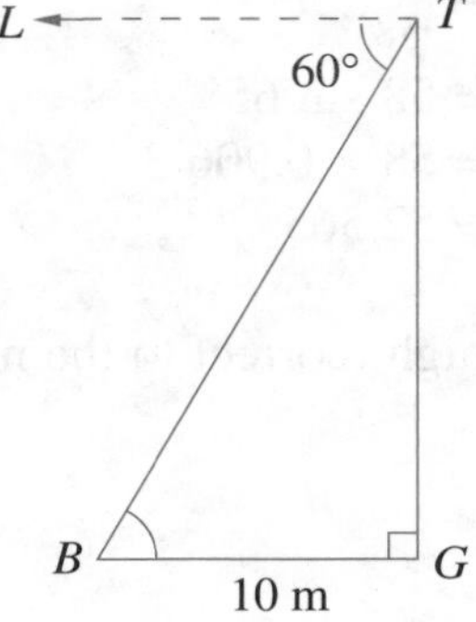

$$\begin{aligned} \hat{B} &= L\hat{T}B \\ &= 60° \\ \tan \hat{B} &= \frac{GT}{BG} \\ \therefore GT &= BG \tan \hat{B} \\ &= 10 \tan 60° \\ &= 10 \times 1.732 \\ &= 17.32 \end{aligned}$$

Thus the tower is 17.3 m high (correct to 3 sig. fig.).

In $\triangle MBG$,

$$\begin{aligned} GM &= \frac{1}{2}(17.32) \\ &= 8.66 \\ \tan \hat{a} &= \frac{GM}{BG} \\ &= \frac{8.66}{10} \\ &= 0.866 \\ \therefore \hat{a} &= 40.9° \quad \text{(correct to 1 dec. pl.)} \end{aligned}$$

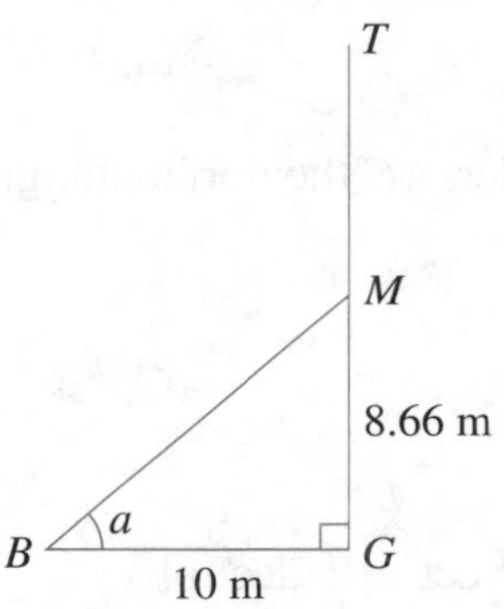

Thus the angle of elevation is 40.9°.

Exercise 10.6

answers on p. 438

1. A ladder, 6 m long, leans against a wall and makes an angle of 60° with the ground. How high up the wall does the ladder reach? How far from the wall is the foot of the ladder?

2. A man starts at O and wishes to reach a point P, 300 m northeast of O. If he gets to P by first walking due north and then due east, how far will he have to walk in each direction?

3. From the top of a building 20 m high, a man watches people walking along the street. If the angle of depression of the foot of a pedestrian is 60°, how far is the pedestrian from the foot of the building?

4. The shadow of a pole is 4 m long when the angle of elevation of the sun is 60°. Find the length of the shadow when the angle of elevation of the sun is 45°.

5. Find the height of a tower if the angle of elevation of the top is 34° at a point 50 m from its foot.

6. The length of the shadow of a 16 m tall tree is 8 m. What is the angle of elevation of the sun?

7. A 5-m ladder leans against a vertical wall with its top at a height 4 m from the ground. What is the approximate size of the angle that the ladder makes with the horizontal?

8. A hill slopes upwards at an angle of 14° with the horizontal. What height does a man reach when he has travelled 100 m up the slope? Give your answer correct to the nearest metre.

9. A man whose eye is 1.5 m above the ground is standing 15 m from a tree which is 12 m high. What is the angle of elevation of the top of the tree from his eye? Give your answer correct to the nearest degree.

10.

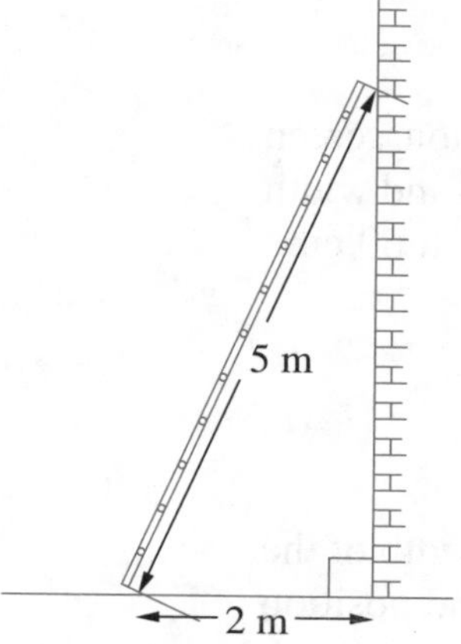

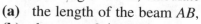

(a) Find the height of the top of the ladder above the ground.
(b) Calculate the angle between the ladder and the ground.

11. The diagram shows part of the roof support in the form of an isosceles triangle ABC. Given that the beam BC is of length 5.4 m, calculate
(a) the length of the beam AB,
(b) the area of $\triangle ABC$.

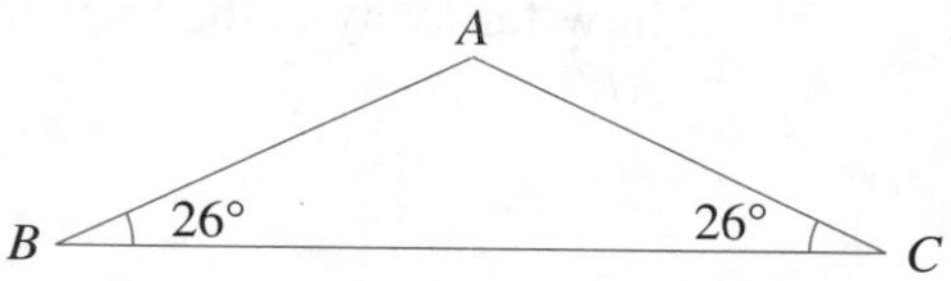

12. (a)

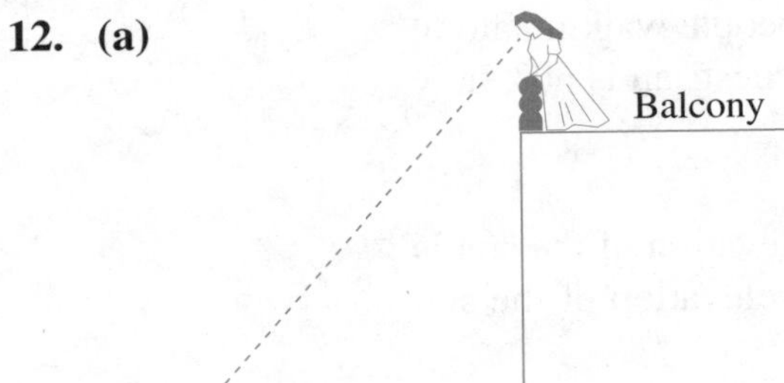

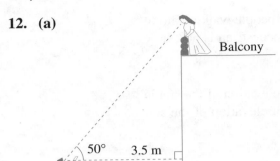

Romeo stands 3.5 metres away from the wall of Juliet's house. Juliet is standing on a balcony. By raising his eyes 50° from the horizontal, Romeo can gaze into Juliet's eyes. Romeo and Juliet are the same height as each other. Calculate the height of the balcony above the ground, giving your answer in metres correct to one decimal place.

(b) In part (a), the distance 3.5 metres was given to the nearest half metre, and the angle 50° was given to the nearest 10°. Write down the limits between which

(i) the distance, and

(ii) the angle must lie. *(C)*

13.

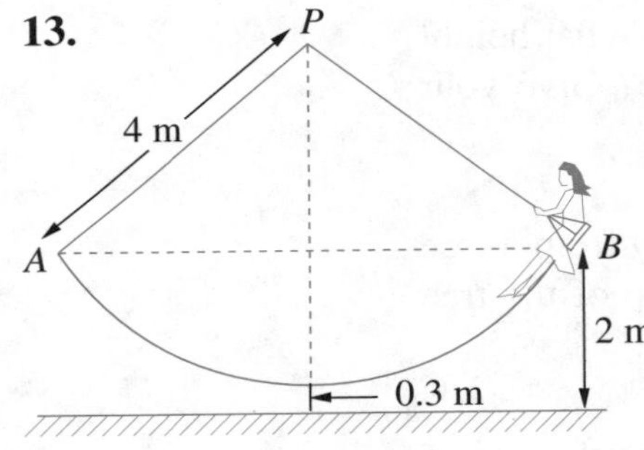

The ropes of a swing are 4 metres long, and the seat is 30 cm above the ground when it is at its lowest point. When Roberta uses the swing, the seat reaches a height of 2 metres above the ground on each side of the vertical.

Calculate the angle APB through which she swings. *(C)*

14. (a)

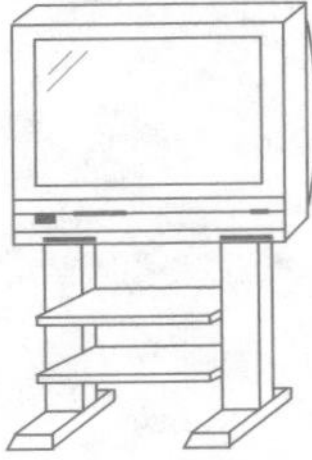

The height and width of a television screen are in the ratio 3 : 4. Find the height and width of a screen with a diagonal of length 60 cm.

(b)

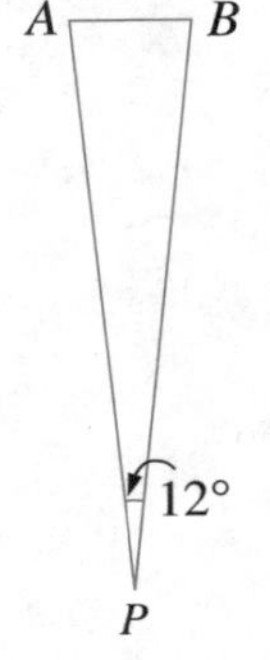

In the diagram, AB represents the width of the television screen in part (a). P is the position of a TV viewer. If $A\hat{P}B = 12°$ and $AP = PB$, how far away is the viewer P from the screen AB?

15. The road leading out of a school runs in a direction 40° to the west of North before joining a major road at a point 440 m away from the school as shown. If this major road runs in a north-south direction, find its shortest distance from the school. Give your answer correct to the nearest metre.

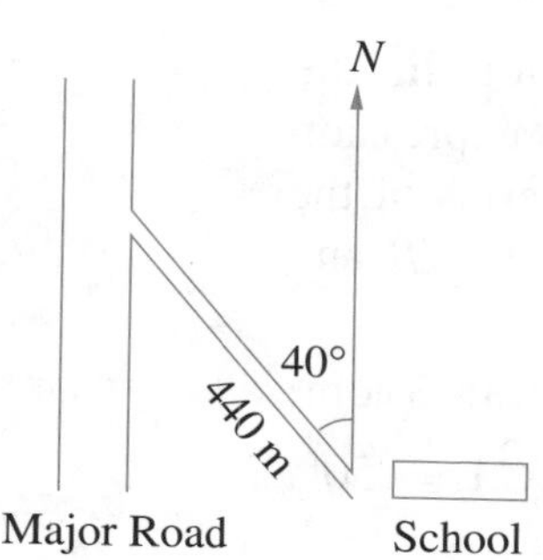

***16.** A see-saw consists of a plank 4.8 m long which is supported by a pivot at its centre and rotates in a vertical plane about the pivot. If the height of the pivot pillar above the ground is 1.0 m, through what maximum angle can the see-saw beam rotate? Give your answer correct to the nearest degree.

***17.** When a plot of land was marked off, the boundary pegs L, M, N and P were as shown in the figure, with PL parallel to NM. The measures of PN, NM, $\hat{P}$ and $\hat{L}$ are shown. Find the distance between the parallel sides PL and NM. Give your answer correct to the nearest metre.

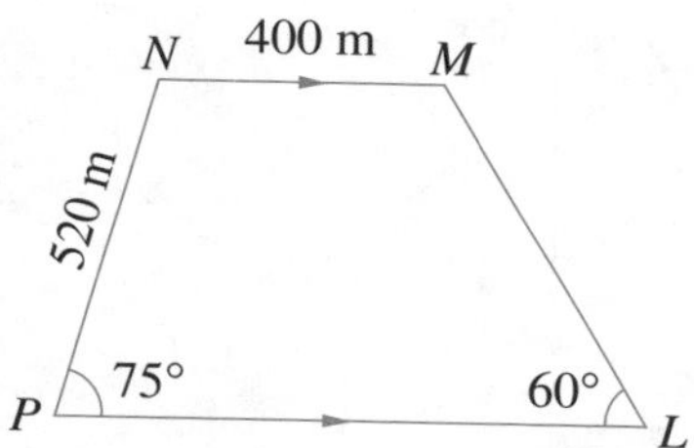

***18.** An observer is at A on the bank of a river and a coconut tree is at P directly across on the opposite bank. A distance AB of 40 m is measured along the bank so that $B\hat{A}P$ is a right angle. $A\hat{B}P$ is found to be 42°.

(a) Find the width of the river.

(b) If the angle of elevation of the top of the coconut tree is 22° from A, find the height of the coconut tree.

(c) Find the angle of elevation of the top of the coconut tree from B.

(d) Find the distance from B to the top of the coconut tree.

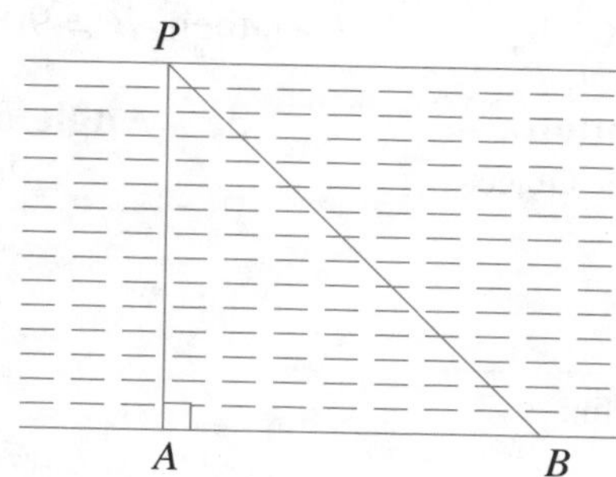

***19.** From the top of a building, the angle of depression of a point on the ground 32 m away from the base of the building is 58°.

(a) How tall is the building?

(b) What is the angle of elevation of a point **(i)** half-way, **(ii)** three-quarter-way up the building?

*20. (a) Using the notation in the diagram, find an expression for the side b in terms of the side c and the angles B and ECA.

(b) Given that c = 38.3 cm, $\hat{B}$ = 20° and $E\hat{C}A$ = 50°, calculate b.

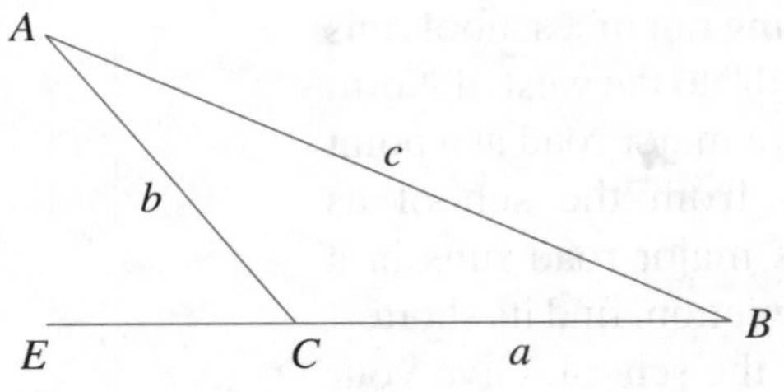

Chapter Review

1. Pythagoras' Theorem

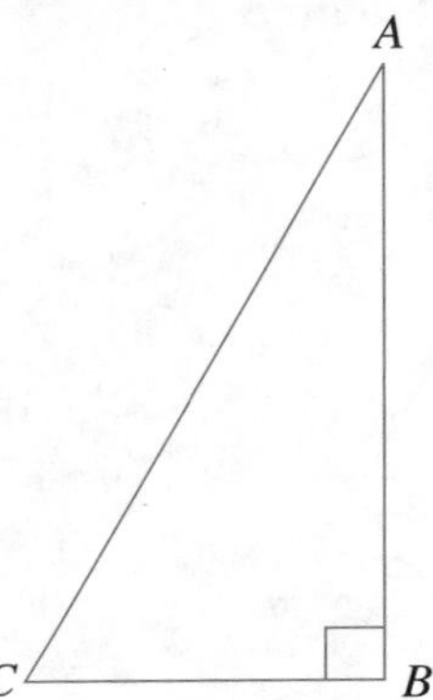

In $\triangle ABC$, if $\hat{B}$ = 90°, then $AB^2 + BC^2 = AC^2$.

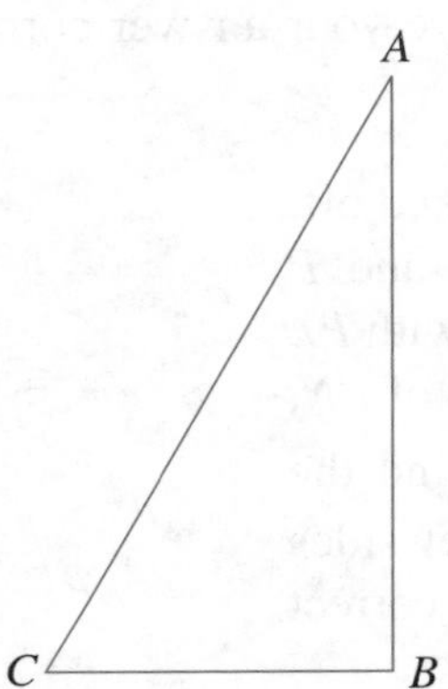

In $\triangle ABC$, if $AB^2 + BC^2 = AC^2$, then $\hat{B}$ = 90°.

2. Angle of Elevation

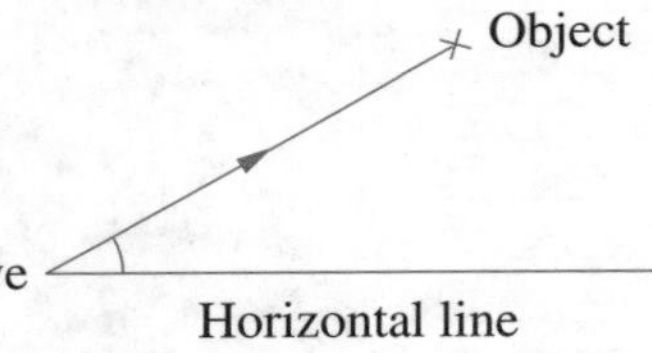

3. Angle of Depression

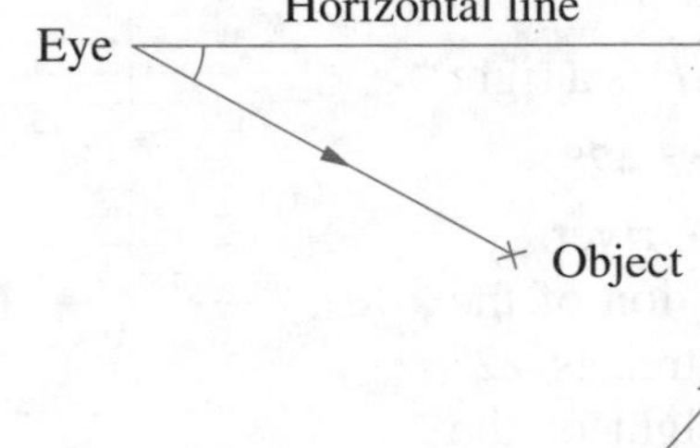

4. Trigonometrical Ratios

$$\sin \hat{A} = \frac{\text{side opposite } \hat{A}}{\text{hypotenuse}}$$

$$\cos \hat{A} = \frac{\text{side adjacent to } \hat{A}}{\text{hypotenuse}}$$

$$\tan \hat{A} = \frac{\text{side opposite } \hat{A}}{\text{side adjacent to } \hat{A}}$$

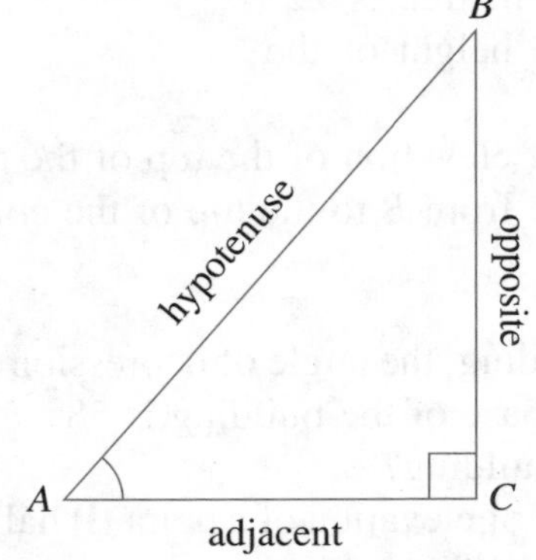

CHALLENGER 10

1. A water-lily originally 10 cm above the water surface is blown 50 cm sideways by a strong wind as shown. Find the depth of the pond.

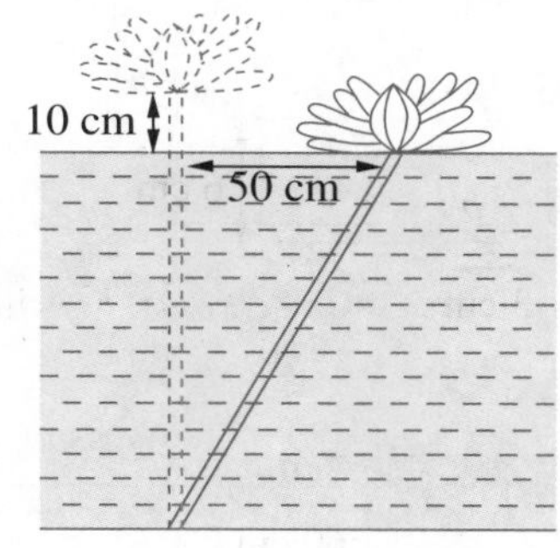

2. The figure shows a cross-section of a cylindrical pipe of diameter 75 cm. The pipe is laid horizontally to carry away water. Find the depth of water if the breadth of the water surface is 60 cm. What will be the breadth if the depth is doubled?

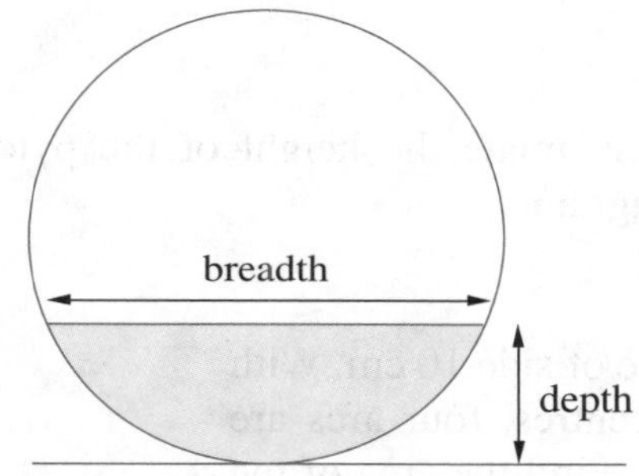

3. A pagoda stands on a hill 100 m above the sea level. If $A\hat{C}D = 60°$ and $B\hat{C}D = 30°$, find the height, AB, of the pagoda.

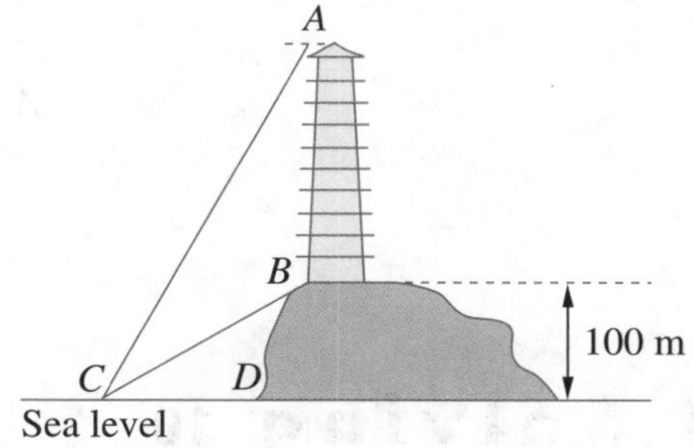

4. When the sun is directly above a point A, a tower CB 190 km north of A casts a shadow BN as shown. If the tower is 100 m tall and the shadow is 3 m long, estimate the radius of the earth. Give your answer correct to 3 significant figures. (*Hint:* Assume that $\triangle BNC$ is a right-angled triangle.)

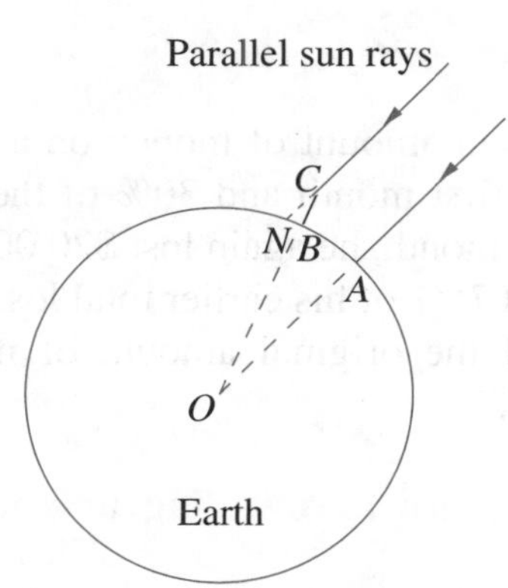

5. David wanted to know the height of a pylon. He made use of his pocket-book to estimate the angles of elevation, $\hat{a}$ and $\hat{b}$, at two points as shown.

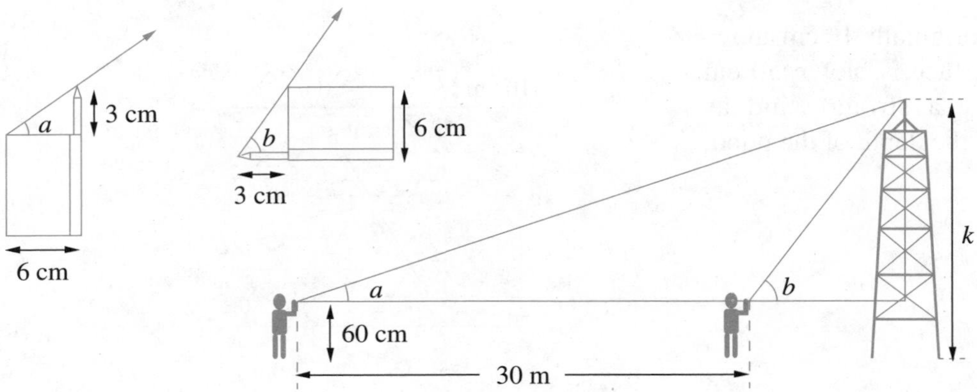

Explain how to estimate the height of the pylon using the information shown in the diagram.

6. *ABCD* is a square of side 10 cm. With the vertices as centres, four arcs are drawn as shown. Find the area of the shaded part.

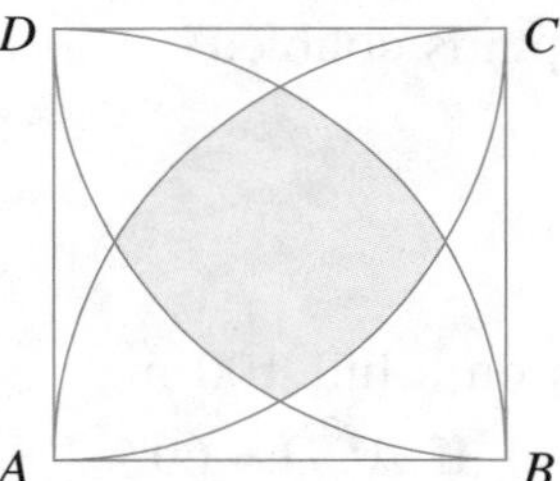

Problem Solving 10

Investment at Risk

Mr Tan Ah Teck invested an amount of money on a high-risk project. He lost 20% of the money in the first month and 30% of the remaining money in the second month. In the third month, he again lost \$20 000. In the fourth month, he made a gain and recovered 75% of his earlier total loss. By then, he actually lost \$9 000 less than 25% of the original amount of money invested. Find the original amount of money.

The strategies to use are **use arrow diagram**, **use equations** and **work backwards**.

Keys: x = money (\$) invested
y = money left after the 3rd loss
$x - y$ = total loss (\$) in 3 months

$$\boxed{x} \xrightarrow{\times 0.8} \boxed{} \xrightarrow{\times 0.7} \boxed{} \xrightarrow{-\,20\,000} \boxed{y} \xrightarrow{+\,0.75(x-y)} \boxed{9\,000 + 0.75x}$$

So $y + 0.75(x - y) = 9\,000 + 0.75x$

$0.25y = 9\,000$

$\therefore\ y = 36\,000$

Now let us work backwards from y to find x.

$$\boxed{100\,000} \xleftarrow{\div\,0.8} \boxed{80\,000} \xleftarrow{\div\,0.7} \boxed{56\,000} \xleftarrow{+\,20\,000} \boxed{36\,000}$$

$\therefore\ x = 100\,000$

So the original amount of money = \$100 000

1. **Generosity** A philanthropist, Mr Li, donated a sum of money to start off a fund-raising campaign. Through the support of the public, the amount collected after one month was 20% of the sum donated by Mr Li. In the second month, the increase of the fund was \$12 800 more than 25% of the fund. In the third month, the increase of the fund was double the two increases in the earlier months put together. Meanwhile Mr Li had agreed to top up the fund to \$168 000 by making a second donation which would be twice the amount of his first donation. How much was Mr Li's first donation?

2. **Team Work** Two jobs can be done effectively if the workers are divided into two teams A and B in the correct ratio. If 5 workers in team A are absent, 2 workers have to be transferred from team B to team A to maintain the correct ratio of workers in the two teams. What is this correct ratio?

3. **Perimeter** Study the following sequence of areas of certain squares:

   49, 4 489, 444 889, 44 448 889, . . .

   What is the perimeter of the square whose area is 444 444 888 889?

4. Triangular Pattern

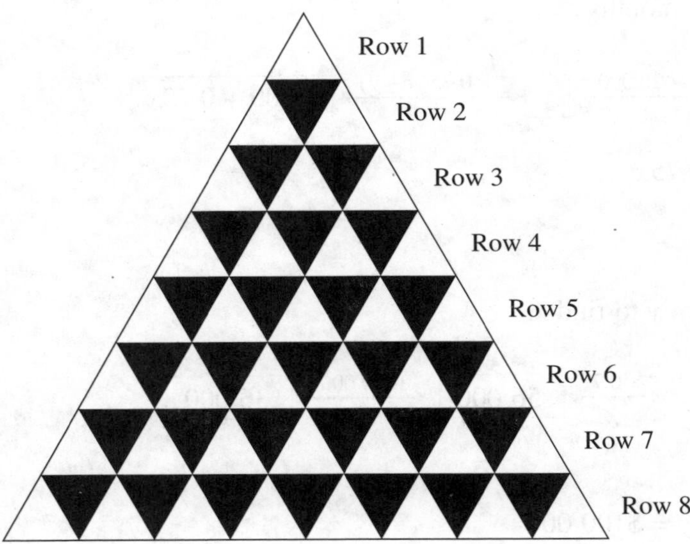

The diagram shows the first eight rows of a continuing pattern of black and white triangles.

(a) Find a formula for each of the following:

(i) the number of triangles in the nth row,

(ii) the total number of triangles in the first n rows,

(iii) the total number of white triangles in the first n rows,

(iv) the total number of black triangles in the first n rows.

(b) Show algebraically that your answer to (a) (ii) is the sum of your answers to (a) (iii) and (iv). (*C*)

Chapter 11

Motion Geometry

Chapter Highlights

- Drawing the reflection of a simple plane figure
- Exploring reflection in the environment
- Drawing the rotation of a simple plane figure, about any point in the plane through angles which are multiples of 90°
- Exploring rotation in the environment
- Drawing the translation of a simple plane figure in the *x-y* plane
- Exploring translation in the environment
- Drawing an enlargement of a given plane figure
- Exploring enlargement (including reduction) in the environment
- Identifying reflection, rotation, translation and enlargement of a given plane figure
- Drawing the image of a figure involving combined movements

11.1 REFLECTION

If you write the letter *R* on a piece of paper and place a mirror upright on the piece of paper as shown, you will see the **reflection** of the letter *R* in the mirror. We say that the reflection 'Я' in the mirror is the **image under reflection** of the letter *R*.

Reflection is a mirror image.

The reflection of a snow-capped mountain on a glacial lake and the mirror image of another vehicle in the rear-view mirror of a car are examples of reflection in the environment.

Class Activity 1

1. (a) Fold a piece of tracing paper into half. Unfold it and draw a line *XY* along the crease. Then draw a $\triangle ABC$ on the right side of *XY*.

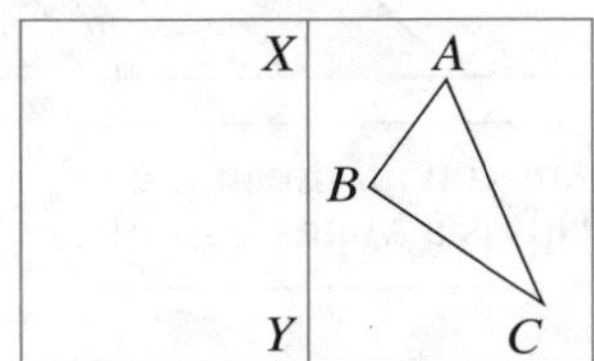

(b) Fold the paper again along *XY* so that the left side of the paper is on top of $\triangle ABC$ as shown.

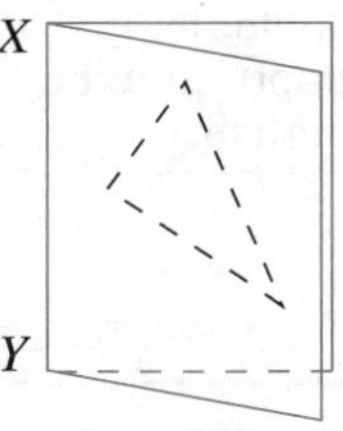

(c) Trace $\triangle ABC$ on to the reverse face of the paper.

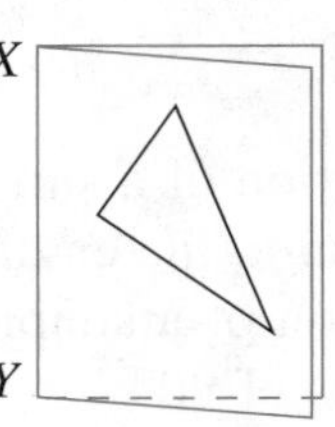

(d) Unfold the paper (you will see through the paper the triangle you have just drawn). This will help you trace the mirror image of $\triangle ABC$.

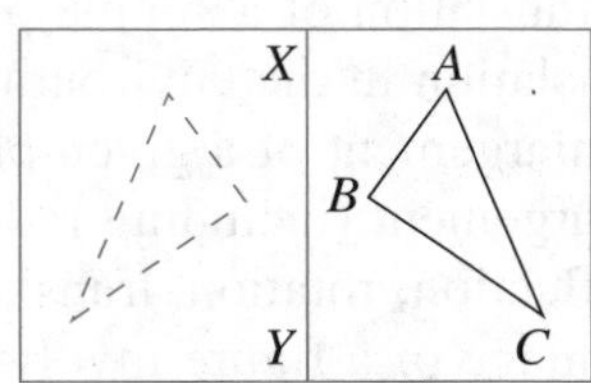

(e) Trace the mirror image of $\triangle ABC$ and name the vertices A', B' and C'. Then join AA', BB' and CC' as shown. We say that $\triangle ABC$ is transformed under a reflection in the line XY to $\triangle A'B'C'$.

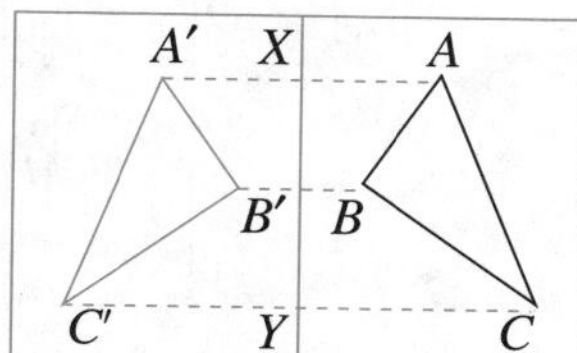

(f) The line XY is called the **line of reflection** (or mirror line). Is XY a perpendicular bisector of AA', BB' and CC'?

(g) A transformation is also known as a **mapping**. Do we also say that $\triangle ABC$ is mapped onto $\triangle A'B'C'$ under a reflection in the line XY?

2.

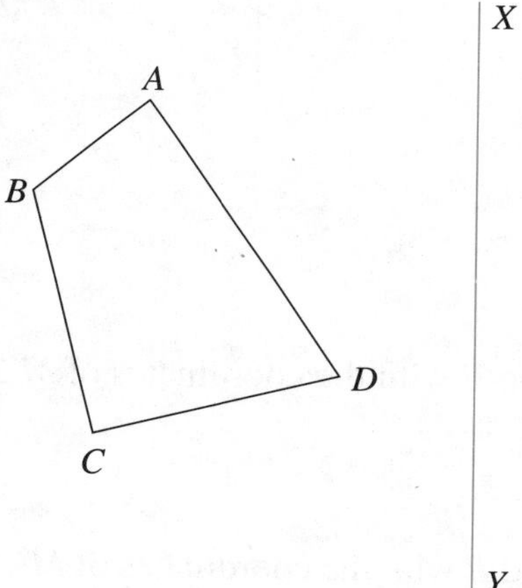

(a) Quadrilateral $ABCD$ is mapped onto quadrilateral $A'B'C'D'$ by a reflection in XY. Copy the quadrilateral $ABCD$ on a piece of tracing paper. Use your geometrical instruments to draw the points A', B', C' and D' which are the mirror images of A, B, C and D, i.e. draw A', B', C' and D' such that XY is the perpendicular bisector of AA', BB', CC' and DD'. Then complete the quadrilateral $A'B'C'D'$.

(b) Fold your paper along the mirror line to find out whether

- **(i)** each line segment of the original figure is equal to the corresponding line segment of the image figure,
- **(ii)** each angle of the original figure is equal to the corresponding angle of the image figure,
- **(iii)** the original figure is congruent to its image figure.

3. **(a)** M' is the image of M when the y-axis is the mirror line. M'' is the image of M when the x-axis is the mirror line. Write down the coordinates of M' and M''.

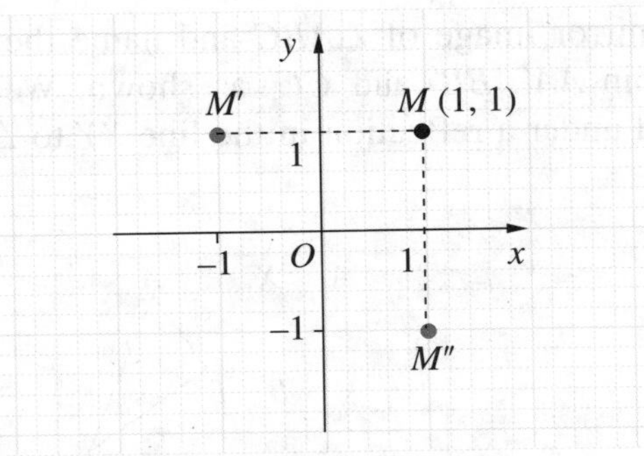

(b) $A'B'$ is the image of AB when the y-axis is the mirror line. $A''B''$ is the image of AB when the x-axis is the mirror line. Write down the coordinates of A', B', A'' and B''.

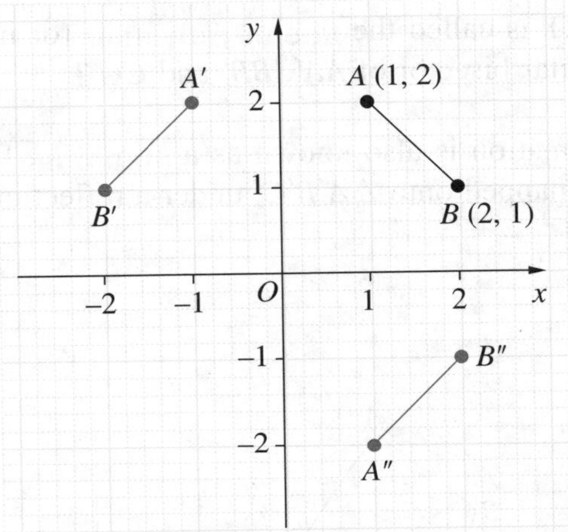

(c) Compare the coordinates of M, A and B with the coordinates of M', A' and B'. What do you notice?

(d) Compare the coordinates of M, A and B with the coordinates of M'', A'' and B''. What do you notice?

4. Give some examples of reflection in daily life.

Remember these:

- **Reflection carries segments into equal segments.**
- **Reflection carries angles into equal angles.**
- **Reflection carries whole figures into congruent whole figures.**

Exercise 11.1

answers on p. 438

1. Copy and draw on graph paper the reflection of each figure with respect to the mirror line XY.

(a)

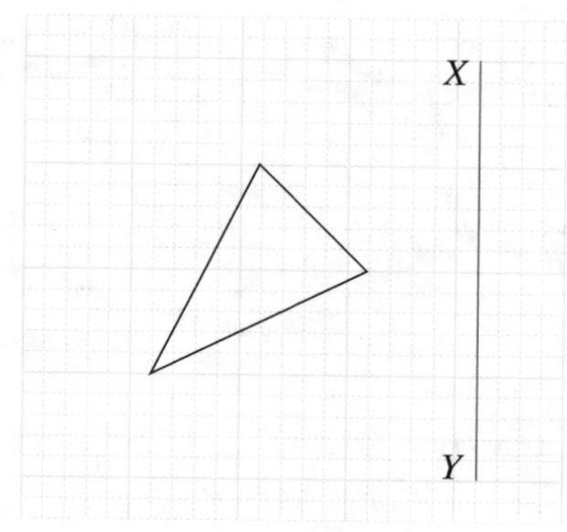

(b)

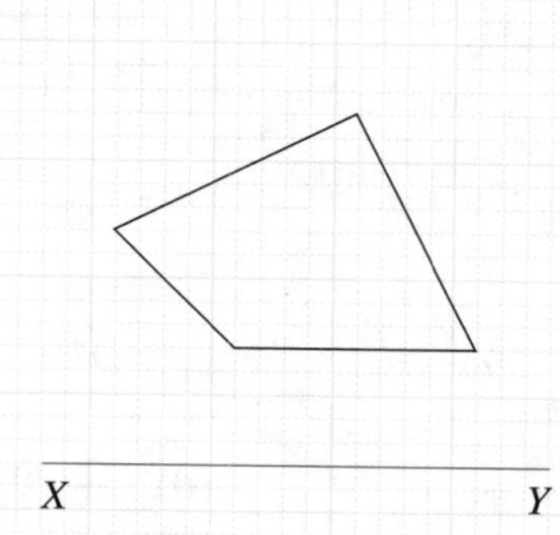

(c)

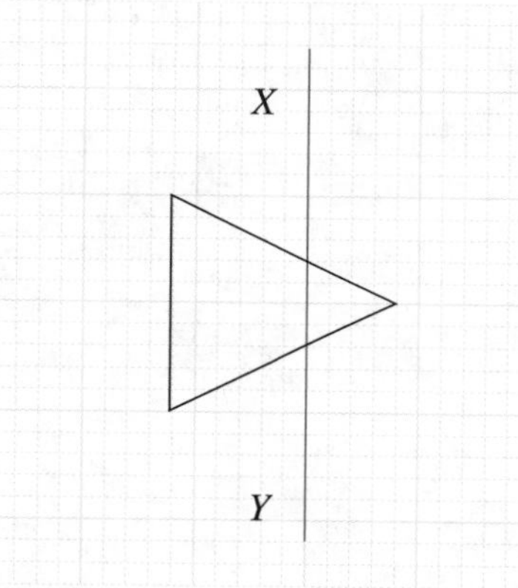

(d)

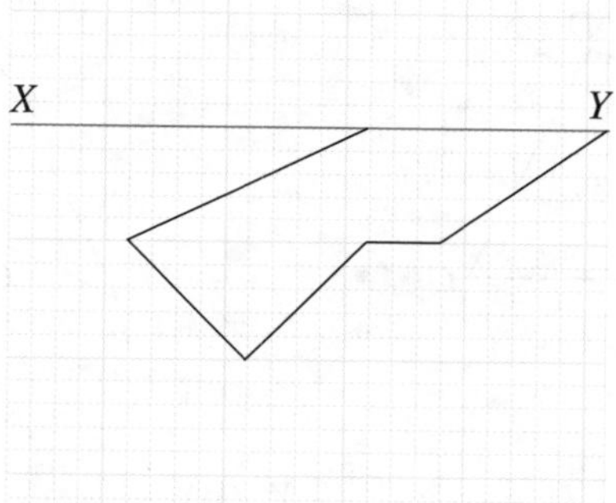

(e)

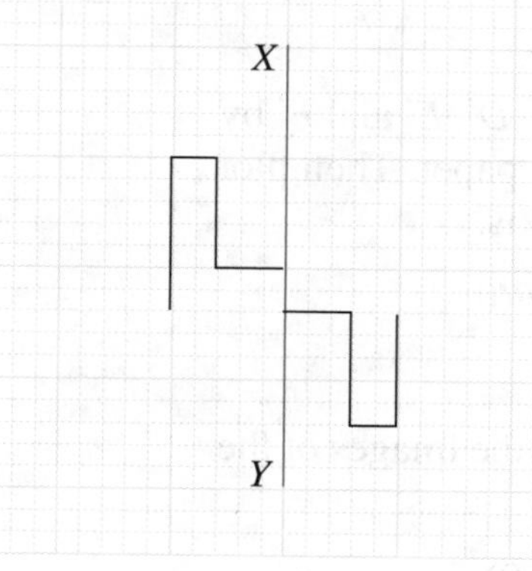

(f)

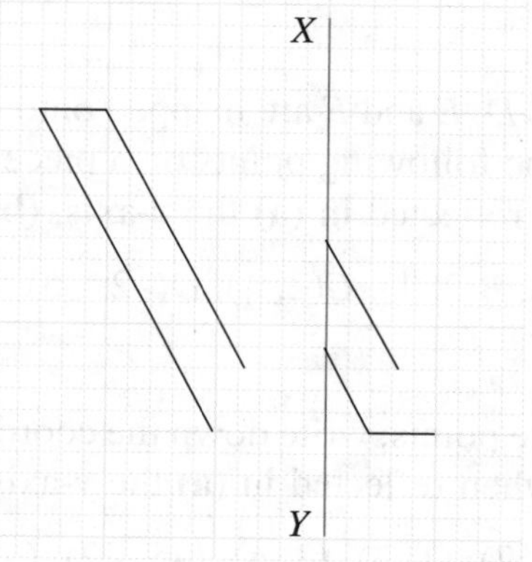

2. The following figures are transformed under reflection in XY. Trace a copy of each figure. Using geometrical instruments, construct the image of each figure. Label the image.

(a)

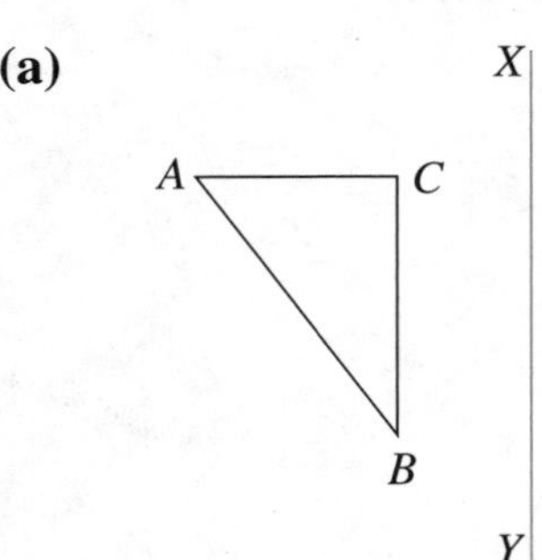

(b)

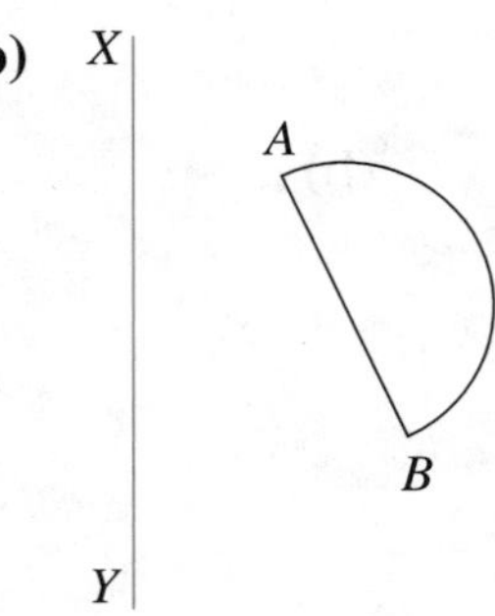

(c)

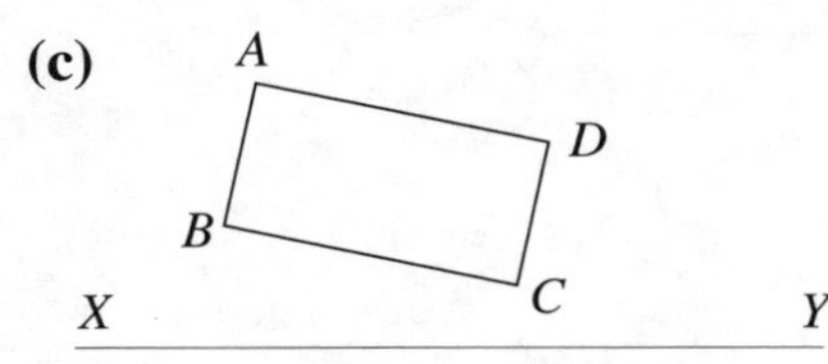

(d)

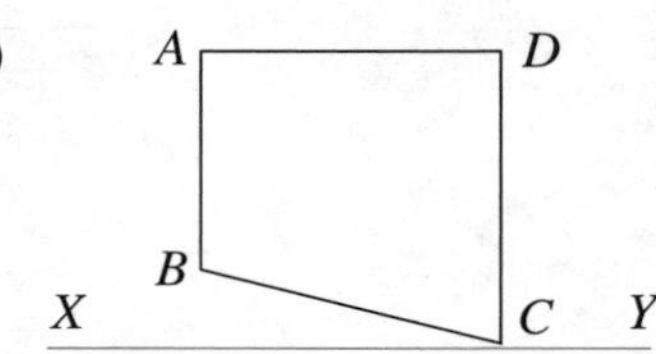

(e)

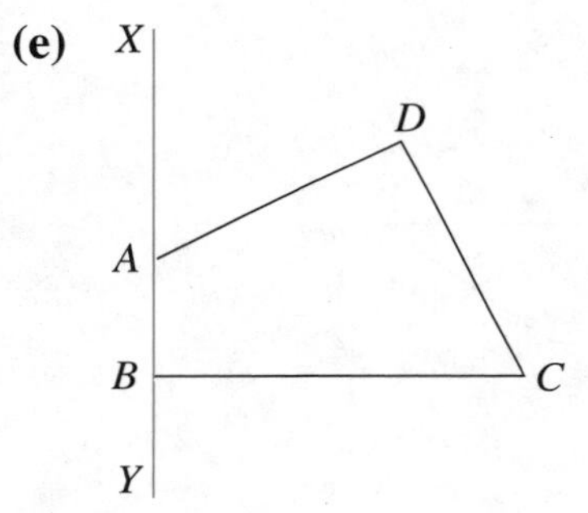

(f)

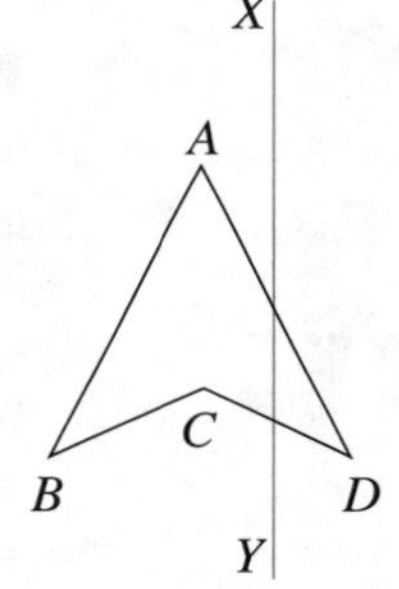

(g)

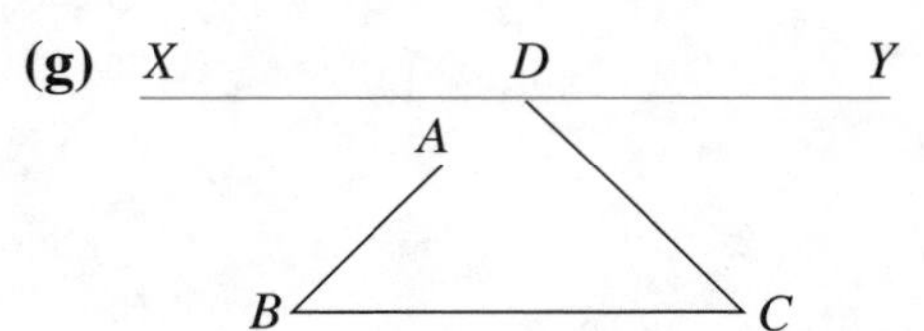

(h)

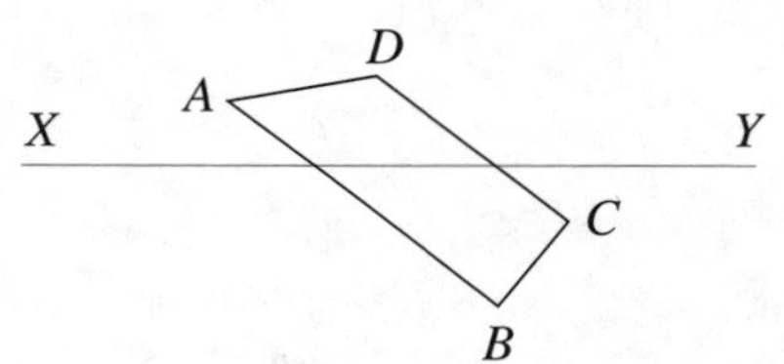

3. The points A, B, C, D, E and F are mapped onto A', B', C', D', E' and F' by a reflection. Plot the following points on a piece of graph paper. Then plot their images when reflected in **(a)** the y-axis, **(b)** the x-axis.

$$A(-2, 1),\ B(3, 1),\ C(2, 4),\ D(-2, -5),\ E(3, 0),\ F(0, 3)$$

4. Without plotting the points, write down the coordinates of the images of the following points when reflected in **(a)** the y-axis, **(b)** the x-axis.

$$(-4, 2),\ (1, 3),\ (3, 4),\ (-5, -2),\ (-3, 0),\ (4, 0)$$

11.2 ROTATION

Draw a letter R on a sheet of paper. Copy it onto a piece of tracing paper. Rotate the tracing paper clockwise about a fixed point O through a certain angle as shown. The letter R in the new position is called the **image of R under a rotation**.

Rotation is turning a point or figure about a fixed point.

We observe rotations in daily life. Examples of rotation are foot drills involving left turns, right turns and about-turns, the turning of the minute and hour hands of a clock, and turning the knobs of equipment.

Class Activity 2

1. **(a)** Copy the figure $OABC$.
   (b) Trace the figure onto a piece of tracing paper.
   (c) Fix the point O with a sharp point and rotate the traced figure through an angle of 90° clockwise as shown. Name the image under rotation as $OA'B'C'$.
   (d) OA is transformed to OA' under rotation through 90° clockwise.
   Is OC transformed to OC' under the same rotation?
   Is OB transformed to OB' under the same rotation also?
   How do you find out?

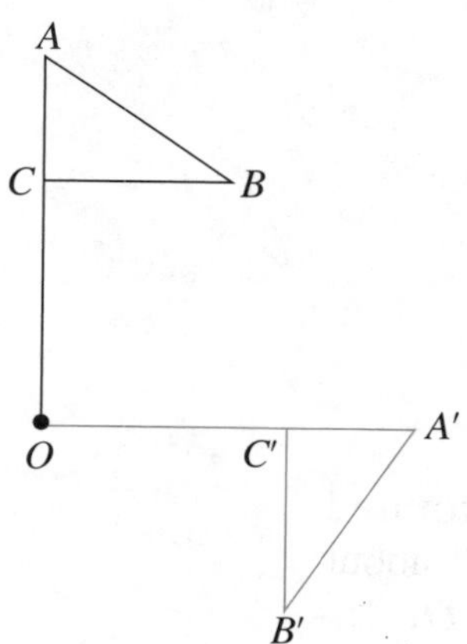

2. State whether each of the following statements is true or false.
   If a figure is transformed under rotation, then
   (a) each line segment of the original figure is equal to the corresponding line segment of the image figure,
   (b) each angle of the original figure is equal to the corresponding angle of the image figure,
   (c) the original figure is congruent to its image figure.

3. (a) A is rotated 90° anticlockwise about the origin O. Its image is A'. Write down the coordinates of A'.

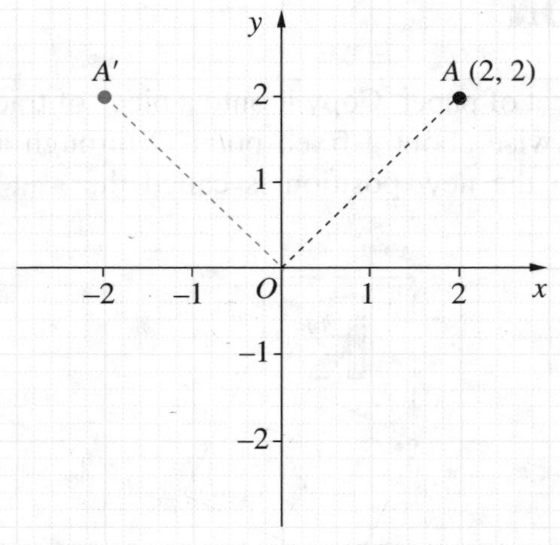

(b) AB is rotated 90° clockwise about the origin O. Its image is $A'B'$. Write down the coordinates of A' and B'.

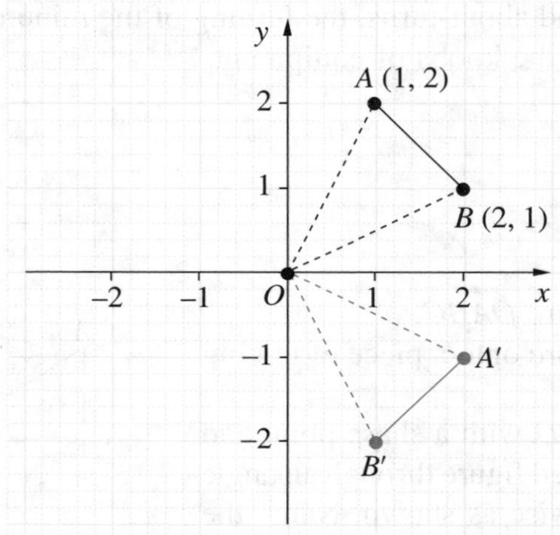

(c) $\triangle ABC$ is rotated through 180° about the origin O. Its image is $\triangle A'B'C'$. Write down the coordinates of A', B' and C'.

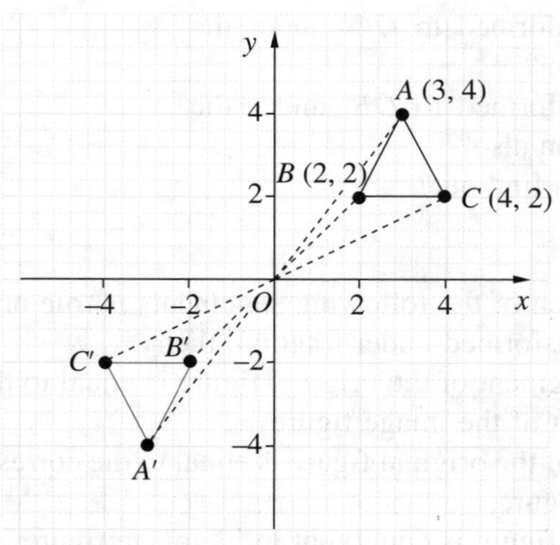

4. Give some examples of rotation in daily life.

Remember these:

> **A rotation carries segments into equal segments.**
> **A rotation carries angles into equal angles.**
> **A rotation carries whole figures into congruent figures**

Worked Example

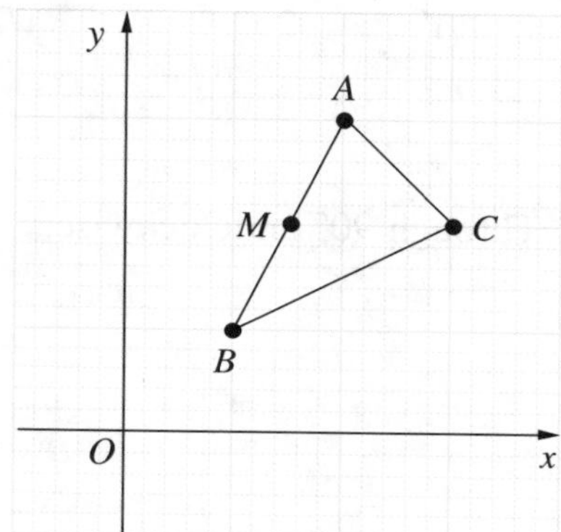

$\triangle ABC$ is mapped onto $\triangle A'B'C'$ under a rotation. Draw and label the image of $\triangle ABC$ under a clockwise rotation

(a) through 90° about A,

(b) through 270° about M.

Solution:

(a)

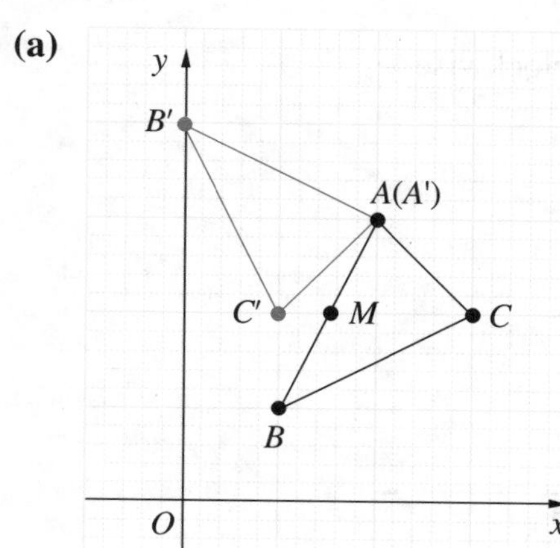

$\triangle A'B'C'$ is the required image.

(b)

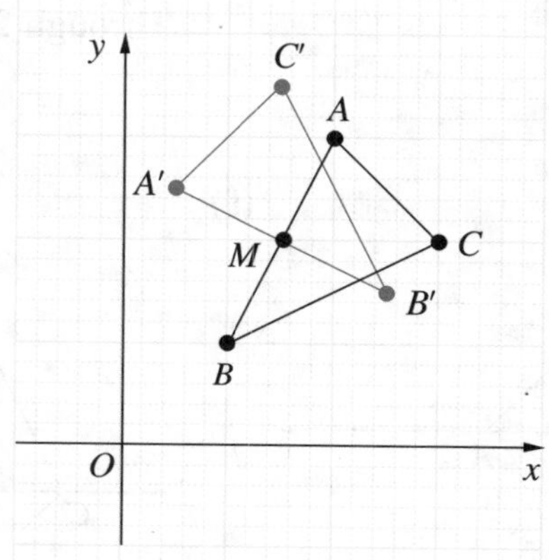

$\triangle A'B'C'$ is the required image.

Note: 270° clockwise rotation is equivalent to 90° anticlockwise rotation.

Exercise 11.2

answers on p. 438

1. Copy the following figures on graph paper. Draw and label the image of each figure under rotation about the origin through an angle as indicated.

(a)

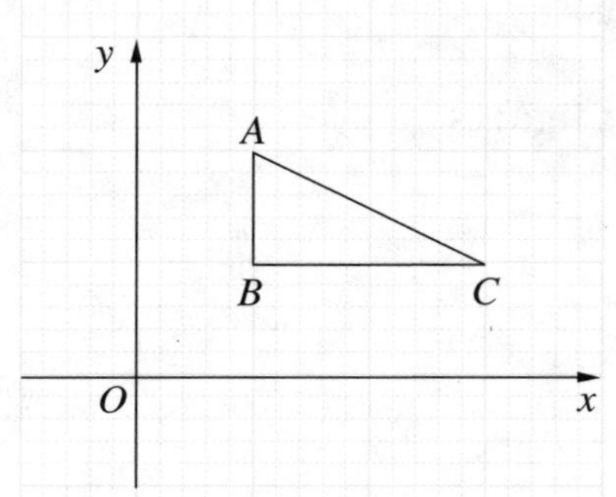

Through 90° clockwise.

(b)

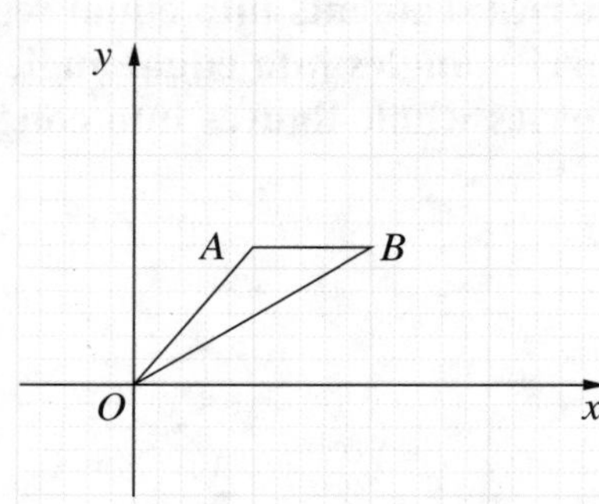

Through 90° anticlockwise.

(c)

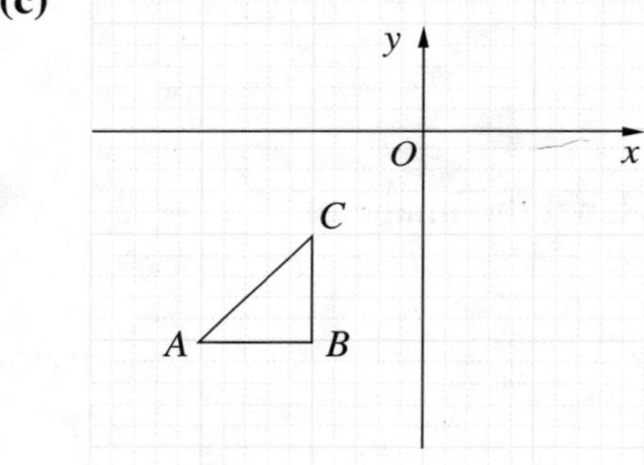

Through 180°.

(d)

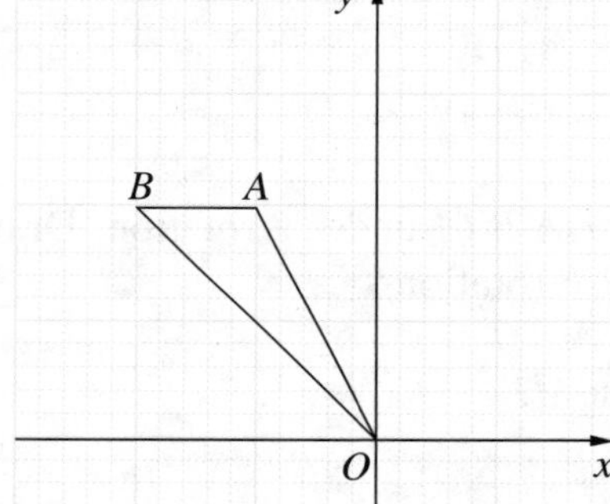

Through 270° anticlockwise.

(e)

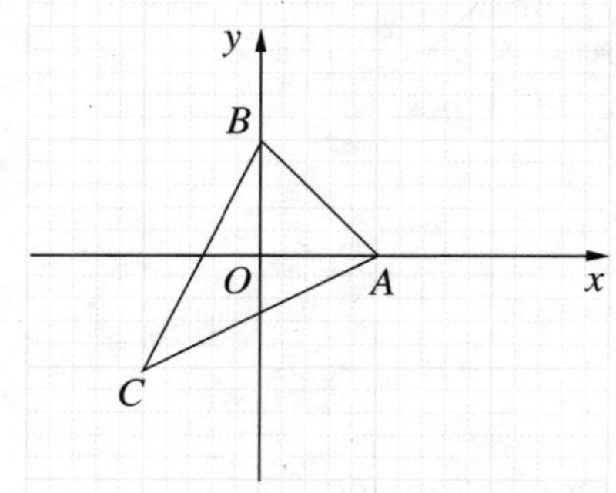

Through 90° clockwise.

(f)

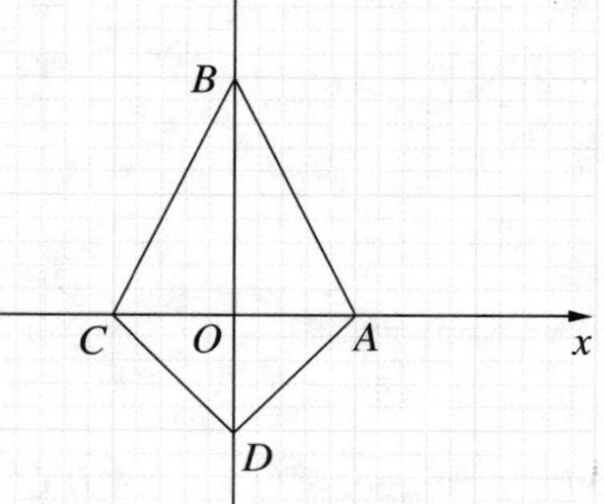

Through 180°.

2. Copy the following figures on graph paper. Draw and label the image of each figure under rotation as instructed.

(a)

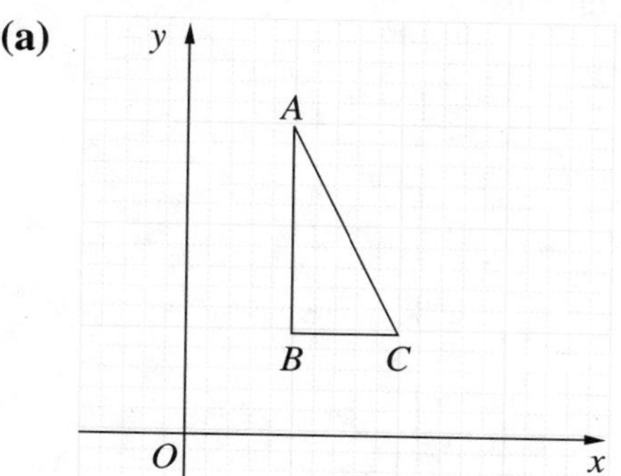

Through 90° clockwise about A.

(b)

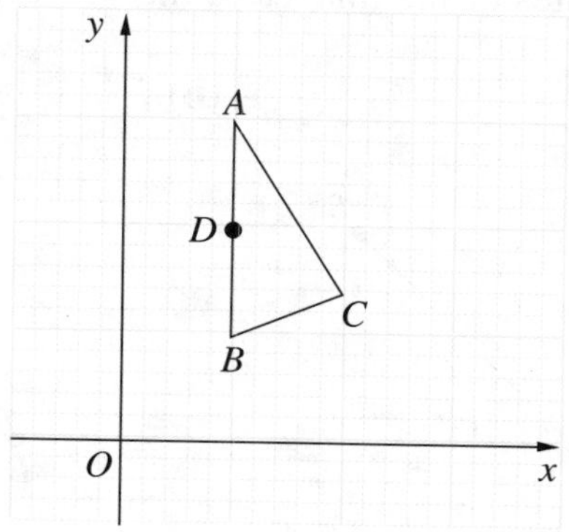

Through 90° anticlockwise about D.

(c)

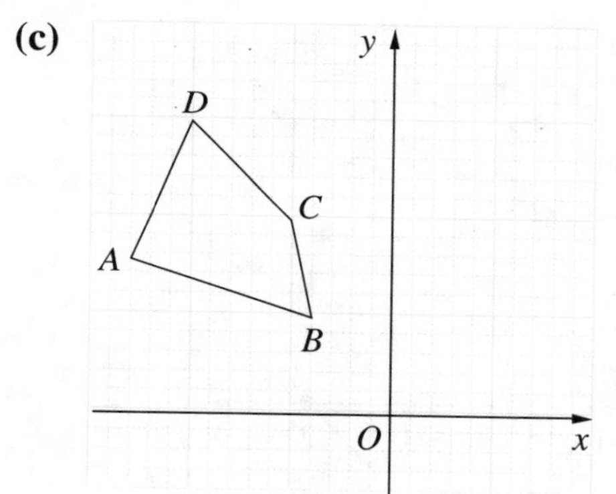

Through 180° about B.

(d)

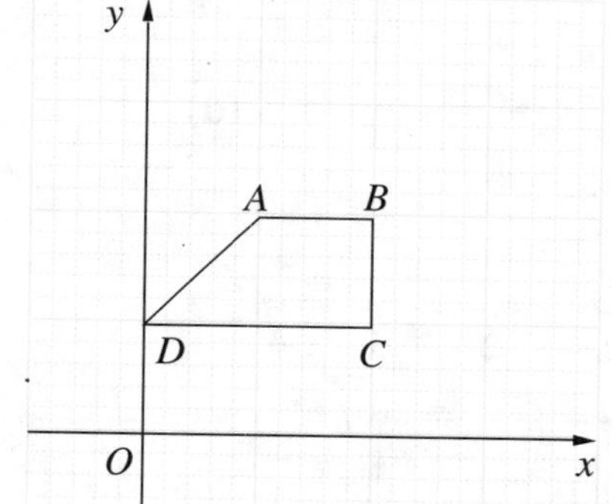

Through 90° anticlockwise about D.

(e)

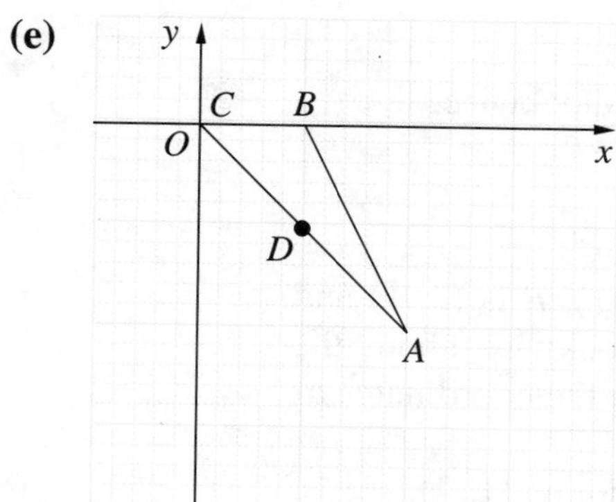

Through 270° anticlockwise about D.

(f)

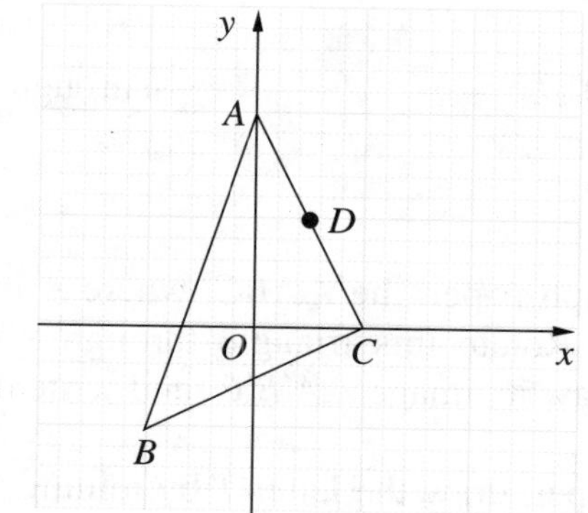

Through 180° about D.

3. Copy the following figures on graph paper. Draw their images under rotation about the origin O. The angle of rotation is shown in each case. Give the coordinates of the images of the vertices in each case.

(a)

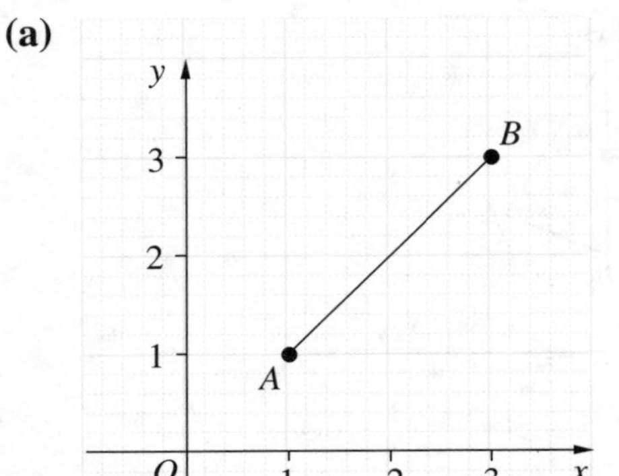

Through 90° anticlockwise.

(b)

y
D
3
C 2
1
E
–3
–2
–1
O
x

Through 90° clockwise.

(c)

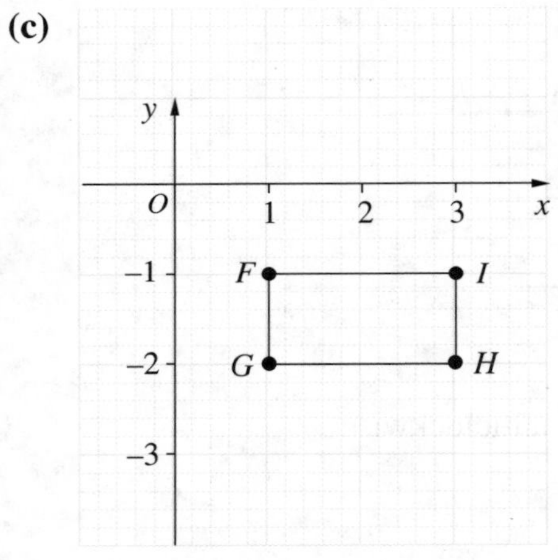

Through 180°.

(d)

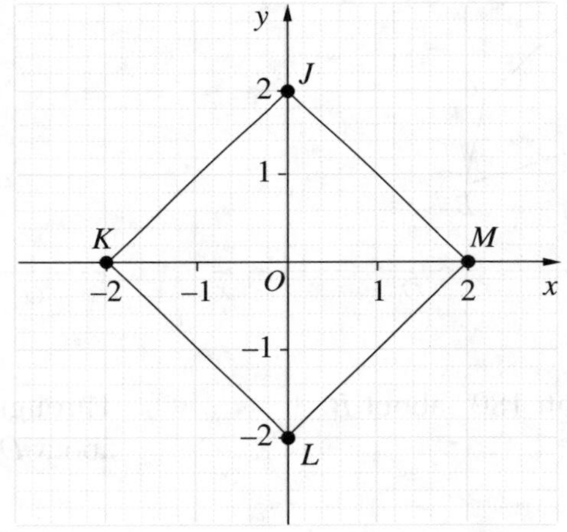

Through 90° clockwise.

4. **(a)** Draw on graph paper, the $\triangle ABC$, where A is (2, 1), B is (3, 1) and C is (1, 2). Rotate this triangle through 90° clockwise about the origin O. Draw its image $\triangle A'B'C'$ and write down the coordinates of A', B' and C'.

(b) On graph paper, draw the letter T by joining the points (1, 4), (2, 4), (2, 2) and (3, 4). This letter is rotated through 180° about the origin O. Draw its image and give the coordinates of the images of the four given points.

11.3 TRANSLATION

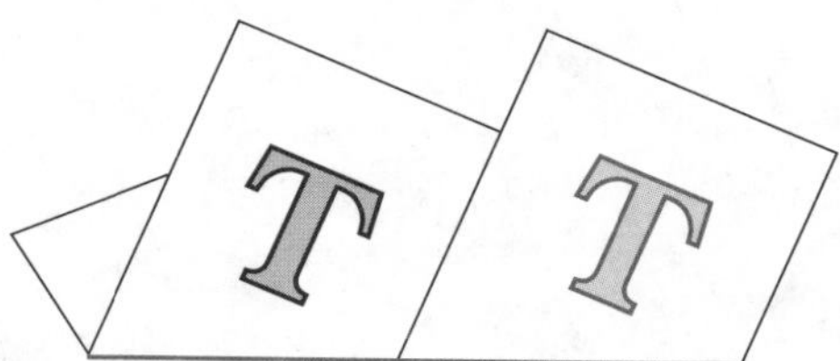

The letter T on the sheet of paper is copied on to a sheet of tracing paper. The two sheets of paper are folded and the tracing paper is slid as shown. Notice that the letter is moved without turning. We say that the letter T is translated. The letter in the new position is called the **image under a translation**.

Translation is the movement of a point or figure by a sliding motion.

A concrete block sliding along a flat surface in a straight line and an aeroplane flying along a linear course are examples of translations in the environment.

Class Activity 3

1.

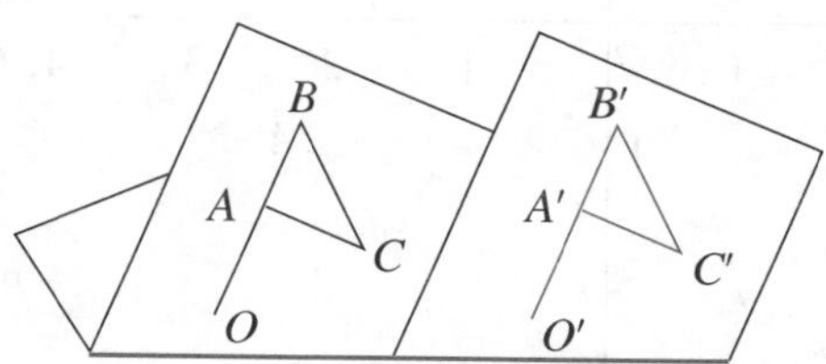

Copy the figure $OABC$ on a sheet of paper and trace the figure on to a tracing paper. Fold the two sheets of paper and slide the tracing paper as shown. Denote the figure on the tracing paper as $O'A'B'C'$. The points O, A, B and C are translated to O', A', B' and C'.

(a) Are the line segments OO', AA', BB' and CC' equal in length?
(b) Are these line segments parallel?

2. State whether each of the following statements is true or false.
If a figure is transformed under translation, then
(a) each line segment of the original figure is equal to the corresponding line segment of the image figure,
(b) each angle of the original figure is equal to the corresponding angle of the image figure,
(c) the original figure is congruent to its image figure.

3. **(a)** A is translated 2 units in the x-direction and 3 units in the y-direction to its image A'. Write down the coordinates of A'.

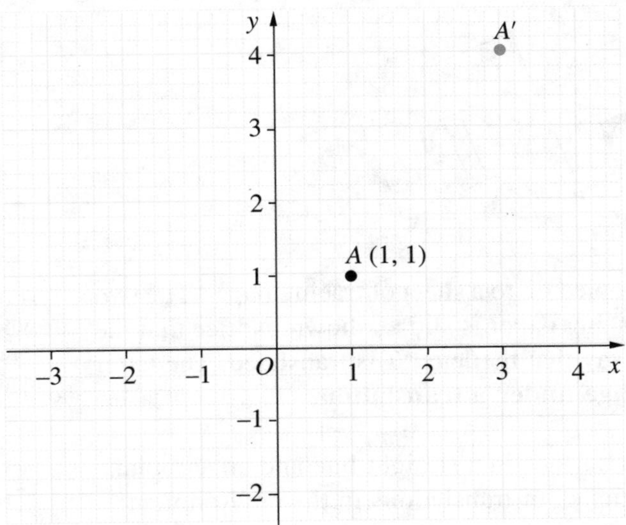

(b) AB is translated 1 unit in the x-direction and –3 units in the y-direction to its image $A'B'$. Write down the coordinates of A' and B'.

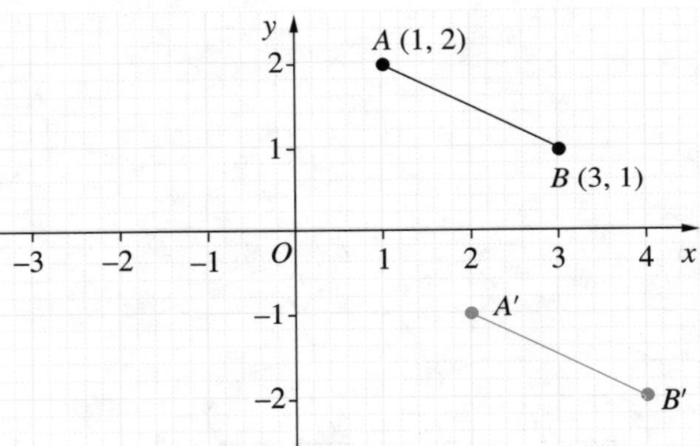

(c) $\triangle ABC$ is translated –4 units in the x-direction and 4 units in the y-direction to its image $\triangle A'B'C'$. Write down the coordinates of A', B' and C'.

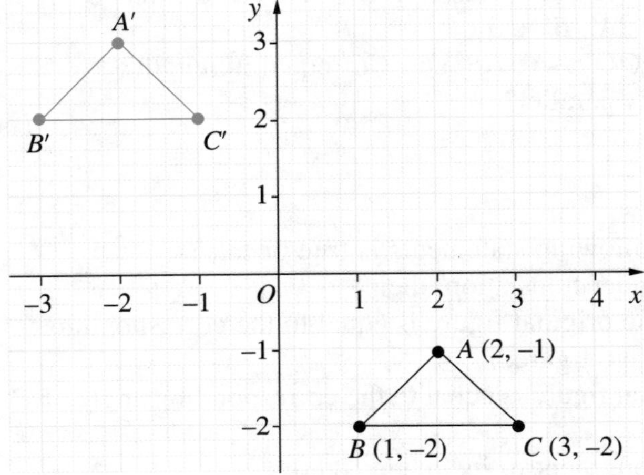

4. Give some examples of translations in daily life.

Remember these:

- **Translation carries segments into equal segments.**
- **Translation carries angles into equal angles.**
- **Translation carries whole figures into congruent figures.**

Exercise 11.3

answers on p. 439

1. Copy the following figures on graph paper and do the translation of each figure as instructed. Draw and label each image.

(a)

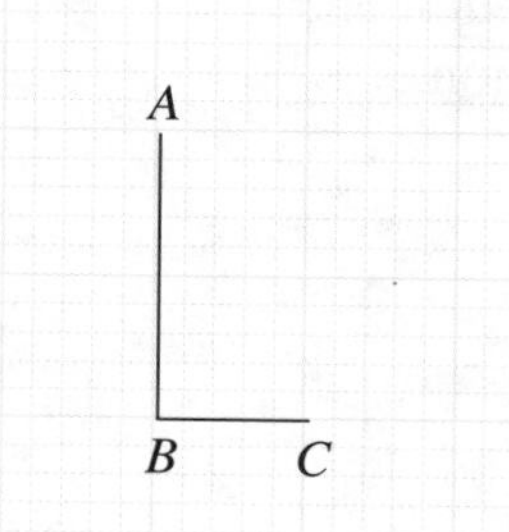

2 cm to the right.

(b)

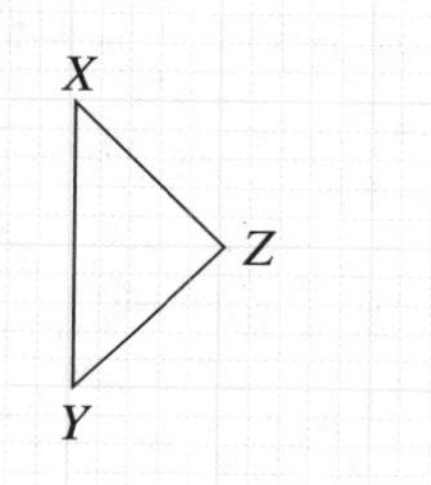

1 cm up and 3 cm to the left.

(c)

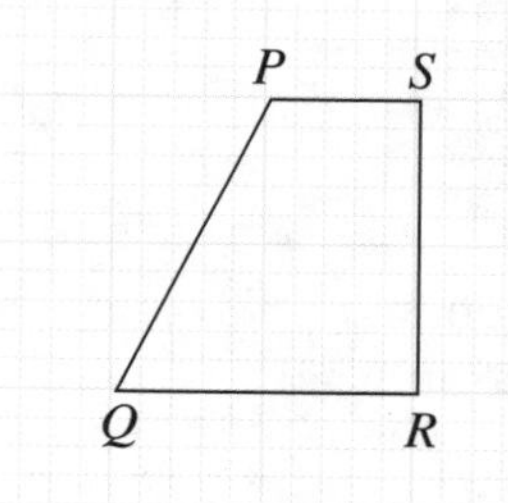

1 cm to the right and 1 cm up.

(d)

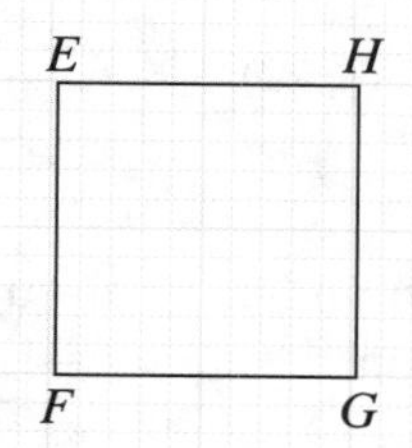

1 cm down and 2 cm to the right.

(e)

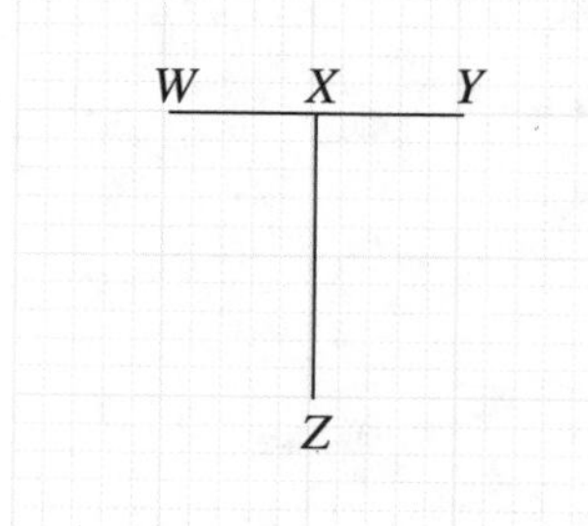

2 cm up and 1 cm to the right.

(f)

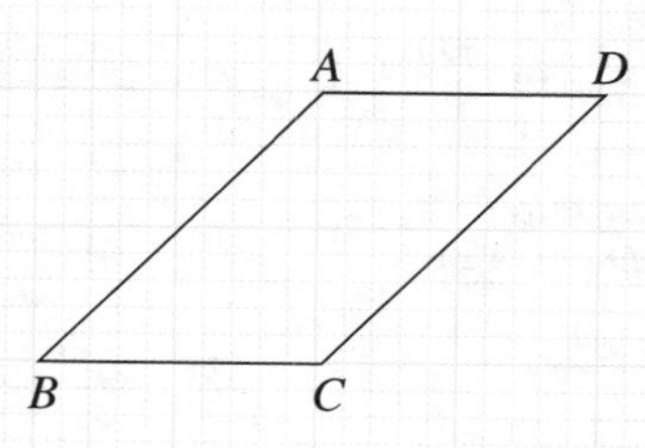

2 cm to the right and 1 cm to the left.

2. Copy the following figures on graph paper and do the translation as instructed. Draw and label each image. Then write down the coordinates of its vertices.

(a)

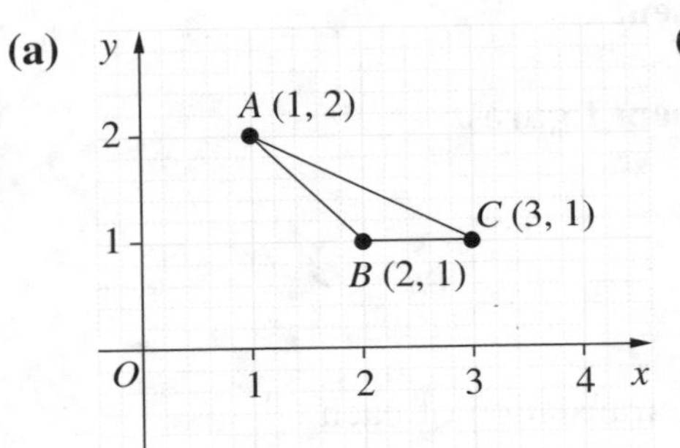

1 unit in the x-direction and –2 units in the y-direction.

(b)

–3 units in the y-direction and 4 units in the x-direction.

(c)

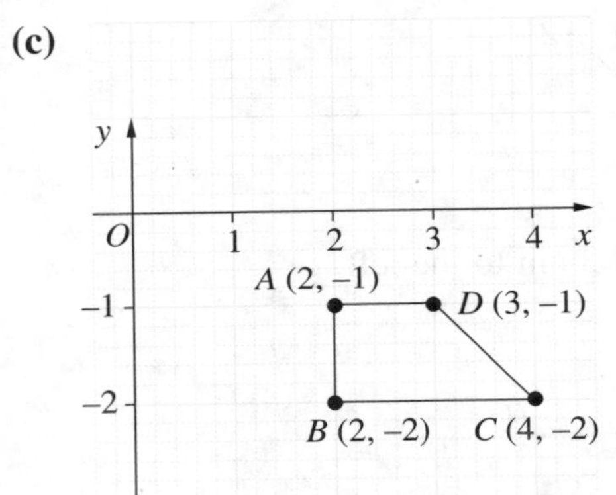

3 units in the y-direction and –3 units in the x-direction.

(d)

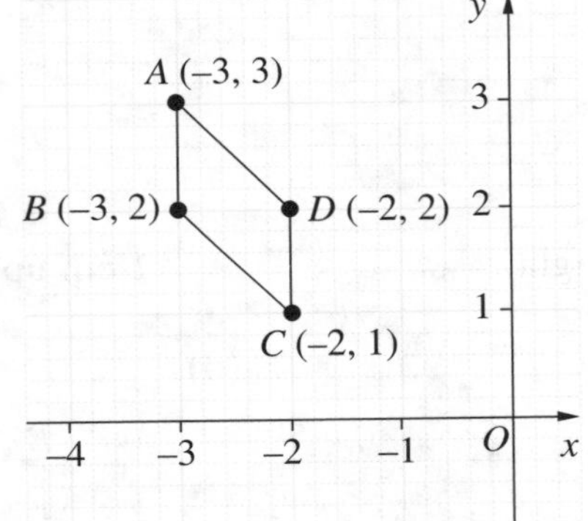

4 units in the x-direction and –4 units in the y-direction.

(e)

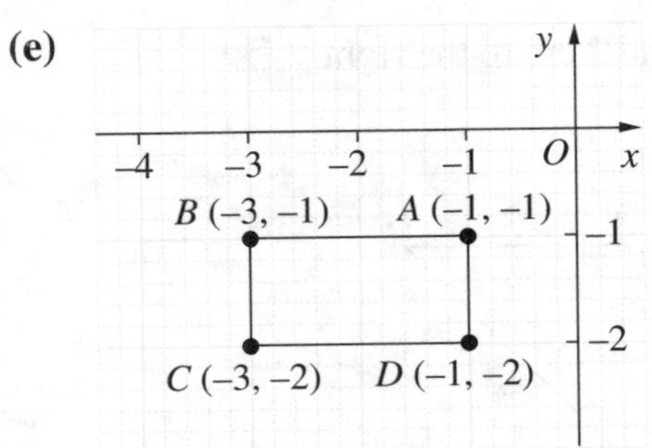

4 units in the x-direction and 3 units in the y-direction.

(f)

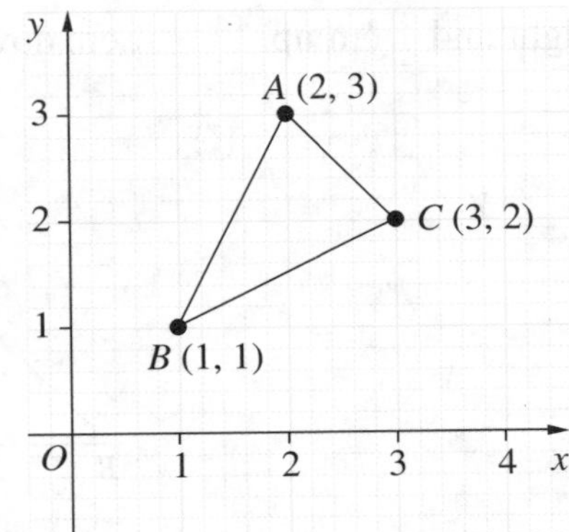

–4 units in the x-direction and –4 units in the y-direction.

11.4 ENLARGEMENT

From what we have learnt so far, we notice that reflection, rotation and translation are **rigid motions**, that is, a figure does not change its shape and size after it has been transformed by these motions.

We shall learn another transformation which is not a rigid motion. Under this transformation, a figure does not change its shape but it changes its size. We call this transformation an **enlargement**.

The projection of a diagram on a screen from an overhead projector and an enlarged copy of a photograph are examples of enlargement in the environment.

Class Activity 4

1. ABC is a given triangle. $\triangle A'B'C'$ is an enlarged copy. The scale used is 5 : 2.

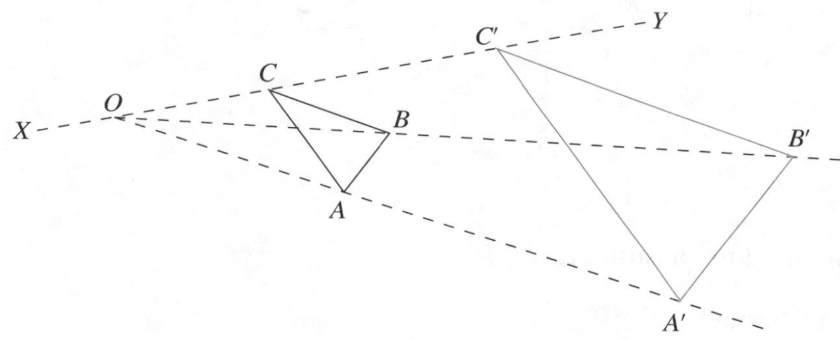

The following steps are used to construct $\triangle A'B'C'$.

Step 1: Draw a line XY through C.

Step 2: Mark points O and C' on XY such that $OC = 2$ cm and $OC' = 5$ cm. (Note that $OC' : OC = 5 : 2$.)

Step 3: From O, draw straight lines through B and A. Construct points B' and A' such that $C'B' \parallel CB$ and $B'A' \parallel BA$ and join $A'C'$ as shown.

We say that $\triangle A'B'C'$ is the image of $\triangle ABC$ under an enlargement with scale factor $\frac{5}{2}$. The point O is called the **centre of enlargement**.

(a) Make the necessary measurements to find out whether

(i) each side of the image is $\frac{5}{2}$ times the corresponding side of the given figure,

(ii) each angle of the image is equal to the corresponding angle of the given figure.

(b) Draw a triangle ABC such that $AB = 2$ cm, $BC = 3$ cm and $AC = 4$ cm. Construct the image of $\triangle ABC$ under an enlargement with scale factor $\frac{3}{2}$.

2. When the scale factor is a proper fraction, the image under enlargement is smaller than the given figure. The following example shows a reduced copy of the given $\triangle PQR$. $\triangle P'Q'R'$ is the image of $\triangle PQR$ under an enlargement with scale factor $\frac{1}{2}$, centre at O.

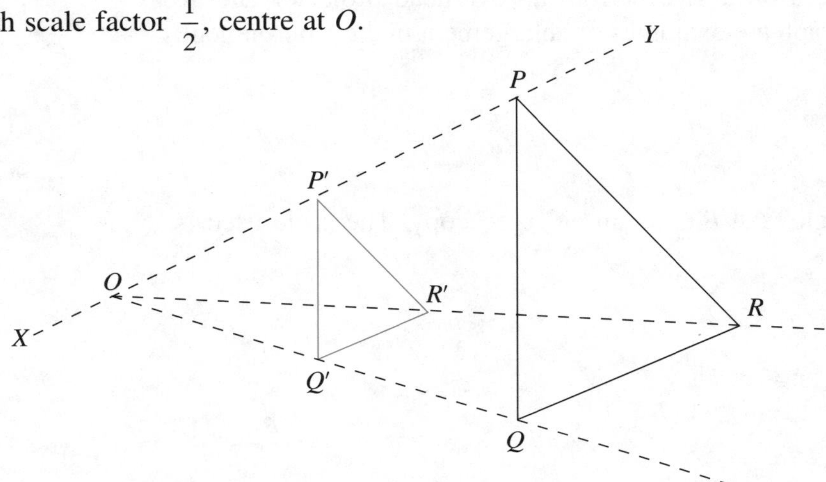

The following steps are used to construct $\triangle P'Q'R'$.

Step 1: Draw a line XY through P.

Step 2: Mark points O and P' on XY such that $OP = 6$ cm and $OP' = 3$ cm. (Note that $OP' : OP = 1 : 2$.)

Step 3: From O, draw straight lines to R and Q.

Step 4: Construct points R' and Q' such that $P'R' \parallel PR$ and $P'Q' \parallel PQ$. Join $Q'R'$ as shown.

(a) Make the necessary measurements to find out whether

(i) each side of the image is $\frac{1}{2}$ of the corresponding side of the given figure,

(ii) each angle of the image is equal to the corresponding angle of the given figure.

(b) Draw a triangle XYZ such that $XY = 6$ cm, $YZ = 4$ cm and $XZ = 8$ cm. Construct the image of $\triangle XYZ$ under an enlargement with scale factor $\frac{2}{3}$.

3. **(a)** $\triangle A'B'C'$ is an enlargement of $\triangle ABC$ with scale factor 2. The centre of enlargement is at the origin O. Write down the coordinates of A', B' and C'.

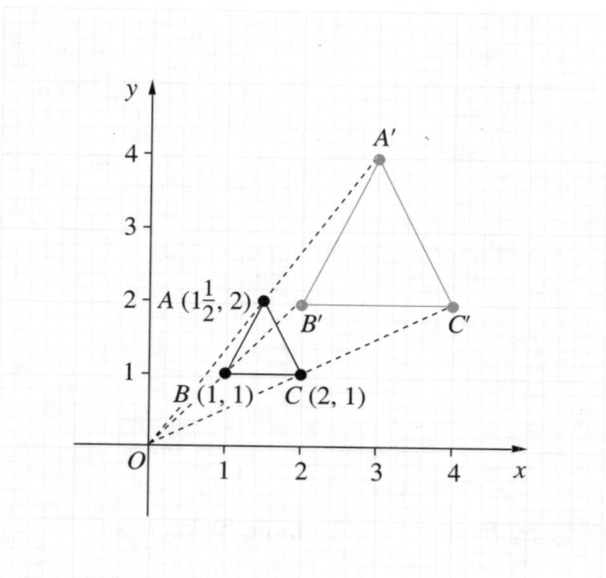

(b) Quadrilateral $A'B'C'D'$ is an enlargement of quadrilateral $ABCD$ with scale factor $\frac{1}{3}$. The centre of enlargement is at the origin O. Write down the coordinates of A', B', C' and D'.

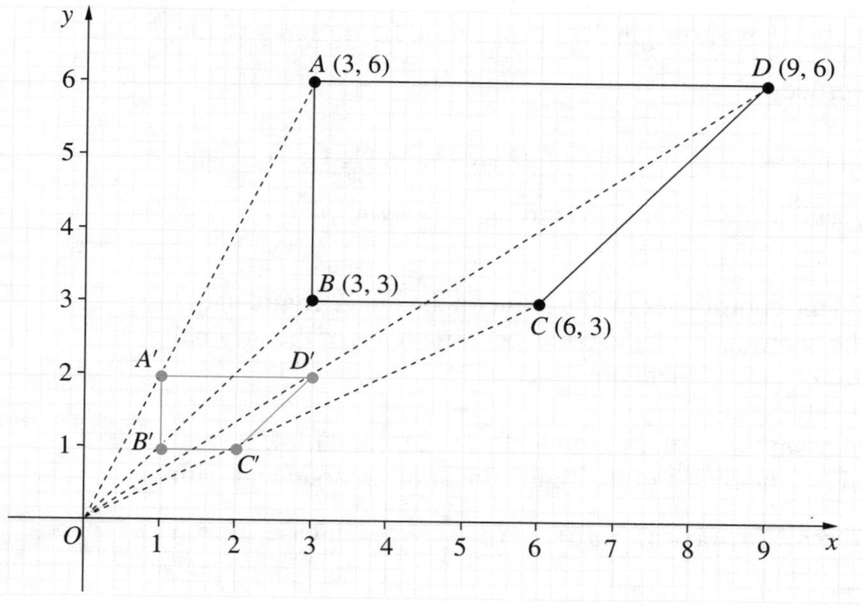

Exercise 11.4

answers on p. 439

1. Copy the following figures. With X as the centre of enlargement, enlarge each figure with the scale factor given.

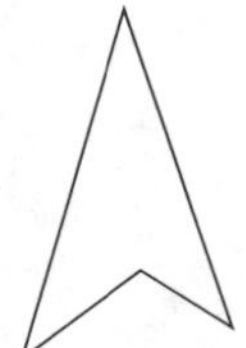

Enlarge by factor 2. Enlarge by factor 3. Enlarge by factor $\frac{3}{2}$.

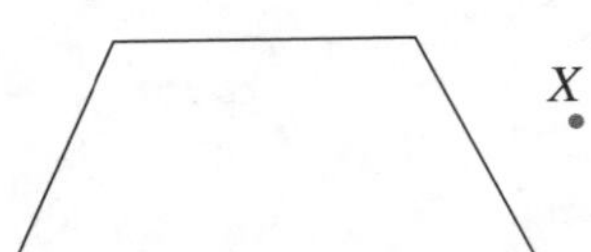

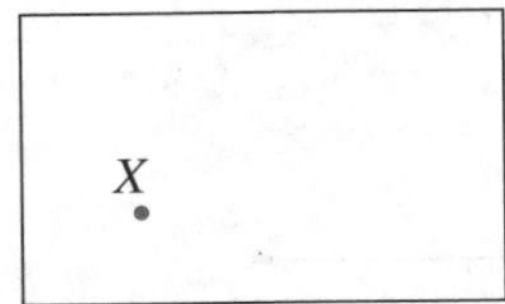

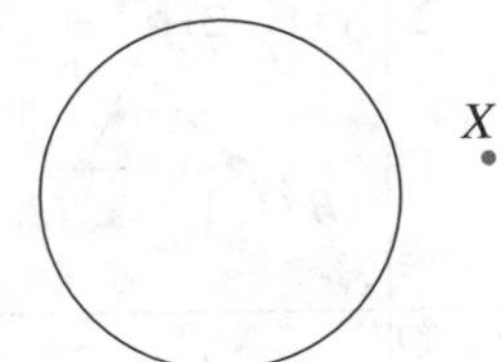

Enlarge by factor $\frac{2}{3}$. Enlarge by factor $\frac{3}{4}$. Enlarge by factor $\frac{5}{2}$.

Use the origin O as the centre of enlargement in each of the following cases.

2. A line segment AB, where A is (1, 1) and B is (3, 3), is enlarged with scale factor 2, centre at the origin. Draw the enlarged segment and give the coordinates of its vertices.

3. A triangle, whose vertices are (3, 3), (1, 1) and (4, 2), is given an enlargement with scale factor $\frac{3}{2}$, centre at the origin. Draw the image figure and give the coordinates of its vertices.

4. Enlarge a square, whose vertices A, B, C and D are (1, 3), (1, 1), (3, 1) and (3, 3) respectively, with scale factor $\frac{2}{3}$, centre at the origin.

5. Describe how to find the coordinates of any point on the image figure under an enlargement if the coordinates of the corresponding point of the original figure and the centre of enlargement are given.

6. $ABCDE$ is a polygon whose vertices are (1, 3), (1, 2), (3, 1), (4, 2) and (5, 4) respectively. Find the image of the figure under an enlargement with (0, 0) as centre and scale factors **(a)** 2, **(b)** $\frac{5}{2}$, **(c)** $\frac{1}{2}$. In each case, sketch the image of the figure.

11.5 COMBINATION OF TRANSFORMATIONS

Transformation is the changing of a figure's position, shape or size.

Worked Example 1

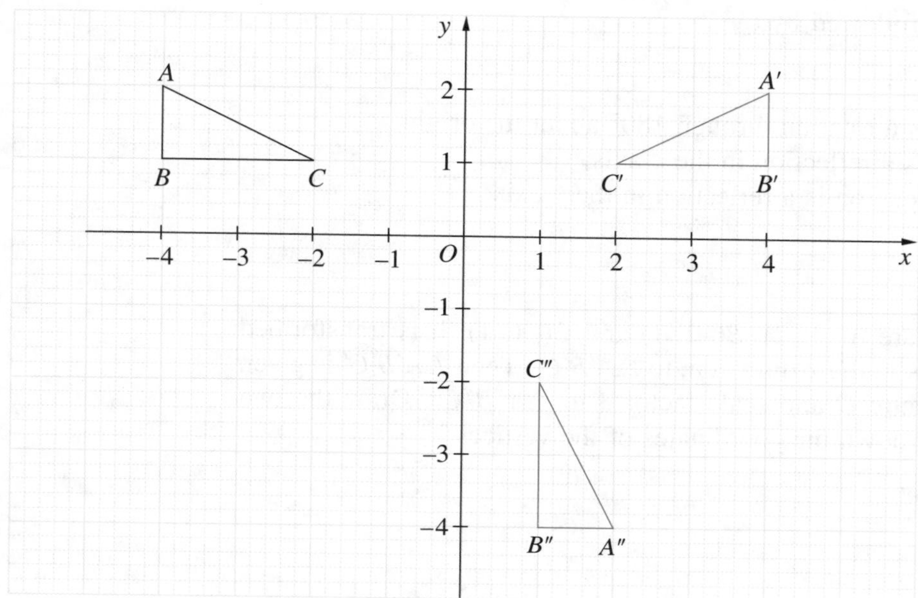

$\triangle ABC$ is mapped onto $\triangle A'B'C'$ under a certain transformation P. $\triangle A''B''C''$ is the image of $\triangle A'B'C'$ under another transformation Q. Describe fully transformation P and transformation Q.

Solution:

Transformation P is a reflection in the y-axis.
Transformation Q is a clockwise rotation through 90° about the origin O.

Worked Example 2

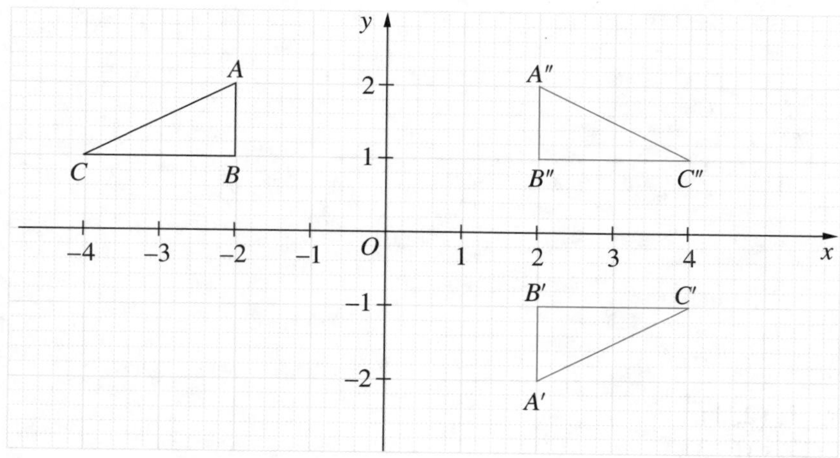

$\triangle ABC$ is given a transformation P followed by a transformation Q. Its two successive images are $\triangle A'B'C'$ and $\triangle A''B''C''$ respectively.

(a) Describe fully transformation P and transformation Q.

(b) Describe a single transformation equivalent to the combined transformations, P followed by Q.

Solution:

(a) Transformation P is a rotation through 180° about the origin.
Transformation Q is a reflection in the x-axis.

(b) The single transformation is a reflection in the y-axis.

Worked Example 3

The vertices of $\triangle ABC$ are $A(-1, 2)$, $B(-2, 1)$ and $C(-1, 1)$. It is transformed under translation, 3 units in the x-direction, to $\triangle A'B'C'$. Then $\triangle A'B'C'$ is given an enlargement with centre O and scale factor 3 to $\triangle A''B''C''$. Draw the two image figures and write down the coordinates of the vertices.

Solution:

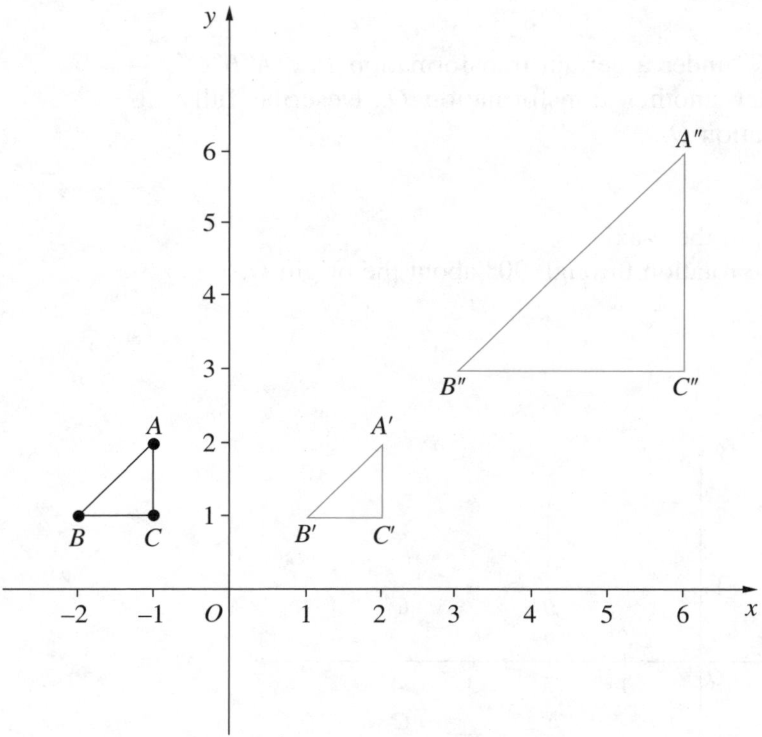

A' is (2, 2), B' is (1, 1) and C' is (2, 1).
A'' is (6, 6), B'' is (3, 3) and C'' is (6, 3).

Exercise 11.5

answers on p. 439

1. In each of the following diagrams, $\triangle A'B'C'$ is the image of $\triangle ABC$ under a transformation P. $\triangle A''B''C''$ is the image of $\triangle A'B'C'$ under a transformation Q. Describe fully transformation P and transformation Q.

(a)

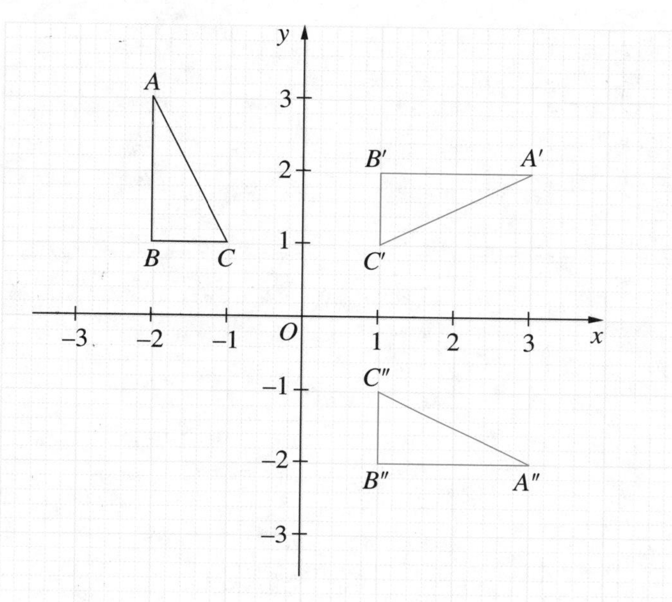

(b)

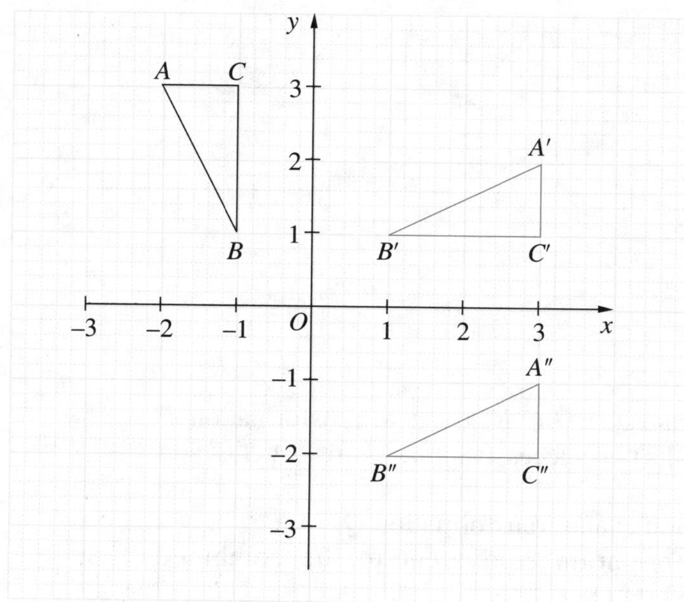

(c)

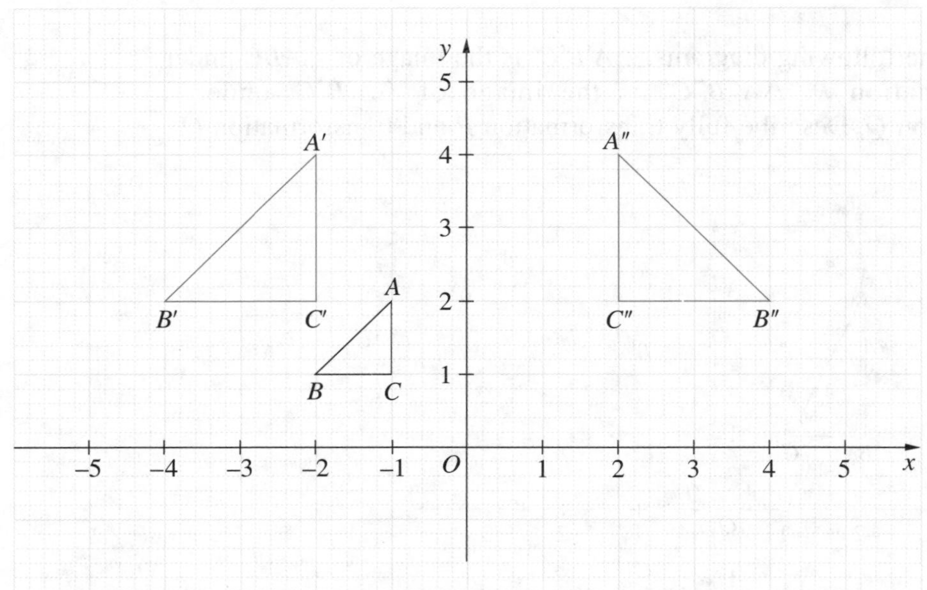

(d)

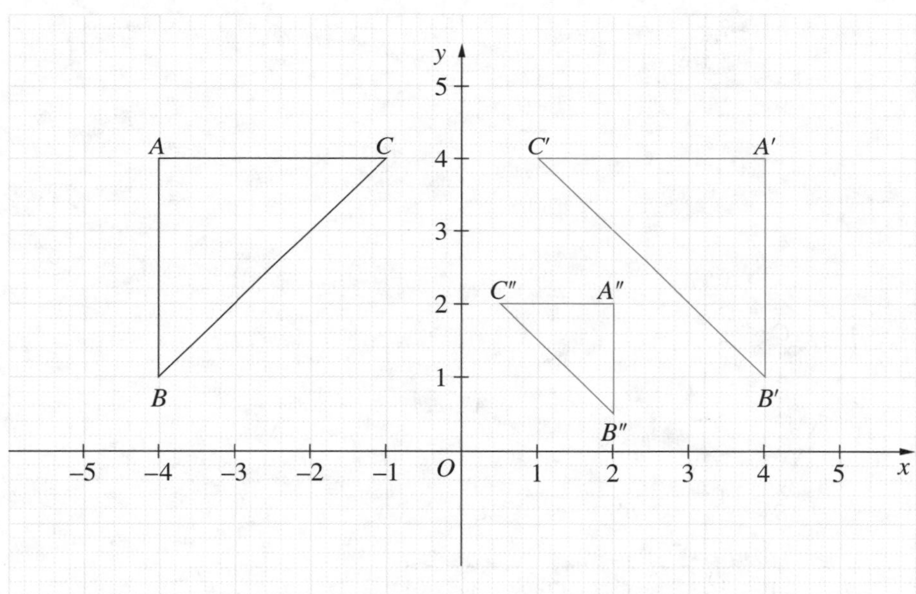

2. In each of the following diagrams, $\triangle ABC$ is given a transformation P followed by a transformation Q. Its two successive images are $\triangle A'B'C'$ and $\triangle A''B''C''$ respectively.

(i) Describe fully transformation P and transformation Q.

(ii) Describe a single transformation equivalent to the combined transformations, P followed by Q.

(a)

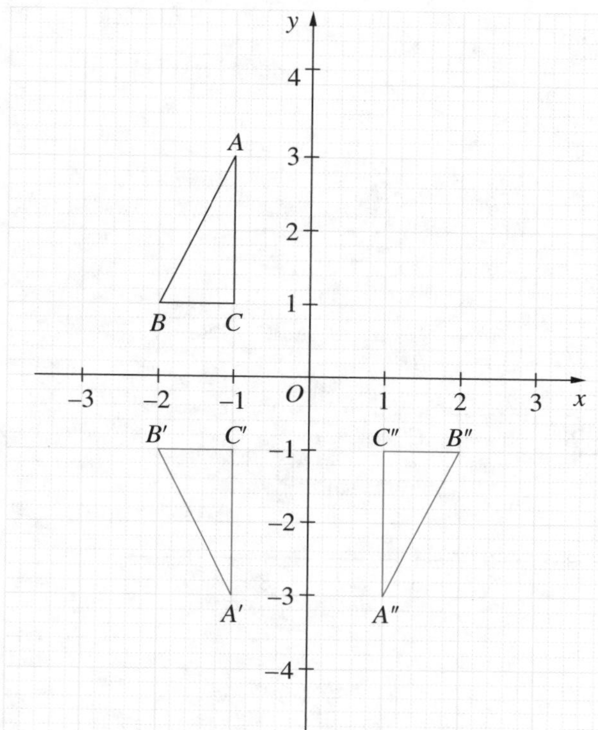
y
x
O
A
B
C
A′
B′
C′
A″
B″
C″
4
3
2
1
−1
−2
−3
−4
−3
−2
−1
1
2
3

(b)

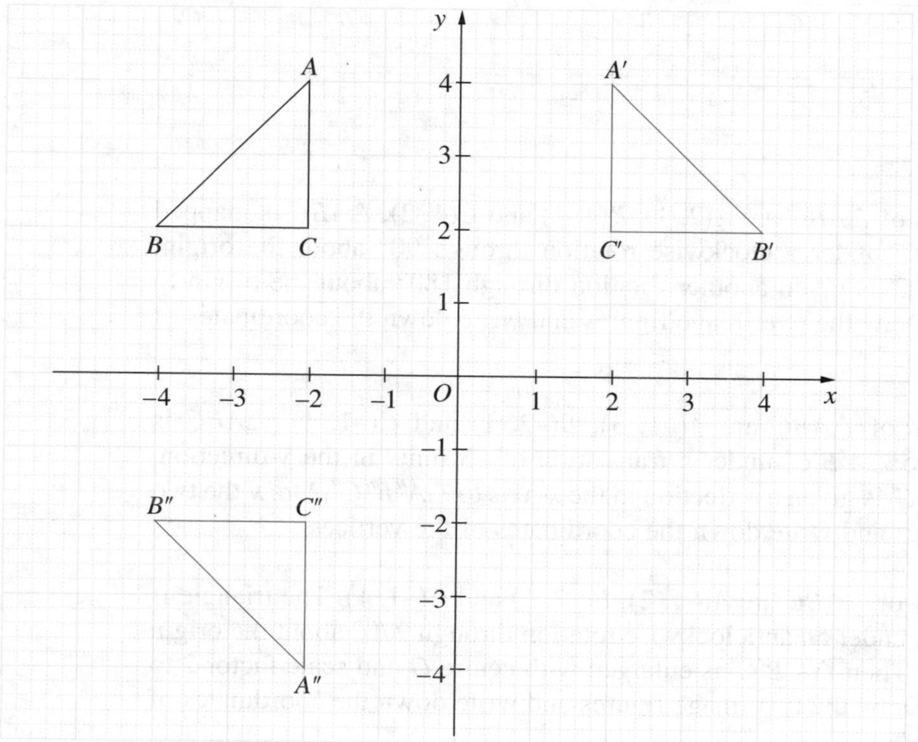
y
x
O
A
B
C
A′
B′
C′
A″
B″
C″
4
3
2
1
−1
−2
−3
−4
−4
−3
−2
−1
1
2
3
4

(c)

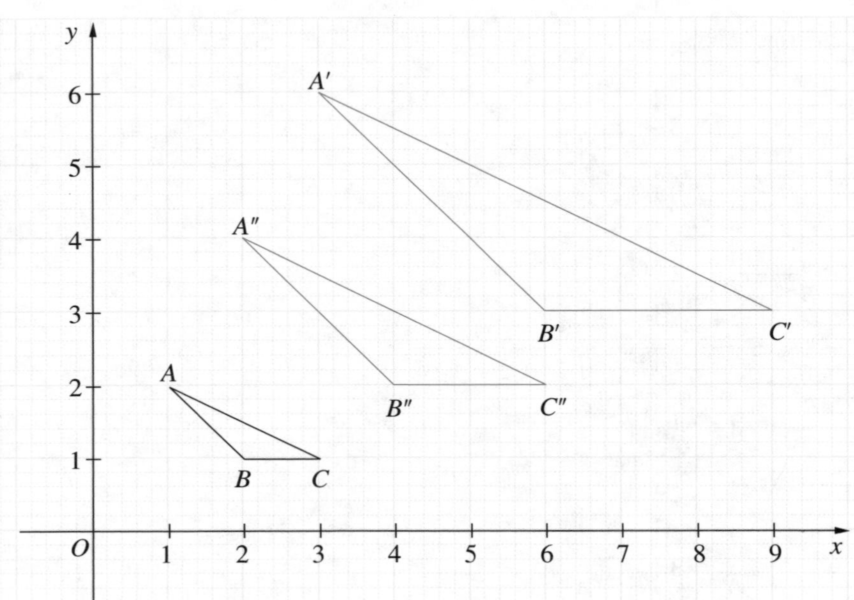

(d)

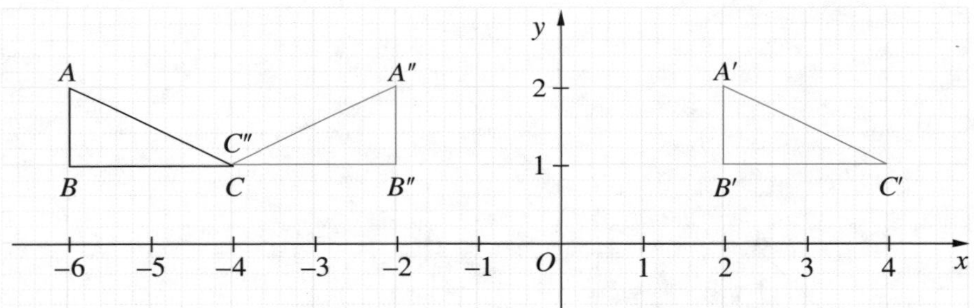

3. The vertices of $\triangle ABC$ are $A(2, 1)$, $B(4, 1)$ and $C(4, 2)$. $\triangle ABC$ is mapped onto $\triangle A'B'C'$ under a clockwise rotation through 90° about the origin. Then $\triangle A'B'C'$ is given another rotation through 180° about the origin to $\triangle A''B''C''$. Draw the two image figures and write down the coordinates of the vertices.

4. The vertices of $\triangle ABC$ are $A(-1, 3)$, $B(-2, 1)$ and $C(-1, 1)$. $\triangle ABC$ is mapped onto $\triangle A'B'C'$ under a translation of -3 units in the y-direction. Then $\triangle A'B'C'$ is given a reflection in the x-axis to $\triangle A''B''C''$. Draw the two image figures and write down the coordinates of the vertices.

5. The vertices of $\triangle ABC$ are $A(-1, 2)$, $B(-2, 1)$ and $C(-1, 1)$. The triangle is transformed under an anticlockwise rotation through 270° about the origin to $\triangle A'B'C'$. Then $\triangle A'B'C'$ is enlarged with centre O and scale factor 2 to $\triangle A''B''C''$. Draw the two image figures and write down the coordinates of the vertices.

6. Points are reflected in the line $x = 3$ and then their images are reflected in the line $y = -2$.
(a) Find the coordinates of the final image of the point (1, 2).
(b) If the point (a, b) remains as (a, b) under these combined reflections, write down the values of a and b.

7. $A(-1, 2)$ is mapped onto A_1 by a reflection in the line $x = 2$. A_1 is mapped onto A_2 by a reflection in the line $x = 4$.
(a) Find the coordinates of A_1 and A_2.
(b) Given that A_2 is the reflection of A in the line $x = k$, find the value of k.

8. Two transformations M and T are defined as follows:
M is a reflection in the x-axis and T is a translation of +3 units parallel to the y-axis.
Find the image of $P(-2, 5)$ under the combined transformation
(a) M followed by T,
(b) T followed by M.

Chapter Review

1. **Reflection**
   - Reflection carries segments into equal segments.
   - Reflection carries angles into equal angles.
   - Reflection carries whole figures into congruent figures.

2. **Rotation**
   - Rotation carries segments into equal segments.
   - Rotation carries angles into equal angles.
   - Rotation carries whole figures into congruent figures.

3. **Translation**
   - Translation carries segments into equal segments.
   - Translation carries angles into equal angles.
   - Translation carries whole figures into congruent figures.

4. **Enlargement**
   - Enlargement carries segments of figures proportionately into corresponding segments of figures.
   - Enlargement carries angles into equal angles.
   - Enlargement carries whole figures into similar figures.

CHALLENGER 11

1. (a) In the figure, AB is 3 cm and O is 4 cm directly below A. Copy the diagram and draw the image of $A'B'$ of AB under a clockwise rotation of 90° about O. Join AA' and BB'. Then draw the perpendicular bisectors of AA' and BB'. What do you notice?

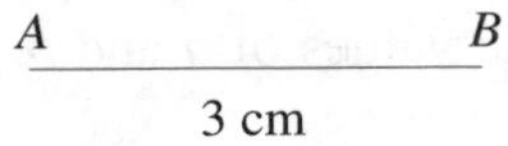

(b) $A'B'$ is the image of AB under a rotation through 90° anticlockwise. Copy the diagram and find the centre of rotation by construction.

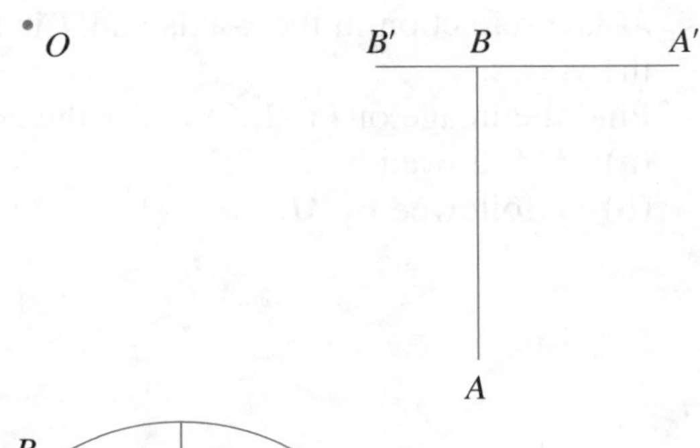

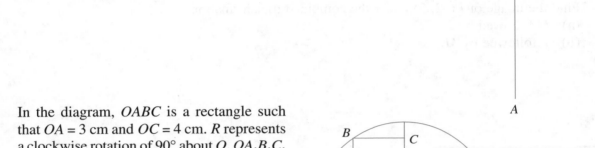

2. In the diagram, $OABC$ is a rectangle such that $OA = 3$ cm and $OC = 4$ cm. R represents a clockwise rotation of 90° about O. $OA_1B_1C_1$ is the image of $OABC$ under R. $OA_2B_2C_2$ is the image of $OA_1B_1C_1$ under R and $OA_3B_3C_3$ is the image of $OA_2B_2C_2$ under R.
(a) Copy the diagram and draw these images on it. Join the points A, A_1, A_2, A_3 and A. Then join the points B, B_1, B_2, B_3 and B.
(b) Find the ratio of the area of $AA_1A_2A_3$ to the area of $BB_1B_2B_3$.

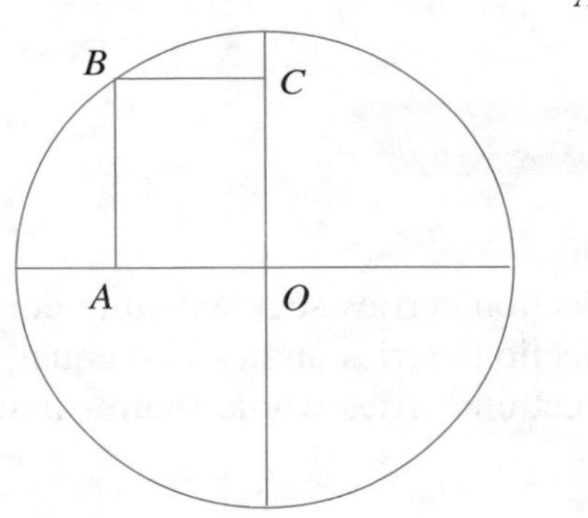

3. 

This pattern is made up of a basic picture and its images under successive transformations. Can you identify the transformations?

Abu says : Reflection followed by reflection followed by reflection.
Bala says : Rotation followed by rotation.
Christina says: Rotation followed by reflection followed by rotation followed by reflection and so on.

Do you agree with what they say? Give reasons.

4. The figure shows eight slung chairs equally spaced on a 'big wheel' with centre O. How can 'chair A' be transformed to occupy the position of chair C?
Study each of the following answers given by four students. If you think an answer is correct, improve on it by giving full description of the transformations required. Draw diagrams to illustrate your answers.

(a) Ali's answer : Translation followed by translation.
(b) Samy's answer: Rotation followed by rotation.
(c) Lihua's answer: Reflection followed by reflection.
(d) Mary's answer : Enlargement followed by enlargement.

5. The figure shows two pieces of cardboard; one is a regular pentagon and the other a square with vertices A, B, C and D. The pentagon is given a clockwise rotation round the square with centre of rotation at A and then at B and so on until the letter R is formed again. Find the sum of all the angles of rotation.

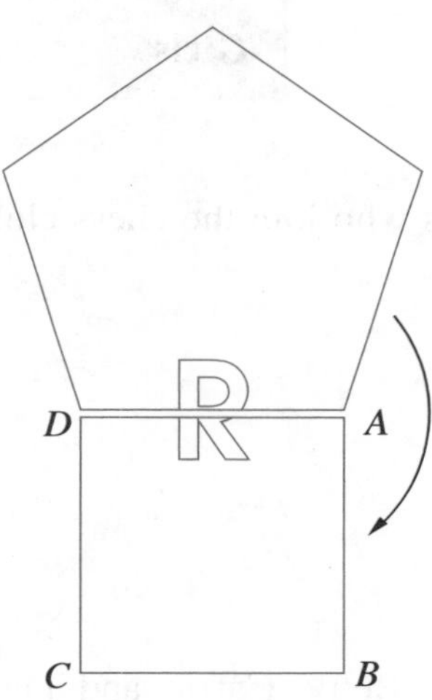

6. In the figure, $\triangle ABC$ is an equilateral triangle. $\triangle A'B'C'$ is its image under an enlargement with centre O. The circle touches the sides of $\triangle ABC$. Find the scale factor of the enlargement.

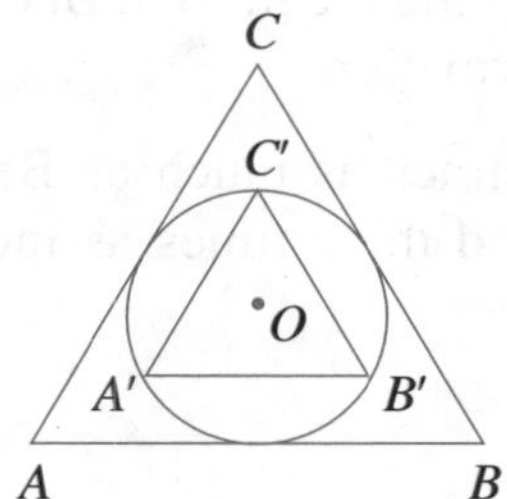

Problem Solving 11

Chess Club

In a school, 25% of the girls and 60% of the boys join the school chess club. In the school chess club, 20% of the members are girls. What percentage of the students of the school join the chess club?

The strategies to use are **make connection** and **use tabulation** with the concept of ratio.

Keys: Bc = Boys who are members of the chess club
Bn = Boys who are not members of the chess club
Gc = Girls who are members of the chess club
Gn = Girls who are not members of the chess club

Let $Bc = 12k$ and $Gc = 3k$. Then $Bn = 8k$ and $Gn = 9k$. Hence complete the table as shown.

$$\frac{Bc}{Gc} = \frac{80\%}{20\%} = \frac{4}{1} = \frac{12}{3}$$

$$\frac{Bc}{Bn} = \frac{60\%}{40\%} = \frac{3}{2} = \frac{12}{8}$$

$$\frac{Gc}{Gn} = \frac{25\%}{75\%} = \frac{1}{3} = \frac{3}{9}$$

	In chess club	**Not in chess club**
Boys	$12k$	$8k$
Girls	$3k$	$9k$

$$\text{Percentage of students who join the chess club} = \frac{12k + 3k}{12k + 3k + 8k + 9k} = \frac{15}{32} \approx 46.9\%$$

1. **Savings** Alan, Betty, Carrie and Dolly earned the same amount of money per month. Find the ratio of Betty's savings to Dolly's savings using the following information.

   Alan spent three times as much as Betty. Dolly spent twice as much as Carrie. Carrie saved three times as much as Dolly. Betty saved twice as much as Alan.

2. **Square within a Square** The area of the shaded part is 15 cm². If x and y are integers, find the possible values of x and y.

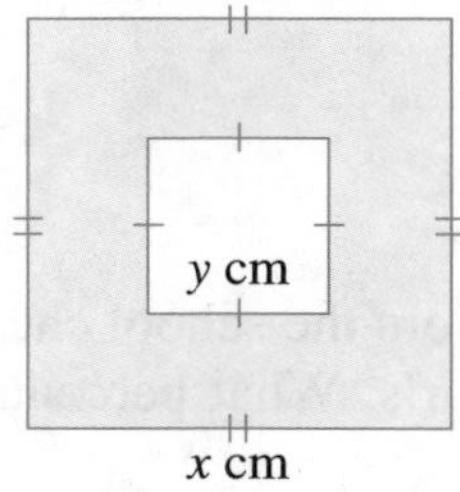

3. Black and White

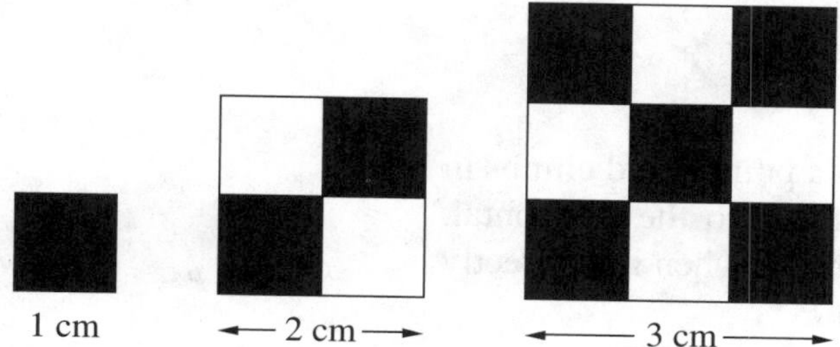

The diagram shows 3 squares, the sides of which are 1 cm, 2 cm and 3 cm respectively. Each of the small squares on the diagram has a side of length 1 cm and alternate squares are coloured black and white.

(a) The number of small squares of each colour used is shown in the following table. Copy and complete the table.

Length of side of given squares	L	1	2	3	4	5
Number of black squares	B	1	2	5		
Number of white squares	W	0	2	4		
Total number of squares	T	1	4	9		

(b) **(i)** How many small white squares will there be when a square of side 11 cm is drawn?

(ii) Find the length of the side of a square when 1 681 small black and white squares are needed to cover it.

(c) Write down a formula connecting T and L.

(d) Write down a formula connecting T and B when,

(i) B is an even number,

(ii) B is an odd number. *(C)*

4. Tea Mixture The table shows that proportions of Grade A, Grade B and Grade C tea in three brands of tea mixtures P, Q and R. If the cost per kg of Brand P and Brand Q tea mixtures are \$8 and \$9 respectively, find the cost per kg of Brand R tea mixture.

Brand \ Grade	*A*	*B*	*C*
P	1	2	2
Q	1	7	2
R	1	1	2

REVISION EXERCISE 3

Revision 3A *(answers on p. 439)*

1. An aircraft leaves a runway at a point P and climbs in a straight line at an angle of 20° to the horizontal. Calculate the height of the aircraft when it is directly over a point N, 2 000 m from P.

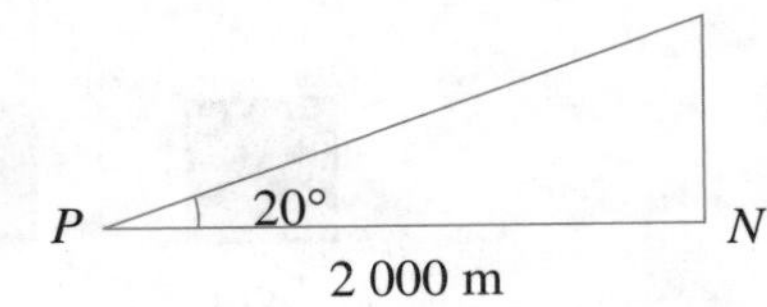

2. Find the values of a and b. Is $\triangle XYZ$ a right-angled triangle?

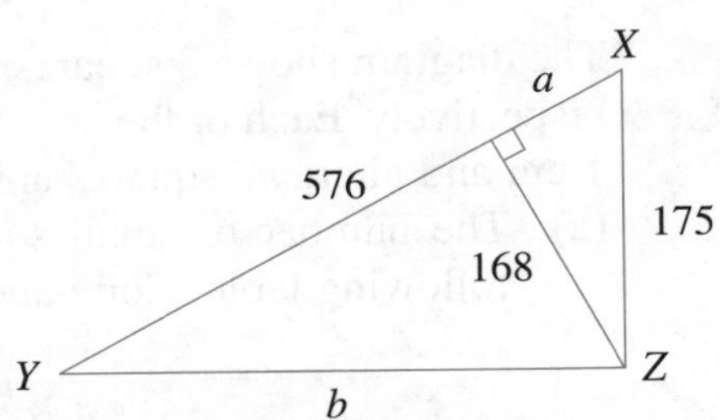

3. Copy the figures and with × as the centre of enlargement, enlarge each figure with the scale factor given.

(a)

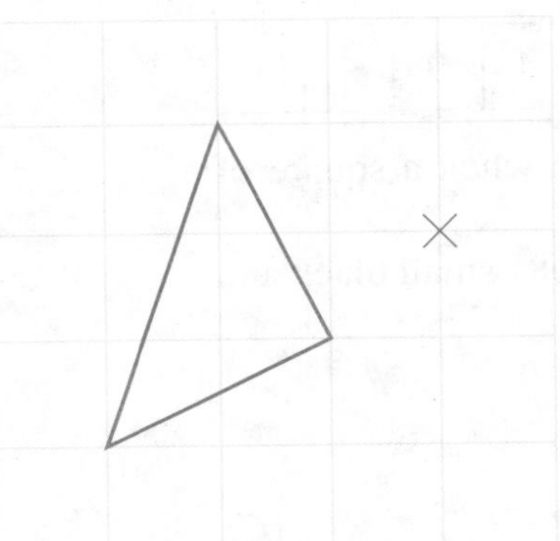

Enlarge by factor 2.

(b)

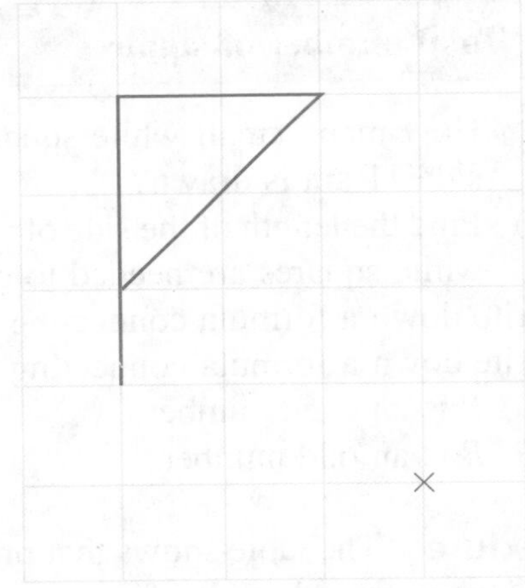

Enlarge by factor $\frac{2}{3}$.

4. Find **(i)** the perimeter, **(ii)** the area of the minor sector of a circle with centre O, radius r and central angle θ if
   (a) $r = 5$ cm, $\theta = 20°$,
   (b) $r = 9.5$ cm, $\theta = 43°$.
   Give your answers correct to the nearest cm or cm^2.
   (Take $\pi = 3.14$.)

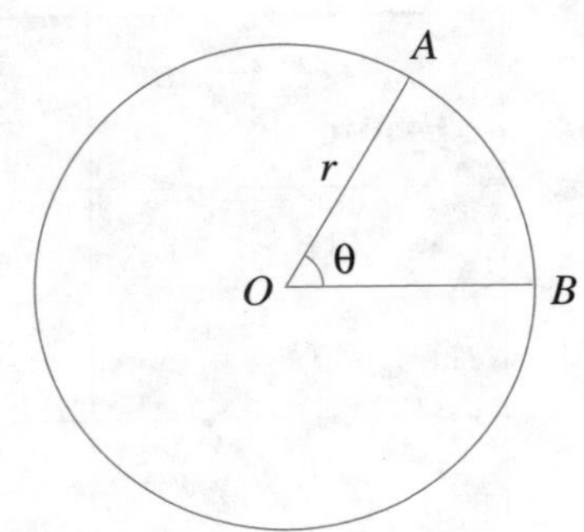

5. Plot the points $A(-4, 2)$, $B(-2, 2)$ and $C(-2, 1)$ on squared paper. Draw $\triangle ABC$. Translate the figure -3 units in the y-direction and then 4 units in the x-direction.
Draw its image and write down the coordinates of the vertices of the image.

6. $\triangle OPQ$ is an enlargement of $\triangle OAB$ with scale factor 3 and centre O. If the area of $\triangle OAB = 15\text{ cm}^2$, find the area of quadrilateral $APQB$.

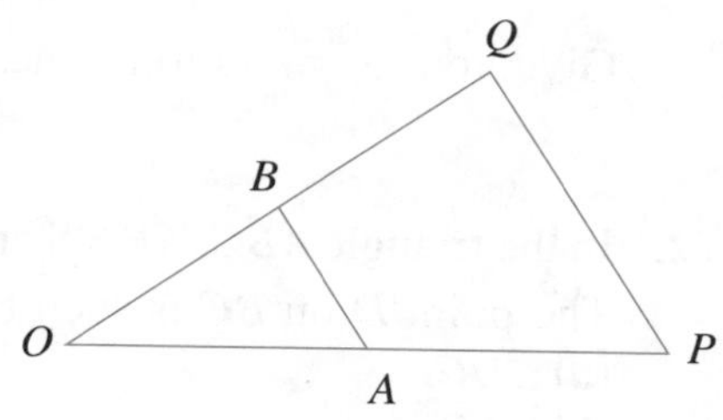

7. The diagram shows two concentric circles of radii 8 cm and 6 cm. Calculate the area of the shaded part. $\left(\text{Take } \pi = \frac{22}{7}.\right)$

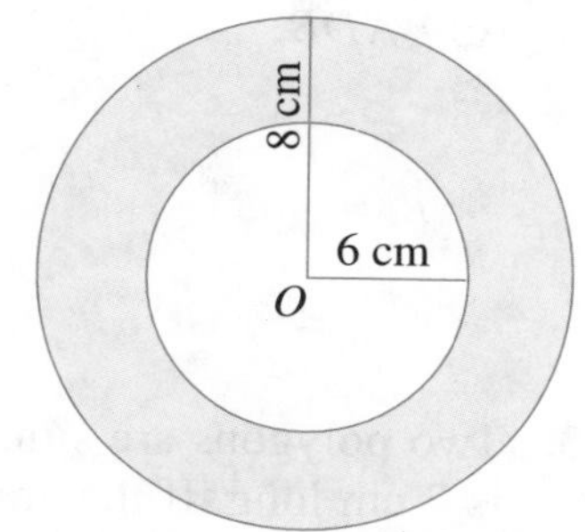

8. Find **(i)** the volume and **(ii)** the total surface area of a cone whose height is h cm, slant height l cm and base radius r cm if
(a) $r = 2$, $h = 4.8$, $l = 5.2$,
(b) $r = 2.1$, $h = 7.2$, $l = 7.5$.

Give your answers correct to the nearest cm^2 or cm^3. $\left(\text{Take } \pi = \frac{22}{7}.\right)$

9.

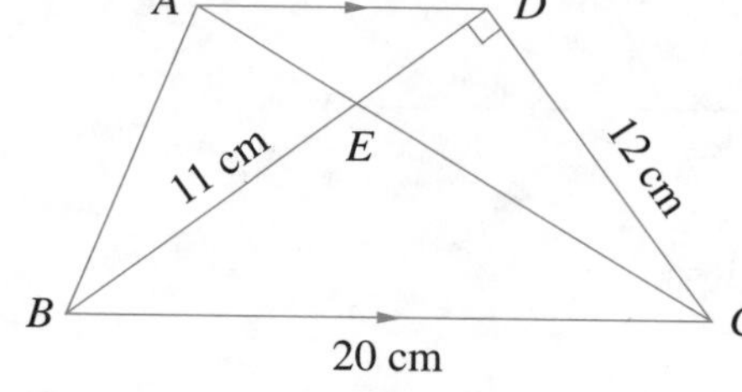

The triangle BDC is right-angled at D and AD is parallel to BC. Given that $BC = 20$ cm, $CD = 12$ cm and $BE = 11$ cm, calculate
(a) BD,
(b) CE,
(c) AD.

10.

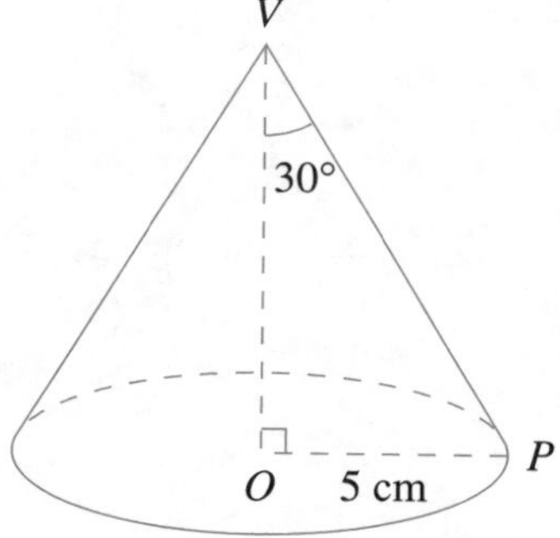

The diagram represents a circular cone standing on a horizontal base of radius 5 cm. V is the vertex of the cone, O is the centre of the base, P is a point on the circumference of the base, and $O\hat{V}P = 30°$.
Calculate
(a) VP,
(b) the circumference of the base of the cone, taking π to be 3.142,
(c) the curved surface area of the cone.

Revision 3B *(answers on p. 439)*

1. Find the volume and surface area of a sphere of radius r cm when r is
(a) 6.4, **(b)** 7.8.
Give your answers to the nearest cm^2 or cm^3. $\left(\text{Take } \pi = \frac{22}{7}.\right)$

2. In the triangle ABC, $AB = 8$ cm, $A\hat{B}C = 90°$ and $A\hat{C}B = 45°$. The point D on BC is such that $BD = 6$ cm. Calculate
(a) DC,
(b) AD,
(c) $A\hat{D}B$.

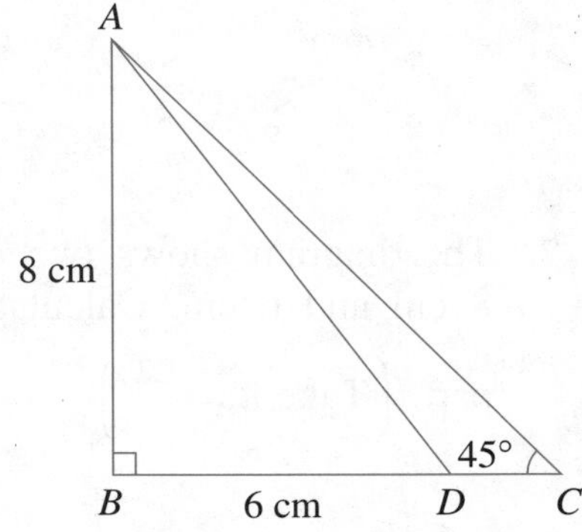

3. Two polygons are similar. The side of one is 3 cm long and the corresponding side of the other is 7 cm long. If the area of the first is 2 m^2, find the area of the other.

4. Plot the points $A(3, 6)$, $B(3, 3)$ and $C(6, 3)$ on graph paper. Enlarge $\triangle ABC$ with scale factor $\frac{1}{3}$.
Draw the image figure and give the coordinates of its vertices.

5. Trace the figures. Using geometrical instruments, construct the image of each figure under reflection with respect to XY and label the image.

(a)

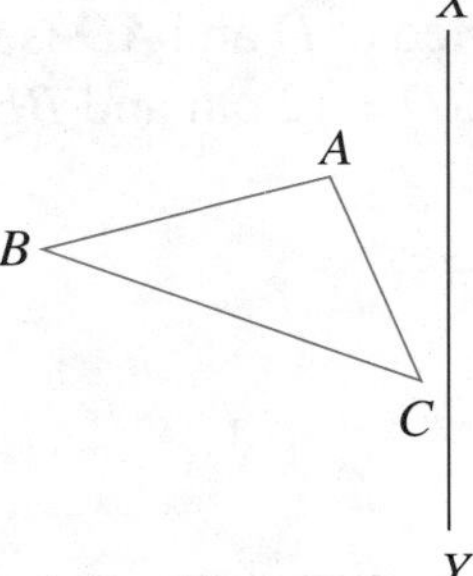

(b)

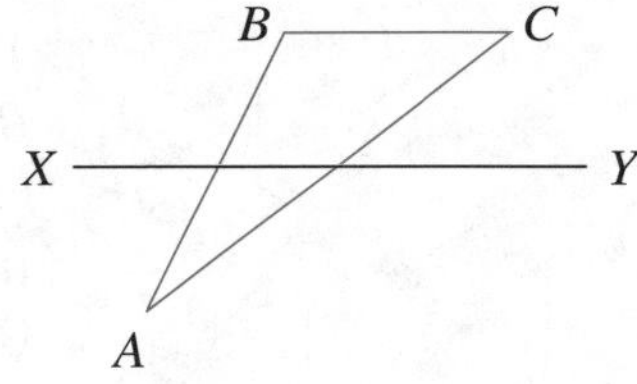

6. Find **(i)** the perimeter, **(ii)** the area of the major sector of a circle with centre O, radius r and central angle θ, if
(a) $r = 6$ cm, $\theta = 210°$,
(b) $r = 5.5$ cm, $\theta = 300°$.
Give your answers correct to the nearest cm or cm^2.
$\left(\text{Take } \pi = \frac{22}{7}.\right)$

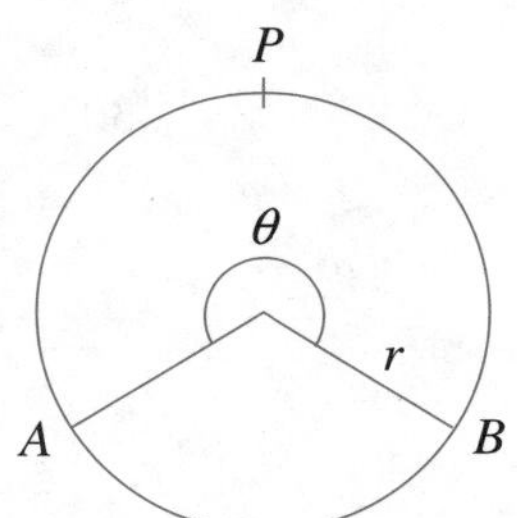

7. A circular pizza of diameter 24 cm costs \$2.75; the same variety of pizza of diameter 32 cm costs \$3.75. They have the same thickness. Which has the better value? Show working to support your answer. *(C)*

8. A wheel of radius 30 cm is turning about a fixed axis at a rate of $1\frac{1}{2}$ revolutions per minute. Calculate
   (a) the angle through which the wheel turns in 30 seconds,
   (b) the distance moved by a point on the rim in 30 seconds. (Take π to be 3.14.)

9. 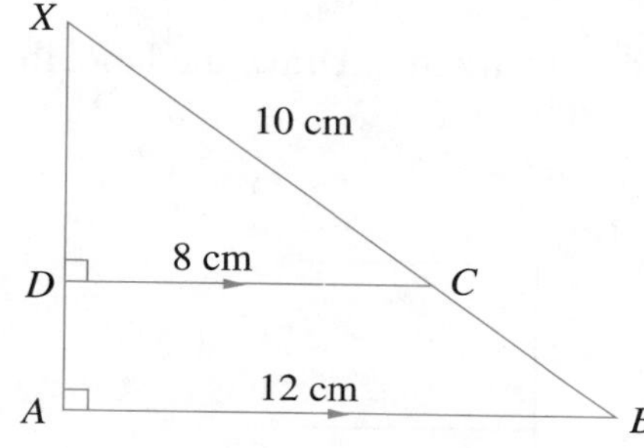

In the diagram, AB is parallel to DC and $B\hat{A}D = C\hat{D}X = 90°$. Given that $XC = 10$ cm, $AB = 12$ cm and $DC = 8$ cm, calculate
   (a) XD,
   (b) BC.

10. 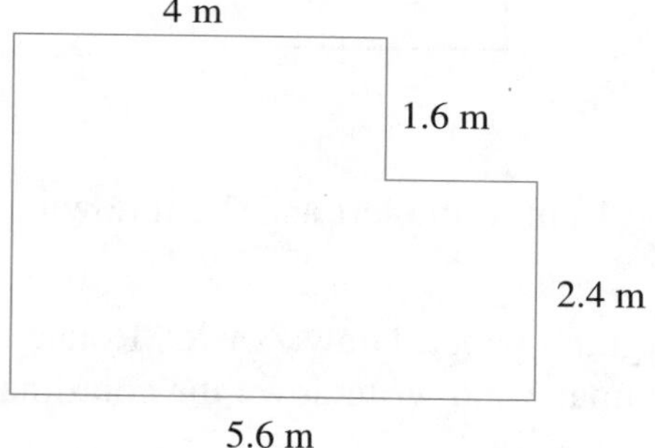

The diagram, which is not to scale, shows the plan of a room. All the angles on the diagram are right angles.
   (a) Draw an accurate plan of the room using a scale of 1 : 40.

A fitted carpet, without a pattern, is to be laid to cover the floor completely. The carpet is supplied in a roll 80 cm wide, to be laid in a series of parallel strips.
   (b) Draw lines on your plan to show how you would lay the strips.
   (c) Find the total length of carpet required.
   (d) The carpet costs \$8.50 per metre length. Calculate the total cost of the carpet. *(C)*

Revision 3C *(answers on p. 439)*

1. The diagram shows a circular wooden reel with a hole H of radius 4 cm in the middle. If the shaded part P is 8 cm wide,
   (a) express in terms of π, the area of H,
   (b) find the value of $\dfrac{\text{area of } P}{\text{area of } H}$.

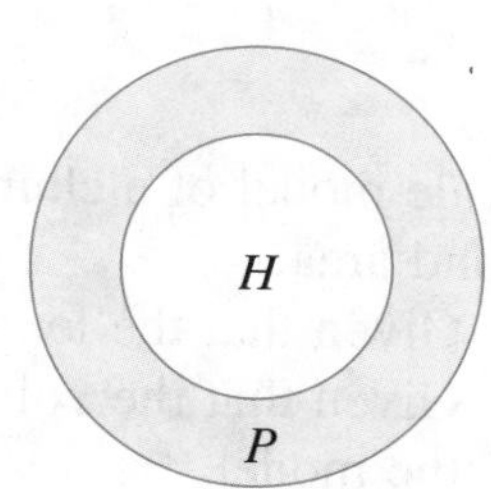

2. A circular piece of cake with radius 14 cm weighs 2.5 kg. A wedge-shaped piece with central angle 72° is cut out. Find the mass and area of the sector of this wedge-shaped piece.

3. A river 20 m wide flows due east between parallel banks. Two points P and Q are 50 m apart on the south bank.

(a) X is a point on the north bank such that $XP = XQ$. Calculate $P\hat{X}Q$.

(b) Y is another point on the north bank such that $Y\hat{Q}P = 90°$. Calculate YP.

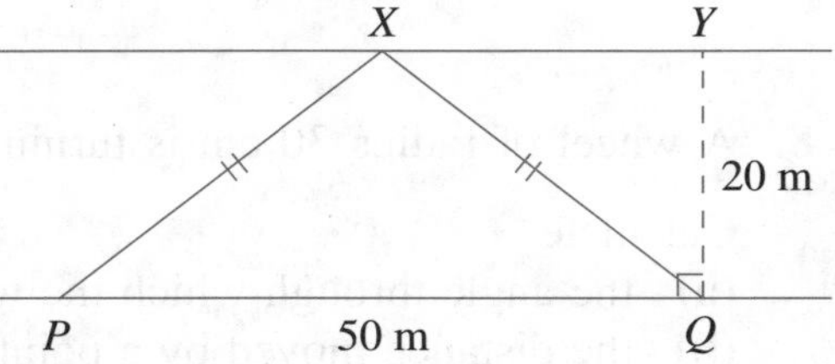

4. Copy the figures on graph papers and do the translation as instructed. Draw and label the images.

(a)

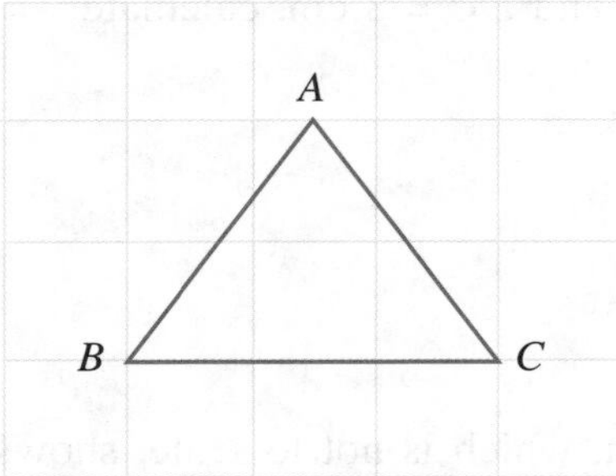

2 cm to the right and 2 cm up.

(b)

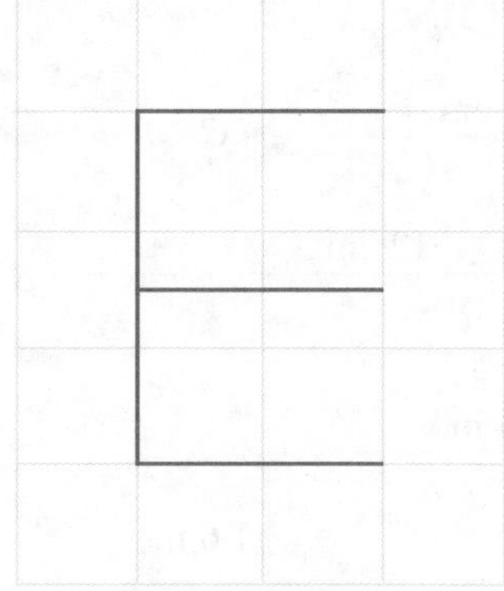

1 cm to the left and 2 cm down.

5. Plot the points $A(-4, 1)$, $B(-3, 3)$ and $C(-2, 2)$ on graph paper. Draw $\triangle ABC$. Rotate the figure through 90° clockwise about the origin O. Draw its image and write down the coordinates of the vertices of the image.

6.

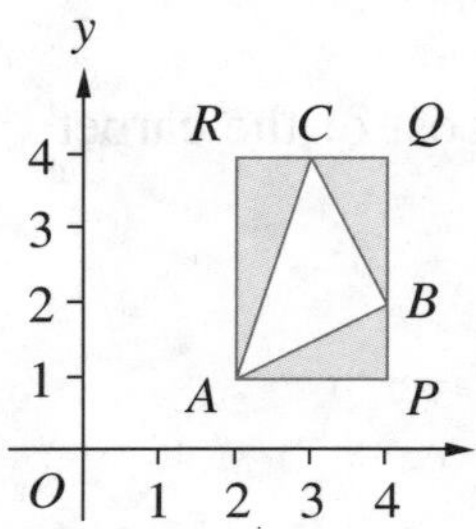

The figure $APQR$ is a rectangle such that AP is parallel to the x-axis. The vertices of $\triangle ABC$ are $A(2, 1)$, $B(4, 2)$ and $C(3, 4)$.

(a) Write down the coordinates of the points P, Q and R.

(b) Calculate the total area of the shaded parts.

(c) Calculate the area of $\triangle ABC$.

7. A scale model of a church is made. The ground area of the model is one hundredth of the actual ground area.

(a) Given that the length of the model is 4 m, calculate the length of the church.

(b) Given that the volume of the church spire is 3 000 m^3, calculate the volume of the spire on the model. *(C)*

8.

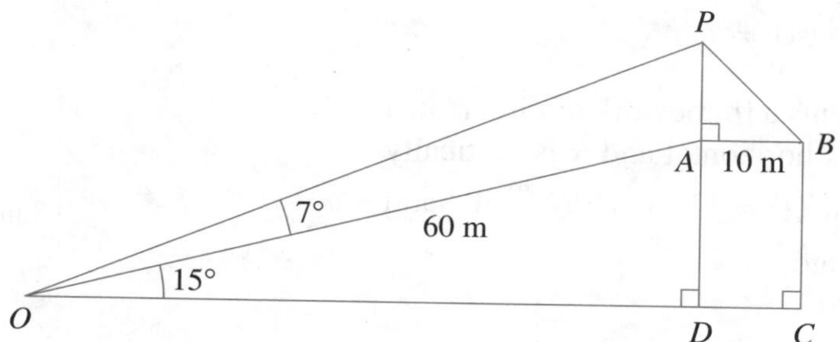

ABCD represents a building with a vertical flagpole *AP* on the roof. The point *O* is on the same level as *C* and *D*. The angle of elevation of *A* from *O* is 15°, $OA = 60$ metres and $P\hat{O}A = 7°$.

(a) Calculate

(i) the height *AD* of the building, **(ii)** the height of the flagpole, *AP*.

(b) Given also that $AB = 10$ metres, calculate the angle of elevation of *P* from *B*. (*C*)

9.

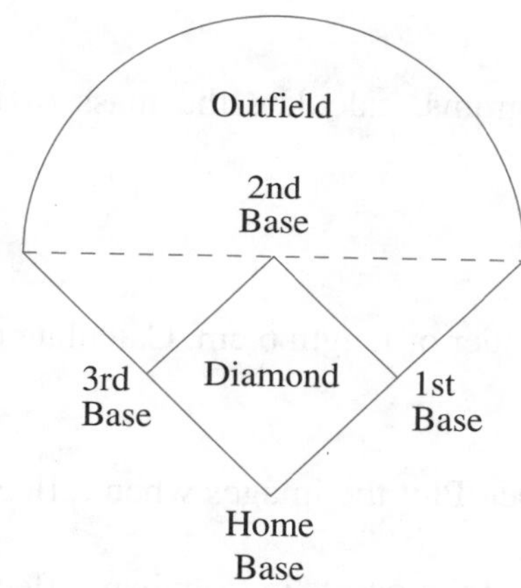

The diagram, which is not to scale, represents a baseball field.

The "diamond" is a square, of side 27.4 m.

(a) Using a scale of 1 cm to represent 5 m, make a scale drawing of the baseball field.

(b) Calculate, for the whole field,

(i) the perimeter, **(ii)** the area,

giving your answers correct to 3 significant figures. (*C*)

10.

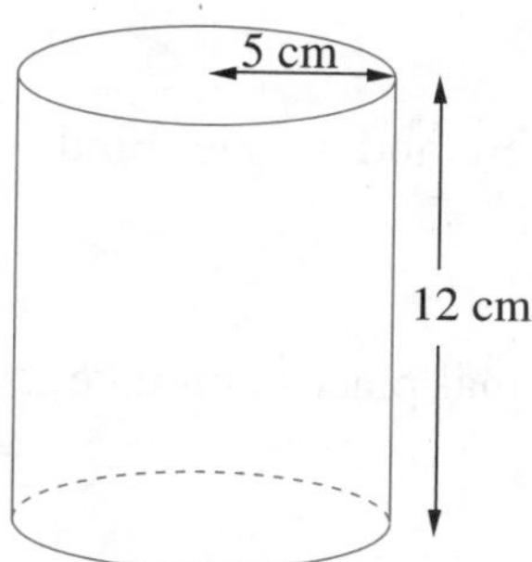

A cylindrical tin of dog food has a radius of 5 cm and a height of 12 cm, as shown in the diagram.

(a) Taking π to be 3.14, calculate

(i) the area of the circular top of the cylinder,

(ii) the volume of the cylinder.

(b) The mass of each tin when full is 1.25 kg and when empty is 150 g. Calculate the mass, in grams, of the contents of a tin.

(c) The tins are packed into rectangular cartons 50 cm long, 30 cm wide and 24 cm high. Find the maximum number of tins each carton will hold. (*C*)

Revision 3D (answers on p. 439)

1. The diagram represents a framework of girders in a vertical plane. PQ is horizontal and R is vertically above Q. $QR = 8$ m, $QS = 11$ m, $R\hat{P}Q = 58°$ and $R\hat{Q}S = 37°$. Calculate
   (a) PQ,
   (b) SN, the height of S above PQ.
   (Give your answers correct to the nearest m.)

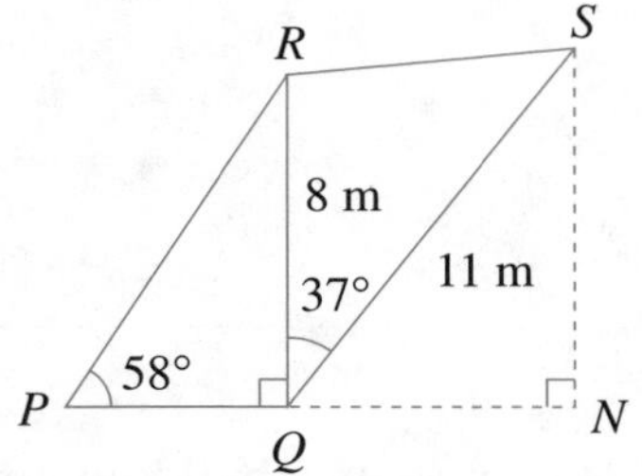

2. **(a)** Calculate the angle turned through by the hour hand of a clock as the time changes from 07 00 to 11 00.
   (b) Calculate the angle turned through by the minute hand during the same period of time.
   (c) Calculate the acute angle between the hour hand and the minute hand at 08 30. *(C)*

3. A solid metal cube has a volume of 125 cm^3.
   (a) Given that 1 cm^3 of the metal has a mass of 9 grams, calculate the mass of the cube, expressing your answer in kilograms.
   (b) Calculate
   (i) the length of each edge of the cube,
   (ii) the total surface area of the cube.
   (c) The cube is melted down and made into a solid cylinder of length 6 cm. Calculate the radius of the cylinder. [Take π to be 3.142.] *(C)*

4. **(a)** Plot the points (1, 2), (2, 4) and (3, 3) on graph paper. Plot the images when reflected about the x-axis.
   (b) Without plotting the points, write down the images of the points in (a) when reflected about the y-axis.

5. The solid is made up of a hemisphere and a cone. Find
   (a) the volume of the cone,
   (b) the volume of the hemisphere.

   Give each answer correct to 2 decimal places and take $\pi = \frac{22}{7}$.

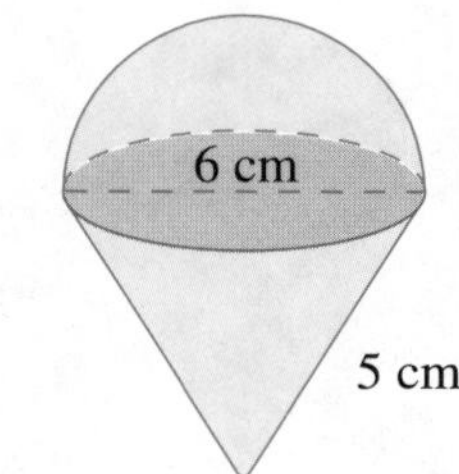

6. The length, breadth and height of a cuboid are 8 cm, 5 cm and 3 cm respectively.
   (a) If the measures of the length and breadth are doubled, how many times is the new volume as large as the original volume?
   (b) If the measures of length, breadth and height are tripled, how many times is the new volume as large as the original volume?

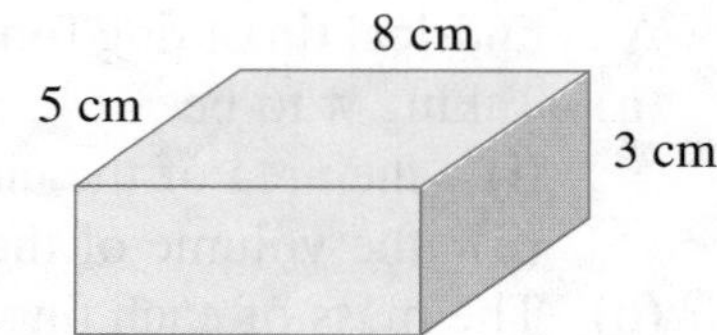

7. The vertices of $\triangle ABC$ are $A(1, 1)$, $B(2, 1)$ and $C(2, 2)$. Transform the figure under a clockwise rotation of 90° about the origin to its image $\triangle A'B'C'$. Then $\triangle A'B'C'$ is given a reflection in the y-axis to $\triangle A''B''C''$. Draw the two image figures and write down the coordinates of the vertices.

8.

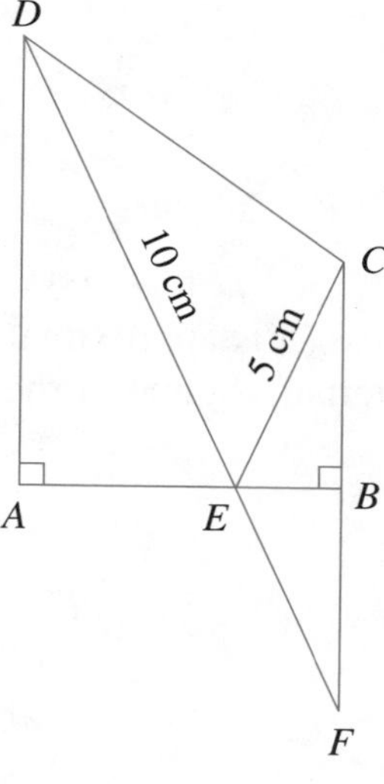

In the diagram, $D\hat{A}B = C\hat{B}A = 90°$, $EC = 5$ cm and $ED = 10$ cm. The point F is the reflection of C in the line AB, and DF intersects AB at E.

(a) State the length of DF.

(b) Given that the area of $\triangle CED$ is $12\frac{1}{2}$ cm^2, show that $D\hat{E}C = 30°$.

(c) Hence calculate the length of CD.

(d) Prove that $\triangle DAE$ is similar to $\triangle CBE$. (You may use any appropriate method. If transformations are used, they must be precisely described.)

(e) Calculate the numerical values of the ratios

(i) $\dfrac{\text{area of } \triangle CBE}{\text{area of } \triangle DAE}$,

(ii) $\dfrac{\text{area of } \triangle CDE}{\text{area of } \triangle CDF}$. *(C)*

9.

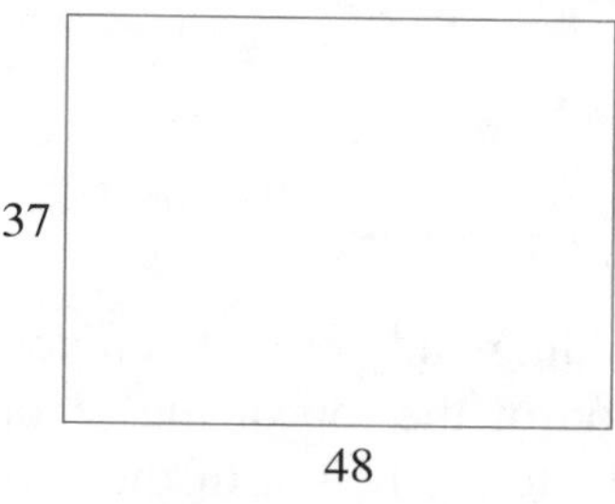

A teacher has a rectangular piece of paper which is 48 cm long and 37 cm wide.

(a) Calculate the perimeter of the piece of paper, giving your answer in metres and centimetres.

(b) The teacher wishes to cut the paper up into squares each of which measures 5 cm by 5 cm. What is the largest number of **whole** squares she can cut out? *(C)*

10. The diagram represents a box, in the shape of a cuboid.

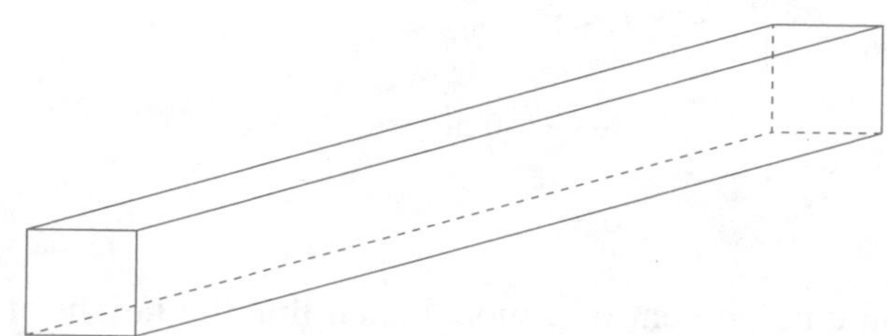

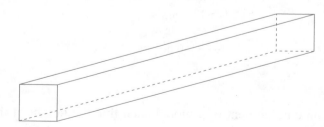

Its internal dimensions are: length 2 m, width 10 cm, height 10 cm.

(a) Calculate the internal volume of the box

(i) in cubic centimetres, **(ii)** in cubic metres.

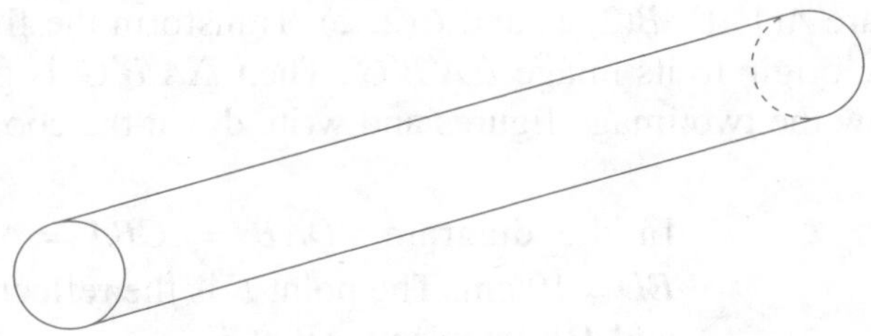

A cylinder fits exactly into the box.

(b) **(i)** Write down the radius of the cylinder.

(ii) Calculate the volume of the cylinder, in cubic centimetres. (π is approximately 3.142)

(c) Express the volume of the cylinder as a percentage of the internal volume of the box. (*C*)

Revision 3E *(answers on p. 440)*

1. **(a)** Find the surface area of a cube whose volume is 27 cm^3.

(b) Find the central angle subtended by an arc of 6 cm of a circle whose radius is 14 cm. $\left(\text{Take } \pi = \frac{22}{7}.\right)$

2. A man stands at a window in a building and observes another building which is 150 m away. He observes that the angle of elevation of the top of the second building is 50° and the angle of depression of its foot is 20°. Calculate the height of the second building.

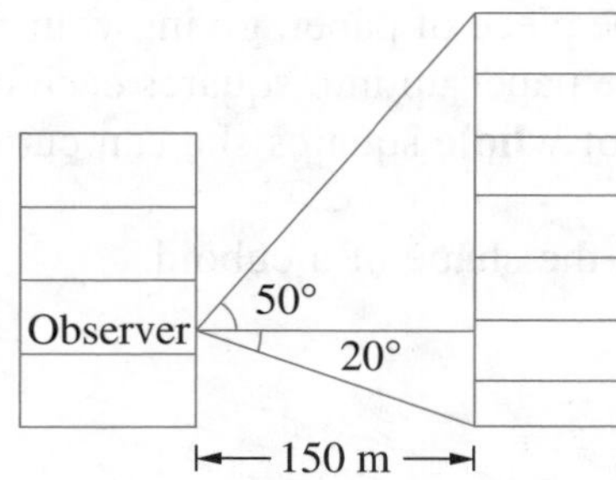

3. An office building is an enlargement of a model such that the height of the building is 30 times the height of the model.

(a) If the volume of the model is v m^3 and that of the building is V m^3, express V in terms of v.

(b) If the floor area of the building is 540 m^2, calculate in m^2 the corresponding area of the model.

4. Copy the following figures on graph paper. Draw and label the image of each figure under rotation about the origin through an angle as indicated.

(a)

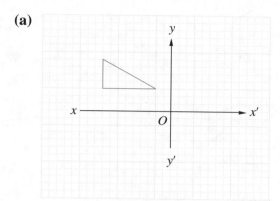

Through 90° clockwise.

(b)

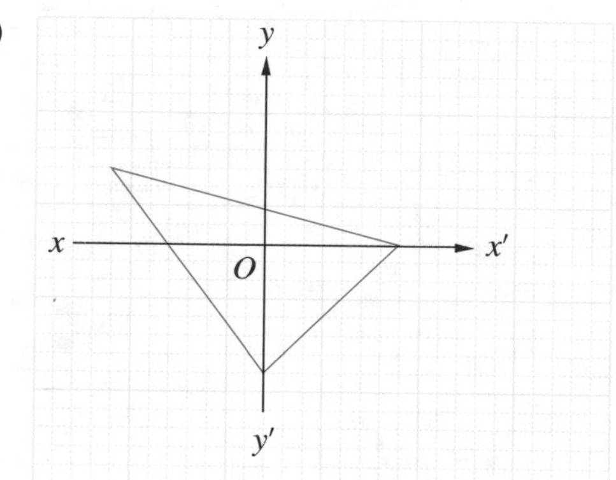

Through 90° anticlockwise.

5. Find the volume of the prism.

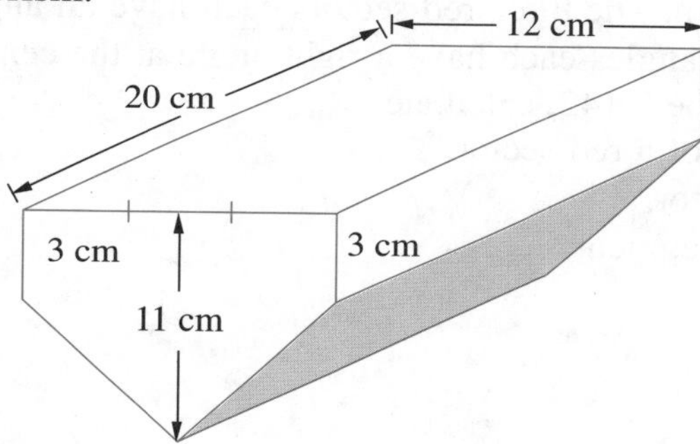

6. The vertices of $\triangle ABC$ are $A(2, 2)$, $B(2, 1)$ and $C(3, 1)$. Transform the figure under 180° rotation about the origin to $\triangle A'B'C'$. Then $\triangle A'B'C'$ is given a reflection in the y-axis to $\triangle A''B''C''$. Draw the two images. Describe a single transformation equivalent to the combined transformations.

7.

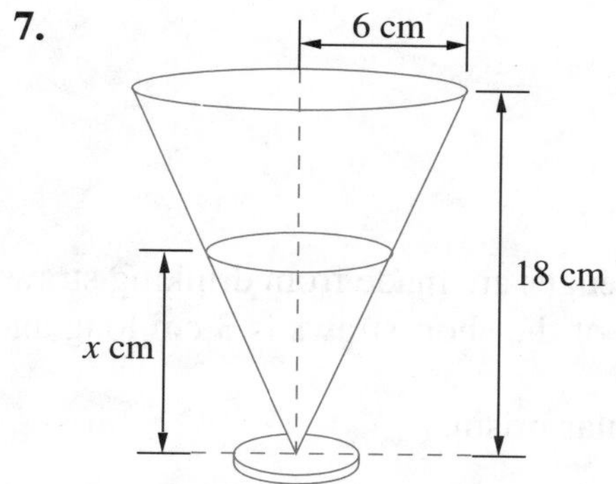

A glass is in the shape of an inverted cone of radius 6 cm and height 18 cm.

(a) Calculate the capacity of the glass. [The volume of a cone of radius r and height h is $\frac{1}{3}\pi r^2 h$, and π is approximately 3.142.]

(b) Milk is poured into the glass to a height of 9 cm. Calculate the volume of milk in the glass.

(c) If the height of milk in the glass is x cm,

(i) find the radius of its surface, in terms of x,

(ii) find a formula for the volume of milk, in terms of π and x,

(iii) show that, when $x = 9$, your formula gives the same answer as in part (b). *(C)*

8.

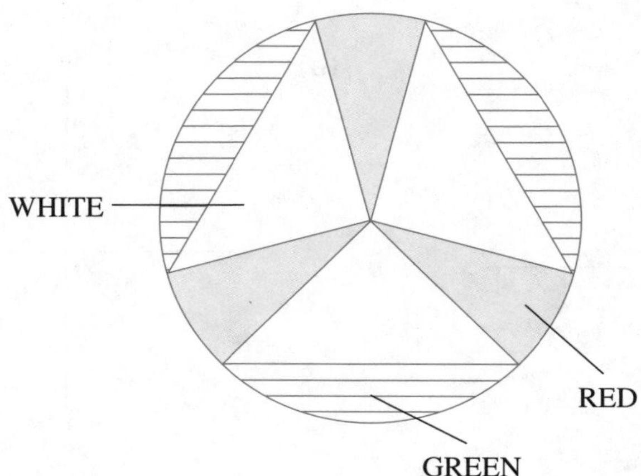

The diagram above shows a new logo, designed in red, white and green, for a car company. The radius of the circle is 5 cm. The three red sectors each have an angle of 30° at the centre of the circle. The three white triangles each have a right angle at the centre of the circle.
Taking the value of π to be 3.142, calculate

(a) the length of an arc of a red sector,

(b) the area of a red sector,

(c) the area of a green segment. (*C*)

9.

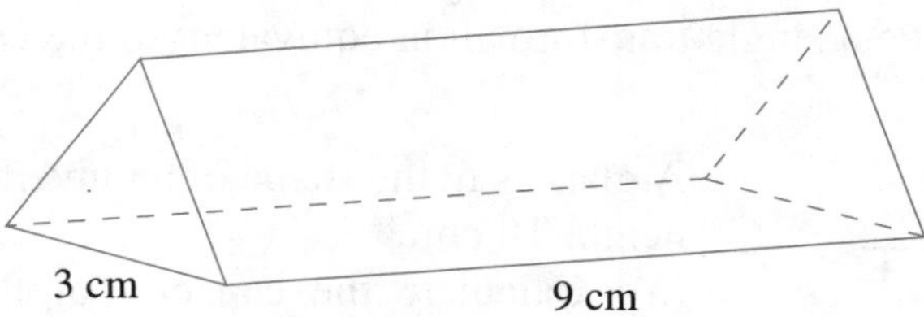

A model of a triangular prism is shown in the diagram. The edges are made from drinking straws and the corners are held together with pieces of wire. Each of the short straws is 3 cm long and each of the long straws is 9 cm long.

(a) Find the total length of straw used to make the triangular prism.

(b) If $2\frac{1}{2}$ cm of wire are needed to hold the straws together at each corner, find the total length of wire required.

(c) Given that the area of the triangular end of the prism is approximately 4 cm^2, calculate the approximate volume of the prism. (*C*)

10. In the diagram, RQ is parallel to BC and RP is parallel to AC. Explain why $\triangle ARQ$ is similar to $\triangle RBP$. Given that $\frac{AR}{RB} = \frac{3}{4}$, calculate the numerical value of the ratios

(a) $\frac{\text{area of } \triangle ARQ}{\text{area of } \triangle RBP}$,

(b) $\frac{RQ}{BC}$,

(c) $\frac{\text{area of trapezium } BRQC}{\text{area of } \triangle ABC}$,

(d) $\frac{RX}{QC}$.

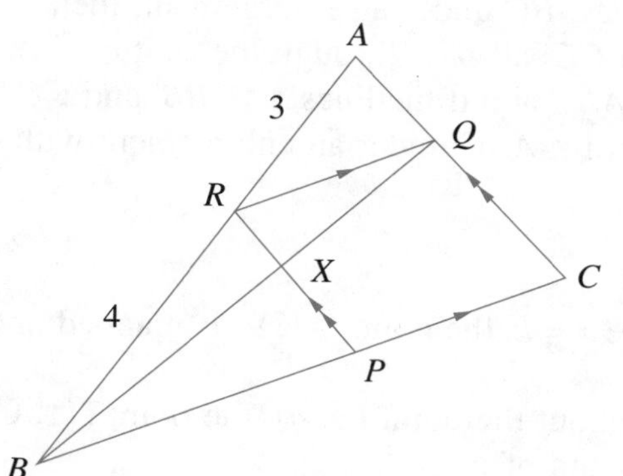

MISCELLANEOUS EXERCISE 3

(answers on p. 440)

1. $\triangle ABC$ and $\triangle A'B'C'$ are drawn on the same sheet of paper. State whether each of the following statements is true or false. If the statement is false, explain why.

(a) If $\triangle A'B'C'$ is an image of $\triangle ABC$ under an enlargement, then $\triangle A'B'C'$ is similar to $\triangle ABC$.

(b) If $\triangle A'B'C'$ is similar to $\triangle ABC$, then $\triangle A'B'C'$ is an image of $\triangle ABC$ under an enlargement.

(c) If $\triangle A'B'C'$ is an image of $\triangle ABC$ under an enlargement, then $\triangle A'B'C'$ is similar to $\triangle ABC$ and the lines AA', BB' and CC' all pass through the centre of enlargement.

(d) If $\triangle A'B'C'$ is similar to $\triangle ABC$ and if the lines AA', BB' and CC' all pass through a point O, then $\triangle A'B'C'$ is an image of $\triangle ABC$ under an enlargement with centre O.

2. **(a)** Under reflection in the line $x = k$, the point $(-1, 9)$ is mapped onto the point $(5, 9)$. Find the value of k.

(b) Under a rotation of 180° about the point (p, q), the point $(11, 0)$ is mapped onto the point $(0, 9)$. Find the value of p and of q.

3.

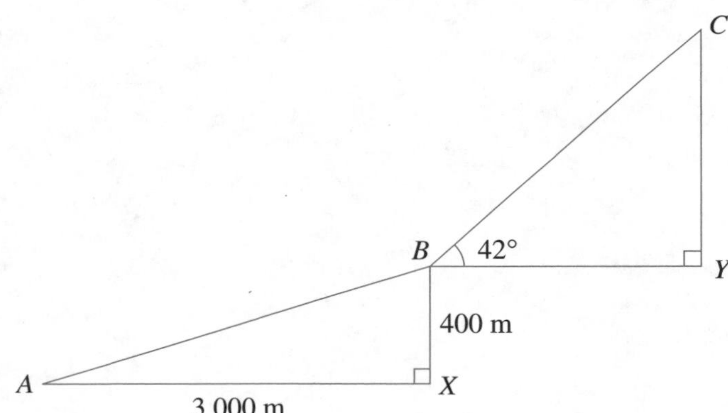

A mountaineer climbed to the top of a mountain along two straight paths AB and BC. He started from point A, at sea level, and climbed the gentle slope to B. He then climbed the steeper section from B to the top of the mountain C.

(a) Given that $A\hat{X}B = 90°$, $AX = 3\ 000$ m and that B is 400 m above sea level, calculate

(i) $B\hat{A}X$,

(ii) the actual distance he walked from A to B, giving your answer correct to the nearest 10 metres.

(b) The point C is 1 250 metres above sea level. Given that $C\hat{Y}B = 90°$ and that $C\hat{B}Y = 42°$, calculate the distance from B to C.

(c) Write down the angle of depression of B from C. *(C)*

4.

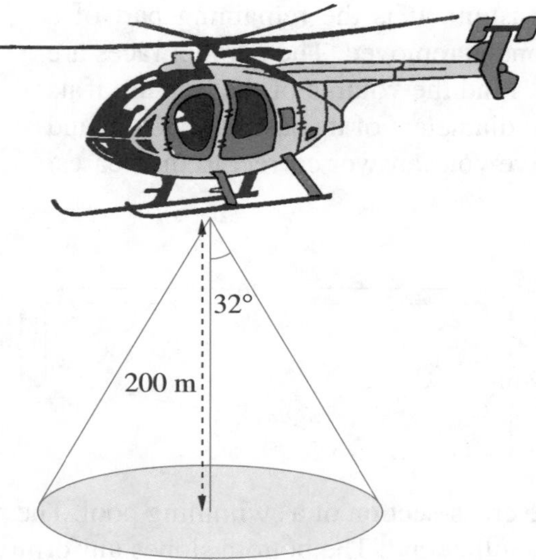

[In this question take π to be 3.142. 1 hectare = 10 000 m^2.]

On a still day, a helicopter hovers at a height of 200 m and sprays the ground with fertilizer. The shaded part of the diagram shows the circular area sprayed.

(a) If the "angle of spray" is 32°, calculate the sprayed area in square metres. Give your answer correct to three significant figures.

(b) The farmer wants to spray a circular area of 3 hectares from the same height. What "angle of spray" should he use? *(C)*

5.

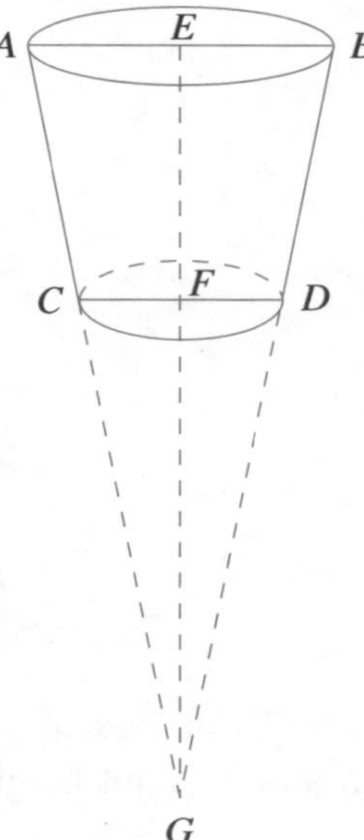

The diagram shows a bucket with a top diameter AB of 36 cm and a base diameter CD of 24 cm. The depth EF of the bucket is 30 cm.

(a) If $FG = x$ cm, show that

$$\frac{x}{x + 30} = \frac{2}{3}.$$

(b) Calculate the value of x.

(c) Calculate the capacity of the bucket in litres.

6. The figure shows a frustum. It is the remaining part of a cone after a smaller cone is removed. The parallel faces are referred to as its bases. Find the volume of the frustum if its height is 15 cm and the diameters of its bases are 30 cm and 20 cm respectively. Give your answer correct to the nearest cubic centimetre.

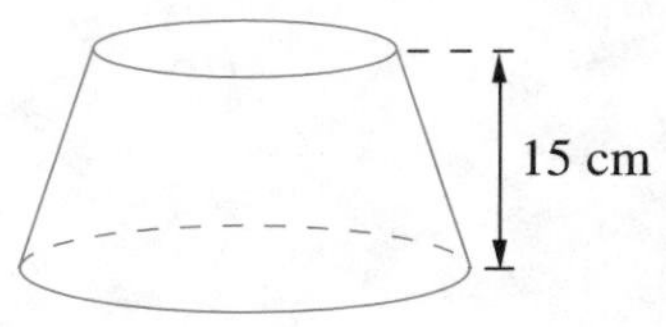

7.

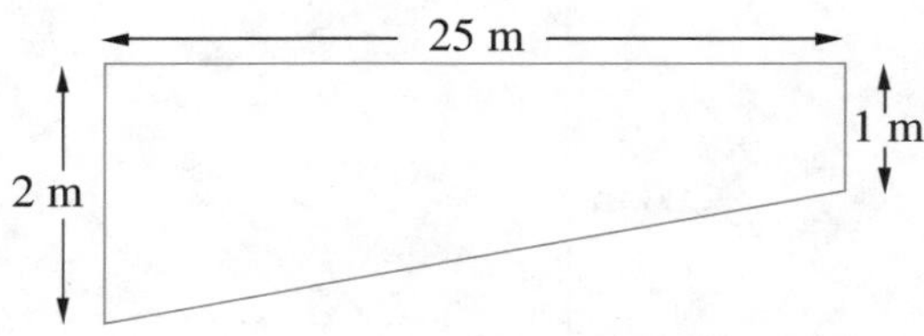

The diagram shows the cross-section of a swimming pool. The pool is 25 m long, 1 m deep at one end and 2 m deep at the other end. The bottom slopes uniformly from one end to the other. Water enters the pool at a constant rate and, from empty, the time taken to fill the pool completely is 3 hours.

(a) Find the area of the cross-section of the pool.

(b) Find the time taken to fill the pool to a depth of one metre at the deep end.

(c) Find the depth of the water at the deep end after 2 hours.

(d) Copy the diagram and draw a sketch graph to represent how the depth of water at the deep end of the pool changes with time.

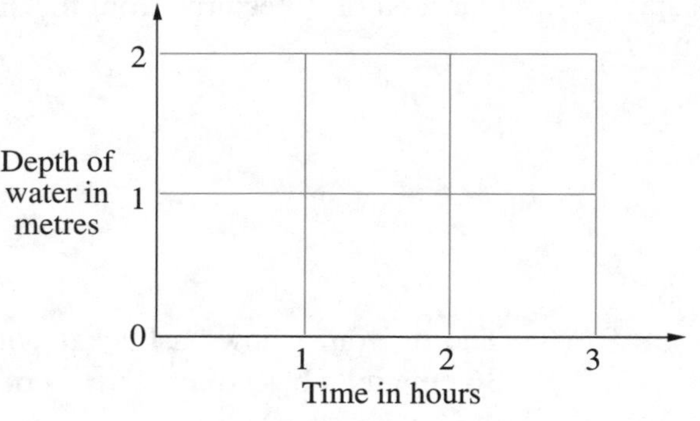

(*C*)

8.

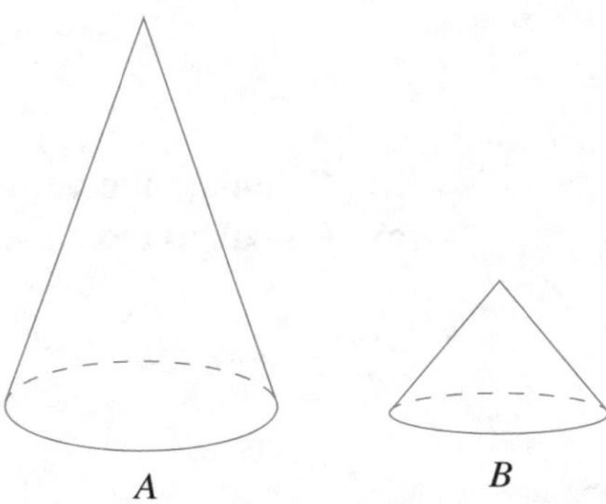

The diagram shows two cones, *A* and *B*. The radius of *A* is 5 cm and its slant height is 13 cm. The radius of *B* is 4 cm and its slant height is 5 cm.

(a) Calculate the vertical height of
  (i) cone A, **(ii)** cone B.

(b) Find the ratio
  (i) volume of A : volume of B,
  (ii) curved surface area of A : curved surface area of B.

9. A firm which manufactures golf balls is experimenting with the packaging of its product. 3 golf balls, each of radius 2.15 centimetres, are packaged in a rectangular box, a cross-section of which is shown in the diagram below. The box is 12.9 centimetres long, 4.3 centimetres wide and 4.3 centimetres high.

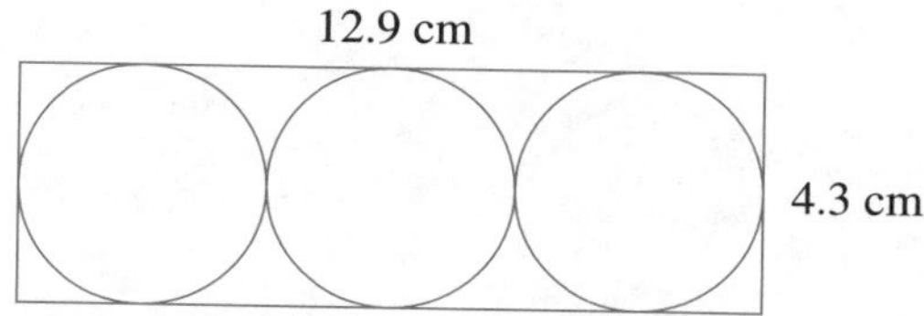

(a) Given that the volume of a sphere of radius r is $\frac{4}{3}\pi r^3$, calculate the amount of space within the box which is unfilled.

The marketing department suggests that an equilateral triangular box of side 11.75 centimetres and height 4.3 centimetres might be more attractive. The diagrams show a plan and side view of the new box.

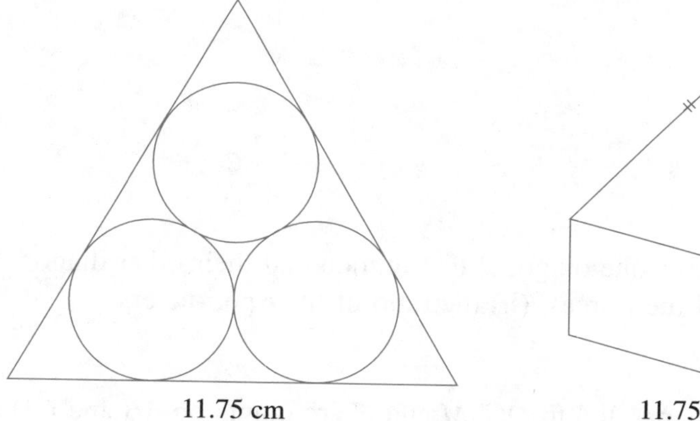

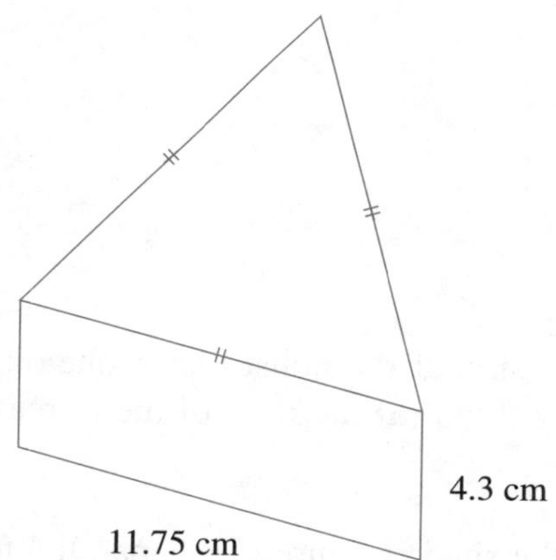

(b) Calculate the amount of space within this new box which is unfilled. [π is approximately 3.142.]

(C)

10. In the figure, $ABCD$ is a trapezium. AD = 12 cm, AB = 24 cm, $\hat{A}$ = 60° and $\hat{B}$ = 45°. Find the area of the trapezium. Give your answer correct to the nearest square centimetres.

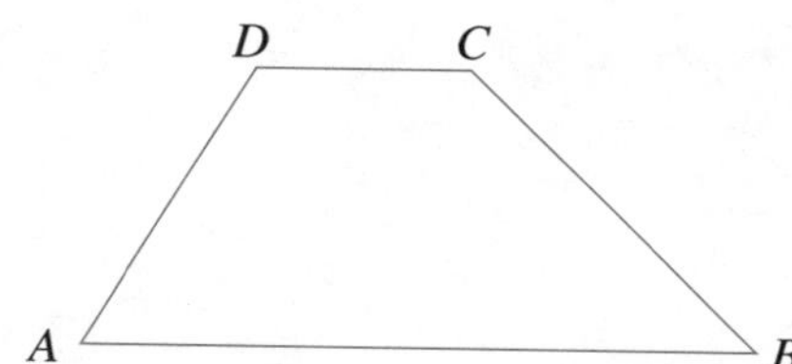

11. Find the ratio $\dfrac{\text{area of } \triangle CDX}{\text{area of parallelogram } ABCD}$.

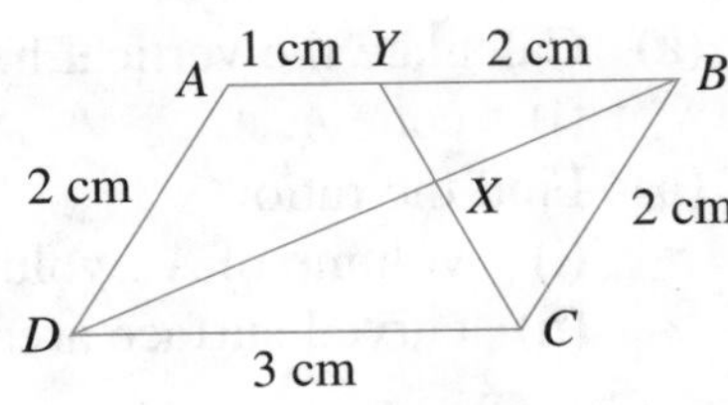

12. In the figure, AOB is a quadrant of radius 7 cm, C is the midpoint of arc AB and CD is perpendicular to AO. Find the area of the shaded part. $\left(\text{Take } \pi = \dfrac{22}{7}.\right)$

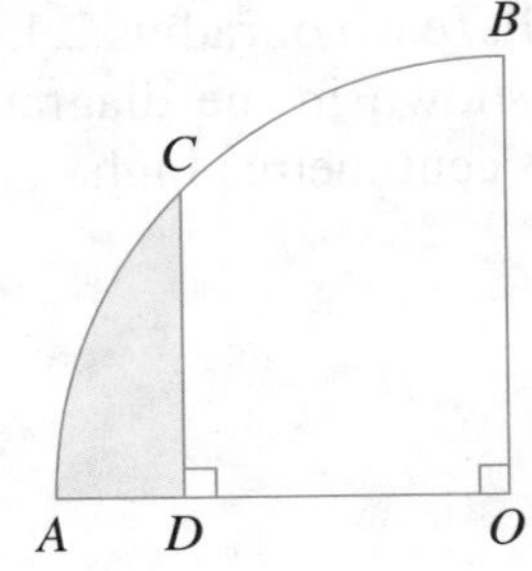

13. In the figure, BD is the bisector of $A\hat{B}C$ and $AB : BC = 2 : 3$. Calculate

(a) the ratio of the area of $\triangle AED$ to the area of $\triangle CEB$,

(b) the lengths of BE and ED if $BD = 7\frac{1}{2}$ cm.

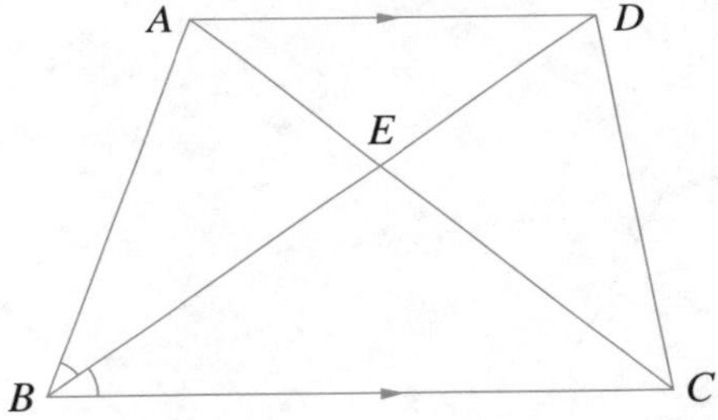

14. Two similar rhombuses have one diagonal in common and their other diagonals are in the ratio 3 : 2. Find **(a)** the ratio of their areas, **(b)** the ratio of their perimeters.

15. In the shaded figure, AB is parallel to DC. M and N are points on AB and CD respectively such that $MN = 10$ cm and $N\hat{M}B = 80°$. If $AB = 14$ cm, calculate the shaded area.

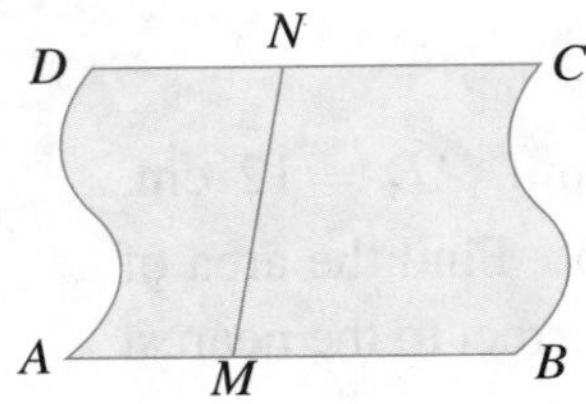

INVESTIGATION 3

1. Think of a 2-digit number.
Add the tens digit to 3 times the ones digit to form the second number and repeat this to get the third number and so on.

For example, 27 , 23 , 11 , 04 , ...

$$\begin{array}{cccc} 27, & 23, & 11, & 04, \ldots\ldots \\ \uparrow & \uparrow & \uparrow & \uparrow \\ \text{start} & 2+3(7) & 2+3(3) & 1+3(1) \end{array}$$

(a) Continue this sequence until you get 30 terms in all. What do you observe?
(b) Use other numbers as your starting numbers to form sequences. What do you observe?

2. Each of the following palindromes is expressed as a product of two numbers.

$$\begin{aligned} 252 &= z \times a \\ 25\,452 &= z \times b \\ 2\,545\,452 &= z \times c \\ 254\,545\,452 &= z \times d \\ 25\,454\,545\,452 &= z \times e \end{aligned}$$

(a) If $z = 4$, find the values of a, b, c, d and e.
(b) If $z = 7$, find the values of a, b, c, d and e.
(c) Investigate for other values of z. What do you observe?

3. Take three consecutive numbers, say 5, 6 and 7. Find their product and add the middle number. What do you notice?
Investigate for three other consecutive numbers. Describe your observation.

4. A 2 by 2 square grid has 1 big and 4 small squares, i.e. a total of 5 squares of all sizes.

(a) Copy and complete the following table.

Dimension of square grid	Total number of squares
1 by 1	1
2 by 2	5
3 by 3	14
4 by 4	30
5 by 5	
6 by 6	
7 by 7	
8 by 8	

(b) How many squares of all sizes are there in a 20 by 20 square grid? Investigate.

Chapter 12

Statistics I

Chapter Highlights

- Collecting, classifying and tabulating data and representing the data by bar graphs and pie charts, including choosing the appropriate statistical method to represent the data
- Reading and interpreting bar graphs, including interpreting tables and drawing the corresponding bar graphs
- Reading and interpreting pie charts, including interpreting tables and drawing the corresponding pie charts
- Reading and interpreting line graphs, including interpreting tables and drawing the corresponding line graphs
- Reading and interpreting pictograms, including interpreting tables and drawing the corresponding pictogram
- Becoming aware of the misuse of statistical displays

12.1 COLLECTION AND PRESENTATION OF DATA

People who work in government, commercial and industrial establishments need statistical information to help them plan their work. For example, the priority in building schools depends on data such as the number of children who are likely to seek admission, the population densities in various regions, etc.

Data is a collection of facts or information.

The data collected are usually presented in tables or charts.

Examples

(a) One morning, four students – Albert, Betty, Carol and Donald – were stationed at a certain point along a road. They worked in pairs to gather information about the flow of traffic for $1\frac{1}{4}$ hours. They recorded the data they have collected as follows:

Data Recorded by Albert and Betty

Time intervals (a.m.)				
8.00–8.15	**8.15–8.30**	**8.30–8.45**	**8.45–9.00**	**9.00–9.15**
T C C C C	*B V C M C*	*B C C C*	*V T B L*	*B L C C*
C T V C M	*C B C C L*	*L T C M*	*C C M M*	*T V C C*
C B T T T	*T M C L T*	*V L C C*	*C C V L*	*T T M M*
T C V C M	*T C C C L*	*C C C B*	*B T C C*	*T C C T*
B C T C T	*C V T C C*	*M C C C*	*M T T C*	*V V V T*
M M T C C	*V V T T C*	*V T L V*	*V B M C*	*C T C M*
T C V C T	*C C T M C*	*L M C C*	*C L L C*	*L C C V*
V C B C T	*T C T C B*	*T C C C*	*T T M V*	*B V*
C T C T M	*C V C T T*	*C C C V*	*V L T L*	
C C C B M	*C C C T C*	*B C C V*	*V T M*	
C T C T C	*T T C M T*	*T C C M*		
C C C T C	*C C C C B*	*C C M C*		
L L C T C	*C B L T M*	*C C C C*		
T C M C T	*M C T C V*	*L B T M*		
C C C T C	*C T C T C*	*C C T C*		
T C B C B	*T C T C M*	*C T B C*		
C T T C L	*C M C T C*	*C M C C*		
C C C C T	*B M C T C*	*T T B T*		
C T C T C	*V C M C C*	*M C*		
B C T V T	*C T T C B*			
C M T V	*C C T C C*			
	T C T T C			
	T C C			
104 vehicles	113 vehicles	74 vehicles	39 vehicles	30 vehicles

B for buses *C* for cars *L* for lorries

M for motorcycles *V* for vans *T* for taxis

MATHSTORY

The father of modern statistics was an Englishman, John Graunt (1620–1674). Graunt studied birth and death records and discovered that more boys than girls were born. He also found that because men were more subject to death from occupational accidents, diseases and war, the numbers of men and women of marriageable age were about equal. His results were published in a book entitled Natural and Political Observations Upon the Bills of Mortality. His work was the first to analyse statistics and to draw conclusions on the basis of such analysis. Graunt's work led to the development of actuarial science which is used by insurance companies.

Data Recorded by Carol and Donald

Comparison of vehicle types through a place

Time (a.m.) / Vehicles	8.00–8.15	8.15–8.30	8.30–8.45	8.45–9.00	9.00–9.15	Number of vehicles
Buses	𝍸 ||	𝍸 ||	𝍸 |	|||	||	25
Lorries	|||	||||	𝍸	𝍸 |	||	20
Cars	𝍸 𝍸 𝍸 𝍸 𝍸 𝍸 𝍸 𝍸 𝍸 𝍸	𝍸 𝍸 𝍸 𝍸 𝍸 𝍸 𝍸 𝍸 𝍸 𝍸 𝍸	𝍸 𝍸 𝍸 𝍸 𝍸 𝍸 𝍸 𝍸	𝍸 𝍸	𝍸 𝍸	165
Taxis	𝍸 𝍸 𝍸 𝍸 𝍸 𝍸	𝍸 𝍸 𝍸 𝍸 𝍸 𝍸	𝍸 𝍸	𝍸 |||	𝍸 ||	85
Vans	𝍸 |	𝍸 ||	𝍸	𝍸 |	𝍸 |	30
Motorcycles	𝍸 |||	𝍸 𝍸	𝍸 |||	𝍸 |	|||	35
Number of vehicles	104	113	74	39	30	

The students recorded their data in different ways.

- Albert and Betty recorded the vehicles they observed without much organisation.
- Carol and Donald recorded their data according to the type of vehicles and in groups of five for easy counting.
- The method used by Carol and Donald is more systematic.

(b) The data in (a) can be organised, classified and tabulated as follows:

The traffic flow at a certain place

Time (a.m.) / Vehicles	8.00–8.15	8.15–8.30	8.30–8.45	8.45–9.00	9.00–9.15	Subtotal
Buses	7	7	6	3	2	25
Lorries	3	4	5	6	2	20
Cars	50	55	40	10	10	165
Taxis	30	30	10	8	7	85
Vans	6	7	5	6	6	30
Motorcycles	8	10	8	6	3	35
Subtotal	104	113	74	39	30	**Total = 360**

Generally, a table has a title and includes subtotals and the total.

(c) The organised data in (b) can be presented in various pictorial forms.

Pie Chart

In a pie chart, the angle of each sector is proportional to the number of items represented.

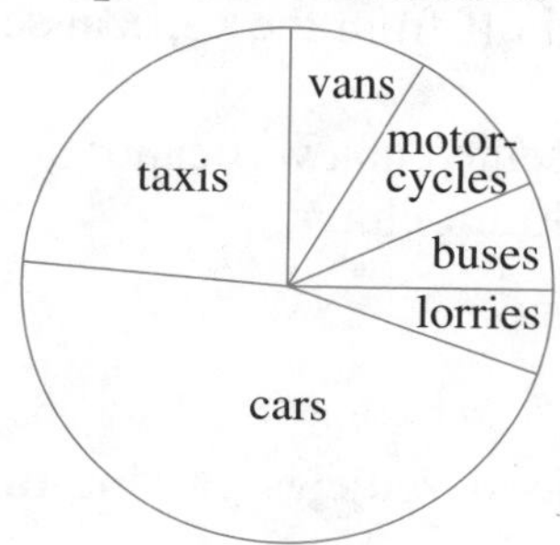

Before the pie chart is drawn, the angle of each sector is calculated as follows:

Buses : $\frac{25}{360} \times 360° = 25°$

Lorries: $\frac{20}{360} \times 360° = 20°$

Cars : $\frac{165}{360} \times 360° = 165°$

Taxis : $\frac{85}{360} \times 360° = 85°$

Vans : $\frac{30}{360} \times 360° = 30°$

Motorcycles: $\frac{35}{360} \times 360° = 35°$

Bar Chart

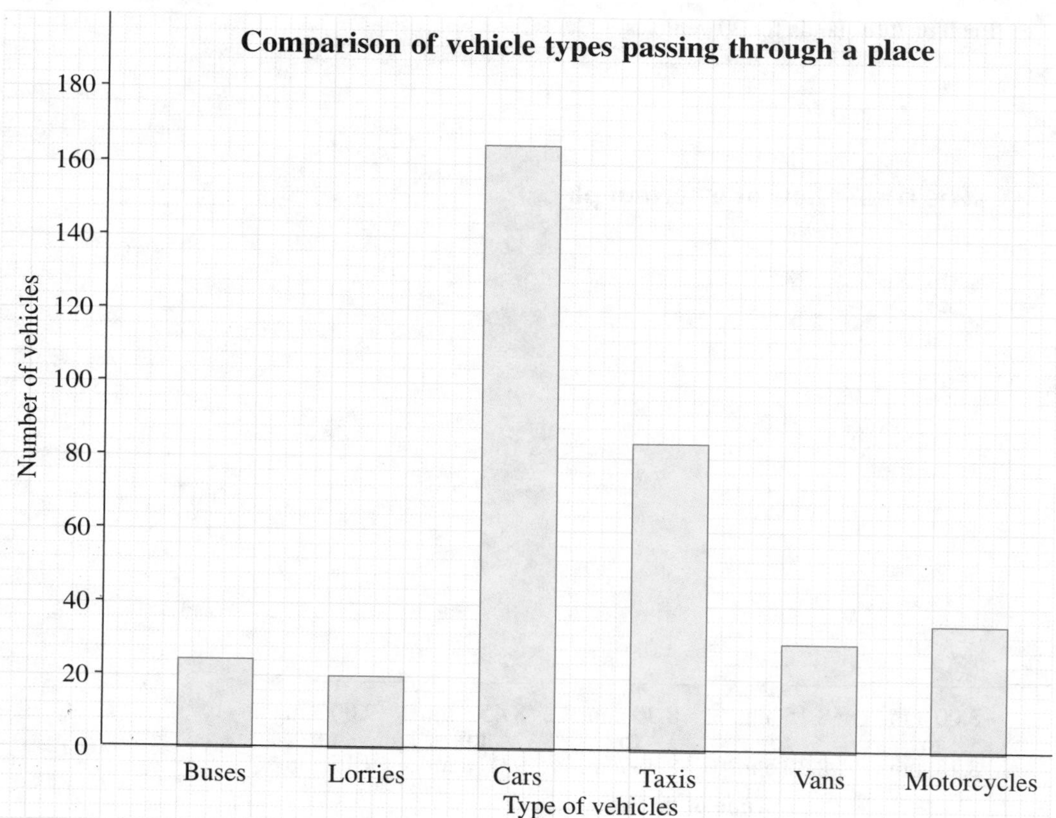

In a bar chart, the bars drawn are of equal width. The values of the various items are represented by the lengths of the bars. For example, the total number of buses recorded as read off from the vertical scale is 25.

A bar chart can be presented in a vertical or horizontal form. A vertical bar chart is also known as a **column chart**.

Pictogram

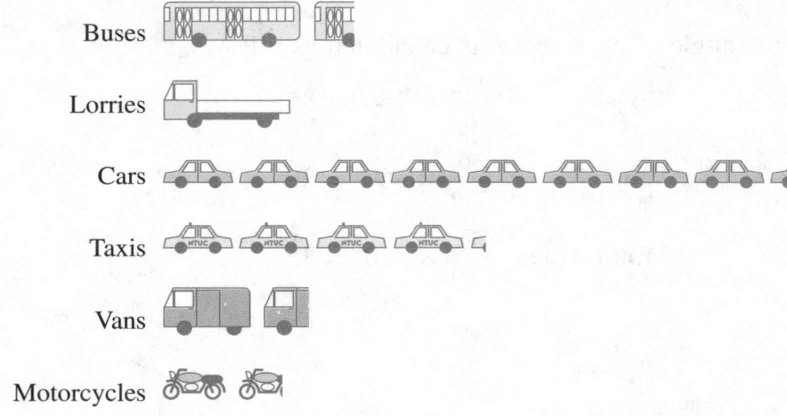

Line Graph

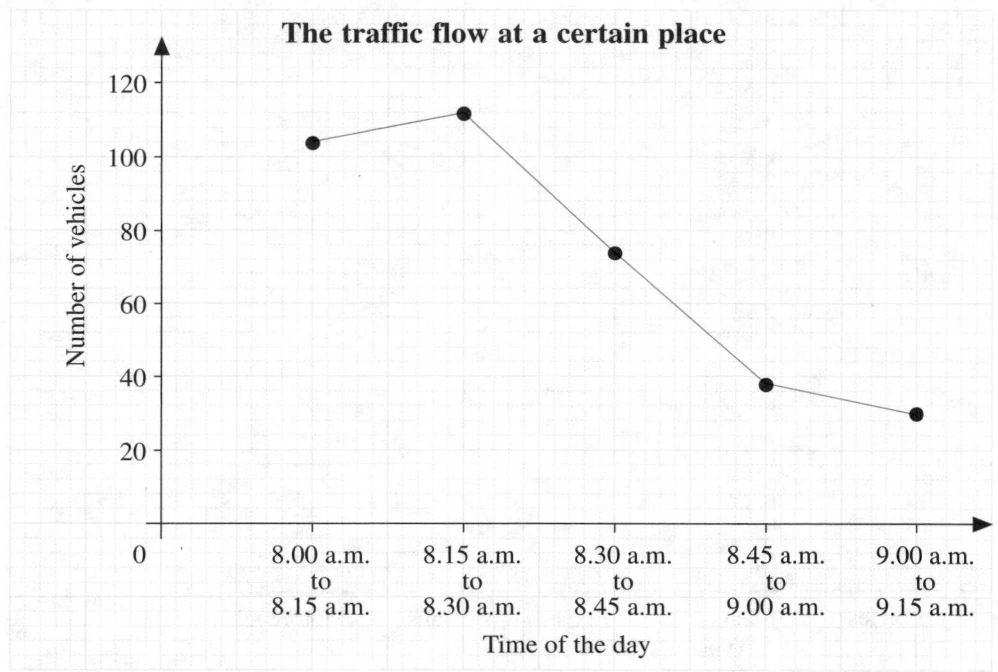

The line graph shows the total number of vehicles recorded at the end of each interval of 15 minutes. The points are joined by line segments to show how the number increases or decreases with time. It tells us that the peak period is from 8.15 a.m. to 8.30 a.m.

However, the intermediate points between the end points of each line segment do not have any meaning in this example.

Comparison of Presentations of Data

Let us examine the advantages and disadvantages of the following presentations.

Tabulation

- It allows comparison of data.
- Accuracy of data is not lost.
- It is less appealing to the readers owing to a lack of visual impact.

Bar Chart

- It is fairly accurate.
- It is easy to draw.
- The values can be easily estimated from the scales.
- The lengths give clear comparison of values with respect to each other.

Pie Chart

- It is not as easy to draw as a bar chart.
- It is not easy to read as the values of the items are represented by the angles of the sectors.
- It gives a good comparison of each part with the whole.

Pictogram

- It is not easy to draw.
- It is not easy to read as the values of the items are sometimes represented by a fractional part of the picture or symbol of the item.
- It is appealing to the readers because of its visual impact.
- It is designed for the layman.

Line Graph

- It is easy to draw.
- The values can be easily read off from the grid lines.
- It is useful to show an upward or a downward trend, a peak or fluctuations.
- The values between the plotted points may not have meaning.

Class Activity

Students are to work in groups for the following activities.

1. Measure the height and mass of each student in the group.
Name: ____________
Height: ____________
Mass: ____________
Construct a table to organise the data collected.
Represent the data by a column graph. (Represent the measurements of the height and mass of each student in two columns, side by side.)

2. Collect the following data.
Number of students who choose red as their favourite colour.
Number of students who choose blue as their favourite colour.
Number of students who choose green as their favourite colour.
Number of students who do not choose any of these colours as their favourite colour.
Construct a table to organise the data collected.
Draw a pie chart to represent the data.

3. Find out the month of birth of each student in the group.
Number of students who were born in the months of January, June and July.
Number of students who were born in the months of March and May.
Number of students who were born in the months of April and August.
Number of students who were not born in these months.
Construct a table to organise the data collected.
Draw a pie chart to represent the data.

Exercise 12.1

1. Select 5 types of books of your choice (for example, mathematics, science, second language, fiction and ghost story) from the school library. For each type, pick 5 books and record the number of times each book has been borrowed in a year. Construct a table to organise the data collected. Use an appropriate display method to present your findings.

2. **(a)** Copy and use this survey form to collect the data.

How I Come to School

Name of student: ____________ Date: ____________

Please put a tick (✓) in the appropriate box.

Walk	☐	Bus	☐	Car	☐
Motorcycle	☐	MRT	☐	Others	☐

(b) Design a similar form to collect data for each of the following surveys.
- My favourite TV programme.
- Places of interest I like to visit.
- My favourite subject in school.
- My favourite game.

(c) Construct a table of your survey. Present your findings with an appropriate display method.

12.2 READING AND DRAWING OF BAR GRAPHS

Worked Example

The bar graph below shows the yearly enrolment in the educational institutions of a certain city from 1995 to 1997.

Bar graph uses a series of horizontal or vertical bars of differing lengths to show information.

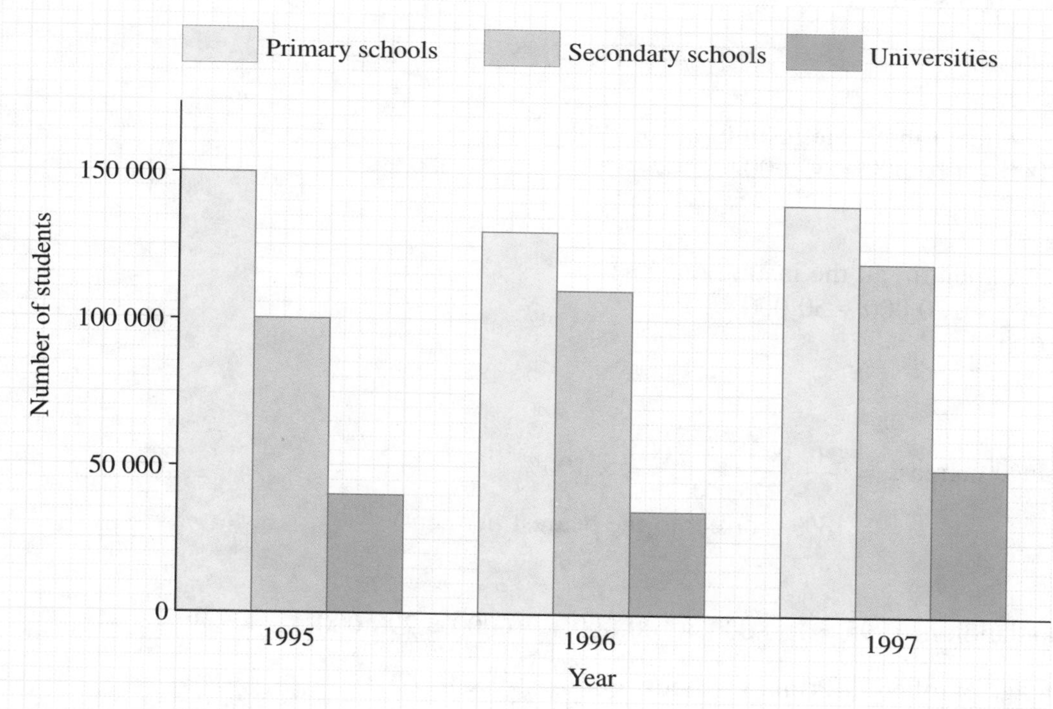

Study the graph and answer the following questions.

(a) Give the total enrolment in each institution from 1995 to 1997.

(b) Give the total enrolment in all the institutions
 (i) in 1996,
 (ii) in 1997.

(c) Find the percentage increase of the total enrolment in all the institutions from 1996 to 1997. Give your answer correct to the nearest per cent.

(d) What percentage of the student population in 1995 was enrolled in
(i) Primary schools,
(ii) Secondary schools,
(iii) Universities?
Give each answer correct to the nearest per cent.

Solution:

(a) Total enrolment in Primary schools from 1995 to 1997
= 150 000 + 130 000 + 140 000
= 420 000

Total enrolment in Secondary schools from 1995 to 1997
= 100 000 + 110 000 + 120 000
= 330 000

Total enrolment in Universities from 1995 to 1997
= 40 000 + 35 000 + 50 000
= 125 000

(b) **(i)** Total enrolment in all the institutions in 1996
= 130 000 + 110 000 + 35 000
= 275 000

(ii) Total enrolment in all the institutions in 1997
= 140 000 + 120 000 + 50 000
= 310 000

(c) The percentage increase $= \dfrac{310\,000 - 275\,000}{275\,000} \times 100\%$
= 13% (correct to the nearest per cent)

(d) Student population in 1995 = 150 000 + 100 000 + 40 000 = 290 000

(i) Percentage enrolled in Primary schools $= \dfrac{150\,000}{290\,000} \times 100\%$
= 52% (correct to the nearest per cent)

(ii) Percentage enrolled in Secondary schools $= \dfrac{100\,000}{290\,000} \times 100\%$
= 34% (correct to the nearest per cent)

(iii) Percentage enrolled in Universities $= \dfrac{40\,000}{290\,000} \times 100\%$
= 14% (correct to the nearest per cent)

Exercise 12.2

answers on p. 440

1. The following bar chart shows a survey on the types of books borrowed by 80 students from a school library in a certain week.

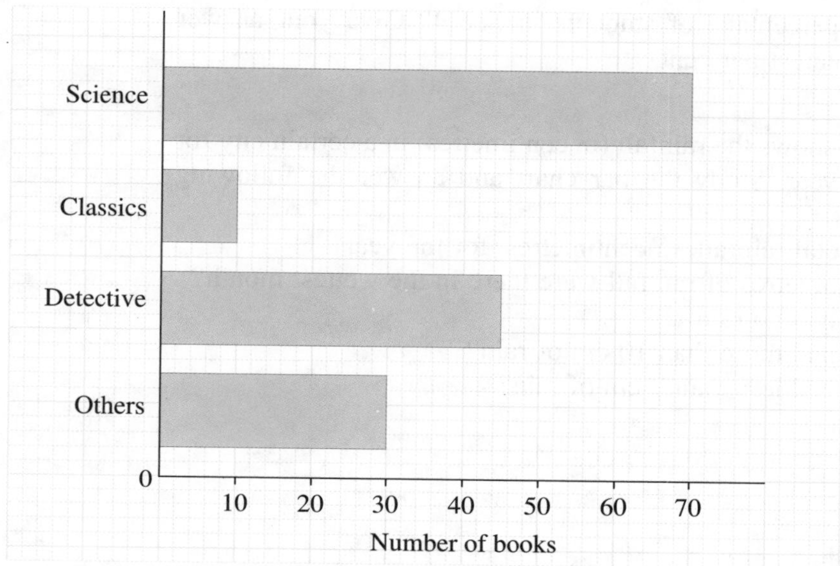

(a) How many books on classics were borrowed?
(b) How many books on science fiction were borrowed?
(c) How many books were borrowed altogether?
(d) What per cent of the books borrowed were detective storybooks?
(e) If every student borrowed at least 1 but not more than 2 books, how many borrowed exactly 2 books?

2.

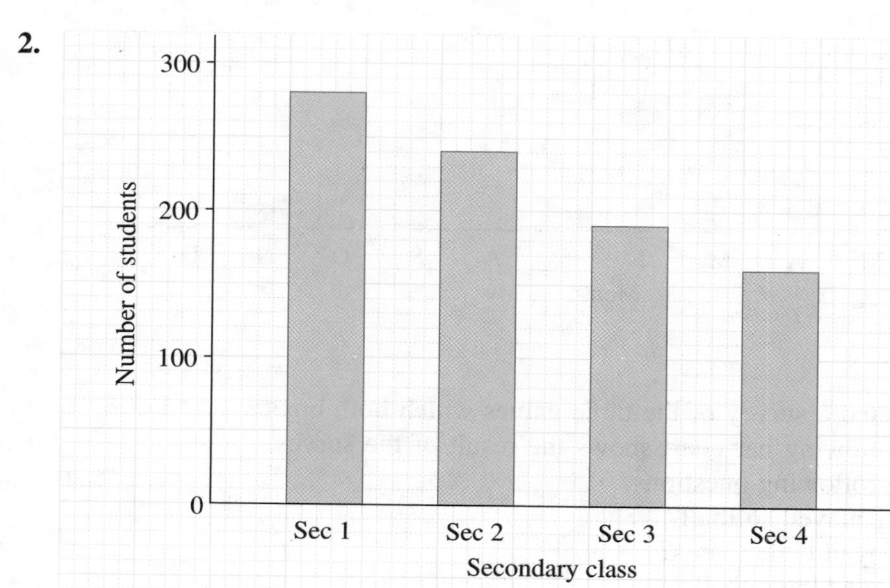

The bar chart shows the student enrolment in a secondary school for a certain year. Study the bar chart and answer the following questions.
(a) How many students were there in Sec 3?
(b) What was the total student population in the school?
(c) Which level had the most students?
(d) Which levels had fewer than 200 students?
(e) What was the percentage of students in Sec 4? Give your answer correct to the nearest per cent.

3. The bar chart below shows the rainfall (in centimetres) in a certain city for each month of the year. Study the bar chart and answer the following questions.
(a) What was the total rainfall, in centimetres, for the year?
(b) How many centimetres of rainfall were there in the wettest month?
(c) Which months had no rainfall?
(d) Which months had more than 10 cm of rain?
(e) Which months had less than 9 cm of rain?

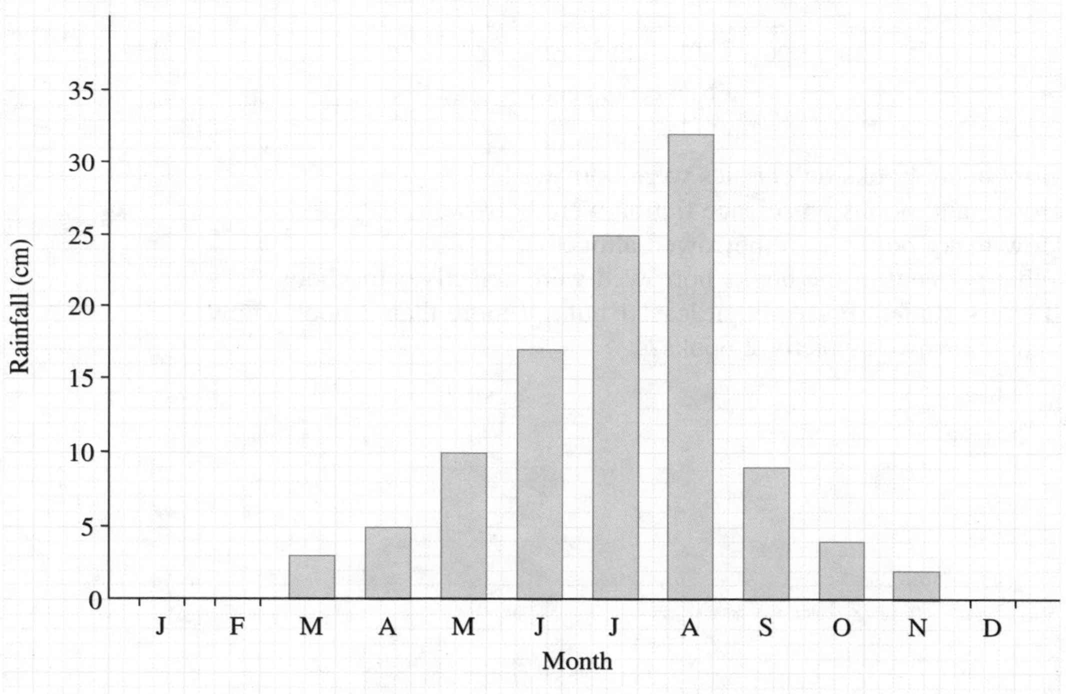

4. A certain school conducted a survey of the three games which both boys and girls played. The following bar chart shows the result of the survey. Study it and answer the following questions.
(a) How many students played softball?
(b) How many boys played table tennis?
(c) How many girls played basketball?

(d) Assuming that each student played only one of these games,
  (i) how many boys played these games,
  (ii) how many girls played these games,
  (iii) what per cent of the students who played these games were girls? Give your answer correct to the nearest per cent.

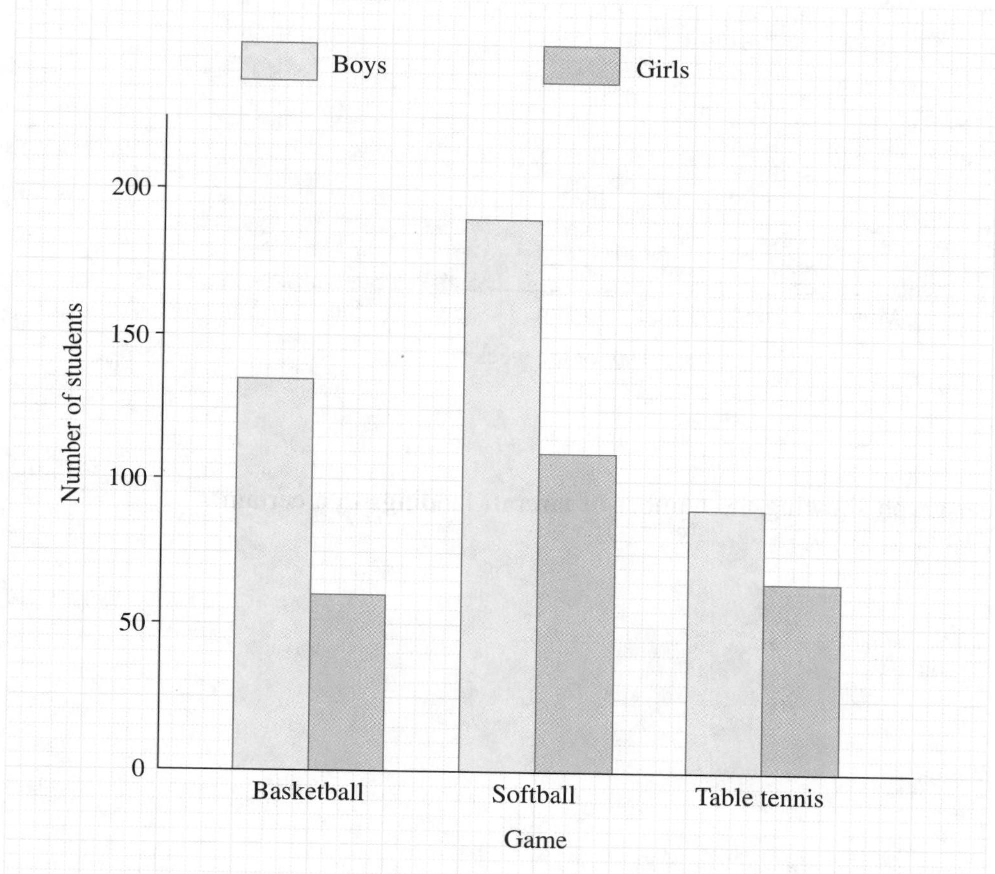

5. The following bar chart shows the daily water consumption for a week in a certain city. Study the bar chart and answer the following questions.
  (a) What was the total water consumption for the week?
  (b) On which day of the week was the water consumption the highest and how much water, in cubic metres, was consumed?
  (c) Which day of the week had the lowest water consumption and how much water, in cubic metres, was consumed?
  (d) On which days of the week did the water consumption exceed 782 000 m^3?
  (e) On which days of the week was the water consumption less than 780 000 m^3?
  (f) What was the difference in the water consumption between Thursday and Friday?

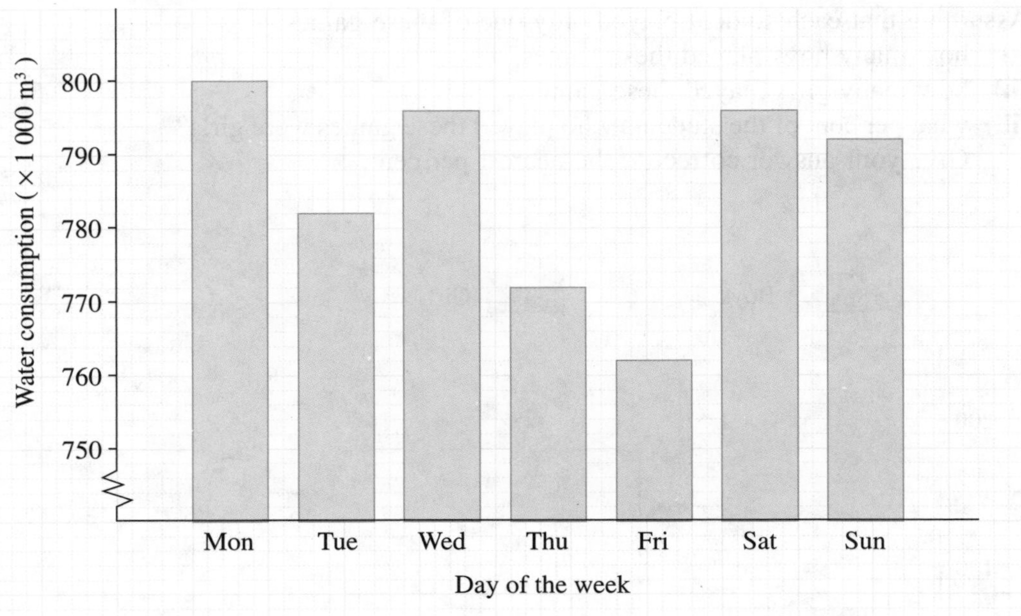

6. Below is a bar graph showing the number of aircraft landings in a certain airport from 1994 to 1997.

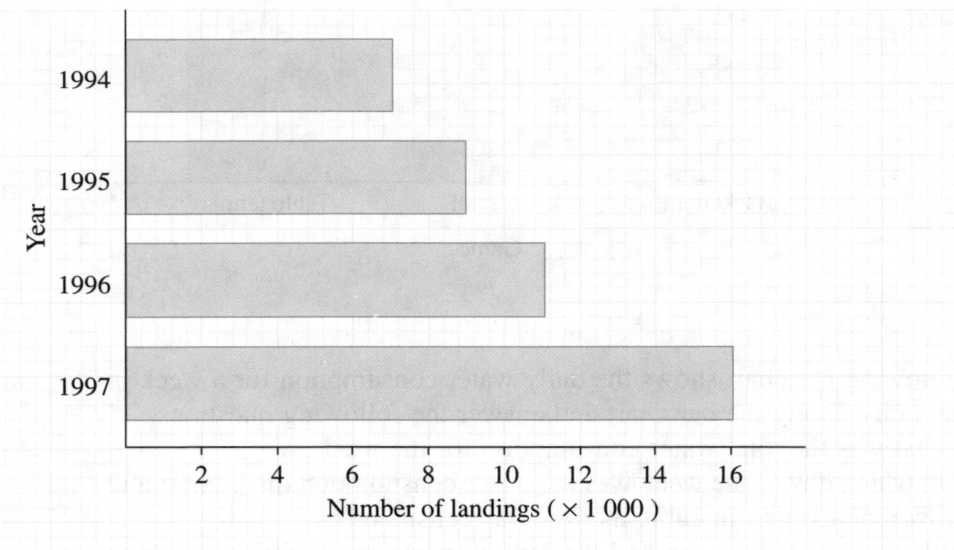

Study the bar chart and answer the following questions.

(a) Find the number of aircraft landings for each year from 1994 to 1997.

(b) If the landing fee for each aircraft was \$250, calculate the total fee collected by the airport in 1994.

(c) What is the percentage increase of landings from 1996 to 1997? Give your answer correct to the nearest per cent.

7. In a certain university, the yearly student intake for the various courses is shown in the bar graph below.

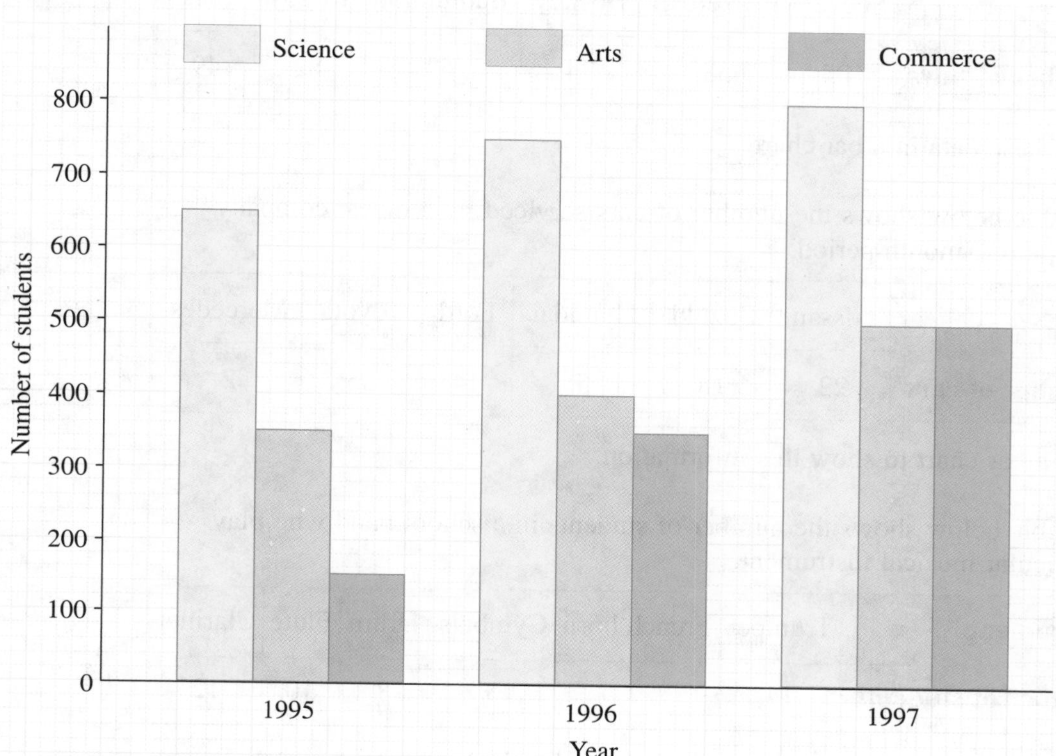

Study the graph and answer the following questions.

(a) Give the total intake for each course from 1995 to 1997.

(b) Give the total intake for the three courses in **(i)** 1995 and **(ii)** 1996.

(c) Give the percentage increase of the total intake for the three courses from 1995 to 1997. Give your answer correct to the nearest per cent.

(d) What percentage of the student intake in 1997 attended the following courses?

(i) Science **(ii)** Arts **(iii)** Commerce

Give your answers correct to the nearest per cent.

8. Below is the result of a survey to find out how 1 040 students go to school.

275 go to school by car
500 go to school by bus
105 go to school by MRT
160 walk to school

(a) Represent the data using a bar chart.

(b) What percentage of the students go to school by bus? Give your answer correct to one decimal place.

9. In a school, the number of boys taking part in each game is shown in the table below.

Game	Soccer	Basketball	Hockey	Badminton	Rugby	Chess
Number of boys	105	53	74	63	82	49

Show these data in a bar chart.

10. The table below shows the number of cars serviced by a motor company during a one-month period.

Car	Nissan	Suzuki	Hyundai	Ford	Toyota	Mercedes
Number of cars	22	18	5	14	35	2

Draw a bar chart to show this information.

11. The table below shows the number of students in a school band who play a particular musical instrument.

Instrument	Trumpet	French horn	Cymbals	Drum	Flute	Clarinet
Number of students	14	9	5	8	10	12

A new member joined the band and chose to play the French horn and three students decided to change from playing the trumpet to beating the drum.

(a) Construct a new table to show the changes using the information given.

(b) The bar chart below is drawn based on the new information. Only two bars are drawn. Copy the bar chart below onto graph paper and draw the other four bars.

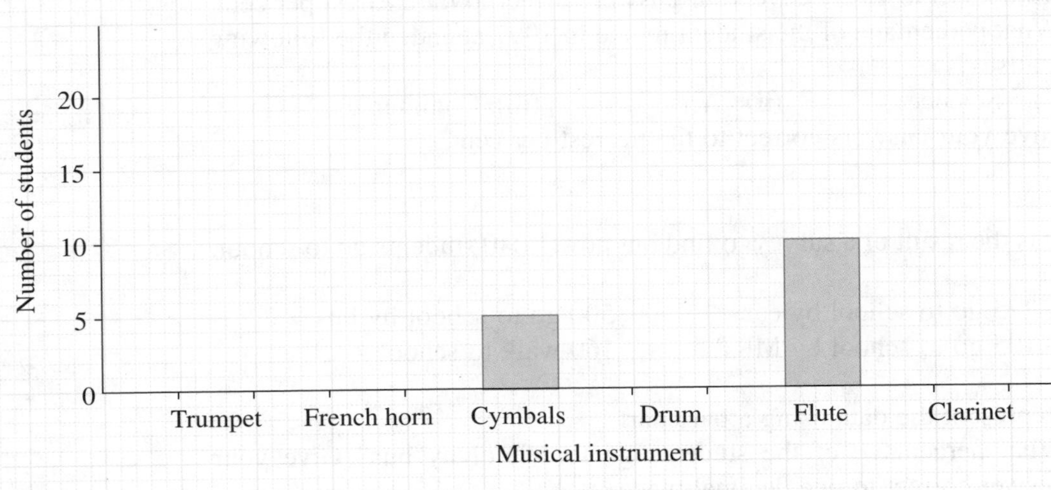

12.3 READING AND DRAWING OF PIE CHARTS

Worked Example

The pie chart represents the number of students and teachers in a certain school.

(a) Measure the angles of the sectors for boys, girls and teachers.

(b) If the total number of students and teachers in the school is 1 800, how many **(i)** boys, **(ii)** girls, **(iii)** teachers are there in the school?

(c) If $\frac{2}{5}$ of the girls are above 12 years old, find the angle of the sector that represents this.

(d) What percentage of the students are boys? Give your answer correct to the nearest per cent.

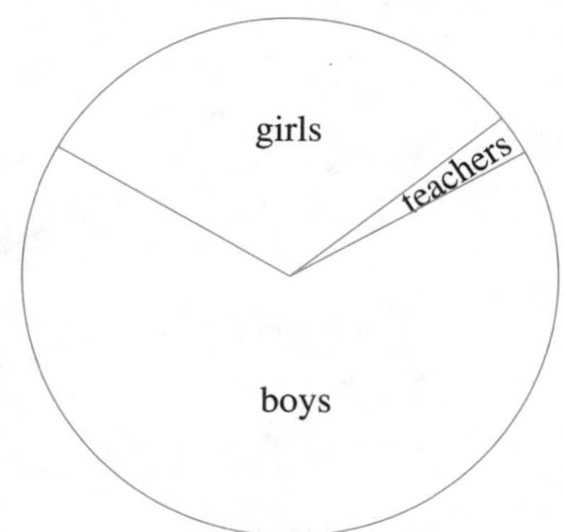

Solution:

(a) For boys, the angle of the sector is 240°.
For girls, the angle of the sector is 110°.
For teachers, the angle of the sector is 10°.

(b) (i) Number of boys $= \frac{240}{360} \times 1\ 800$
$= 1\ 200$

(ii) Number of girls $= \frac{110}{360} \times 1\ 800$
$= 550$

(iii) Number of teachers $= \frac{10}{360} \times 1\ 800$
$= 50$

(c) Angle of the sector for girls above 12 years old $= \frac{2}{5} \times 110°$
$= 44°$

(d) Number of students $= 1\ 200 + 550$
$= 1\ 750$

Percentage of boys $= \frac{1\ 200}{1\ 750} \times 100\%$
$= 69\%$ (correct to the nearest per cent)

Exercise 12.3

answers on p. 440

1. The pie chart below represents the sales of fruits by a fruiterer. If the total sales amounted to $5 400, calculate the amount collected for each type of fruits sold.

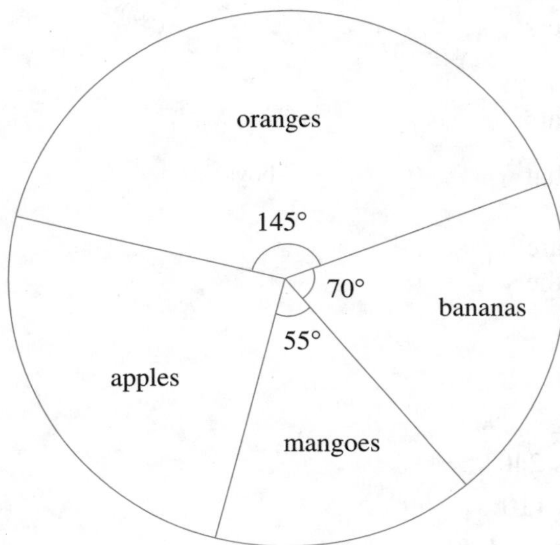

2. The pie chart below shows the number of different types of books loaned out by a library in a week. If the total number of books loaned out was 180, find, by making the necessary measurements, the number of each type of books borrowed from the library.

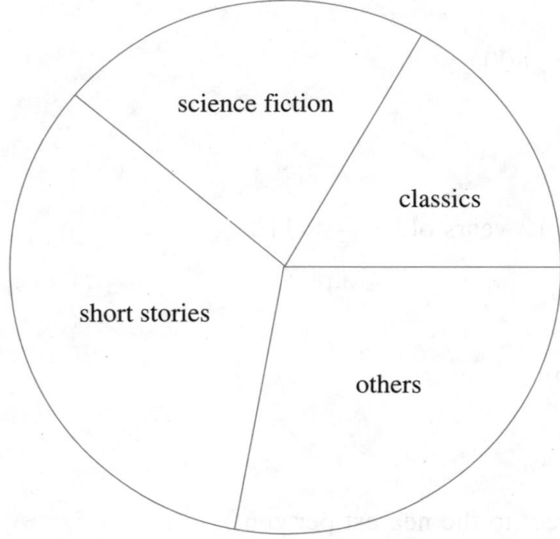

3. A man earned $1 080 a month. He spent 15% of it on rent, 50% on food, 10% on transport, 20% on others and saved the rest. Copy and complete the pie chart below for the given information.

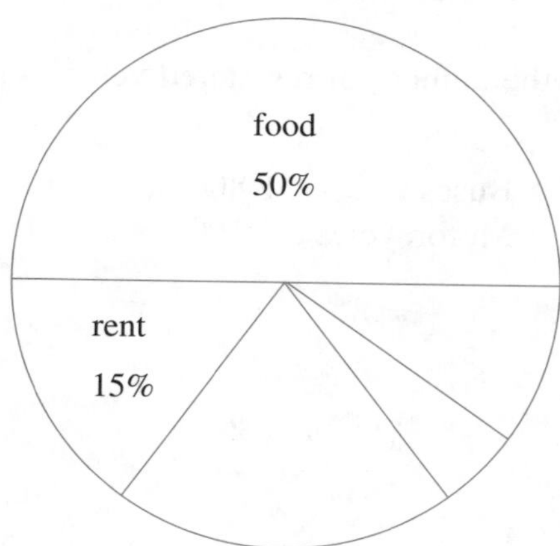

4. A family with an income of $1 800 spent it as follows:

Food	$700	Transport	$150
Rent	$250	Savings	$200
Others	$500		

(a) Represent these data on a pie chart.
(b) What percentage of the income was spent on food? Give your answer correct to one decimal place.

5. The pie chart below represents the number of students and teachers in a certain school.

(a) Measure the angles of the sectors for boys, girls and teachers.
(b) If the total number of students and teachers in the school is 3 600, how many **(i)** boys, **(ii)** girls, **(iii)** teachers are there in the school?
(c) If $\frac{3}{4}$ of the boys are above 12 years old, find the angle of the sector that will represent this on the same pie chart.

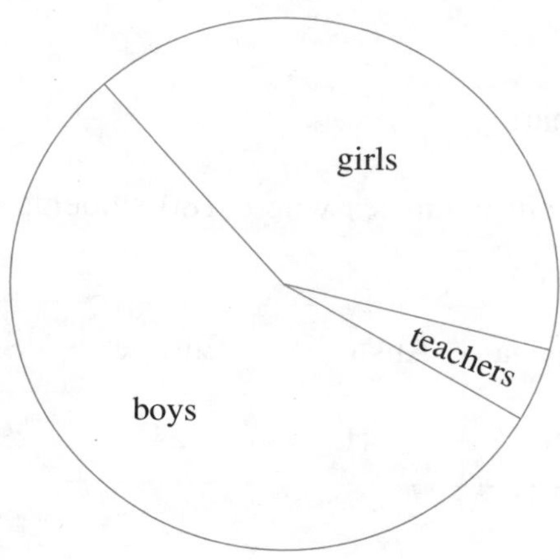

6. A survey of a certain school showed that out of 720 students, 400 preferred pop music, 200 semi-classical and 120 classical.
   (a) Represent this information using a pie chart.
   (b) What percentage of the students preferred semi-classical music?

7. It was estimated that in a certain city, the number of registered vehicles at the end of 1997 was as follows:

Cars	10 500	Buses	1 800
Taxis	4 200	Motorcycles	5 100

   Represent the data on a pie chart.

8. 1 080 students of a certain school named the subject they like best. The pie chart shows the result of the survey. By measuring the angle of each sector, find the number of students belonging to each group. Then express the number in each group as a percentage of the total number of students.

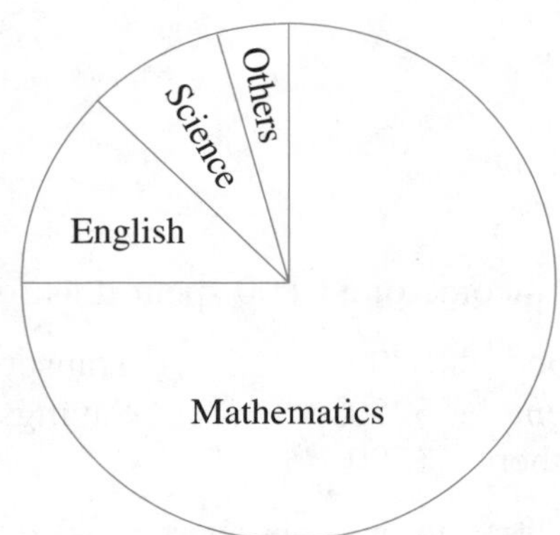

9. The table below shows the number of periods allotted to each subject in a class timetable per week.

Subject	Number of periods
English	8
Second Language	6
Mathematics	8
Science	6
Literature	3
Geography	3
History	3

   Show this information on a pie chart.

10. The table below shows the different countries where 180 students spent their school holidays.

Countries	Malaysia	Australia	Europe	USA
Number of students	86	41	24	29

   Represent the data on a pie chart.

11. The table below shows how 240 students travelled to school from their homes.

Method	Walk	Bus	Car	Motorcycle	MRT
Number of students	100	65	25	10	40

Draw a pie chart to illustrate the information.

12. Visitors to a National Park were asked to vote for their favourite animal. The results are shown on the given pie chart.

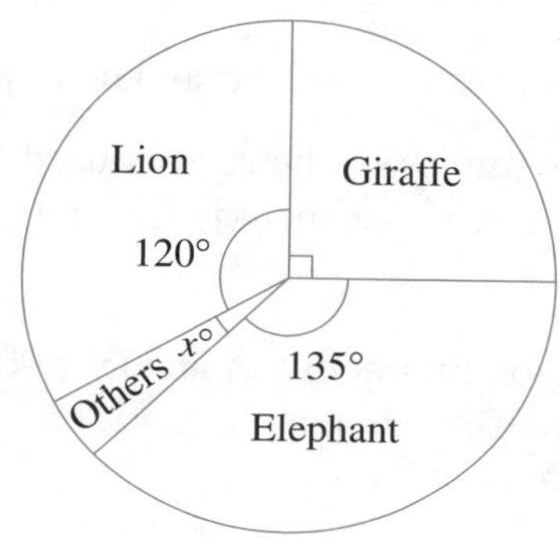

(a) Calculate
   (i) the value of x,
   (ii) the percentage of visitors who voted for giraffes.

(b) Calculate the number of people who took part in the survey, given that elephants obtained 20 more votes than lions. (*C*)

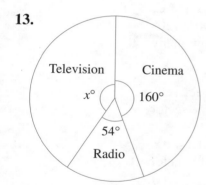

13. The girls in a school were asked to choose their favourite form of entertainment from television, cinema and radio. Their replies are represented in the pie chart.

(a) Calculate the value of x.

(b) 400 of the girls chose the cinema. Find the total number of girls in the school.

(c) Find the percentage of girls who chose the radio. (*C*)

14.

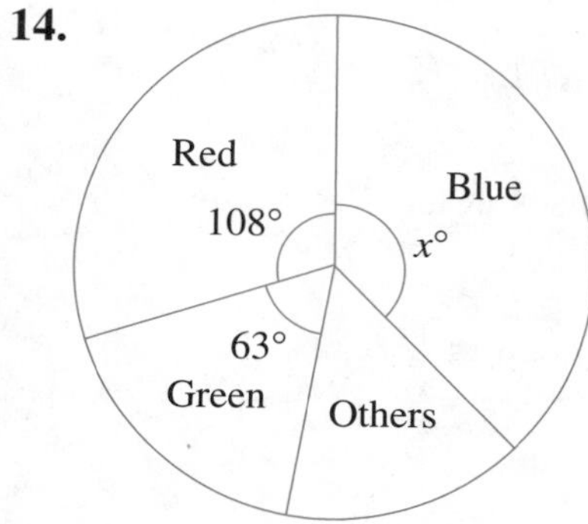

Each member of a class of 40 girls was asked to name her favourite colour. Their choices are represented on the given pie chart.

(a) If 15 said they liked blue, calculate the value of x.

(b) Find the number who said they liked green.

(c) Find the percentage of the class who said they liked red. (*C*)

15.

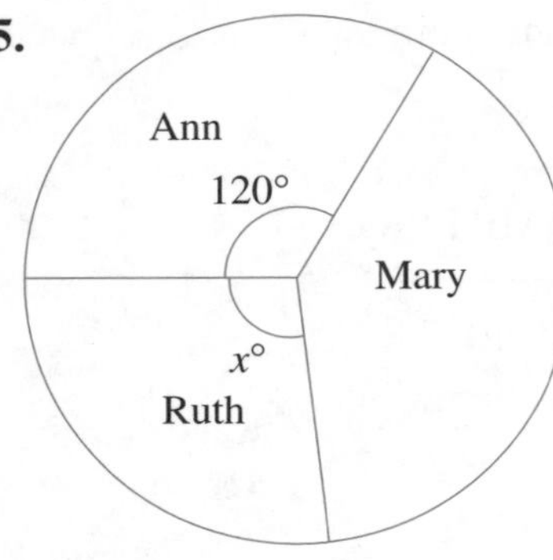

Ann, Mary and Ruth have 3 000 stamps between them. Ruth has 800 stamps. The pie chart represents the number of stamps each girl has.

(a) **(i)** How many stamps does Ann have?

(ii) Calculate the value of x.

(b) Ruth has 500 more used stamps than unused stamps. How many used stamps does she have? *(C)*

16. A pie chart is made to show how Mr Brown's total salary is spent. Income tax takes up 20% of his total salary, and he pays $12\frac{1}{2}$% of the remainder in rent. Calculate the angles of the sectors used to represent

(a) the amount he pays for income tax and

(b) his rent. *(C)*

17. A firm sells 90 kg of commodity A and $(x + 90)$ kg of commodity B. When these sales are represented on a pie chart, commodity A is represented by a sector of angle 45°. Find x. *(C)*

18. A sum of money is divided in the ratio 1 : 3 : 5. Draw a pie chart to illustrate this division. Indicate the angles of the sectors clearly.

19. Draw a pie chart to represent the sales of three commodities A, B and C, given that the angles of the sectors representing A, B and C are 90°, 120° and 150° respectively. If the total sale is 480 tonnes, calculate how many tonnes of each commodity are sold.

20. **(a)** The sales of two commodities A and B are 7 kg and 11 kg respectively. If these sales are represented by a pie chart, find the angle of the sector representing the sale of A.

(b) The sales of three commodities P, Q and R are in the ratio 1 : 4 : x. When these sales are represented by a pie chart, the angle of the sector representing the sale of P is 10°. Find x. *(C)*

12.4 READING AND DRAWING OF LINE GRAPHS AND PICTOGRAMS

Worked Example 1

The following table shows the number of people alighting from the buses at a certain bus terminal at 15-minute intervals on a working day.

Time (a.m.)	7.45–8.00	8.00–8.15	8.15–8.30	8.30–8.45	8.45–9.00	9.00–9.15
Number of people	51	62	59	100	318	40

Represent this information using a line graph and answer the following questions.

(a) Which is the busiest period?

(b) In your opinion, suggest one explanation in general terms for any trend of the line graph.

Solution:

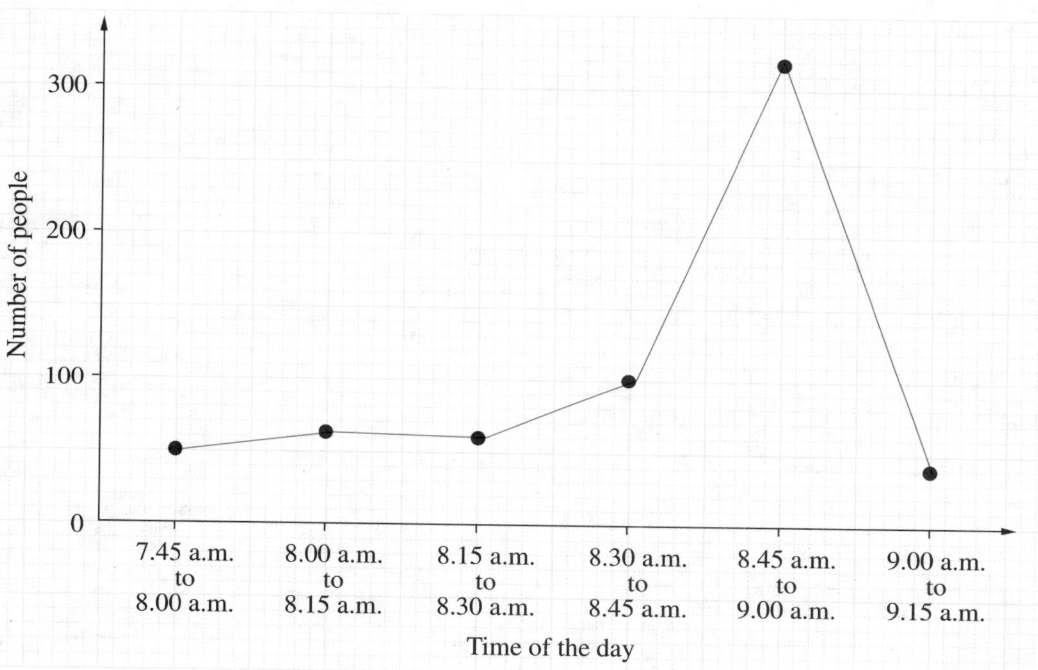

(a) The busiest period is from 8.45 a.m. to 9.00 a.m.

(b) The big rush between 8.45 a.m. and 9.00 a.m., and the trickle after 9.00 a.m. suggests that work begins at 9.00 a.m. for the majority of the people and they work at places within 15 minutes of walking distance from the bus terminal.

Worked Example 2

The table below shows the profit made by a trading firm in a six-month period.

Month	January	February	March	April	May	June
Profit	\$20 000	\$25 000	\$12 500	\$7 500	\$30 000	\$22 500

Illustrate these figures on a pictogram.

Solution:

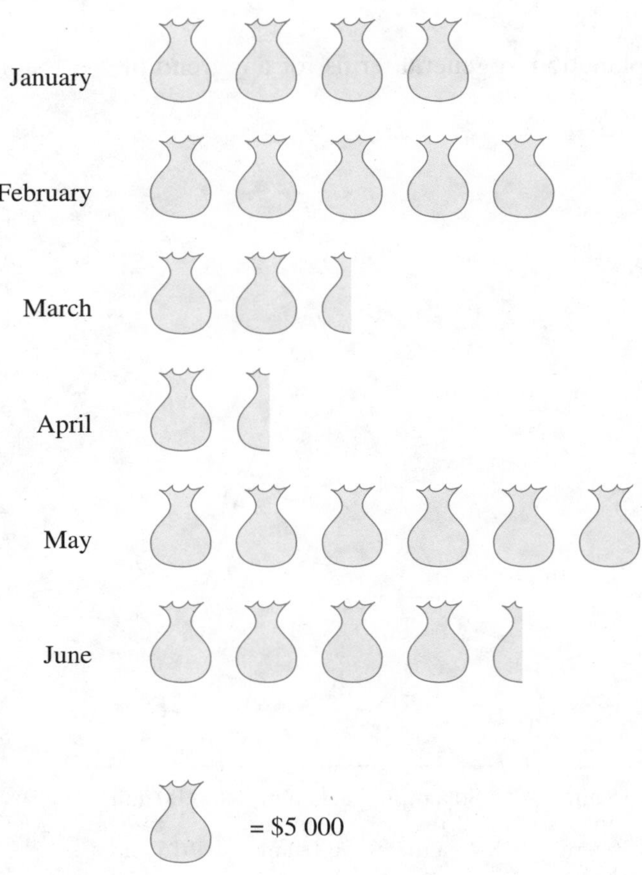

Exercise 12.4

answers on p. 441

1. The table below shows the population (to the nearest 100) of a town for the given period 1945–1990.

Year	Population	Year	Population
1945	9 200	1970	22 100
1950	12 500	1975	26 900
1955	14 600	1980	29 800
1960	16 400	1985	34 200
1965	18 800	1990	40 500

(a) Draw a line graph to show the population growth of the town.
(b) At which period did the population increase most rapidly?

2. The table below shows the number of people visiting the zoo each day for one particular week.

Day	Monday	Tuesday	Wednesday	Thursday	Friday	Saturday	Sunday
Number of people	1 250	1 895	2 360	2 565	2 840	5 290	6 550

(a) Draw a line graph to show this information.
(b) Describe in general terms any peculiar features of the line graph.

3. Examine the rough graphs below, and suggest an explanation in general terms of any trends which you may have observed in each line graph.
(a) *Taxi fares for a journey*

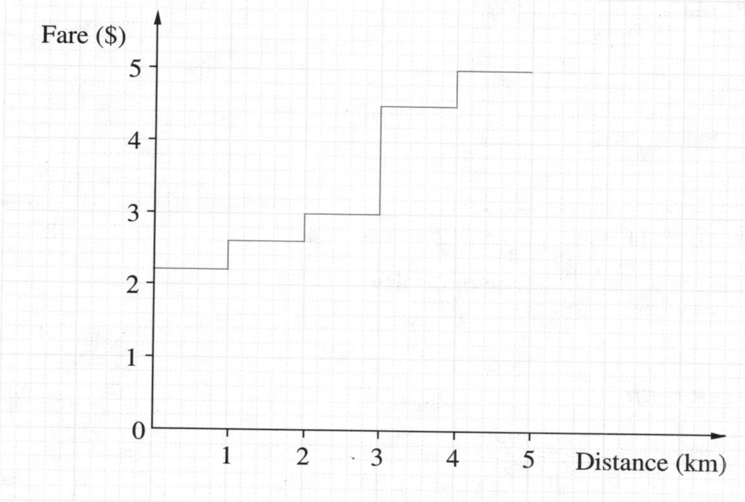

(b) *A man's yearly expenditure from 22 to 62 years old*

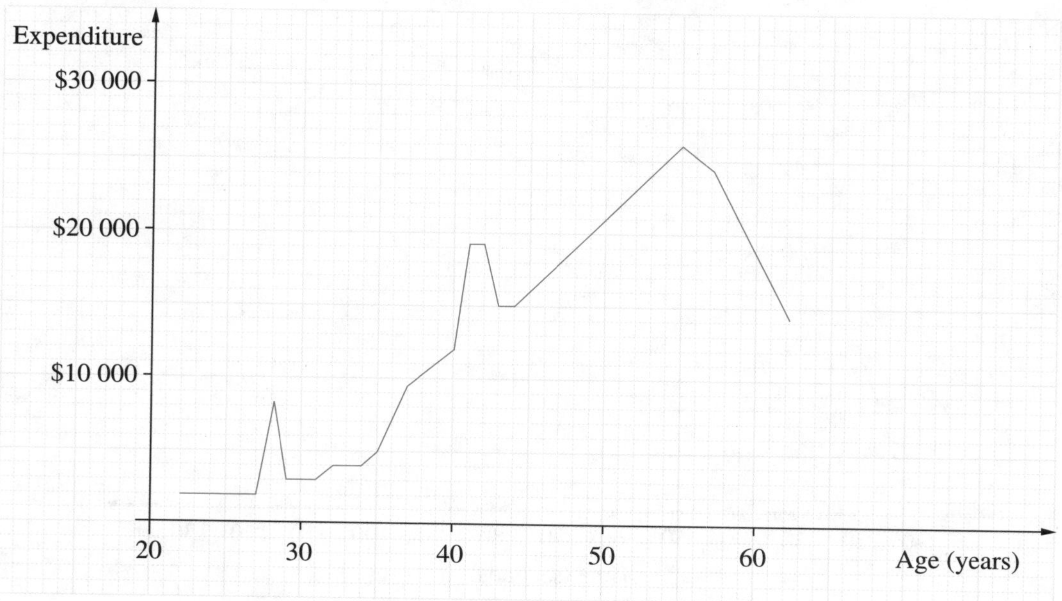

(c) *Number of vehicles passing a certain point along a road in Singapore on a working day*

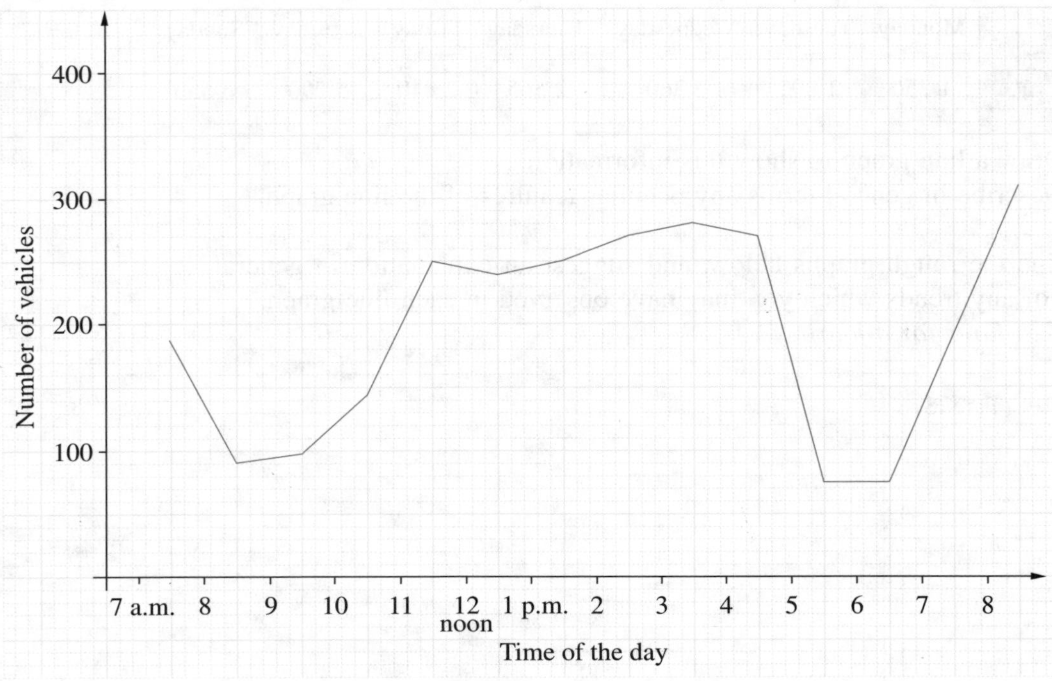

(d) *Time taken to travel in a lift*

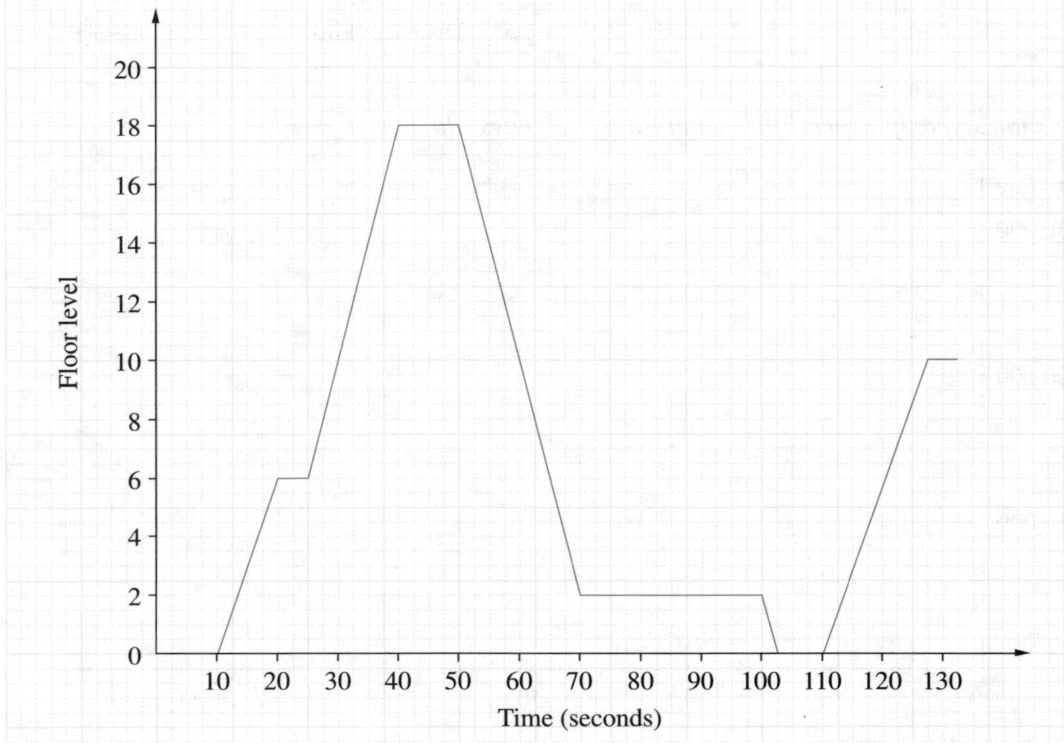

4. The table below shows the number of 'O' level passes obtained by 115 students of a school.

Number of passes	0	1	2	3	4	5	6	7	8
Number of students	5	4	10	12	25	32	18	6	3

Draw a pictogram to illustrate the above data.

5. The table below shows the size of T-shirts worn by a class of Sec 2 students.

Size	Small	Medium	Large	Extra large
Number of students	28	11	2	1

Illustrate these figures using a pictogram.

6. The table below shows the sale of rackets and bats at a shop during a one-month period.

Type of racket or bat	Tennis	Badminton	Squash	Table Tennis
Number sold	120	90	65	54

Represent the above data using a pictogram.

7. The pictogram below is meant to show the sale of hot drinks in a coffee house for a day.

(a) Write in general terms your comments on the pictogram.
(b) If you were asked to improve on it, show how you would draw it.

8. Here are the sketches of four line graphs.

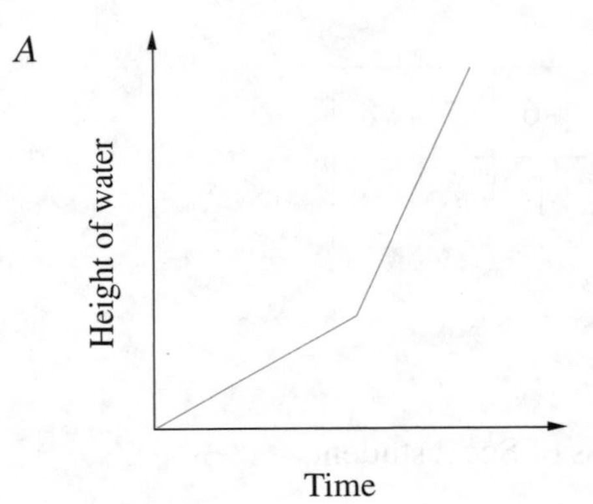

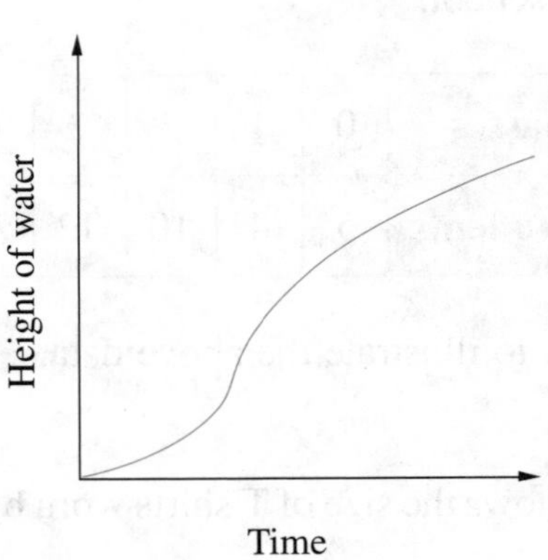

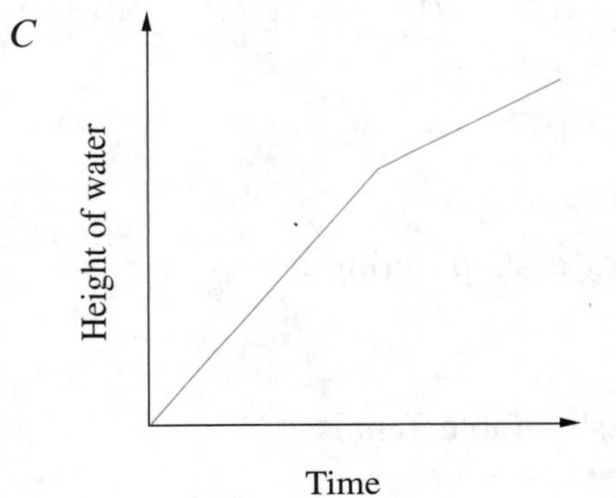

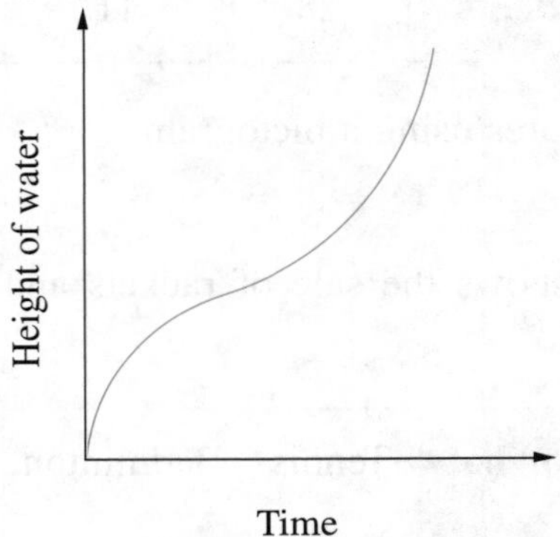

(a) Choose the correct graph to describe the following situation.
Water is added steadily into a tub in which a tin of milk is placed in its upright position. The height of water is recorded at regular time intervals and a height-time graph is plotted.

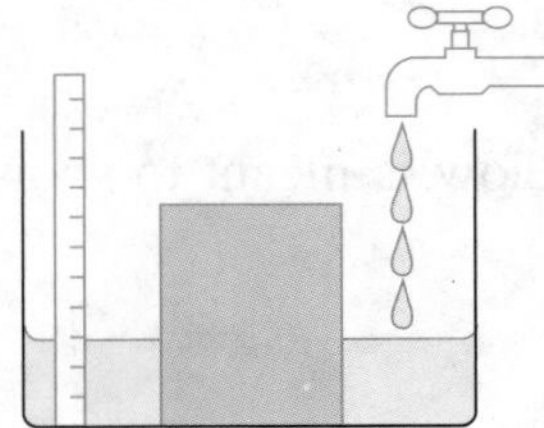

(b) Choose the correct graph to describe the new situation where the tin is made to lie on its side instead of standing upright.

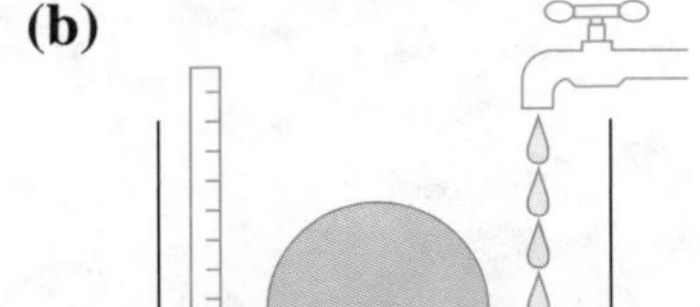

9. **(a)** Water is added steadily to the container on the right and the height of water is recorded at regular time intervals. Sketch a graph to show the height-time relationship for the situation.

(b) Repeat (a) for each of the following containers.

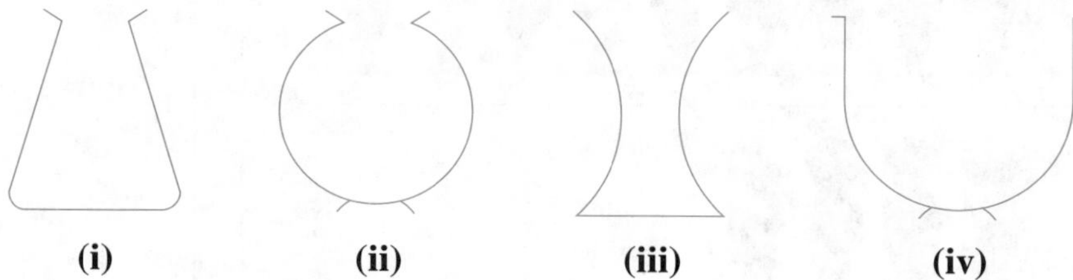

10. **(a)** A conical flask with a piece of plasticine in it is placed in a tub as shown. Water is added steadily into the tub and the height of water is recorded at regular time intervals. Sketch a graph to show the height-time relationship for this situation.

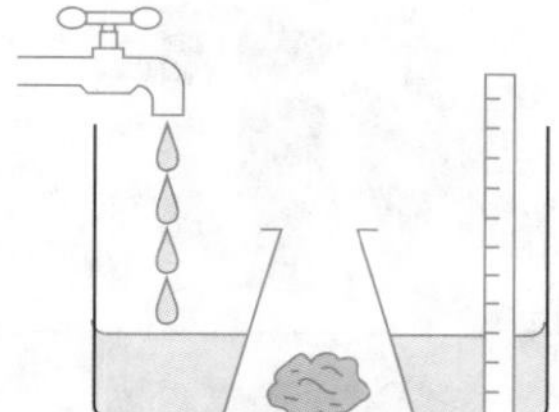

(b) Sketch a graph to show the new situation where a bowl is used to replace the conical flask.

Chapter Review

Presentation of Data

The statistical data collected can be presented in various ways.

Examples:

Tabulation

Game	Soccer	Basketball	Hockey	Chess
Number of boys	180	80	50	50

Pictogram

Number of boys who play the following games

Soccer	
Basketball	
Hockey	
Chess	

Each picture represents 20 boys.

Pie Chart

Proportion of boys who play these games

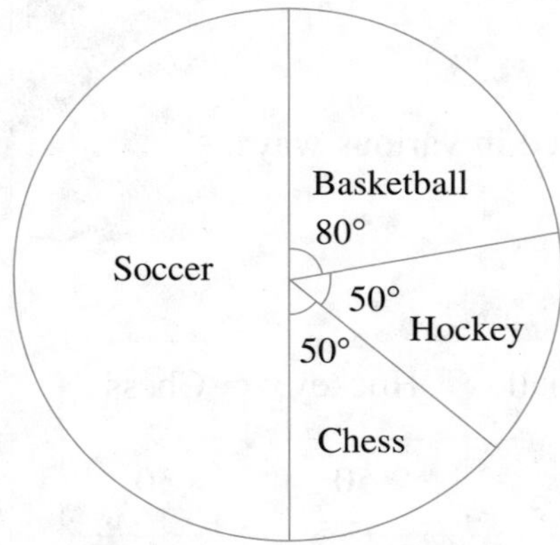

Bar Chart

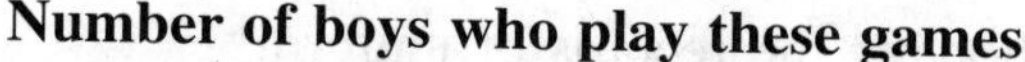

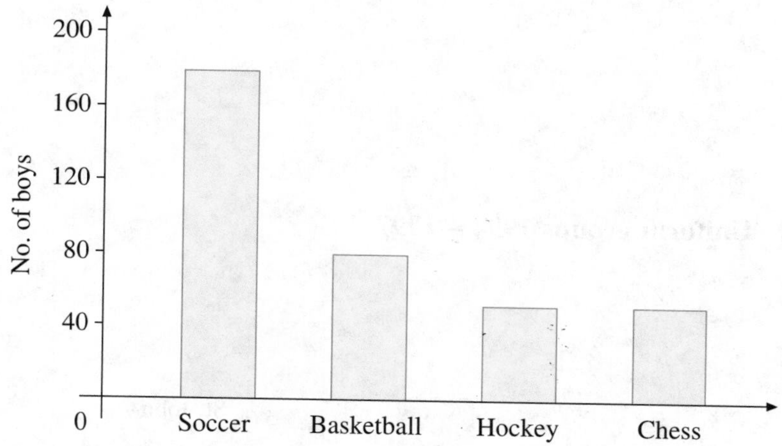

Line Graph

Boys who failed the Physical Fitness Test

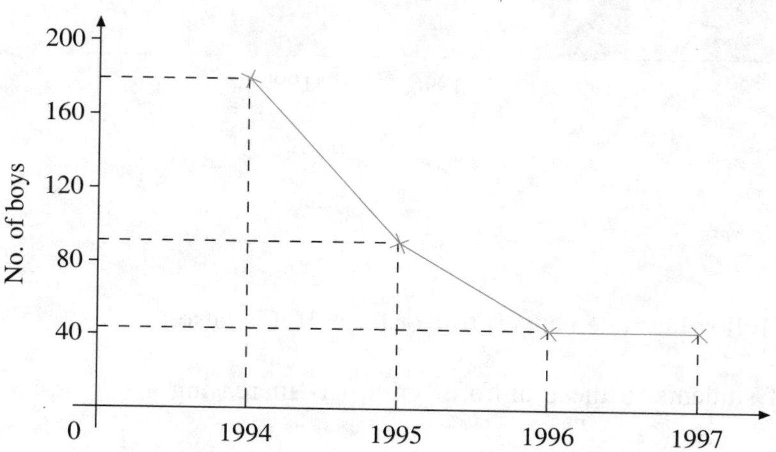

CHALLENGER 12

1. The following is a component bar chart showing the records of uniform groups.

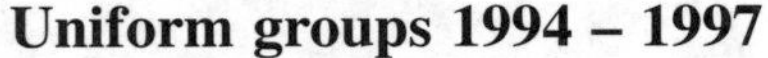

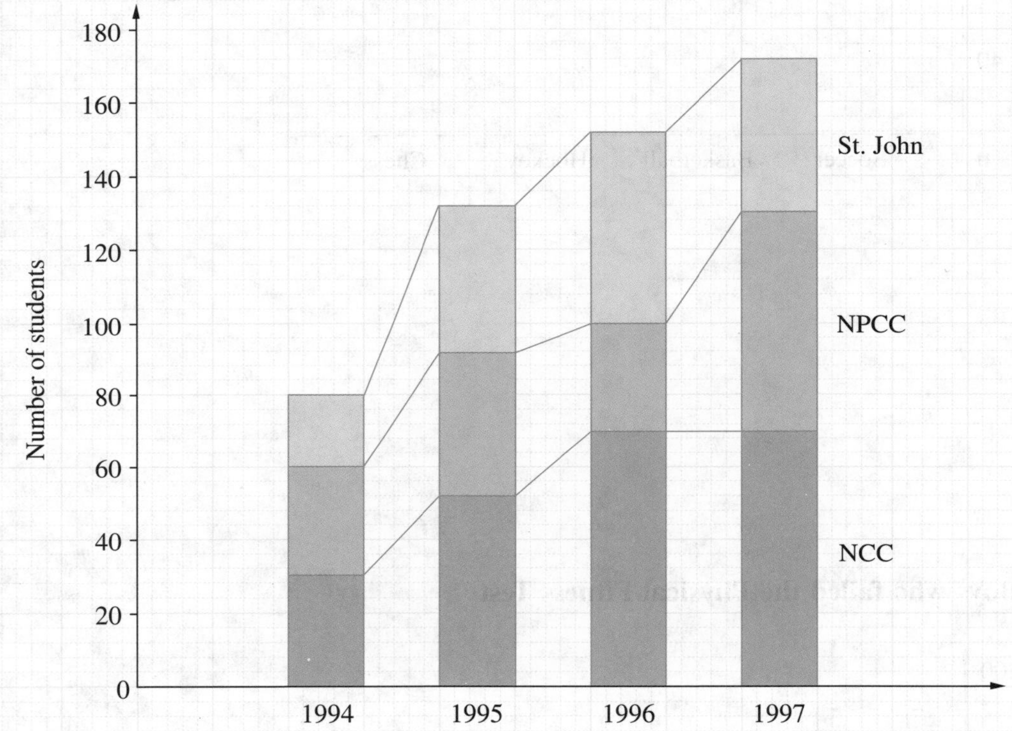

State whether each of the following statements is true or false. If it is false, explain why.

(a) The total number of students in these uniform groups is increasing every year.
(b) The number of students in NPCC is increasing every year.
(c) The number of students in NCC is increasing every year.
(d) The number of students in the St. John is increasing every year.

2. Referring to question 1 above, complete the following table to show the breakdown of club membership for each year on a percentage basis.

	NCC	NPCC	St. John
1994	%	%	%
1995	%	%	%
1996	%	%	%
1997	%	%	%

3. Referring to question 2, draw a component bar chart in percentages (i.e. the vertical axis is in percentages instead of in actual quantities).

4. Referring to question 1, draw a pie chart of radius 6 cm to show the number of students in the three uniform groups for 1997. Draw the corresponding pie chart for 1994 using an appropriate radius so that the total number of students in the uniform groups for these two years may be compared.

5. The pie chart shows how 120 workers are divided into various salary groups.

(a) How many more workers belong to the group '\$2 000 to \$3 000' than the group 'Below \$2 000'?

(b) If $\frac{2}{3}$ of the workers belonging to the group 'Below \$2 000' earn more than \$1 000 a month, how many workers do not earn more than \$1 000 a month?

(c) If 15% of the workers belong to the sector '\$3 001 to \$4 000', how many workers earn more than \$4 000 a month?

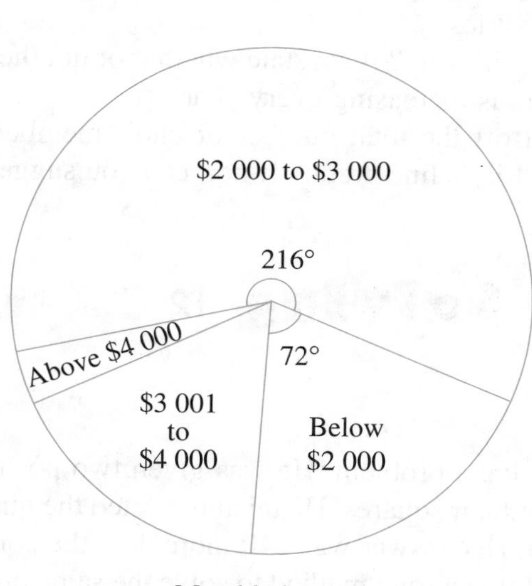

Monthly income

6. The following dual bar chart shows the number of boys and girls in a school choir from 1994 to 1997. Notice that a line graph is drawn in the same diagram.

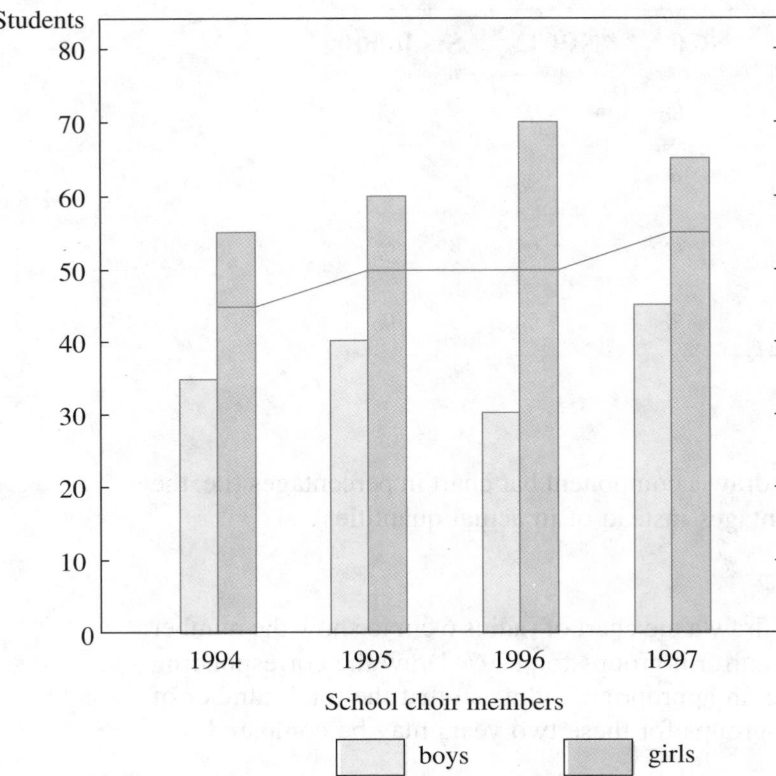

Lily, who added in the line graph, claims that it shows how the total number of choir members varies.

(a) Do you agree with Lily? If so, state whether or not the total number of choir members is increasing every year.

(b) Can you read off the total number of choir members for each year directly from Lily's line graph? If not, can you suggest how this may be done?

Problem Solving 12

Double Mistakes

Samad was asked to solve a problem. He was given two positive integers and asked to find the sum of their squares. He misinterpreted the question and found the square of their sum. His answer was 240 more than the correct answer. His classmate Ali used the same wrong method to solve the same problem but he got the right answer, because he mistakenly wrote one of the given numbers as 2. Do you have enough information to find the two given numbers?

The strategies to use are **use equation** and **guess and check**.

Let us denote the two given numbers as x and y.

Then
$$x^2 + y^2 = (x + y)^2 - 240$$
$$x^2 + y^2 = x^2 + 2xy + y^2 - 240$$
$$\therefore xy = 120 \quad \text{.....................} \quad (1)$$

Also
$$x^2 + y^2 = (x + 2)^2$$
$$\therefore y^2 = 4(x + 1) \quad \text{.....................} \quad (2)$$

Now find x for which $4(x + 1)$ is a square number.
Try $x = 3, 8, 15, \ldots$

Since equations (1) and (2) are satisfied by taking $x = 15$ and $y = 8$.
$\therefore$ the given numbers are 15 and 8.

1. **Two Squares** The perimeter and area of the smaller square are P_1 cm and a_1 cm^2 respectively. The perimeter and area of the bigger square are P_2 cm and a_2 cm^2 respectively. Given that P_1, a_1, P_2 and a_2 are integers and that $P_1 + a_2 = 153$ and $P_2 + a_1 = 108$, find the sides of the two squares.

2. **Possible Routes** A man walks from X to Y. He is allowed to walk along the path in East and North directions only. How many different ways can he take to reach Y from X?

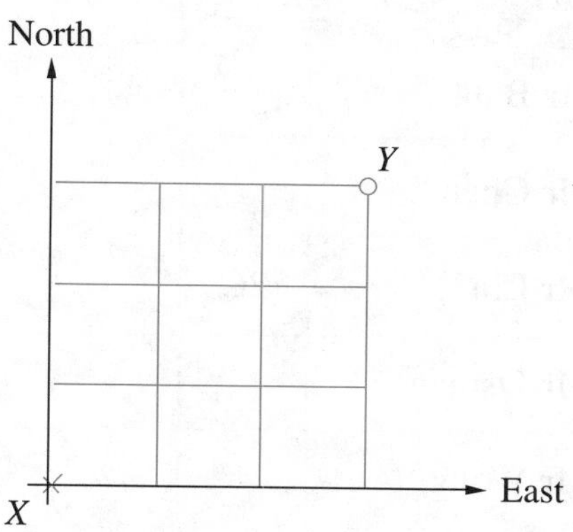

3. **Lucky Number** Chee Keong's lucky number is SIX. To him SIX means LUCK. Can you find a solution for his puzzle below? (There are many solutions. If you are lucky, you may find six.)

$$\begin{array}{r} FIVE \\ +\quad ONE \\ \hline LUCK \\ \hline \end{array}$$

Rules:

- Replace each letter by a digit to make the addition correct.
- Use the same digit for the same letter and different digits for different letters.

4. **Chess Tournament** Ali, the reporter for his school's newsletter, asked five teachers to forecast the results of a chess tournament. The following is the gist of the interview.

Ali : Which one of the five teams, do you think, will be the champion?
Mr Wong : Sec 2B
Mr Lin : Sec 2C
Ali : What about the 2nd place?
Mr Wong : Sec 2E
Mr Lin : Sec 2D
Ali : What about the 3rd place?
Mr Bala : Sec 2A
Mr Chen : Sec 2E
Ali : What about the 4th place?
Mr Bala : Sec 2C
Mr Osman : Sec 2B
Ali : What about the 5th place?
Mr Wong : Sec 2A
Mr Chen : Sec 2D

(a) Complete the following table.

Chess Tournament Forecasts

Teacher \ **Placing**	1st	2nd	3rd	4th	5th
Mr Bala					
Mr Chen					
Mr Lin	2C				
Mr Osman					
Mr Wong					2A

(b) After the tournament, the newsletter reported that each teacher had made at least one correct forecast, but did not publish the tournament results. Do you now have enough information to work out the results by reasoning? If so, complete the table below.

Placing	1st	2nd	3rd	4th	5th
Team					

Chapter 13

Statistics II

Chapter Highlights

- Making frequency tables and reading, interpreting and drawing histograms, including presenting the information from a histogram in the form of a frequency table
- Finding the mean, median and mode of a frequency distribution
- Distinguishing the purpose for which mean, median and mode are used

13.1 FREQUENCY DISTRIBUTION

The following table shows the respective height, body mass, age and daily pocket money of Students *A* to *J*. Each measure is corrected to the nearest unit.

Student	Height in cm	Mass in kg	Age	Pocket money in $
A	130	40	14	7
B	131	42	15	5
C	130	41	16	5
D	132	42	14	5
E	135	44	17	6
F	133	43	15	8
G	130	42	16	5
H	134	42	13	7
I	134	43	14	4
J	131	45	14	7

Table 13.1

If you study the list, you will notice that it contains four sets of numerical data. We shall call these data **scores**. **Frequency** is a term used to indicate the number of times a particular score occurs. The four sets of scores can be presented as **frequency distributions** as follows:

A frequency distribution is a table or graph that shows how often a value or an event occurs.

(a)

Height to the nearest cm	130	131	132	133	134	135
Number of students	3	2	1	1	2	1

Table 13.2(a)

(b)

Mass to the nearest kg	40	41	42	43	44	45
Number of students	1	1	4	2	1	1

Table 13.2(b)

(c)

Age at the last birthday	13	14	15	16	17
Number of students	1	4	2	2	1

Table 13.2(c)

(d)

Pocket money in $	4	5	6	7	8
Number of students	1	4	1	3	1

Table 13.2(d)

Tables such as these are called **frequency tables**. The numbers in the top row of each table represent the scores and the numbers in the bottom row represent the corresponding frequencies.

A frequency table is one which shows all the values obtained in order of size and the frequency of each value.

MATHSTORY

Not only are statistics frequently used, they are also frequently abused. Benjamin Disraeli (1804–1881), an English prime minister, once remarked, 'There are 3 kinds of lies: lies, damned lies and statistics'. People sometimes deliberately use statistics to mislead others. This has been seen in advertising. More often, the misuse of statistics is the result of misinterpreting what the statistics actually mean.

Histogram

We can draw diagrams to represent the frequency tables of the ten students' heights, masses, birthdays and amounts of pocket money. The most appropriate diagrams in such cases are **histograms**.

To draw a histogram to represent a frequency distribution of scores, e.g. students' heights, mark intervals of equal length on a horizontal number line and mark each score in order of size at the centre of each interval. Then, with each interval as base, draw a rectangle whose *area* represents the frequency of the corresponding score.

(a) *Histogram for the heights of the ten students*

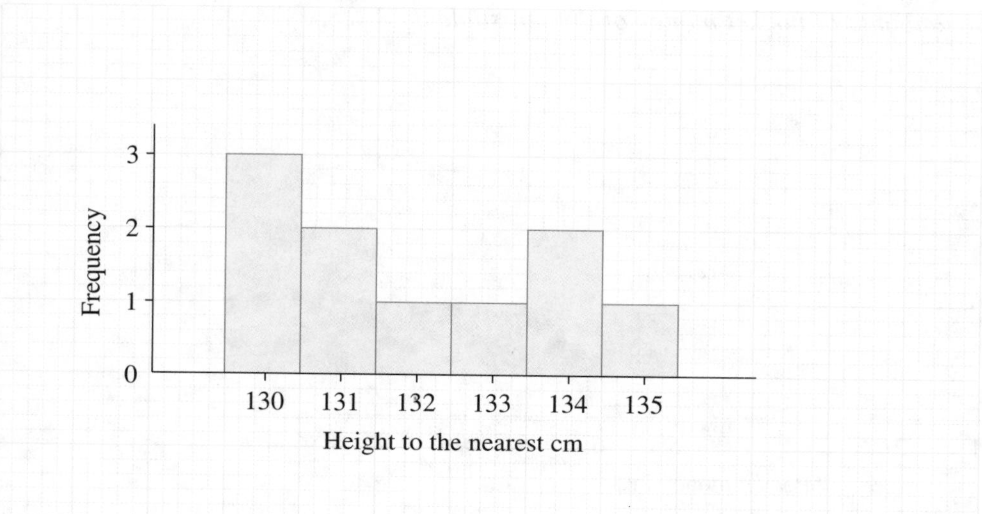

(b) *Histogram for the masses of the ten students*

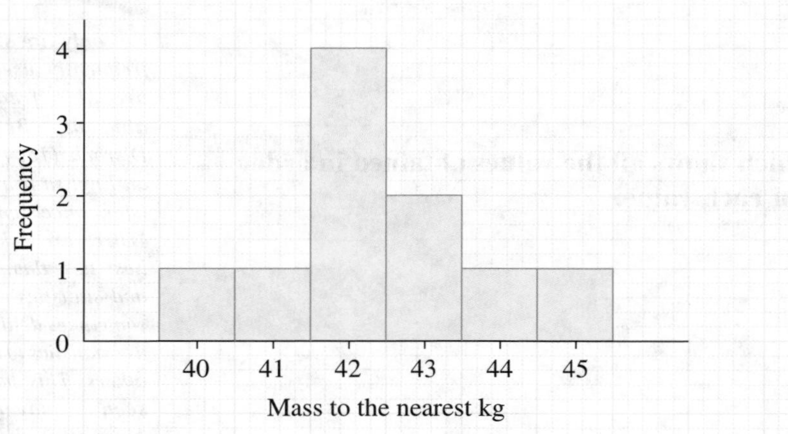

(c) *Histogram for the ages at the last birthday of the ten students*

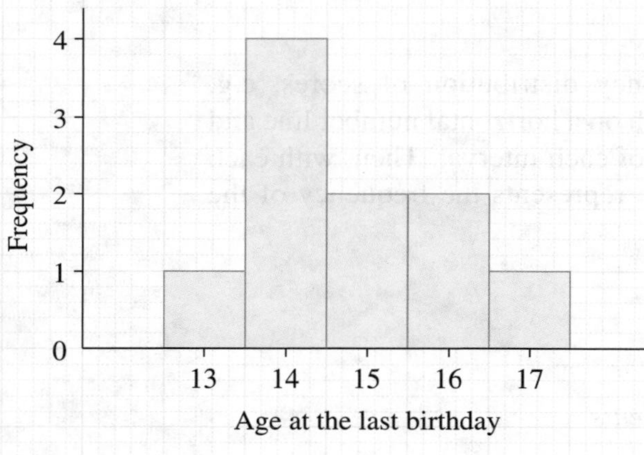

(d) *Histogram for the amounts of pocket money of the ten students*

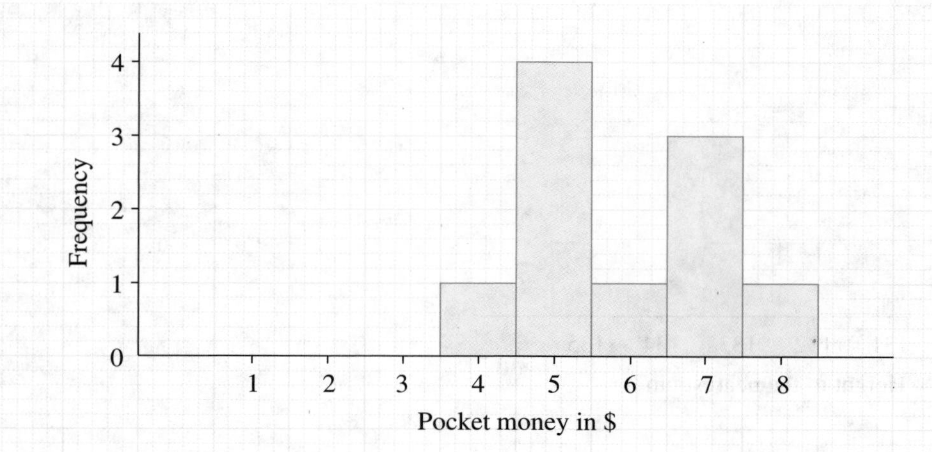

Worked Example

Below are the scores awarded in a test to a class of 40 students.

1	7	6	4	7	5	2	5	2	5
2	1	4	2	1	6	1	4	7	4
3	2	5	1	1	4	1	6	3	3
4	5	2	7	3	3	3	4	4	4

Draw **(a)** a frequency table, **(b)** a histogram for the data.

Solution:

(a)

Marks scored	1	2	3	4	5	6	7
Number of students	7	6	6	9	5	3	4

(b)

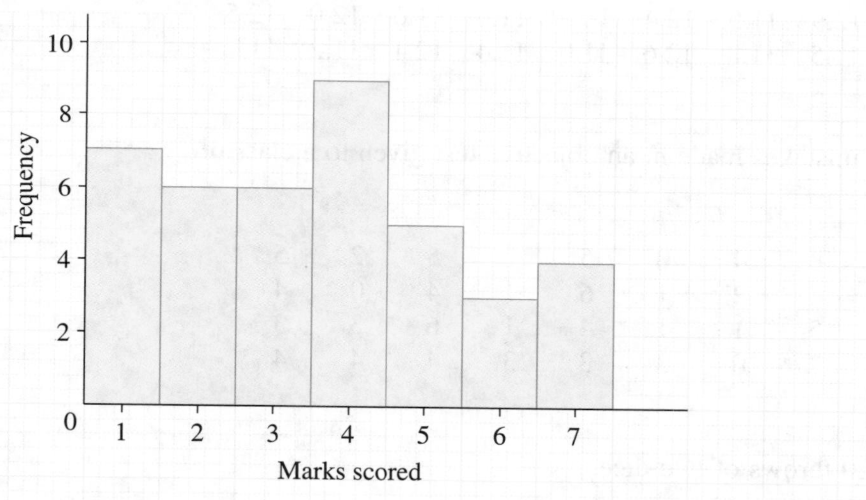

Note: Use tally marks to help you construct the frequency table like this:

Score	Tally marks	Frequency
1	~~////~~ //	7
2	~~////~~ /	6
3	~~////~~ /	6
4	~~////~~ ////	9
5	~~////~~	5
6	///	3
7	////	4

Exercise 13.1

answers on p. 441

1. Construct a frequency table for each of the following sets of data.

(a) The number of correct answers obtained by 40 girls in a Mathematics test.

1	3	2	3	4	5	5	8	9	5
5	1	7	6	3	4	8	10	5	6
6	7	1	6	7	5	8	5	9	5
6	5	7	4	3	8	5	10	10	9

(b) The times clocked by 30 boys during a school athletics heat in the 100-metre race. (Time is recorded in seconds.)

11.2	12.1	12.6	11.2	12.6	11.4	10.8	12.3	11.8	12.8
11.8	10.9	12.9	11.5	12.4	10.9	11.6	11.6	12.0	12.5
10.9	11.9	11.5	11.8	12.6	11.0	11.4	12.1	11.2	11.7

(c) The number of mistakes made in an objective test given to a class of 40 students.

1	0	6	4	0	5	2	5	2	5
2	1	4	2	1	6	1	4	0	4
3	2	5	1	1	4	1	6	3	3
4	5	2	0	3	3	3	4	4	4

(d) The scores of 20 throws of two dice.

2	11	3	5	9	6	8	9	7	5
7	12	6	4	10	8	7	6	8	6

2. Answer these questions by studying the following histogram for the masses of 14 students.

(a) What is the smallest mass?
(b) How many students weigh 58 kg?
(c) What is the most common mass?
(d) How many students weigh
  (i) at least 60 kg,
  (ii) more than 60 kg,
  (iii) less than 60 kg,
  (iv) not more than 60 kg?

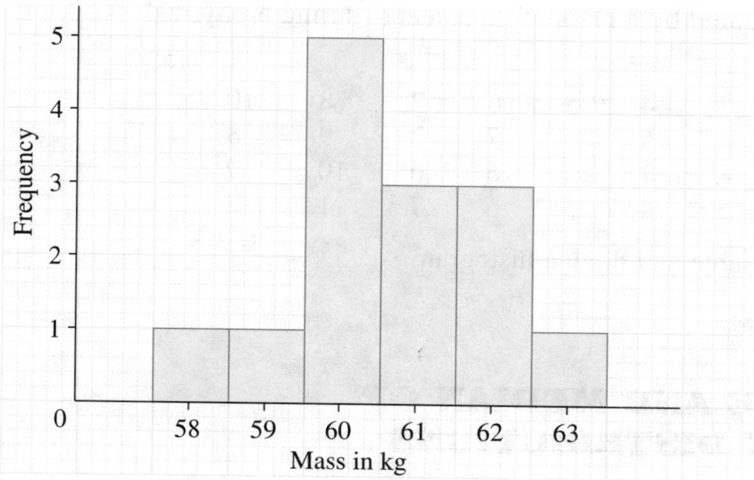

3. The histogram below shows the marks scored by the students in a class test.

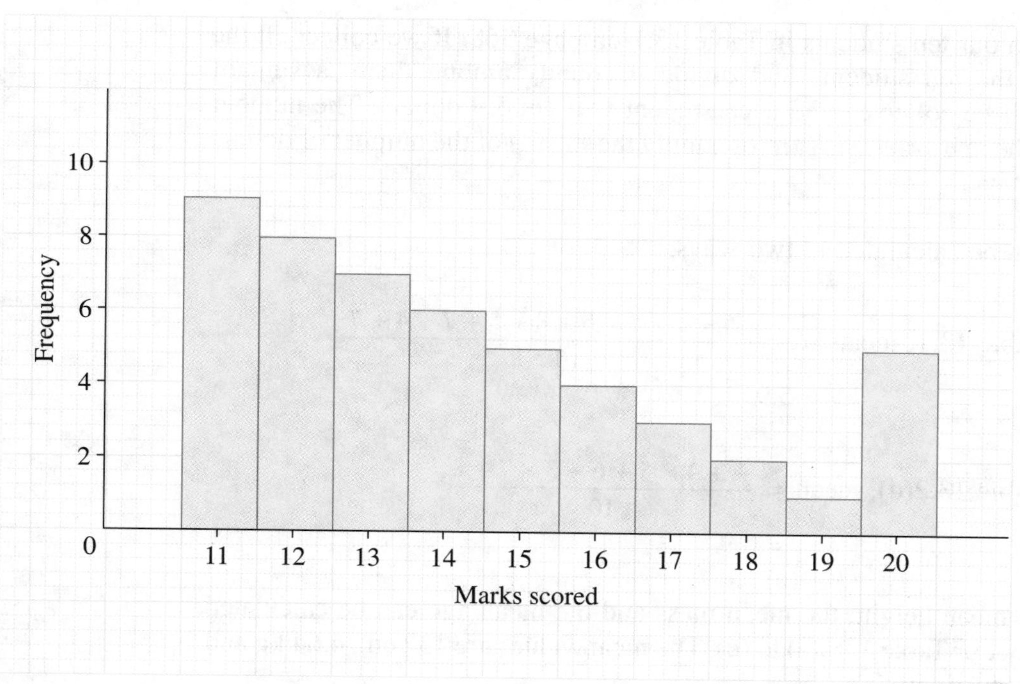

(a) How many students scored 15 marks?
(b) What was the most frequent score?
(c) What was the frequency in (b)?
(d) How many students were there altogether?

4. Here is a list of points scored by a class of 40 students during a physical fitness test.

1	2	2	3	4	5	6	7	8	10
2	4	3	4	5	6	7	7	9	8
3	5	6	6	7	5	6	6	10	9
4	6	5	3	4	5	6	7	1	8

Construct the frequency table and draw a histogram.

13.2 MEAN, MODE AND MEDIAN OF FREQUENCY DISTRIBUTIONS

When all the statistical data have been collected and presented as a frequency distribution, the statistician then starts to analyse the data. An important aspect of data analysis is to find the average score, the middle score or the most frequent score.

Mean

Let us refer to our ten students in Table 13.1 on page 368. If we collect all the money from the ten students and divide it equally among them, a sum of 59 dollars will be collected and each student will get 5.9 dollars. The number 5.9 is called the **arithmetic mean** (or simply the **mean**) of the number of dollars the students have.

The mean can be calculated in two ways.

(a) From Table 13.1, mean $= \dfrac{7 + 5 + 5 + 5 + 6 + 8 + 5 + 7 + 4 + 7}{10}$

$= 5.9$

(b) From Table 13.2(d), mean $= \dfrac{4 + 4 \times 5 + 6 + 3 \times 7 + 8}{10}$

$= 5.9$

Similarly the mean height, the mean mass and the mean age can be calculated from Table 13.1 or Table 13.2(a) to (c). The mean values are 132 cm, 42.4 kg and 14.8 years respectively.

> **The mean of a set of scores is the number obtained by adding the scores and dividing the sum by the total number of scores.**

Mode

Let us look at Table 13.2(a) to (d) again and find out which height, mass, age and amount of pocket money occur most frequently. We observe that 130 cm, 42 kg, 14 years and \$5 occur most frequently in their respective tables.

The score that occurs most often in a distribution is called the mode.

A frequency distribution may have more than one mode.

Example

In histogram *X*, the mode is 3. In histogram *Y*, the modes are 2 and 4.

(a) *Histogram X*

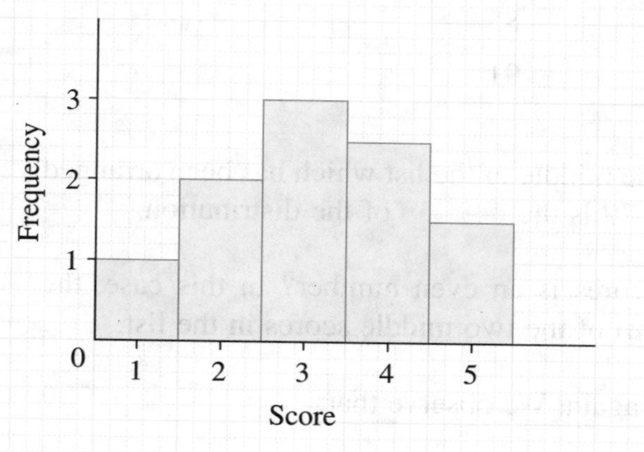

(b) *Histogram Y*

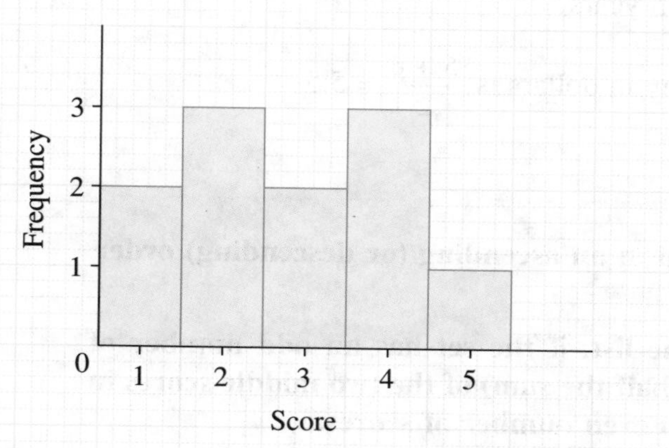

Median

Sometimes we are interested in the middle score of the distribution.

Suppose we list the members of a class in ascending order of the scores they obtained in a test as follows:

Pupils	Test Scores
K	58
L	63
M	64
N	75
O	79
P	82
Q	85
R	85
S	91

We observe that the score 79 is in the middle of the list which has been arranged in an ascending order. We say that 79 is the **median** of the distribution.

What happens if the number of scores is an even number? In this case, the median is the average (half the sum) of the two middle scores in the list.

Let us look at Table 13.2(a) to (d) again. We observe that:

(a) median height is $\frac{131 + 132}{2} = 131.5$ cm

(b) median mass is 42 kg

(c) median age is $\frac{14 + 15}{2} = 14.5$ years

(d) median sum of pocket money in dollars is $\frac{5 + 6}{2} = 5.5$

If a set of scores is arranged in an ascending (or descending) order, the median is defined as:

> **The middle score in the list, if the set has an odd number of scores; or the average (half the sum) of the two middle scores in the list, if the set has an even number of scores.**

Worked Example 1

Find the mean, mode and median of each of the following sets of scores.

(a) 2, 2, 2, 4, 5, 7, 6

(b) 2, 6, 5, 5, 4, 2, 1, 2, 3, 5

Solution:

(a) The mean is $\dfrac{2 + 2 + 2 + 4 + 5 + 7 + 6}{7} = \dfrac{28}{7}$

$= 4$

The mode is 2.

The median is 4.

Note: 2, 2, 2, ④, 5, 6, 7.

(b) The mean is $\dfrac{2 + 6 + 5 + 5 + 4 + 2 + 1 + 2 + 3 + 5}{10} = \dfrac{35}{10}$

$= 3.5$

The modes are 2 and 5.

The median is $\dfrac{3 + 4}{2} = 3.5$

Note: 1, 2, 2, 2, ③, ④, 5, 5, 5, 6.

Worked Example 2

The following frequency table represents the points scored by a group of boys in a game.

Number of points scored	1	2	3	4	5	6
Number of boys	2	4	5	2	3	0

(a) Draw a histogram for the data.

(b) What is the mode of the distribution?

(c) What is the median of the distribution?

(d) How many boys played the game?

(e) What is the mean of the distribution?

Solution:

(a)

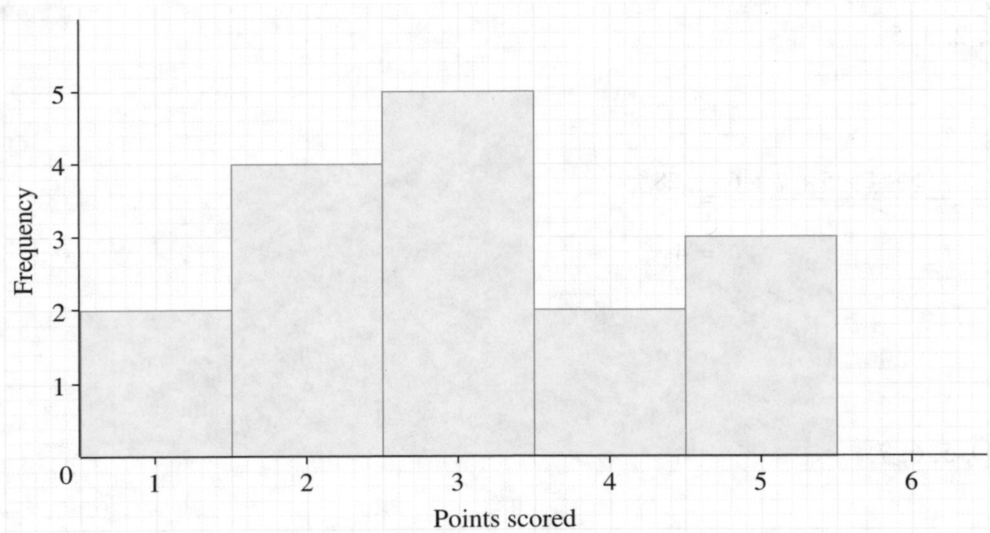

(b) 3 is the mode of the distribution.

(c) 3 is the median of the distribution.

(d) The total number of boys who played the game is 2 + 4 + 5 + 2 + 3 = 16

(e) The mean of the distribution is

$$\frac{(2 \times 1) + (4 \times 2) + (5 \times 3) + (2 \times 4) + (3 \times 5)}{16} = 3$$

Note: For (c), we list the points scored by all the boys like this:

1, 1, 2, 2, 2, 2, 3, ③, ③, 3, 3, 4, 4, 5, 5, 5

and take the average of the two middle scores, which is 3.

Exercise 13.2 

answers on p. 441

1. Find the mean, median and mode of the following sets of scores.

(a)	1	2	2	3	4	5						
(b)	4	4	6	8	9							
(c)	2	6	5	5	5	7						
(d)	2	4	6	8	8	8						
(e)	46	78	97	45	67	99	57	46	65			
(f)	11.1	10.1	9.8	9.7	9.9	11.1	10.2	10.1	9.8	9.6	10.4	9.8

2. Below is a list of grades obtained by a class of 40 students in a Mathematics test.

1	2	2	2	2	2	4	5	5	6
1	2	3	3	3	4	4	5	5	6
1	3	3	3	3	4	4	5	5	6
2	3	3	3	4	4	4	5	6	6

(a) Present the results in a frequency table.
(b) Draw a histogram of the distribution.
(c) What is the mode?
(d) What is the median?
(e) What is the mean?

3. 3 coins were tossed 20 times. The list below shows the number of heads for each toss.

2	3	2	1	3	1	1	0	1	1
3	1	2	2	1	3	0	2	2	2

(a) Present the data in a frequency table.
(b) Draw a histogram of the distribution.
(c) What are the mode and median of the distribution?
(d) Find the mean number of heads per toss.

4. A test is conducted on a sample of 20 gas lighters in order to find out how long each lighter, when filled with gas, would continue to remain lighted. The following data are recorded to the nearest minute.

127	130	127	128	126	128	126	127	125	130
129	128	129	128	132	128	126	125	124	126

(a) Construct a frequency table for the data.
(b) Draw a histogram of the distribution.
(c) What are the mode and median of the distribution?
(d) Find the mean burning life of the gas in the lighters.

5. The beads in 20 boxes were counted. The number of beads in each box is given below.

57	58	61	58	59	62	58	60	58	56
60	61	59	60	60	56	55	61	63	58

(a) Construct a frequency table.
(b) Draw a histogram of the distribution.
(c) What are the mode and median of the distribution?
(d) What is the mean number of beads per box?

6. In an objective test, the students were asked to answer ten questions. The histogram below shows the number of questions attempted by the students.

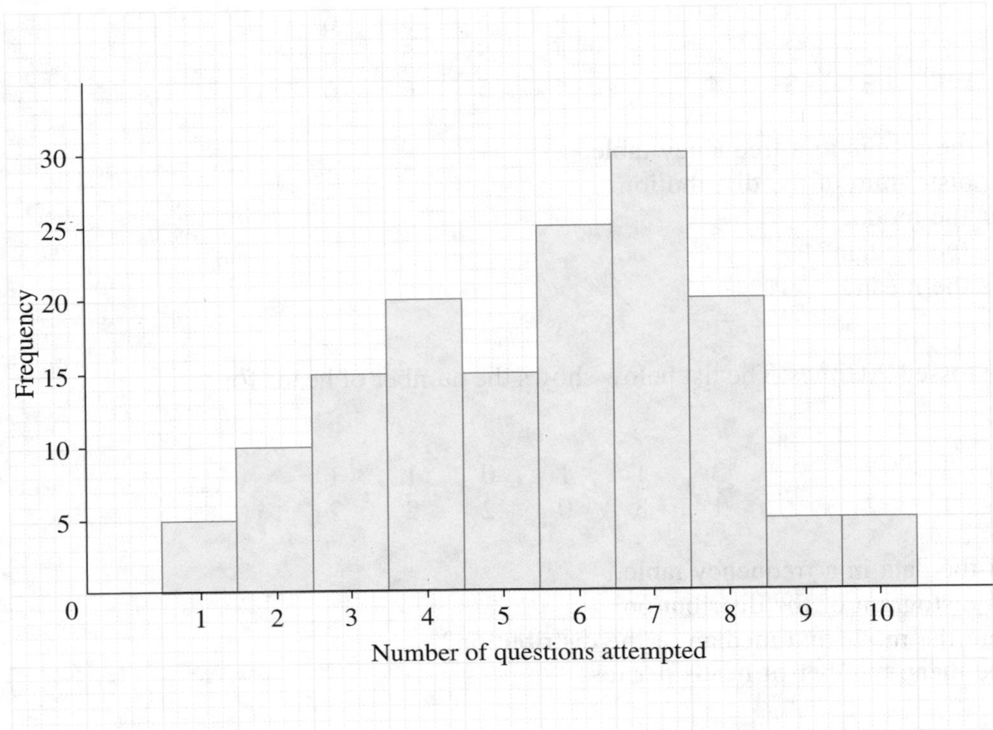

(a) Present this information in a frequency table.

(b) **(i)** How many students attempted 6 questions or less?

(ii) How many students attempted 8 questions or more?

(iii) How many students attempted exactly 7 questions?

(c) How many students took the test?

(d) Find the mean, mode and median of the number of questions attempted.

7. Two dice were thrown together and the two numbers were added together to arrive at a score. This was repeated for 30 throws. The results are given below.

Score	2	3	4	5	6	7	8	9	10	11	12
Frequency	1	1	0	4	7	8	5	2	1	1	0

(a) Draw a histogram of the distribution.

(b) What are the mode and median of the distribution?

(c) What is the mean score?

8. Every member of a group of women was asked how many children she had. The bar chart illustrates the results of this survey.

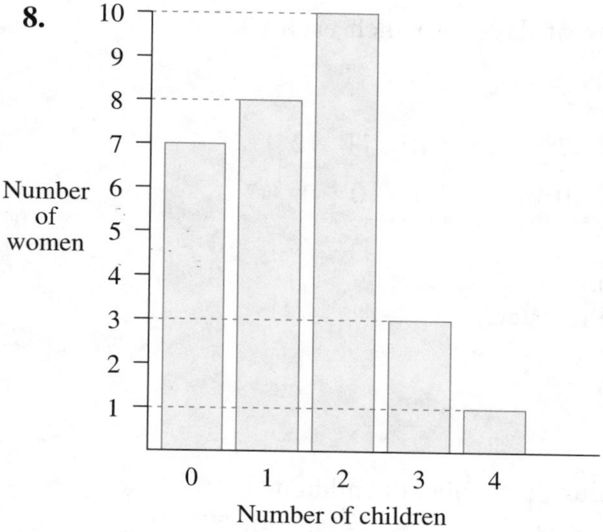

Find

(a) the number of women in the group,

(b) the modal number of children,

(c) the median number of children. *(C)*

9. The bar chart shows the number of telephone calls made by a businessman on each day of a week.

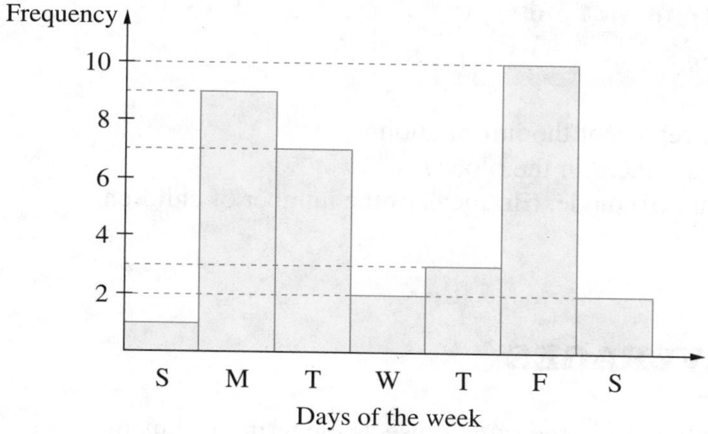

(a) Calculate the total number of calls made during the week.

(b) On which day was the modal number of calls made?

(c) Calculate the mean number of calls made per day during the week. Give your answer correct to one decimal place. *(C)*

10.

Number of points scored	1	2	3	4	5	6
Number of students	0	5	1	2	4	3

The frequency table above represents the points scored by a group of students in a physical fitness test.

(a) Draw a histogram to represent the data.

(b) **(i)** What is the median? **(ii)** What is the mode?

(c) Find the mean score of the students in the physical fitness test.

11. A class register was taken to check the number of days on which each student was absent in a year.

Number of days	0	1	2	3	4	5	6	7	8	9	10	11	12
Number of students	25	6	1	2	1	1	2	0	0	0	1	0	1

(a) Present the data in the form of a histogram.
(b) What is the total number of students in the register?
(c) **(i)** What is the mode of the distribution?
(ii) What is the median of the distribution?
(iii) What is the mean of the distribution?

12. A survey on 50 families in a block of flats regarding the number of children in each family is recorded here.

Number of children in the family	0	1	2	3	4	5
Number of families	1	10	12	5	16	6

(a) Draw a histogram to represent the information.
(b) How many children are there in the block?
(c) What is the **(i)** median, **(ii)** mode, **(iii)** mean of the number of children in a family?

13.3 TYPES OF AVERAGES

The term 'average' is commonly used in the same sense as the term 'arithmetic mean'. In statistics however, the arithmetic mean is one type of averages. The median and the mode are other types of averages. Thus, it is necessary to state quite clearly which type of average we are referring to.

Often, an average is chosen as a typical value for some purpose as the following problems show.

Class Activity

1. Suppose a tailor was asked to make sports caps for a class of 28 students, and the head measurements were given as follows:

Measurement in cm	54	54.5	55	55.5	56	56.5	57	57.5
Frequency	1	1	2	8	5	5	3	3

(a) What is the mean head measurement of these students?
(b) Suppose only one size is to be made. Would the tailor choose the mean?
(c) What is the modal head measurement?
(d) Will the mode represent the group better? Why?
(e) When we say the 'average' student wears a certain size, are we referring to the mode or the mean?

2. The monthly salaries earned by the employees of a small firm are as follows:

2 executive officers earn	$850 each
2 clerks earn	$700 each
4 typists earn	$650 each
1 office boy earns	$600

(a) What is the mean salary paid by the firm?
(b) Is the mean a good 'representative' of the data on salaries for this firm?
(c) If the money available for salaries was evenly distributed, how much would each employee of the firm get?

3. Suppose the firm mentioned in question 2 above employs a manager and pays him $2 000.
(a) What is the mean salary of the employees then?
(b) Is the mean affected by the value $2 000?
(c) Is the mean salary a good 'representative' of the earnings of these employees?
(d) What is the median salary?
(e) Does the median give a better indication of the average salary of these employees?
(f) What is the mode of the salaries?
(g) A unionist says that the 'average' salary of the employees is $650. For what purpose is $650 chosen as a representative salary? (*Note:* Ask your teacher to explain the responsibilities of a unionist.)

Exercise 13.3

answers on p. 441

1. Tony went into a shop. He noted that there were 6 pairs of BR shoes and their prices were $10, $56.80, $58, $58, $58 and $58.80.
(a) What type of averages did Tony think was used in the poster before entering the shop?
(b) What type of averages did the shopkeeper actually use for his poster?

Renovation SALE!

BR Shoes
Average Price
Less Than
$50

(c) Did the shopkeeper lie? Was his poster misleading? Write down what you think.
(d) Tony did not buy any shoes from the shop. Was he short of money? What do you think?

2. The salaries of 7 employees of a firm are as follows:

$2 100, $2 400, $2 550, $2 600, $2 800, $2 850, $3 000

The employer gives each employee a raise and their respective new salaries are:

$ 2 200, $2 520, $2 700, $2 860, $2 920, $3 000, $3 200

The employer claims that his employees' salaries have been given an average increase of 10%.

(a) Which type of average is used by the employer when he makes his claim?
(b) What is the actual percentage increase of the total salaries?
(c) What is the actual percentage increase of the mean salary?

3. Which statistical averages (mean, mode or median) are being referred to in the following questions about daily pocket allowance.
For each question, if your answer involves more than one of the averages, rank them from 'most likely' to 'least likely'.

(a) The average pocket money of the students in class A is $3.47.
(b) The average student in class B has $5.00 pocket money.
(c) The average student in class C has pocket money exceeding $3.00.
(d) On the average, Samy has $4.00 pocket allowance.
(e) One half of the students in class D each has more than $3.00 pocket money.
(f) Peter has $4.00 pocket money; this is the average pocket money for his class.

Chapter Review

1. A **frequency table** is one which shows all the values obtained in order of size and the frequency of each value.

Example:

Points scored	1	2	3	4	5
Number of students	1	4	2	2	1

2. A **histogram** is used to represent a frequency table.

Example: From (1)

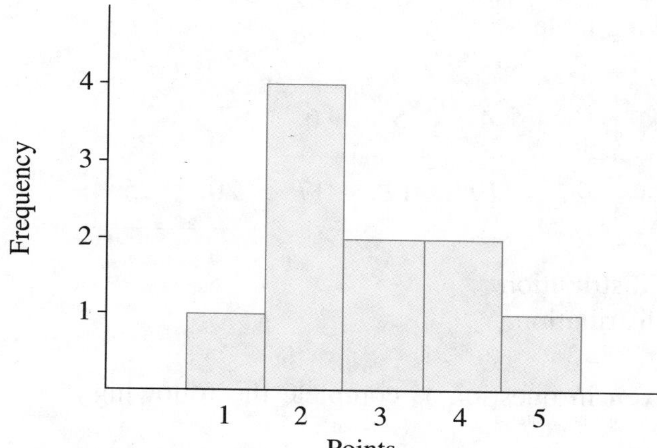

3. The **mean** of a set of scores is the number obtained by adding the scores and dividing the sum by the total number of scores.

Example: From (1)

$$\frac{(1 \times 1) + (4 \times 2) + (2 \times 3) + (2 \times 4) + (1 \times 5)}{10} = \frac{28}{10}$$
$$= 2.8$$

The mean number of points is 2.8. The mean may not always be a whole number.

4. The **mode** is the score that occurs most often in a distribution.

Example: From (1)
The mode of the distribution is 2.

A frequency distribution may have more than one mode.

5. If a set of scores is arranged in an ascending (or descending) order, the **median** is defined as
(i) the middle score in the list, if the set has an odd number of scores,
(ii) the average (half the sum) of the two middle scores in the list, if the set has an even number of scores.

Example: From (1)

$$\frac{2 + 3}{2} = 2.5$$

The median of the distribution is 2.5.

CHALLENGER 13

1. The distribution of the number of 'O' level passes gained by a group of 120 students is shown in the following table.

Number of 'O' level passes	3	4	5	6	7	8
Number of students	27	19	12	17	20	25

(a) Draw a histogram for the distribution.
(b) Draw a pie chart for the distribution.

2. (a) Using the information given in question 1, complete the following table.

Number of 'O' level passes	Number of students
3	
4 to 5	
6 and above	

(b) Draw a pie chart to illustrate the information given in the table in (a).
(c) Draw a histogram to illustrate the information given in the table in (a).
(d) Which feature of the information is more apparent on the pie chart than on the histogram?

3. Compare the two histograms in question 1 and question 2. Describe briefly in what way they are alike and in what way they are different.

4. A survey of weekly pocket money received by 30 students in a class revealed that exactly one third received less than \$10 and exactly one third received \$30 or more. Assuming that each student received less than \$40, draw a histogram to illustrate this information.

5. (a) The mean of three numbers a, b and c is 7 and the mean of five numbers a, b, c, d and e is 13. Find the mean of d and e.

(b) Find, without using the calculator, the mean of $1\frac{1}{6}$, $1\frac{1}{2}$, $2\frac{1}{3}$, $3\frac{1}{4}$, $3\frac{2}{3}$, $-2\frac{1}{2}$, $-5\frac{1}{4}$ and $-\frac{1}{6}$.

6. 11 students took a test consisting of only 5 questions. The frequency distribution of the number of questions correctly answered had a mode of 3, a median of 4 and a mean of 3.6.

(a) Do you have enough information to complete the following table? If so, complete it.

Number of correct answers	0	1	2	3	4	5
Number of students						

(b) Is there more than one possible answer for (a)? If so, give the other answer(s).

Problem Solving 13

Soccer League Cards

John and Peter had 32 Soccer League cards each. They were admiring each other's cards. They then decided to play a game with their cards. The rules are as follows:

- They would play four games.
- They would put all the 64 cards on the table and would not keep any cards until all four games are played.
- After each game, the loser would give half of what he has to the winner.

Although they each won two games and lost two games, John found that he lost 6 cards to Peter. Explain why.

The strategies to use are **use tabulation** and **guess and check**.

Games	John's results/Number of John's cards		
	Case (1)	Case (2)	Case (3)
1st	won/48	won/48	lost/16
2nd	won/56	lost/24	won/40
3rd	lost/28	won/44	won/52
4th	lost/14	lost/22	lost/26

So John lost 6 cards as in Case (3).

Note: Under the same condition that 'they each won two games and lost two games', there should be 3 more cases in which Peter lost cards to John.

1. **Mother and Daughter** When Mary's age was x years, her mother's age was 13 years more than twice her age. Mary's age is now $2x$ years. Find an expression for her mother's present age. If the mother is twice as old as the daughter now, find the daughter's present age.

2. **Two Squares** The figure is made up of two squares whose areas are in the ratio 4 : 1. If the shaded area is x cm^2 and its perimeter is x cm, find the value of x.

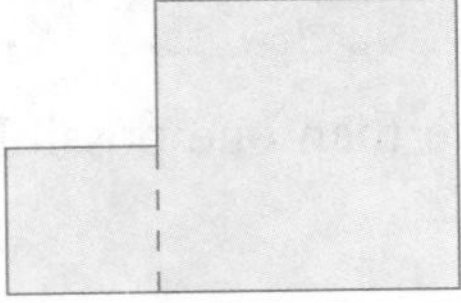

3. **Winning Strategies** Two players play a game of 'picking rubber bands'. Some rubber bands are placed on a table. Each player takes turns to pick up either 1 or 2 rubber bands at a time. The player who picks up the last lot wins the game. Play this game with a friend using 40 rubber bands. How can you win the game if you are given the chance to start first?

4.

Soccer	Matches			Goals	
	Won	Drawn	Lost	For	Against
Team A	2	0	0	7	2
Team B	1	0	1	3	5
Team C	0	0	2	2	5

The above table shows some data for three soccer matches played between teams A, B and C.

Using the above information, complete the table given below.

Soccer Teams	Goals scored by		
	A	B	C
A vs B			*
A vs C		*	
B vs C	*		

Chapter 14

More Algebraic Manipulations

THE GREAT MANIPULATOR (PART II)
Hey! Big Bro! Since you're so good at manipulating algebraic expressions, can you help me with this one?
NEW PAPER
Sure, little Bro! But this time it's going to cost you money.
Man, he really knows how to manipulate.

Chapter Highlights

- Identifying like terms in a polynomial, including stating the degree of an algebraic term
- Adding and subtracting polynomials
- Multiplying polynomials, including simplifying expressions involving multiplication addition and subtraction of polynomials
- Dividing polynomials
- Distinguishing between equations and identities
- Finding unknown coefficients of terms and constant terms in identities
- Expressing one variable of an algebraic expression in terms of another variable, including forming an algebraic expression from two given expressions by elimination of one variable

14.1 ADDITION AND SUBTRACTION OF POLYNOMIALS

Expressions such as $x^3 - 2x^2 + 7x - 12$ are known as **polynomials**. Each term of a polynomial has a **degree** which is the index of the variable of the term. For example in $x^3 - 2x^2 + 7x - 12$,

A polynomial is an expression made up of more than one algebraic term.

x^3 has degree 3,
$-2x^2$ has degree 2,
$7x$ has degree 1,
-12 is a constant and is said to have degree 0.

The degree of a polynomial is the highest degree of all its terms. In this example, the degree of the polynomial is 3. A polynomial is usually arranged in descending order but it can also be arranged in ascending order. For example,

$$-12 + 7x - 2x^2 + x^3.$$

Worked Example 1
Add $(3x^4 - 2x^3 + 2x^2 + 1)$ to $(x^3 - 2x^2 + 7x - 12)$.

Solution:

$$\begin{aligned}(x^3 - 2x^2 + 7x - 12) + (3x^4 - 2x^3 + 2x^2 + 1) &= x^3 - 2x^2 + 7x - 12 + 3x^4 - 2x^3 + 2x^2 + 1 \\ &= 3x^4 - x^3 + 7x - 11\end{aligned}$$

Alternative solution:

$$\begin{array}{rrrrrr} & & x^3 & -2x^2 & +7x & -12 \\ + & 3x^4 & -2x^3 & +2x^2 & & +1 \\ \hline & 3x^4 & -x^3 & & +7x & -11 \\ \hline \end{array}$$

$\therefore$ the answer is $3x^4 - x^3 + 7x - 11$.

Worked Example 2
Subtract $(7x^4 - 3x^2 + 5x - 5)$ from $(x^3 - 3x^2 + 5x)$.

Solution:

$$\begin{aligned}(x^3 - 3x^2 + 5x) - (7x^4 - 3x^2 + 5x - 5) &= x^3 - 3x^2 + 5x - 7x^4 + 3x^2 - 5x + 5 \\ &= -7x^4 + x^3 + 5\end{aligned}$$

Alternative solution:

$$\begin{array}{rrrrrr} & & x^3 & -3x^2 & +5x & \\ + & -7x^4 & & +3x^2 & -5x & +5 \\ \hline & -7x^4 & +x^3 & & & +5 \\ \hline \end{array}$$

$\therefore$ the answer is $-7x^4 + x^3 + 5$.

Note: Instead of doing subtraction, we change the sign of each term of $7x^4 - 3x^2 + 5x - 5$ and do addition.

Exercise 14.1 

answers on p. 442

1. Write down the degree of each of the following terms.
   (a) $3x^2$ (b) $-5x^3$ (c) $8x$
   (d) $-9x^6$ (e) 12 (f) -12

2. Pick out the 'like' terms in each of the following polynomials.
   (a) $x^2 + xyz + x^2 + xyv$
   (b) $a^3 + b^2a + 2a^3 + 3b^2a^2$
   (c) $3xy + 7x^2y + xy + 2xy^2$
   (d) $7x^4y^5z^3 + (-2)x^3y^3z^3 + x^4y^5z^3 + x^2y^2z^2$
   (e) $ab^3c^2 + a^2bc^3 + a^3b^2c + (-1)ab^3c^2$
   (f) $4^2xy^2 + 3x^2y + 3^3x^2y^2 + 4^3x^2y^2$
   (g) $2^3a^2b + 2^4a^2b + 2^5a^2b + 2^4ab^2$

3. (a) Add $(x^3 - 5x^2 + 3x - 8)$ to $(x^4 + 2x^3 + x^2 - 4x + 5)$.
   (b) Add $(x^4 + 4x - 3)$ to $(x^5 + 8x^3 + 4)$.
   (c) Subtract $(x^5 - 3x^4 + 2x^3 - x - 1)$ from $(2x^5 + 8x^2 + 5)$.
   (d) Subtract $(2x^5 - 2x^4 + 7x^3 + 5)$ from $(x^6 + 5x^4 + 8x^3 - 1)$.

4. Rewrite each of the following polynomials in its simplest form.
   (a) $(3x^2 + 7x) + (2x^2 - 8x)$
   (b) $(-2p + 4q) - (p - 7q)$
   (c) $(3x - 2y + 5z) + (7x - 3z) + (-2y + 7z)$
   (d) $(2d^3 - 6d^2 + 3d - 3) - (-d^2 + 6d - 2)$
   (e) $(3x^2 - 5xy + 7y^2) + (2xy - 5y^2 - x^2)$
   (f) $(n^2 - 6n^3 - n + 2) - (10n^3 + n + 2 - n^2)$
   (g) $(2x + 3y) - (5x - 2y) + (3x - 7y)$
   (h) $-6(1 - x + x^2) + 4(x^2 - 2x + 5)$

5. What polynomial must be added to $(3a^2 - a)$ to give $(4a - 3)$?

6. From what polynomial must $(3x^2 - 2x + 1)$ be subtracted to give $(x + x^2)$?

7. Subtract the sum of $(3x^2 - 2xy + 3y^2)$ and $(-5x^2 + 4xy - 2y^2)$ from $(3x^2 + 7xy - 2y^2)$.

8. From the sum of $(2a^2 + 3a - 1)$ and $(-5a^2 - 3)$, subtract the sum of $(3a^2 + 3a + 4)$ and $(4a + 5)$.

14.2 MULTIPLICATION OF POLYNOMIALS

Worked Example

Multiply:

(a) $4x^2 - 2x + 1$ by $3x^2$

(b) $3x^2 - 2x - 4$ by $5x + 3$

(c) $3x^3 - x + 2$ by $x - 4$

Solution:

(a)
$$\begin{aligned} 3x^2(4x^2 - 2x + 1) &= (3x^2)(4x^2) + (3x^2)(-2x) + (3x^2)(1) \\ &= 12x^4 + (-6x^3) + 3x^2 \\ &= 12x^4 - 6x^3 + 3x^2 \end{aligned}$$

(b)
$$\begin{aligned} (5x + 3)(3x^2 - 2x - 4) &= 5x(3x^2 - 2x - 4) + (3)(3x^2 - 2x - 4) \\ &= 15x^3 - 10x^2 - 20x + 9x^2 - 6x - 12 \\ &= 15x^3 - x^2 - 26x - 12 \end{aligned}$$

Note: Multiplication of polynomials is the same as expansion of the product of polynomials.

Alternative method:

$$\begin{array}{lcrrrr} & & & 3x^2 & -\ 2x & -\ 4 \\ & & \times & & 5x\ + & 3 \\ \hline 3(3x^2 - 2x - 4) & \longrightarrow & & 9x^2 & -\ 6x & -\ 12 \\ 5x(3x^2 - 2x - 4) & \longrightarrow & 15x^3 & -\ 10x^2 & -\ 20x & \\ \hline (5x + 3)(3x^2 - 2x - 4) & \longrightarrow & 15x^3 & -\ x^2 & -\ 26x & -\ 12 \\ \hline \end{array}$$

(c)
$$\begin{array}{rrrrr} & 3x^3 & & -\ x & +\ 2 \\ \times & & & x & -\ 4 \\ \hline & -\ 12x^3 & & +\ 4x & -\ 8 \\ 3x^4 & & -\ x^2 & +\ 2x & \\ \hline 3x^4 & -\ 12x^3 & -\ x^2 & +\ 6x & -\ 8 \\ \hline \end{array}$$

$\therefore (3x^3 - x + 2)(x - 4) = 3x^4 - 12x^3 - x^2 + 6x - 8$

Note: In the first line, a blank space between $3x^3$ and $-x$ is left for the term $0x^2$, but since $0x^2 = 0$, it is usually omitted.

From the preceding examples, we should be able to conclude that to multiply two polynomials, we multiply each term of one of the polynomials by each term of the other, and simplify the results.

Exercise 14.2 

answers on p. 442

1. Multiply:

(a) $7a^2 + 1$ by $3a^2$
(b) $2d^2 + 3d - 1$ by (-5)
(c) $b^2 - b - 4$ by $(-2b)$
(d) $y^5 - y^3 + 1$ by y^3
(e) $7 - n + 2n^3$ by $(-n^5)$
(f) $3 - 2t - t^5$ by t^2

2. Expand the following. Show your working either in a horizontal or in a vertical arrangement.

(a) $2x(x^5 + 2x + 3)$
(b) $(3x + 2)(2x - 3)$
(c) $(5m - n)(3m + 2n)$
(d) $(x^2 + x + 2)(x - 3)$
(e) $(a^2 - 2a + 4)(a + 3)$
(f) $(2x^2 + 3x + 1)(-2x^3 + 2)$
(g) $(5a^2 + 3a - 2)(2a^2 - 3a + 1)$
(h) $(-3m^2 - 4)(2m^2 + m + 1)$
(i) $(7n^5 - 2n^4 + 3n^2 - 1)(3n^3 - n + 2)$
(j) $(3x^2 - 2x + 7)(-x^3 + x - 2)$

3. Simplify the following expressions.

(a) $(x - 1)(x^2 + 2x + 2) + (3x^2 - 1)(2x^2 - 4x + 3)$
(b) $(a + b)^2 - (a - b)^2$
(c) $(8y^4 + 3y^3 - y^2 + 1)(y - 3) - (4y^3 + 4)(y^2 - 1)$
(d) $(4x^3 - 2x^2 + x - 1)(2x + 1) + (x^3 - 1)(x^2 - x + 1)$
(e) $(x - 1)(x^4 + x - 1) - (x^3 + 1)(x^2 - 2x + 3)$
(f) $(x^4 - x + 1)(x^2 + 1) + x^2(x - 1)(2x + 1)$

14.3 DIVISION OF POLYNOMIALS (OPTIONAL)

Examples

(a) Consider the division of 19 by 5.

```
                     3   →  Quotient
Divisor  ←   5 ) 19   →  Dividend
                    15
                    ——
                     4   →  Remainder
```

The dividend, divisor, quotient and the remainder are related as follows:

$$19 = 5 \times 3 + 4$$

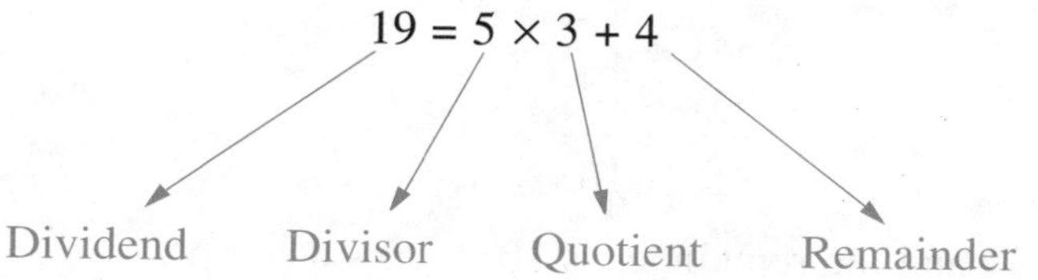

(b) Consider the division of $2x^3 + x^2 - x - 4$ by $x - 2$.

$$
\begin{array}{rrl}
 & 2x^2 + 5x + 9 & \rightarrow \text{Quotient} \\
\text{Divisor} \leftarrow \; x - 2 \,) & 2x^3 + x^2 - x - 4 & \rightarrow \text{Dividend} \\
 & 2x^3 - 4x^2 & \\
 & 5x^2 - x & \\
 & 5x^2 - 10x & \\
 & 9x - 4 & \\
 & 9x - 18 & \\
 & 14 & \rightarrow \text{Remainder}
\end{array}
$$

As in (a), we have the following relationship.

$$2x^3 + x^2 - x - 4 = (x - 2)(2x^2 + 5x + 9) + 14$$

Dividend Divisor Quotient Remainder

Note: The procedure is as follows:

1. To get the first term of the quotient, use this relationship: 1st term of quotient $\times$ 1st term of divisor $\rightarrow$ 1st term of dividend i.e. $(?) \times x \rightarrow 2x^3$. Thus we have $2x^2$.
2. Multiply $2x^2$ by $(x - 2)$ to get $2x^3 - 4x^2$.
3. Subtract $2x^3 - 4x^2$ from the dividend, ignoring the term -4 for the time being, to get $5x^2 - x$.
4. To get the 2nd term of the quotient, use this relationship: 2nd term of quotient $\times$ 1st term of divisor $\rightarrow$ 1st term of the resulting expression from step 3 i.e. $(?) \times x \rightarrow 5x^2$.
5. Similarly, the last term of the quotient can be obtained.

Worked Example

Find the quotient and remainder when $x^4 + x^3 - 2x + 1$ is divided by $x - 3$.

Solution:

$$
\begin{array}{rr}
 & x^3 + 4x^2 + 12x + 34 \\
x - 3 \,) & x^4 + x^3 \qquad - 2x + 1 \\
 & x^4 - 3x^3 \\
 & 4x^3 \\
 & 4x^3 - 12x^2 \\
 & 12x^2 - 2x \\
 & 12x^2 - 36x \\
 & 34x + 1 \\
 & 34x - 102 \\
 & 103
\end{array}
$$

The quotient is $x^3 + 4x^2 + 12x + 34$ and the remainder is 103.

Exercise 14.3

answers on p. 442

1. Divide each of the following by $x - 2$. Give the quotient and remainder for each division.

(a) $4x^4 + 2x^3 + x^2 - 2x + 1$ **(b)** $2x^4 + 2x^3 + 3x$

(c) $x^3 + x^2 + 2x + 1$ **(d)** $4x^3 + 2x^2 + 2x - 3$

2. Divide each of the following by $x + 2$. Give the quotient and remainder for each division.

(a) $2x^3 - 2x^2 + 2$ **(b)** $x^4 + x^3 - x^2 + 4$

(c) $3x^3 - 2x - 2$ **(d)** $2x^4 + x^3 - 3x^2 + 3x$

3. Divide each of the following by $2x - 1$. Give the quotient and remainder for each division.

(a) $4x^4 + x^2 + 3x - 5$ **(b)** $2x^4 + 5x^3 - x^2 - x + 2$

(c) $6x^4 - 3x^3 + 2x^2 + 11x - 6$ **(d)** $-2x^3 - 3x^2 + 8x + 5$

4. Divide each of the following by $x^2 + x + 2$. Give the quotient and remainder for each division.

(a) $4x^4 + 3x^3 + 9x^2 + 4$ **(b)** $3x^5 + 2x^4 - 8x^2 - 11x - 6$

(c) $2x^5 + 2x^3 - 5x^2 - x + 4$ **(d)** $3x^4 + 2x^3 + 9x^2 + 2x + 10$

14.4 ALGEBRAIC FRACTIONS AND FRACTIONAL EQUATIONS

Examples

(a) Consider the division of 704 by 184.

$$704 \div 184 = \frac{704}{184} = \frac{88 \times 8}{23 \times 8} = \frac{88}{23} \text{ or } 3\frac{19}{23}$$

or

$$704 \div 184 = 3\frac{152}{184} = 3\frac{19}{23} \text{ or } \frac{88}{23}$$

$$\begin{array}{r} 3 \\ 184\overline{)704} \\ \underline{552} \\ 152 \end{array}$$

Notice that when dealing with real numbers, we may express the quotient as an improper fraction or a mixed number using either method as shown above. In arithmetic, we customarily prefer $3\frac{19}{23}$ to $\frac{88}{23}$ as the answer.

(b) Consider the division of $x^2 - 2x - 3$ by $x^2 - 1$.

$$\begin{aligned}(x^2 - 2x - 3) \div (x^2 - 1) &= \frac{x^2 - 2x - 3}{x^2 - 1} \\ &= \frac{(x+1)(x-3)}{(x+1)(x-1)} \\ &= \frac{x-3}{x-1}\end{aligned}$$

or

$$\begin{aligned}(x^2 - 2x - 3) \div (x^2 - 1) &= 1 - \frac{2x+2}{x^2 - 1} \\ &= 1 - \frac{2(x+1)}{(x+1)(x-1)} \\ &= 1 - \frac{2}{x-1}\end{aligned}$$

$$\begin{array}{r} 1 \\ x^2 - 1\,\overline{)\,x^2 - 2x - 3} \\ \underline{x^2 \qquad\quad - 1} \\ -2x - 2 \end{array}$$

Note that we can show

$$\frac{x-3}{x-1} = 1 - \frac{2}{x-1}$$

using either of the following methods.

e.g.

$$\begin{aligned}\text{LHS} &= \frac{x-3}{x-1} \\ &= \frac{(x-1)-2}{x-1} \\ &= 1 - \frac{2}{x-1} \\ &= \text{RHS}\end{aligned}$$

or

$$\begin{aligned}\text{RHS} &= 1 - \frac{2}{x-1} \\ &= \frac{x-1-2}{x-1} \\ &= \frac{x-3}{x-1} \\ &= \text{LHS}\end{aligned}$$

In algebra, we customarily accept $\frac{x-3}{x-1}$ as the answer for $\frac{x^2 - 2x - 3}{x^2 - 1}$, in the simplest form.

Worked Example 1

Simplify:

(a) $\dfrac{x^2 + x - 6}{2x^2 - 3x - 2}$ **(b)** $\dfrac{3x + 9}{4x^2 + 4x - 24}$

Solution:

(a) $$\frac{x^2+x-6}{2x^2-3x-2} = \frac{(x-2)(x+3)}{(2x+1)(x-2)} \quad \left(x \neq -\frac{1}{2}, x \neq 2\right)$$

$$= \frac{x+3}{2x+1}$$

(b) $$\frac{3x+9}{4x^2+4x-24} = \frac{3(x+3)}{4(x+3)(x-2)} \quad (x \neq -3, x \neq 2)$$

$$= \frac{3}{4(x-2)}$$

Note: For (a), when the denominator of the expression is factorised, the product $(2x + 1)(x - 2)$ tells us that if $x = -\frac{1}{2}$ or 2, the denominator is zero and the expression is undefined. Since the possibility that $x - 2 = 0$ is to be excluded, we are allowed to divide the numerator and the denominator of the expression by $(x - 2)$ to simplify it. Similarly for (b), we are allowed to simplify the expression by cancelling $(x + 3)$.

Worked Example 2

Solve the following equations.

(a) $\dfrac{x^2+x-6}{2x^2-3x-2} = 0$ **(b)** $\dfrac{x^2+x-6}{2x^2-3x-2} = \dfrac{6}{7}$

Solution:

(a) $$\frac{x^2+x-6}{2x^2-3x-2} = 0$$

$$\frac{(x-2)(x+3)}{(2x+1)(x-2)} = 0$$

$$\frac{x+3}{2x+1} = 0 \quad (x \neq 2)$$

$$x + 3 = 0 \quad \left(x \neq -\frac{1}{2}\right)$$

$$\therefore x = -3$$

Alternative method:

$$\frac{x^2+x-6}{2x^2-3x-2} = 0$$

$$x^2 + x - 6 = 0$$

$$(x-2)(x+3) = 0$$

$$x = 2 \quad \text{or} \quad x = -3$$

Check: Put $x = 2$ in original equation

$$\frac{(2)^2+2-6}{2(2)^2-3(2)-2} = \frac{0}{0} \quad \text{(Indeterminate)}$$

So $x = 2$ (rejected)

Put $x = -3$ in original equation

$$\frac{(-3)^2 + (-3) - 6}{2(-3)^2 - 3(-3) - 2} = \frac{0}{25} = 0$$

So $\qquad x = -3 \quad$ (accepted)

Note: The given equation is undefined if the denominator $2x^2 - 3x - 2$, i.e. $(2x + 1)(x - 2)$, is zero. So, the possibility that $x = -\frac{1}{2}$ or $x = 2$ is automatically excluded. But, in this alternative method, we have not factorised the denominator and so, we do not know that the root $x = 2$ needs to be rejected. Thus, the 'checking stage' is most important as this tells us that $x = 2$ is to be rejected.

(b)

$$\frac{x^2 + x - 6}{2x^2 - 3x - 2} = \frac{6}{7}$$

$$\frac{(x - 2)(x + 3)}{(2x + 1)(x - 2)} = \frac{6}{7}$$

$$\frac{x + 3}{2x + 1} = \frac{6}{7} \quad (x \neq 2)$$

$$7x + 21 = 12x + 6$$

$$15 = 5x$$

$$\therefore x = 3$$

Alternative method:

$$\frac{x^2 + x - 6}{2x^2 - 3x - 2} = \frac{6}{7}$$

$$7x^2 + 7x - 42 = 12x^2 - 18x - 12$$

$$5x^2 - 25x + 30 = 0$$

$$x^2 - 5x + 6 = 0$$

$$(x - 3)(x - 2) = 0$$

$$\therefore x = 3$$

or $\qquad x = 2$

Check: Put $x = 3$ in original equation

$$\frac{3^2 + 3 - 6}{2(3)^2 - 3(3) - 2} = \frac{6}{7}$$

So $\qquad x = 3 \quad$ (accepted)

Put $x = 2$ in original equation

$$\frac{2^2 + 2 - 6}{2(2)^2 - 3(2) - 2} = \frac{0}{0}$$

So $\qquad x = 2 \quad$ (rejected)

Exercise 14.4

answers on p. 442

1. Find the quotients as algebraic fractions of the following divisions.
   (a) Divide $x^2 - 1$ by $(x + 1)^2$.
   (b) Divide $x^2 + 2x + 1$ by $x^2 - 1$.
   (c) Divide $4x^2 - 8x + 3$ by $4x^2 + 2x - 12$.
   (d) Divide $2x^2 - 8x + 8$ by $x^2 - 3x + 2$.

2. Simplify the following algebraic fractions.
   (a) $\dfrac{(x+1)^2}{1 - x^2}$ (b) $\dfrac{x^2 - 2x + 1}{1 - x^2}$
   (c) $\dfrac{2x^2 - 14x + 24}{x^2 - 8x + 15}$ (d) $\dfrac{8 - 18x^2}{9x^3 - 12x^2 + 4x}$

3. (a) Simplify $\dfrac{6x^2 - 28x - 10}{6x^2 + 24x - 270}$.
   (b) Solve the following equations.
   (i) $\dfrac{6x^2 - 28x - 10}{6x^2 + 24x - 270} = 0$ (ii) $\dfrac{6x^2 - 28x - 10}{6x^2 + 24x - 270} = \dfrac{7}{33}$

4. (a) Simplify $\dfrac{3x^2 - 24x + 45}{2x^2 - 8x - 10}$.
   (b) Solve the following equations.
   (i) $\dfrac{3x^2 - 24x + 45}{2x^2 - 8x - 10} = 0$ (ii) $\dfrac{3x^2 - 24x + 45}{2x^2 - 8x - 10} = \dfrac{3}{4}$

5. (a) Simplify $\dfrac{6x^2 - x - 12}{4x^2 - 12x + 9}$.
   (b) Solve the following equations.
   (i) $\dfrac{6x^2 - x - 12}{4x^2 - 12x + 9} = 0$ (ii) $\dfrac{6x^2 - x - 12}{4x^2 - 12x + 9} = 1$

6. (a) Simplify $\dfrac{x^2 + x - 2}{x^2 - 4}$.
   (b) Solve the following equations.
   (i) $\dfrac{x^2 + x - 2}{x^2 - 4} = 0$ (ii) $\dfrac{x^2 + x - 2}{x^2 - 4} = 3$

7. (a) Simplify $\dfrac{6x^2 - 19x + 8}{4x^2 + 10x - 6}$.
   (b) Solve the following equations.
   (i) $\dfrac{6x^2 - 19x + 8}{4x^2 + 10x - 6} = 0$ (ii) $\dfrac{6x^2 - 19x + 8}{4x^2 + 10x - 6} = 10$

8. **(a)** Simplify $\dfrac{5}{2x-5}+\dfrac{1}{7x+1}$.

(b) Solve the following equations.

(i) $\dfrac{5}{2x-5}+\dfrac{1}{7x+1}=0$ ***(ii)** $\dfrac{5}{2x-5}+\dfrac{1}{7x+1}=\dfrac{37}{36}$

9. **(a)** Simplify $\dfrac{1}{x+3}-\dfrac{2}{1-3x}$.

(b) Solve the following equations.

(i) $\dfrac{1}{x+3}-\dfrac{2}{1-3x}=0$ ***(ii)** $\dfrac{1}{x+3}-\dfrac{2}{1-3x}=\dfrac{5}{7}$

10. **(a)** Simplify $\dfrac{x+3}{x^2+x}+\dfrac{x-3}{x^2-1}$.

(b) Solve the following equations.

(i) $\dfrac{x+3}{x^2+x}+\dfrac{x-3}{x^2-1}=0$ ***(ii)** $\dfrac{x+3}{x^2+x}+\dfrac{x-3}{x^2-1}=\dfrac{1}{2}$

14.5 ALGEBRAIC MANIPULATION

Identities

Study the following equations.

$$7(3x+8)=21x+56 \quad \text{.........................} \quad (1)$$
$$3x+8=3x+8 \quad \text{.........................} \quad (2)$$
$$3x=3x \quad \text{.........................} \quad (3)$$

Notice that if both sides of equation (1) are multiplied by $\frac{1}{7}$, we obtain equation (2). If -8 is added to both sides of equation (2), we obtain equation (3). Thus the three equations above are equivalent equations. Notice also that these equations are true sentences for all values of x. Equations which are true for all values of the variable involved are called **identities**.

Examples

(a) $2x^2-x+3=ax^2-x+b$
(b) $3x^3+x^2-x+1=3x^3+ax^2+bx+1$
(c) $(2x+1)(x-1)=ax^2+bx-1$

If the algebraic sentences in (a), (b) and (c) are identities, find the values of a and b.

(a) By comparing the coefficients and the constant terms, we have $a=2$, $b=3$.
(b) Similarly $a=1$, $b=-1$.
(c) By expanding the left hand side, we have $2x^2-x-1=ax^2+bx-1$. Hence, $a=2$, $b=-1$.

Note: For emphasis, we sometimes use '≡' to mean 'is identically equal to'.

Worked Example

Find a and b for the following identities.

(a) $x(2x - 1) \equiv 2x^2 + ax + b$

(b) $x^2 - 3x + 2 \equiv (x - 1)(ax - b)$

Solution:

(a) $x(2x - 1) \equiv 2x^2 + ax + b$

$2x^2 - x \equiv 2x^2 + ax + b$

Hence, $a = -1$, $b = 0$.

(b) $x^2 - 3x + 2 \equiv (x - 1)(ax - b)$

$x^2 - 3x + 2 \equiv ax^2 - ax - bx + b$

$x^2 - 3x + 2 \equiv ax^2 - (a + b)x + b$

Hence, $a = 1$, $b = 2$.

Check $-(a + b) = -(1 + 2) = -3$ which is correct.

Alternative solution:

(a) $x(2x - 1) \equiv 2x^2 + ax + b$

Put $x = 0$.

Then $0 = b$.

Put $x = 1$.

Then $1 = 2 + a + b$

$1 = 2 + a + 0$

$a = -1$

(b) $x^2 - 3x + 2 \equiv (x - 1)(ax - b)$

Put $x = 0$.

Then $2 = -1(-b)$

$b = 2$

Put $x = 2$.

Then $4 - 6 + 2 = 2a - b$

$0 = 2a - 2$

$a = 1$

Exercise 14.5

answers on p. 442

1. State whether the following equations are identities.

   (a) $3x + 5 = 2x - 7$

   (b) $x - 24 = 8x - 192$

   (c) $5x + (86 - x) = 86 + 4x$

   (d) $6y + 7 = 3y + 7$

   (e) $4(18t - 7) + 40 = 3(4 + 24t)$

   (f) $7m - 3 = (6m - 24) + 8m$

   (g) $(4t - 6) + 6t = -6 + 10t$

   (h) $(8u - 21) + 54 = 4u + (5 + 6u)$

2. Find the values of a and b for each of the following identities.
   (a) $3x^2 + 2x - 1 \equiv ax^2 + bx - 1$
   (b) $2x^3 - 4x^2 + x - 2 \equiv 2x^3 + ax^2 + bx - 2$
   (c) $4x^3 + 3x^2 - x - 3 \equiv ax^3 + 3x^2 - x + b$
   (d) $3x^3 + x - 5 \equiv 3x^3 + ax^2 + x + b$

3. Find the values of a and b for each of the following identities.
   (a) $(2x - 1)(x + 1) \equiv ax^2 + x + b$
   (b) $(3x + 2)(x - 1) \equiv 3x^2 - ax + b$
   (c) $(4x - 3)(x + 2) \equiv ax^2 + bx - 6$
   (d) $(x + 8)(2x - 1) \equiv 2x^2 + ax + b$

4. Find the values of a and b for each of the following identities.
   (a) $x(3x + 1) = 3x^2 + ax + b$
   (b) $x(2x - 1) = ax^2 - x - b$
   (c) $2x^2 + x - 3 = (x - 1)(ax + b)$
   (d) $2x^2 - 5x - 3 = (ax + b)(x - 3)$

14.6 MANIPULATION OF EXPRESSIONS

Worked Example 1

If $y = 2x - 1$ and $x = 2z - 1$, express y in terms of z.

Solution:

$$\begin{aligned} y &= 2x - 1 \\ &= 2(2z - 1) - 1 \\ &= 4z - 2 - 1 \\ &= 4z - 3 \end{aligned}$$

Worked Example 2

If $y = 3x + 1$ and $y = \frac{z - 1}{3}$, express

(a) x in terms of y,

(b) x in terms of z.

Solution:

(a)
$$\begin{aligned} y &= 3x + 1 \\ y - 1 &= 3x \\ \frac{y - 1}{3} &= x \\ \therefore x &= \frac{y - 1}{3} \end{aligned}$$

(b)
$$\begin{aligned} x &= \frac{y - 1}{3} \\ &= \frac{\left(\frac{z - 1}{3}\right) - 1}{3} \\ &= \left(\frac{z - 1}{3} - \frac{3}{3}\right) \times \frac{1}{3} \\ &= \frac{z - 1 - 3}{3} \times \frac{1}{3} \\ &= \frac{z - 4}{9} \end{aligned}$$

Exercise 14.6 

answers on p. 442

1. Express x in terms of y if:
   (a) $y = x + 1$
   (b) $y = 2x + 1$
   (c) $y = 5x - 3$
   (d) $y = \frac{2x - 1}{3}$

2. (a) If $y = 3x - 2$ and $x = 3z - 2$, express y in terms of z.
   (b) If $y = 4x + 1$ and $x = 4z + 1$, express y in terms of z.
   (c) If $y = 3x + 4$ and $x = 3z + 4$, express y in terms of z.
   (d) If $y = 6 - 7x$ and $x = 6 - 7z$, express y in terms of z.

3. If $y = 2x - 5$ and $y = \frac{z + 5}{2}$, express
   (a) x in terms of y,
   (b) x in terms of z.

4. If $y = 3x + 7$ and $y = \frac{z - 7}{3}$, express
   (a) x in terms of y,
   (b) x in terms of z.

5. If $y = 5x - 6$ and $y = \frac{z + 6}{5}$, express
   (a) x in terms of y,
   (b) x in terms of z.

Chapter Review

1. **Polynomials**
   - Expressions such as $x^3 + 3x^2 + 5x - 3$ are known as polynomials.
   - When we subtract a polynomial Q from a polynomial P, we change the sign of each term of Q and do addition.

$$\overbrace{(2x^3 + 3x^2 + 4x - 5)}^{P} - \overbrace{(x^3 - 2x^2 + 5x - 6)}^{Q}$$
$$= 2x^3 + 3x^2 + 4x - 5 - x^3 + 2x^2 - 5x + 6$$

   - Multiplication of polynomials is the same as expansion of the product of polynomials.

- The dividend, divisor, quotient and remainder are related as follows:

$$
\begin{array}{rrl}
 & 2x^2 + 3x + 5 & \rightarrow \text{Quotient} \\
\text{Divisor} \leftarrow \quad x - 1 \,\big) & 2x^3 + x^2 + 2x - 1 & \rightarrow \text{Dividend} \\
 & \underline{2x^3 - 2x^2} & \\
 & 3x^2 + 2x & \\
 & \underline{3x^2 - 3x} & \\
 & 5x - 1 & \\
 & \underline{5x - 5} & \\
 & 4 & \rightarrow \text{Remainder}
\end{array}
$$

- When dividing one polynomial by another, the 'quotient' may be given as an algebraic fraction.

Example: $(x^2 - 2x - 3) \div (x^2 - 9) = \dfrac{x^2 - 2x - 3}{x^2 - 9}$

$$= \frac{(x + 1)(x - 3)}{(x + 3)(x - 3)}$$

$$= \frac{x + 1}{x + 3}$$

2. Identities

Equations which are satisfied by all values of x are called identities.

Example: $x^2 - 4 = (x + 2)(x - 2)$

3. Manipulation of Equations

Given an equation relating x and y and another equation relating y and z, we can express x in terms of z.

Example: $y = 2x - 1$ and $y = \dfrac{z + 1}{2}$

$$x = \frac{y + 1}{2}$$

$$= \frac{\left(\dfrac{z + 1}{2}\right) + 1}{2}$$

$$= \frac{z + 1 + 2}{2} \times \frac{1}{2}$$

$$= \frac{z + 3}{4}$$

CHALLENGER 14

1. If $r = \dfrac{C}{\sqrt{(1 - C^2)(k - 1)}}$, express C in terms of r and k, assuming that $0 < C < 1$ and $k > 1$.

2. Express $2 - \dfrac{2a - c}{a - c} - \dfrac{a + c}{2(c - a)}$ as a single fraction.

3. Solve $\dfrac{x + 2}{2x + 5} + \dfrac{2}{x + 1} = 0$.

4. Simplify $\dfrac{1}{x + 1} - \dfrac{1}{x - 1} + \dfrac{2}{x^2 + 1} + \dfrac{4}{x^4 + 1}$.

5. **(a)** If $(x + 1)(x + 2) = v$, express $x(x + 3)$ in terms of v. Hence find the value of $(x + 1)(x + 2)$ when $x(x + 1)(x + 2)(x + 3) + 1 = 0$.
   (b) Find the value of $(x - 1)(x + 2)$ such that

$$x(x + 1)(x - 1)(x + 2) + 1 = 0.$$

6. Solve $\dfrac{1}{p - 3} - \dfrac{1}{p + 1} = 2\left(\dfrac{1}{p + 3} - \dfrac{1}{p + 5}\right)$.

Problem Solving 14

Square Roots

If x and y are integers, solve

$$\sqrt{x} + \sqrt{y} = \sqrt{1\,996}.$$

The strategies to use are **use equations** and **guess and check**.

The strategy of using equations includes using algebraic skills to manipulate an equation.

$$\sqrt{x} + \sqrt{y} = \sqrt{1\,996}$$
$$\sqrt{x} = \sqrt{1\,996} - \sqrt{y}$$
$$(\sqrt{x})^2 = (\sqrt{1\,996} - \sqrt{y})^2$$
$$x = 1\,996 - 2\sqrt{1\,996}\sqrt{y} + y$$
$$\sqrt{4 \times 1\,996y} = 1\,996 + y - x$$
$$\sqrt{4 \times 4 \times 499y} = 1\,996 + y - x$$

Try $y = 499$, $\quad 4 \times 499 = 1\,996 + 499 - x$

$$\therefore x = 499$$

So x and y are both equal to 499.

1. Trapezium and Parallelogram $ABCD$ is a rectangle. E and G are midpoints of AB and DC respectively. If the area of the trapezium $FCDH$ is 20 cm^2, find the area of parallelogram $EFGH$.

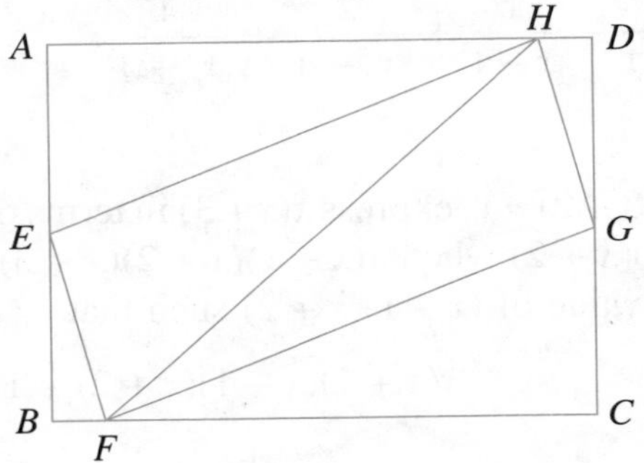

2. Hot and Cold Drinks At a class gathering, the boys took cold drinks and the girls took hot drinks. The total amount spent on cold drinks was 44% more than the amount spent on hot drinks. If the boys took hot drinks and the girls took cold drinks instead, the total amount spent on cold drinks would be equal to that spent on hot drinks. What fraction of the pupils were boys?

3. Forecasts Four matches were played between eight soccer teams: A, B, C, D, E, F, G, H. The following forecasts were made by three men:

Forecast X: Winners – A, B, F, G
Forecast Y: Winners – B, C, E, F
Forecast Z: Winners – E, F, G, H

If each of these forecasts is exactly 75% correct, which four teams won? Find out also which team was beaten by which team in each match.

4. Two Unknowns If x and y are integers, solve

$$\sqrt{x} + \sqrt{y} = \sqrt{1\,998}.$$

REVISION EXERCISE 4

Revision 4A *(answers on p. 443)*

1. Taking the hours of daylight on a certain day to be from 07 20 to 20 40, calculate the angles of a pie chart designed to show the periods of daylight and of darkness on that day.

2. **(a)** Find the mean of each of the following sets of numbers.
   (i) 5, 6, 7, 10, 12
   (ii) 305, 306, 307, 310, 312
   (b) Given that 9 is the mean of 2, x, 10, 12 and 15, find x. *(C)*

3. A pie chart is drawn to represent three values. The angles of two of the sectors are 146° and 160°. Express the third sector as a percentage of the whole pie chart.

4. The mean of three numbers is 13.
   (a) Calculate the sum of the three numbers.
   (b) Seven other numbers have a mean of 23. Calculate the mean of the ten numbers. *(C)*

5. For a certain question on a mathematics examination paper, a candidate could score 0, 1, 2, 3, 4 or 5 marks. The marks scored for this question by 40 candidates are shown in the table below.

Marks	0	1	2	3	4	5
Number of candidates	3	4	7	5	10	11

Find **(a)** the mode, **(b)** the median and **(c)** the mean. *(C)*

6. 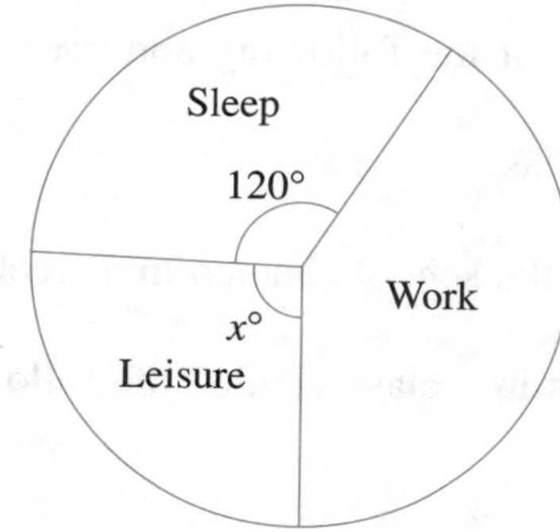

The pie chart shows how a bus driver divides up the 24 hours of his day between working, sleeping and leisure activities.
   (a) Express his sleeping time as a fraction of his day, giving your answer as a fraction in its lowest terms.
   (b) If he has 7 hours of leisure time each day, calculate the value of x.
   (c) He works for 9 hours each day. What percentage of each day does he work? *(C)*

7. **(a)** Multiply $(8a^3 + 3)$ by $4a^2$.
   (b) Divide $(4x^3 - 5x - 9)$ by $(2x - 3)$.

8. **(a)** Add $(x^3 - 3x^2 + 3x - 8)$ to $(2x^4 + 2x^3 - x^2 + 2x + 5)$.
   (b) Subtract $(3x^2 - 2xy + 2y^2)$ from $(4x^2 + 5xy - y^2)$.

9. If $y = 3x - 5$ and $y = \frac{z-5}{2}$, express

(a) x in terms of y, **(b)** x in terms of z.

10. **(a)** Simplify $\frac{2xy - 2y^2 + x - y}{4y^2 - 1}$.

(b) Solve the following.

(i) $\frac{5y - 2y^2 + 3}{4y^2 - 1} = 0$ **(ii)** $\frac{5y - 2y^2 + 3}{4y^2 - 1} = -\frac{4}{3}$

Revision 4B *(answers on p. 443)*

1. **(a)** The mean of the five numbers x, 2, 3, 5 and 9 is 3. Find x.

(b) A pie chart is drawn to represent three commodities. The angles of two of the sectors are 107° and 208°. Express the third sector as a percentage of the whole pie chart. *(C)*

2. The mean of the three numbers p, q and r is 9, and the mean of the five numbers p, q, r, x and y is 11. Find the mean of x and y. *(C)*

3. The distribution of the number of examination passes gained by a group of 100 students is shown in the following table:

Number of examination passes	1	2	3	4	5	6
Number of students	12	15	24	26	15	8

For this distribution, find **(a)** the mode, **(b)** the median and **(c)** the mean. *(C)*

4. State which type of diagram you would use to illustrate each of the following and give brief reasons for your choice.

(a) The examination results of the various subjects for your class.

(b) The exports of a country for 5 different years.

(c) The number of students buying different types of food in the school canteen in a week.

5. A survey of weekly pocket money received by the 30 students in a class yielded the following results:

Amount of pocket money (in cents)	20	30	50	60	75	100
Number of students receiving this amount	2	6	8	3	10	1

(a) Write down the mode of this distribution.
(b) Find the median.
(c) Calculate the mean.

(*C*)

6. The sale of 3 commodities *A*, *B* and *C* are 68 kg, 25 kg and x kg respectively. The total sales amount to 100 kg.
   (a) Find the value of x.
   (b) Express the sale of *A* as a percentage of the total sales.
   (c) If the sales are represented by a pie chart, find the angle of the sector representing the sale of *B*.

(*C*)

7. (a) What polynomial must be added to $(4a^2 - a)$ to give $(3a - 4)$?
   (b) From what polynomial must $(4x^2 - 2x + 1)$ be subtracted to give $(x^2 + x)$?

8. (a) Multiply $(2x + 3)$ by $(-3x^3 + 2x^2)$.
   (b) Divide $(6x^4 + 13x^3 + 12x^2 + 11x + 8)$ by $(2x + 3)$.

9. If $a = 2b - 6$ and $a = \frac{c + 6}{3}$, express
   (a) b in terms of a,
   (b) b in terms of c.

10. (a) Simplify $\frac{6x^2 - 19xy + 8y^2}{6x^2 + 15xy - 9y^2}$.
    (b) Solve the following.
    (i) $\frac{6x^2 - 38x + 32}{6x^2 + 30x - 36} = 0$
    (ii) $\frac{6x^2 - 38x + 32}{6x^2 + 30x - 36} = -\frac{29}{39}$

Revision 4C *(answers on p. 443)*

1. A teacher asked 24 children to name their favourite fruit. Their replies are illustrated by the bar chart below. Illustrate the same information on a clearly labelled pie chart.

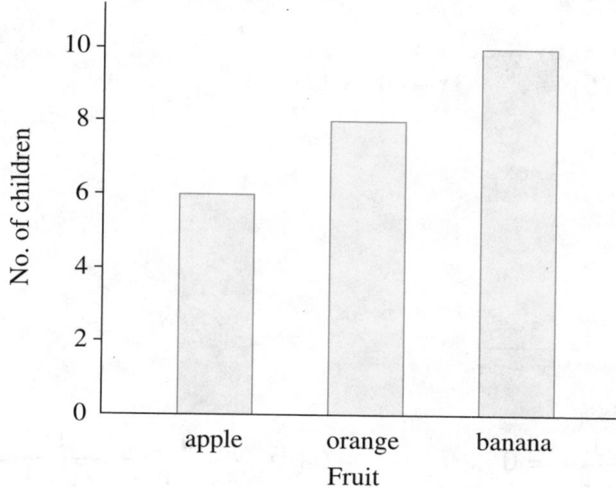

2. Find
(a) the mode,
(b) the mean and
(c) the median of the set of numbers 1, 4, 5, 8, 9, 8, 8, 7, 4.

3.

x	1	2	4	6	12
Frequency	12	6	3	2	1

In a game, the score x occurs with the frequency shown in the table.
(a) Find the mean score.
(b) If the different values of the frequencies are represented on a pie chart, calculate the number of degrees in the sector representing $x = 6$.

4. Write down five different positive integers whose median is 8 and whose mean is 6. *(C)*

5. The pie chart illustrates how the expenditure of a certain family is divided among various items.

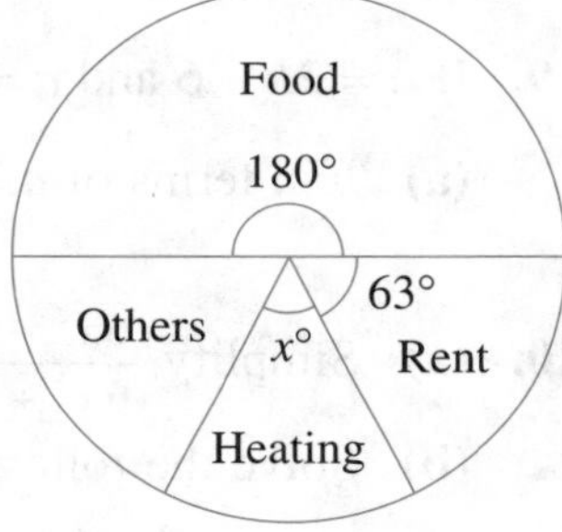

(a) Find what percentage of the total expenditure is spent on
(i) food,
(ii) rent.
(b) Given that $12\frac{1}{2}\%$ of the total expenditure is spent on heating, find x.

6. **(a)** The median of a set of 6 numbers is $2\frac{1}{2}$. Given that five of the numbers are 8, 1, 2, 11 and 1, find the sixth number.
(b) The mean of a set of 8 numbers is 3 and the mean of a different set of 12 numbers is x. Given that the mean of the combined set of 20 numbers is 9, calculate x.

7. From the sum of $(2a^2 + 5a - 2)$ and $(-3a^2 - 4)$, subtract the sum of $(3a^2 + 3a + 5)$ and $(4a + 3)$.

8. **(a)** Multiply $(3x^2 - x + 8)$ by $(-2x^3 + x - 3)$.
(b) Divide $(4x^5 - 2x^4 + 6x^3 - x^2 + 3x - 6)$ by $(2x - 1)$.

9. If $p = 3 - 7m$ and $p = \frac{9 - n}{2}$, express
(a) m in terms of p,
(b) m in terms of n.

10. **(a)** Simplify $\frac{5y}{2x - 5y} + \frac{3y}{21x + 3y}$.
(b) Solve the following.
(i) $\frac{10}{4x - 10} + \frac{1}{7x + 1} = 0$ **(ii)** $\frac{10}{4x - 10} + \frac{1}{7x + 1} = \frac{111}{22}$

MISCELLANEOUS EXERCISE 4

(answers on p. 443)

1. A six-sided dice is thrown 29 times. The results are shown in the table below.

Number shown on dice	1	2	3	4	5	6
Frequency	8	7	5	2	3	4

(a) For these results, write down
  (i) the mode,
  (ii) the median.

(b) The dice is thrown one more time. Find the number shown on the dice if the mean of the 30 throws is to be exactly 3. (*C*)

2.

Number of goals scored per match	0	1	2	3	4
Number of matches	2	6	8	10	4

The number of goals scored by a football team during each of 30 matches is shown in the table.

(a) Write down the modal number of goals scored per match.

(b) Write down the median number of goals scored.

(c) Calculate the mean number of goals scored, giving your answer correct to one decimal place.

(d) Copy the diagram. Represent the data in the table by drawing a bar chart on your diagram, shading it clearly. (*C*)

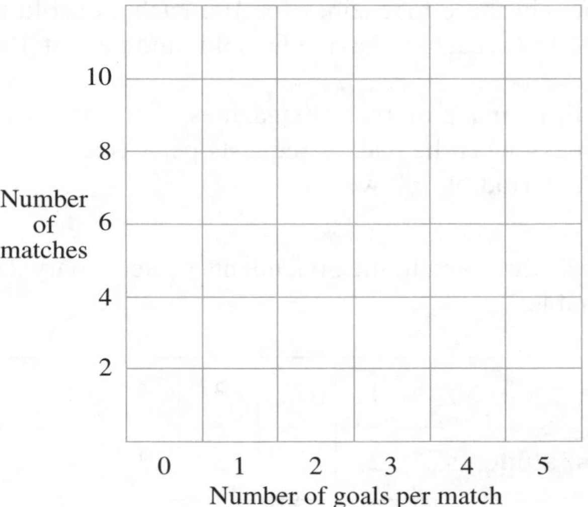

3. A man proposes to plant 500 trees. Of these, 200 are to be Mango trees, 175 are to be Palm trees and the rest are to be Rubber trees.
The pie chart illustrates the distribution.

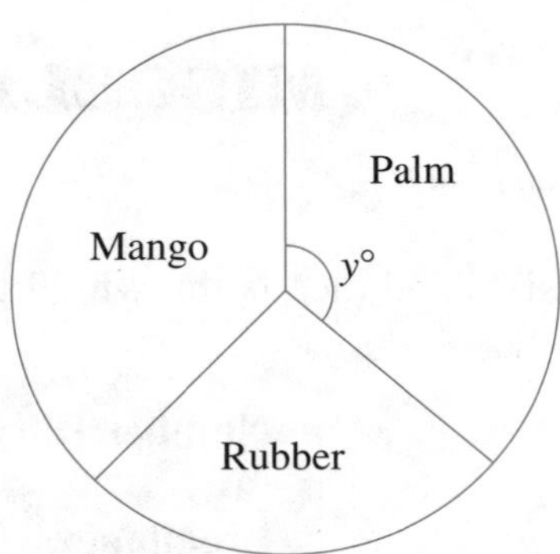

(a) Calculate y.
(b) Following a change in government grants, the man decides to increase the number of Rubber trees by 80%, keeping the numbers of Mango and Palm trees the same as before.

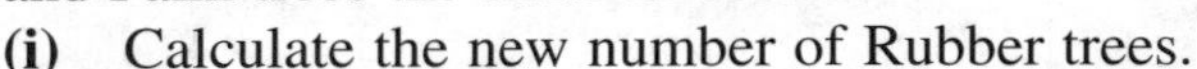

(i) Calculate the new number of Rubber trees.
(ii) What fraction of the new total number of trees will be Mango trees? Give your answer in its lowest terms. (*C*)

4. **(a)** The distribution of 100 values of a variable x is shown in the table.

x	0	1	2	3	4	5	6
Frequency	20	30	25	16	5	2	2

For this distribution, find
(i) the mode, **(ii)** the median, **(iii)** the mean.

(b) A newsagent recorded the number of requests for a certain weekly magazine over a period of 100 successive weeks. The results are shown in the table below.

No. of requests per week	17	18	19	20	21	22	23
Frequency	20	30	25	16	5	2	2

(i) Using your result from (iii) above, state the mean number of requests per week.

The newsagent bought these magazines for 10¢ each and sold them for 20¢ each. He thus made a profit of 10¢ on each magazine he sold, and he lost 10¢ on each magazine which remained unsold.
Calculate the profit he made on these magazines
(ii) for the 20 weeks when he had 17 requests per week,
(iii) for the whole period of 100 weeks. (*C*)

5. **(a)** A Mathematics test was given to the 30 students of Secondary 2A. Their marks were shown in the following table:

Marks	1	2	3	4	5	6	7	8	9
Number of students	2	0	3	3	6	5	5	4	2

(i) Draw a histogram to illustrate this information.
(ii) Draw a vertical line to mark the position of the median.
(iii) State the mode.
(iv) Calculate the mean.

(b) The same Mathematics test was given to the 20 students of Secondary 2B.
(i) These students' marks had a mean of 4.6. Calculate the mean of the marks obtained by the 50 students from the two classes as a whole.
(ii) The mode of the marks obtained by Secondary 2B was 4. Do you now have enough information to find the mode for the whole group of 50 students?

6. Simplify:

(a) $\left(\frac{1}{a+b}\right)\left(\frac{1}{a}+\frac{1}{b}\right)$ **(b)** $\left(\frac{1}{a}-\frac{1}{b}\right) \div (a-b)$

7. Simplify:

(a) $\frac{3x^2-2xy}{x^2y}+\frac{5xy-y^2}{xy^2}$ **(b)** $\frac{3x^2+11x-4}{6x^2+26x+8}$

8. Simplify:

(a) $\frac{3a-b}{ab}+\frac{4b-c}{bc}-\frac{5c-a}{ca}$ **(b)** $\left(\frac{a-b}{c-a}\right)\left(\frac{b-c}{a-b}\right)\left(1-\frac{c^2}{a^2}\right)$

9. Solve the following equation.

$$\frac{6x^2+22x-8}{3x^2+13x+4}=1$$

10. If $x=\frac{b-a}{a+b}$ and $y=\frac{ax+b}{ax-b}$, express y in terms of a and b.

11. If $\frac{x}{3}=\frac{1+t}{1-t}$ and $y=3(1-t)$, express y in terms of x.

12. If $x=\frac{m-1}{m+1}$ and $y=\frac{3m-1}{3m+1}$, express y in terms of x.

13. If $y=\frac{3x-1}{x+1}$ and $z=\frac{3y+2}{4y-1}$, express z in terms of x.

14. If $\frac{1}{x}+\frac{1}{y}=\frac{1}{a}$ and $x+y=b$, find the following in terms of a and b.

(a) xy **(b)** x^2+y^2

15. If $m=\frac{1-3n}{n+3}$, find $m+n$ in terms of

(a) n only, **(b)** m only.

INVESTIGATION 4

1. Take any two-digit number, say 23, as your starting number.
Write down the product of the digits of your starting number to get your 1st number.
Write down the product of the ones digits of your starting number and 1st number to get your 2nd number.
Write down the product of the ones digits of your 1st number and 2nd number to get your 3rd number.
Similarly get your 4th number and so on. For example, start with 23. Then

$$\begin{aligned} &\text{1st number } \mathbf{6} \leftarrow 2 \times 3 \\ &\text{2nd number } \mathbf{18} \leftarrow 3 \times 6 \\ &\text{3rd number } \mathbf{48} \leftarrow 6 \times 8 \\ &\text{4th number } \mathbf{64} \leftarrow 8 \times 8 \end{aligned}$$

(a) Continue your sequence. What do you observe?
(b) Using 32 as your starting number, form another sequence, compare the patterns in (a) and (b).
(c) Investigate using other numbers as starting numbers. Describe your observation.

2. If today is Monday, in 7 days' time it will be Monday again. What day of the week will it be in 10^{10} days' time? Investigate. Explain your strategies.

3. **(a)** John has discovered some 'crazy fractions' which can be reduced to the lowest terms in a peculiar way. For example,

$$\frac{\cancel{13}13}{\cancel{37}37} = \frac{13}{37} \qquad \frac{\cancel{1313}13}{\cancel{3737}37} = \frac{13}{37} \qquad \frac{\cancel{131313}13}{\cancel{373737}37} = \frac{13}{37}$$

Can you find other 'crazy fractions'?

(b) Ali has also discovered another type of 'crazy fractions' which can also be reduced to the lowest terms in a peculiar way. For example,

$$\frac{1\cancel{9}}{\cancel{9}5} = \frac{1}{5} \qquad \frac{1\cancel{99}}{\cancel{99}5} = \frac{1}{5} \qquad \frac{1\cancel{999}}{\cancel{999}5} = \frac{1}{5}$$

Can you find other 'crazy fractions'? Investigate.

4. A circle can be drawn to divide the inside of a square into 2 parts.

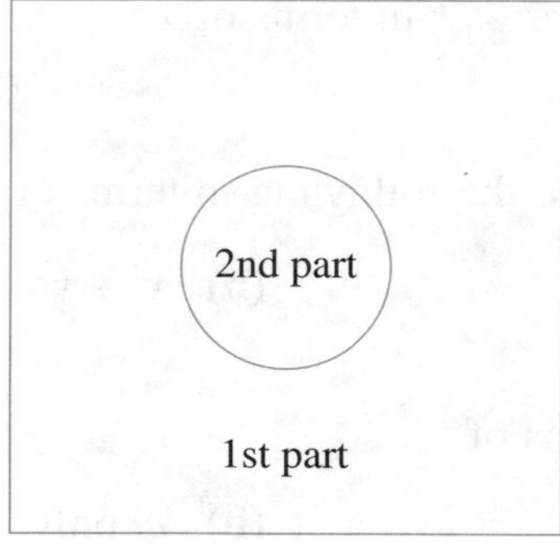

(a) Copy and complete the following table.

Number of circles	1	2	3	4	5	6	7	8	9	10
Maximum number of parts	2	4	8							

(b) How many parts will you get if 20 circles are drawn? Investigate.

ASSESSMENT 1

Paper I *(answers on p. 443)* **50 marks** **1 h**

Answer all the questions without using the calculator.

1. Factorise $12 + 2a - 4a^2$. [2]

2. Solve the simultaneous equations.

$$3x + 2 = x$$
$$4xy - 4 = 5$$

[2]

3. Solve the inequality $\frac{3}{2}(4x - 7) \leqslant \frac{2}{3}(2x + 5)$. [2]

4. Solve the equation $21x^2 + 14 = 3x + 32$. [2]

5. $\triangle PQR$ has vertices $P(-1, 2)$, $Q(-1, 4)$ and $R(-2, 4)$. Draw this triangle on graph paper. Then draw the image of $\triangle PQR$ under [1]

(a) a clockwise rotation of 90° about the origin O. Label the image $P'Q'R'$. [1]

(b) a reflection in the line $y = 0$. Label the image $P''Q''R''$. [1]

6. Express the following in standard form $A \times 10^n$ correct to 3 significant figures.

$$\frac{20.2 \times 10^{-3} \times 1.21 \times 10^{-1}}{33 \times 10^{-7} \times 101 \times 10^{5}}$$

[3]

7. Solve the equation.

$$\frac{4(2a - 1)}{5} + \frac{2(3 - a)}{4} = \frac{3}{10} - \frac{2a}{5}$$

[3]

8. A and B shared a sum of money in the ratio 7 : 5. If B gave A \$8, then A would have twice as much as B would have. How much money did each have at first? [3]

9. 20% of a class of 40 students were girls. When some new girls joined the class, the percentage of girls increased to 36%. How many new girls joined the class? [3]

10. The solid shown is made up of a rectangular prism and two identical right square pyramids. Find the volume of the solid if the rectangular prism measures 2 cm by 2 cm by 6 cm and the height of the solid is 24 cm.

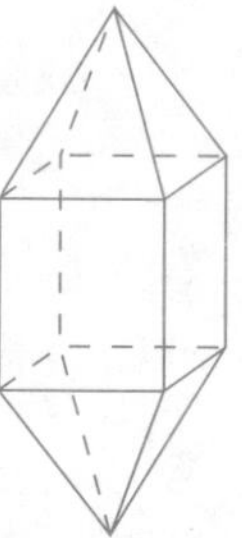

[3]

11. Using a scale of 2 cm to 1 unit on each axis, draw the graphs of the following equations for values of x from –3 to 3.

$$3x - 7y = -2$$
$$5y - 2x = 3$$

Use the graphs to solve the equations. [4]

12.

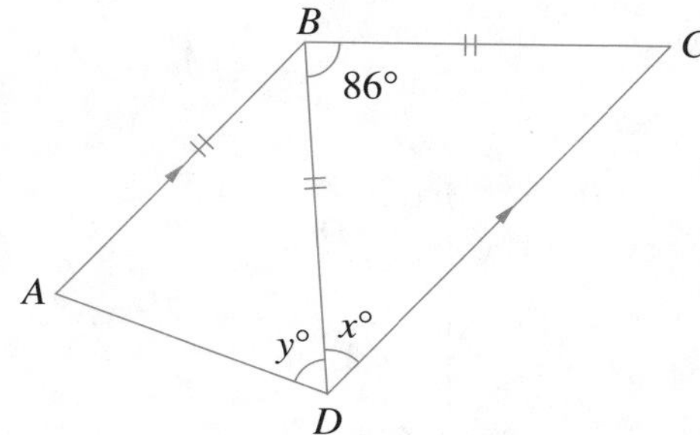

In the diagram, $BA = BD = BC$, $D\hat{B}C = 86°$ and AB is parallel to DC. Calculate the value of
(a) x,
(b) y. [4]

13.

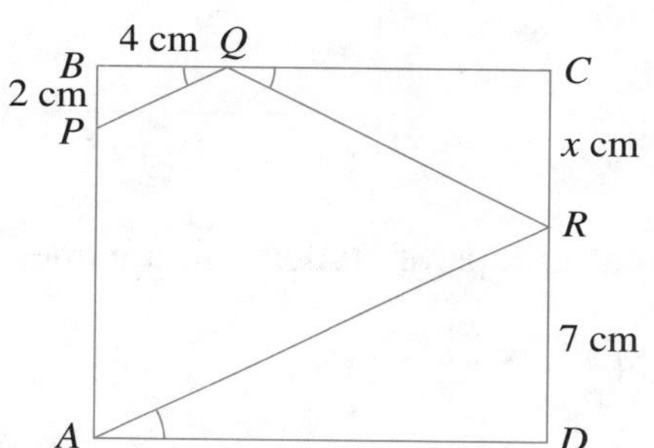

In the figure, $ABCD$ is a rectangle and $PQRA$ is made up of straight lines such that the marked angles are equal. Given that $BP = 2$ cm, $BQ = 4$ cm, $DR = 7$ cm and $CR = x$ cm,
(a) write down QC in terms of x, [2]
(b) find the value of x. [2]

14. A car took 6 hours to travel from town P to town Q. A bus took 9 hours to travel from town Q to town P. Both the car and the bus started their journey at noon. At what time would they pass each other along the same road? [4]

15. A boy who could run x km/h carried a message for 3 km from A to B and passed it to another boy who could run 1 km/h faster than the first boy. The second boy carried the message for 5 km from B to C. The second boy took 50% more time than the first boy to deliver the message. How fast did each boy run? [4]

16. A shopkeeper sold 2 articles at \$150 each. He made a profit of 20% for one article but a loss of 20% for the other. Find the overall profit or loss from the two sales. [4]

Paper II *(answers on p. 444)* **50 marks** **1 h 15 min**

Answer all the questions. You may use the calculator.

Section A (22 marks)

1. The areas of the bases of two similar mugs are in the ratio 9 : 16.
(a) Find the ratio of the heights of the mugs. [2]
(b) Given that the volume of the larger mug is 640 cm^3, find the volume of the smaller mug. [2]

2. Find the volume and the total surface area of a solid circular cone whose height is 8.4 cm and base radius is 6.3 cm. Give your answers correct to the nearest cm^2 or cm^3. Take $\pi = 3.14$. [4]

3. The figure shows an inverted cone of height 30 cm. If 1 cup of water is added into the cone, the water level rises to 10 cm.

(a) How many more cups of water must be added into the cone to bring the water level to 20 cm? [2]

(b) How many cups of water are needed to fill the cone to the brim? [2]

30 cm

4. Find the area of a quadrilateral whose vertices are $A(1, 3)$, $B(3, 2)$, $C(5, 5)$ and $D(2, 6)$.

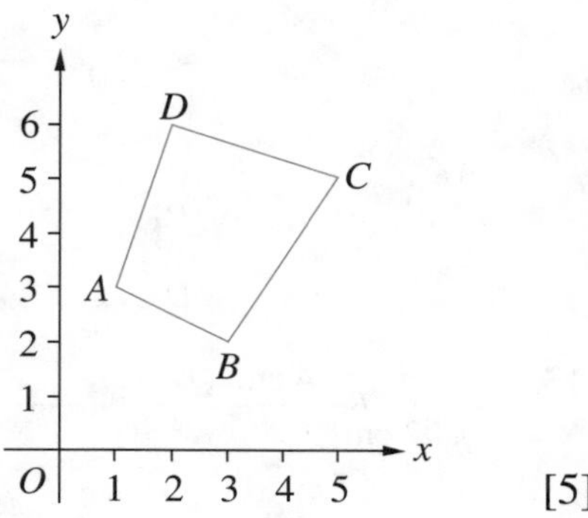

[5]

5. The tables below show the points scored by 3 different groups of students in a game.

(a)

Points	0	1	2	3	4	5
No. of students	2	2	4	2	1	p

Give the value of p if the median is 4 points. [2]

(b)

Points	0	1	2	3	4	5
No. of students	12	13	8	q	8	6

Give a possible value of q if the mode is 3 points. [1]

(b)

Points	0	1	2	3	4	5
No. of students	3	r	1	2	1	4

Calculate r if the mean is 2 points. [2]

Section B (28 marks)

6. The monthly expenditure of Mr Li's family was \$1 200. 20% of this amount was spent on transport and \$800 on food. The rest was miscellaneous expenditure.

(a) Draw a pie chart to represent the expenditure. Indicate the angles of the sector clearly. [4]

(b) If his miscellaneous expenditure made up 8% of his monthly salary, find his salary. [2]

7. The diagram represents a step ladder standing on horizontal ground. $ABCD$ and $ADEF$ are rectangles, $AB = AF = 3$ m, $AD = 0.5$ m, $BE = 1$ m apart and G is a point on the ground such that $DG \perp CE$. Calculate

(a) $C\hat{D}E$, [4]

(b) DG. [3]

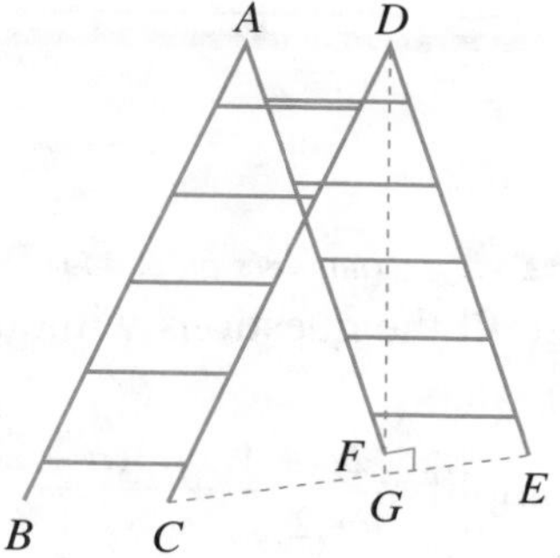

8. Samy bought 100 apples at x cents each and 80 pears at y cents each. He put 5 apples and 4 pears in each bag and sold the bags for $(8x + 6y)$ cents each.

(a) Write down, in terms of x and y, an expression for

(i) the amount of money he spent on the fruit, [1]

(ii) the total amount of money obtained from the sale of the bags of fruit. [2]

(b) Given that his cost was \$40 and his profit on the transaction was 55%, find the value of x and of y. [4]

9. **(a)** $p = 3 \times 7$
$q = 7 \times 7$
$r = 3 \times 3$
Express

(i) 37×7 in terms of p and q, [1]

(ii) 73×37 in terms of p, q and r. [2]

(b)

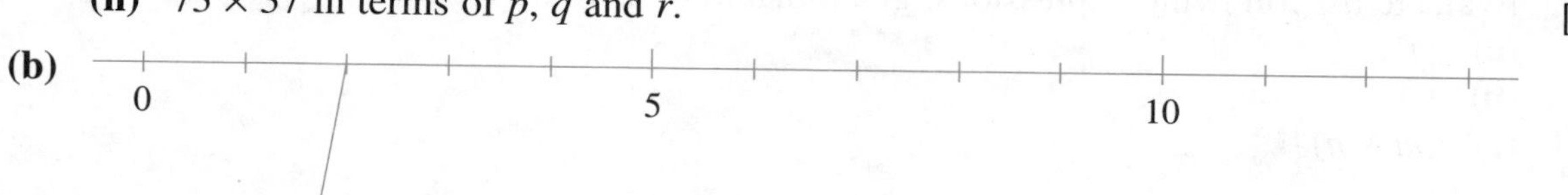

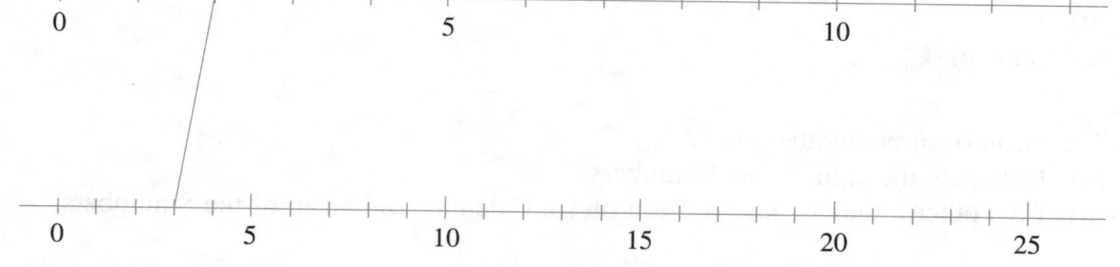

The diagram shows that

3 joins to 2

(i) The rule for joining numbers on the two lines is:

'Divide by 3 and then add x.'

Write down the value of x. [1]

(ii) On the diagram, draw a line showing where 12 joins to. [1]

(iii) Find the number to which 18 joins to. [1]

(iv) Find the number which joins to 9. [2]

ASSESSMENT 2

Paper I *(answers on p. 444)* **50 marks** **1 h**

Answer all the questions without using the calculator.

1. Simplify $\frac{2a-1}{2}+\frac{3(a+2)}{3}-\frac{a+4}{4}$. [2]

2. Solve the inequality $\frac{2}{3}-\frac{1}{3}x>\frac{4}{3}x+\frac{2}{5}$. [2]

3. Factorise the following.

(a) $25x^2-16y^2$ [1]

(b) $9a^2+12ab+4b^2$ [1]

4. Solve the simultaneous equations.

$$\frac{2}{5}y+\frac{1}{4}x=1$$

$$\frac{1}{2}x-\frac{1}{5}y=7$$ [2]

5. Evaluate the following expressions, given that $m=-2$ and $n=3$.

(a) m^n

(b) n^m

(c) $(m+n)^{m+n}$ [3]

6. The mean of three numbers is 12.

(a) Calculate the sum of the 3 numbers. [1]

(b) Five other numbers have a mean of 18. Calculate the mean of the 8 numbers. [2]

7. Find the coordinates of the image of (1, 3) under

(a) a translation which moves the point 2 units in the x-direction and 4 units in the y-direction, [1]

(b) an anticlockwise rotation of 90° about (0, 0), [1]

(c) a reflection about the line $y=2$. [1]

8. The ratio of the breadth to the perimeter of a rectangle is 1 : 6. If the area is 32 cm^2, find the breadth of the rectangle. [4]

9. A pie chart is drawn to represent the quantities of five commodities. The angles for four of the sectors are 85°, 96°, 48° and 77°. Express the fifth sector as a percentage of the whole pie chart. [3]

10. A worker is paid \$5 an hour during the usual working hours and \$7 an hour for overtime work. He worked for 48 hours and received \$248. How many hours of overtime did he work? [3]

11. Each wheel of Ali's bicycle has a diameter of 56 cm.

(a) Calculate the circumference of each wheel of Ali's bicycle. $\left[\text{Take } \pi = \dfrac{22}{7}.\right]$ [2]

(b) Calculate how far Ali has cycled when the rear wheel has rotated 125 times. Give your answer in metres. [2]

12. At the beginning, the number of boys to the number of girls who wished to take part in a walkathon was 3 : 1. Later, 15 new boys and 13 new girls joined the event so that the number of boys was twice as many as the number of girls. How many boys joined the event at the beginning? [4]

13. The distance between two towns X and Y is 210 km. Car A travels from X to Y at a uniform speed of 75 km/h. Car B travels from Y to X at a uniform speed of 65 km/h along the same road. If both cars start at noon, when will they pass each other? [3]

14. A man makes a profit of 20% by selling pineapples at 3 for \$2.55. Find his gain or loss percent if he sells them at \$10.71 per dozen. [4]

15.

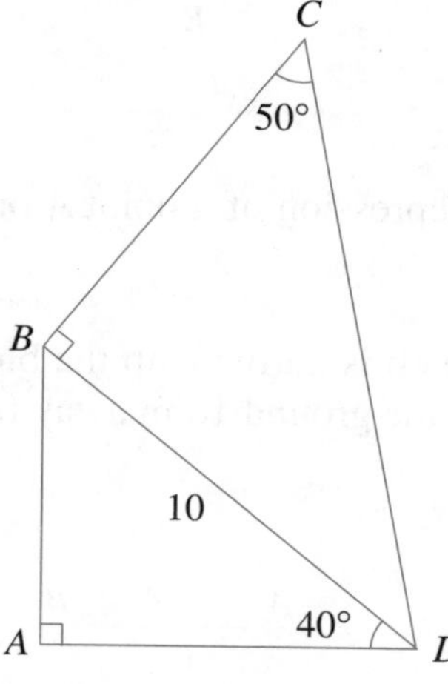

In the triangles ABD and BCD, $B\hat{A}D = C\hat{B}D = 90°$, $B\hat{D}A = 40°$ and $B\hat{C}D = 50°$.

(a) Write down a single word used to describe how the triangles are related.

(b) Given that $BD = 10$ cm, calculate

(i) AD, **(ii)** BC.

[sin 40° = 0.64; cos 40° = 0.77; tan 40° = 0.84] [4]

16. Calculate the length of

(a) CG, [2]

(b) GF. [2]

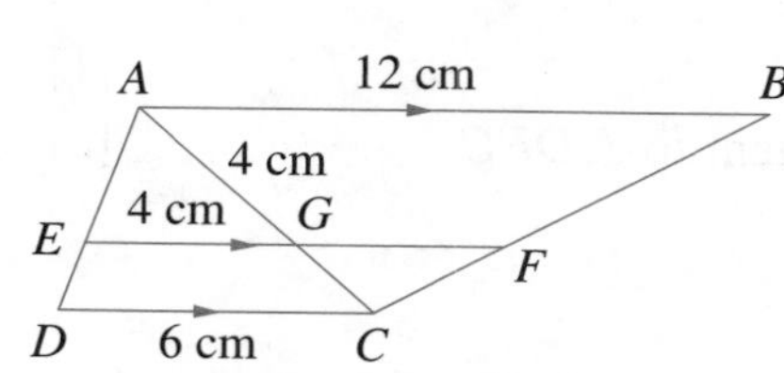

Paper II *(answers on p. 444)* **50 marks** **1 h 15 min**

Answer all the questions. You may use the calculator.

Section A (22 marks)

1. John and Michael had \$370 altogether. If John spent $\frac{2}{5}$ of his money and Michael spent \$50 of his money, then they would have the same amount of money left. How much did each have at the beginning? [4]

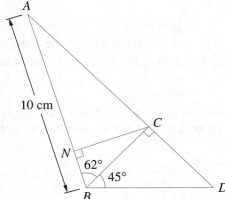

2. In the figure, ACD is a straight line, calculate the length of

(a) CD, [2]

(b) AN. [2]

A

10 cm

C

N

62°

45°

B

D

3. $ABCD$ is a rectangle. If $AB = 10$ cm and $A\hat{E}D = 120°$, find the area of the rectangle. [4]

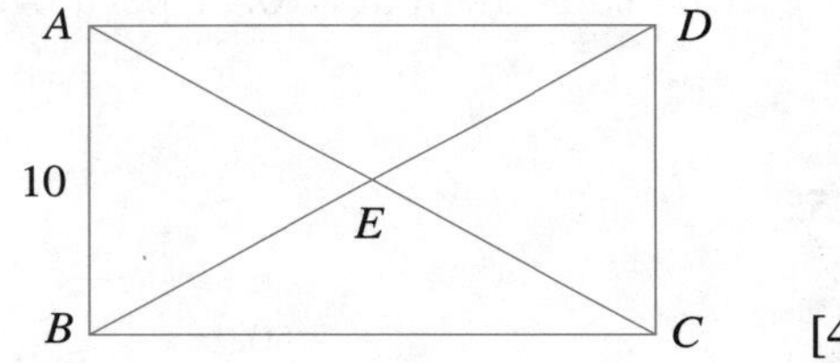

4. From the top of a high rise apartment block, the angle of depression of a point A on the ground 20 m away from the base of the apartment block is 60°.

(a) How tall is the apartment block? [1]

(b) What is the angle of elevation from A of a point X which is halfway up the block? [2]

(c) What is the angle of depression from X of a point Y on the ground 10 m away from the base of the apartment block? [2]

Give your answers correct to the nearest metre or degree.

5. In the figure, AB is parallel to ED, FA is parallel to DC, $EF = CB$ and $EFCB$ is a straight line. Show that

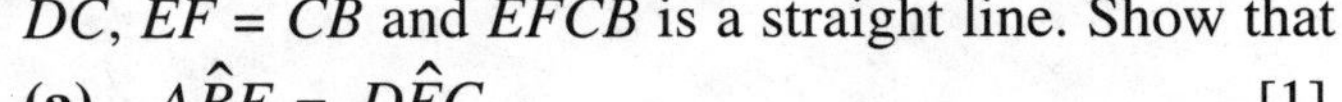

(a) $A\hat{B}F = D\hat{E}C$, [1]

(b) $A\hat{F}B = D\hat{C}E$, [1]

(c) $\triangle ABF$ is congruent to $\triangle DEC$. [3]

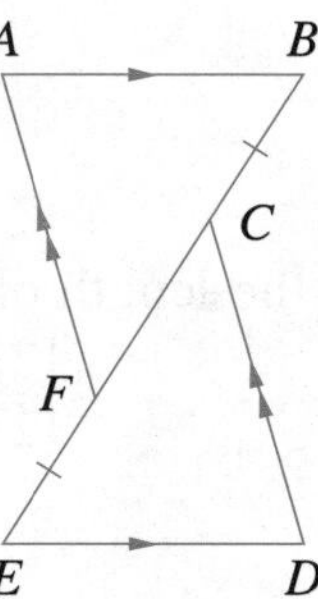

Section B (28 marks)

6. A map is drawn to a scale of 1 : 40 000.

(a) Calculate the actual distance, in kilometres, represented by 1 cm on the map. [1]

(b) Two towns are 25 km apart. Calculate, in centimetres, their distance apart on the map. [2]

(c) On the map, a housing estate has an area of 30 cm^2. Calculate, in square kilometres, the actual area of the estate. [3]

7.

Time	12 00	12 05	12 10	12 20	12 30	12 40	13 00
Distance	0	5	10	10	15	20	30

The table above is a distance-time table of a journey taken by a car.

(a) Represent the journey by a travel graph.
(Use 1 cm to represent 5 minute-interval along the horizontal axis and 1 cm to represent 5 km along the vertical axis.) [3]

(b) Use your graph to answer the following questions.

(i) What is the average speed of the car for the whole journey? [2]

(ii) Describe briefly what happens between 12 10 and 12 20. [2]

8. Samy assists his uncle as a barber on Sundays. He gives some of his earnings to his uncle. The table below shows part of his records.

Date	**Samy's earnings**	**Earnings given to Samy's uncle**
29 Nov	\$50	\$28
6 Dec	\$62	\$34
13 Dec	\$44	\$25
20 Dec	\$52	\$29
27 Dec	\$60	\$33

(a) Describe in words the rule that decides the amount that Samy gives to his uncle? [3]

(b) If the amount Samy earns is S dollars and his uncle's share is U dollars, write down a formula connecting S and U. [2]

(c) On the average, what percentage of Samy's earnings was given to his uncle? [2]

9. On New Year Day, Mary put some money into an empty money box. Each week after that, she put a fixed amount of money into the box. She did not take any money out.
The following table shows how much money is in the box.

Number of weeks after New Year Day	3	4	5	8	q	x
Total amount of money ($)	55	67	79	p	175	y

(a) Calculate
(i) the value of p, **(ii)** the value of q. [2]
(b) Calculate how much money Mary put into the box on New Year Day. [2]
(c) Write down the formula which gives y in terms of x. [2]
(d) If m weeks after New Year Day, Mary's savings are 13 times as much as her savings n weeks after New Year Day, express m in terms of n. [2]

ANSWERS

Chapter 1

Exercise 1.1 (p. 6)

1. (a) 11^7 (b) 5^3 (c) 18^{12}
(d) 6^7 (e) 7^2 (f) 13^{12}
(g) 2^{13} (h) 2^4 (i) 7^{25}
(j) 5^{15} (k) 5^3 (l) 5^{24}
(m) $7^6 \times 11^7$ (n) $\frac{11^2}{5^5}$ (o) $\frac{3^{11}}{2^9}$
(p) $17^5 \times 11^9$ (q) $\frac{17^2}{7^7}$ (r) $7^7 \times 2$

2. (a) 12^3 (b) 7^2 (c) $\left(\frac{2}{3}\right)^3$
(d) 6^3 (e) 3^4 (f) $\left(\frac{5}{6}\right)^2$
(g) 6^3 (h) 3^3 (i) 6^6
(j) 2^2 (k) 6^2 (l) 6^4
(m) 6^5 (n) 3^2 (o) 2^{10}
(p) 2^4 (q) 30^3 (r) 3^8

4. (a) $\frac{16}{81}$ (b) $\left(\frac{2}{3}\right)^{16}$

Exercise 1.2 (p. 11)

1. (a) 11^2 (b) $\frac{1}{7^{16}}$ (c) $\frac{1}{5^{12}}$
(d) $\frac{1}{5^3}$ (e) 3^2 (f) 7^6
(g) $\frac{1}{7^2}$ (h) $\frac{1}{5^4}$ (i) $\frac{1}{3^8}$
(j) $\frac{1}{2^7}$ (k) 3^{10} (l) 3^{12}
(m) 5^3 (n) $\frac{1}{7^9}$ (o) 2^8
(p) $\frac{1}{7^6}$ (q) $\frac{1}{5^{16}}$ (r) $\frac{1}{5^{12}}$

2. (a) $\frac{2^4}{5^{11}}$ (b) $\frac{5^2}{3}$ (c) $\frac{11^2}{7^2}$
(d) $\frac{1}{7^2 \times 17^3}$ (e) $\frac{5^4}{2^2}$ (f) $\frac{2^{20}}{5^2}$
(g) $\frac{1}{3^4 \times 2^2}$ (h) $\frac{1}{7^4 \times 3^{16}}$ (i) $5^5 \times 7^2$
(j) $\frac{11^{11}}{5^6}$ (k) $\frac{1}{2^{12} \times 7^{10}}$ (l) $\frac{1}{2^5 \times 7^{12}}$

3. (a) $\frac{1}{225}$ (b) $\frac{1}{3\ 125}$ (c) $\frac{8}{27}$
(d) $\frac{1}{7\ 776}$ (e) $\frac{1}{16}$ (f) $\frac{81}{250}$
(g) $\frac{1}{1\ 728}$ (h) $\frac{1}{243}$ (i) 1 728 000
(j) $\frac{1}{900}$ (k) 9 (l) $23\frac{7}{16}$

4. (a) -3^7 (b) 2^2 (c) -4^5
(d) $\frac{1}{6^4}$ (e) 5^4 (f) 2^4

5. (a) $1\frac{1}{40}$ (b) 1

Exercise 1.3 (p. 13)

1. (a) a^9 (b) p^{13} (c) x^{13}
(d) b^{12} (e) y^{24} (f) a^5b^7
(g) $x^{12}y^9$ (h) $m^{10}n^{14}$ (i) p^9q^5
(j) $r^8s^{11}t^{10}$ (k) a (l) t^2
(m) a^2 (n) x^3 (o) a^2b^3
(p) m^5n^3 (q) a^{10} (r) b^9
(s) x^{11} (t) y^{11} (u) m^{10}

2. (a) $\frac{1}{a}$ (b) b^4 (c) $\frac{1}{c^4}$
(d) p (e) $\frac{a^6}{b^7}$ (f) $\frac{s^3}{r^7}$
(g) $\frac{1}{x^6y}$ (h) $\frac{q^4}{p^2}$ (i) $\frac{1}{tu^3}$
(j) $\frac{1}{b^6}$ (k) $\frac{1}{p^2}$ (l) 1
(m) $\frac{1}{r^{12}}$ (n) $\frac{a^2}{b^7}$ (o) $\frac{y^5}{x^5}$
(p) $\frac{1}{p^3q^9}$ (q) $\frac{s^5}{t^9}$ (r) u^2v^4
(s) $\frac{1}{u^2}$ (t) $\frac{1}{w^4}$ (u) x^{10}
(v) y^{14} (w) z^5 (x) 1

Exercise 1.4 (p. 18)

1. (a) 500 000 (b) 0.000 428
(c) 1 690 000 000 000 000 000
(d) 501 000 000 (e) 238 600
(f) 7 750 (g) 0.000 000 001 2
(h) 0.000 002 01 (i) 35 000 000

2. (a) 1.231×10^2 (b) 1.2×10^{-2}
(c) 3.4×10^{-3} (d) 3.212×10
(e) 3.001×10^{-1} (f) 3.4×10^9
(g) 3.40×10^9 (h) $3.400\ 00 \times 10^9$
3. (a) 2.35×10^4 (b) 1.29×10^6
(c) 1.245×10^4 (d) 2.903×10^5
(e) 1.23×10^2 (f) 2.3×10
(g) 2.12×10^0 (h) 9.12×10^{-1}
(i) 4.236×10^{-2} (j) 5.804×10^{-3}
(k) 4.21×10^{-4} (l) 4.2×10^{-4}
4. 4.87×10^2 5. 5.03×10^2
6. (a) 1.38×10^5 (b) 1.81×10^{-8}
(c) 5.00×10^{-3} (d) 8.93×10^7
(e) 8.70×10^{-1} (f) 4.76×10^{-5}
7. (a) 29 979 000 000 cm/s
(b) 6.06×10^{23} (c) 7×10^{-5} m^3
8. (a) 1.7×10^4 (b) 2.91×10^3
(c) 1.75×10^7 (d) 3.7×10^{-5}
(e) 7.9×10^{-4}
9. (a) 4.24×10^5 (b) 9.6×10^9
(c) 5.43×10^3 (d) 7.29×10^6
(e) 6.344×10^{-2} (f) 2.064×10^{-4}
(g) 2.112×10^4 (h) $2.050\ 2 \times 10^7$
(i) 1.41×10^{-3} (j) 2.52×10^{-7}

Chapter 2

Exercise 2.1 (p. 28)

1. (a) (i) (b) (iii) (c) (ii) (d) (ii) (e) (iii)
(f) (i) (g) (i) (h) (iii) (i) (ii)
2. (a) $9x^2 + 6x + 1$ (b) $25x^2 + 30x + 9$
(c) $36x^2 + 48x + 16$ (d) $4x^2 + 4xy + y^2$
(e) $16x^2 + 16xy + 4y^2$ (f) $25x^2 - 10x + 1$
(g) $9x^2 - 12x + 4$ (h) $49x^2 - 70x + 25$
(i) $16x^2 - 8xy + y^2$ (j) $25x^2 - 30xy + 9y^2$
(k) $x^2 - 1$ (l) $x^2 - 36$
(m) $x^2 - y^2$ (n) $9x^2 - 1$
(o) $4x^2 - 9y^2$ (p) $25x^2 + 60xy + 36y^2$
(q) $49x^2 - 126xy + 81y^2$ (r) $64x^2 - 80xy + 25y^2$
3. (a) 400 (b) 1 600 (c) 9 975
(d) 9 975 (e) 89 999 (f) 1 997
(g) 998 001 (h) 810 000 (i) 990 025
(j) 160 000 (k) 250 000 (l) 638 401
(m) 1 (n) 1 000 000 (o) 0
(p) 1 001
4. (a) 9 800 (b) 996 000 (c) 99 600 000
(d) 10 000 (e) 10 000 (f) 1 000 000
(g) 10 000 (h) 199

Exercise 2.2 (p. 31)

1. (a) $2xy + 2xz$ (b) $6mp + 3mq$
(c) $4xw + 4xy + 8xz$ (d) $y^5 - y^4 + y^3$
(e) $-7n^2 + n^3 - 2n^5$ (f) $3a^2 + 21a$
(g) $10p^2 + 25p$ (h) $4a^3 - 32a^2$
(i) $7m^3 - 7m^2 - 21m$
(j) $9v^4 + 27v^3 - 18v^2 + 36v$
(k) $2xp + 2yp + 3xq + 3yq$ (l) $3a^3 - a^2b - 3ab^3 + b^4$
(m) $5m^3 - mn + 5m^2n^2 - n^3$ (n) $2x^2 + 7x + 5$
(o) $12x^2 + x - 6$ (p) $12x^2 - 7x - 10$
(q) $2x^2 - 11x + 15$ (r) $18x^4 - 48x^2y + 14y^2$
2. (a) $a^3 + a^2 - 2a + 12$ (b) $x^3 - 2x^2 - x - 6$
(c) $2a^3 + 9a^2 + 11a + 6$ (d) $x^3 + 6x^2 + 4x - 5$
(e) $27a^3 + 18a^2 - 12a - 8$ (f) $-10a^3 + 17a^2 + a - 6$
(g) $6x^3 + 7x^2y - 7xy^2 - 6y^3$ (h) $x^3 - 2x^2y - 2xy^2 - 3y^3$
(i) $ax + bx + cx + ay + by + cy + az + bz + cz$
(j) $p^3 + qp + r^3p + p^2q^2 + q^3 + r^3q^2 + p^2r^2 + qr^2 + r^5$
(k) $x^6 + x^3 + 2x^2 - 2x + 2$
(l) $3m^4 + 11m^3 + 7m^2 + 5m + 6$

Exercise 2.3 (p. 33)

1. (a) $m(n + p)$ (b) $x(y - z)$
(c) $p(q + 2)$ (d) $r(3 - s)$
(e) $5(x + 2)$ (f) $7(a + 1)$
(g) $2(6p - 1)$ (h) $x(x + 1)$
(i) $y(1 + x)$ (j) $3a(b + 3c + 2d)$
(k) $m(n + p + q)$ (l) $p(q + r + 1)$
(m) $y(3x + 4z - 5)$ (n) $a(b + c + 3d)$
2. (a) $(3x + 2)(x + 1)$ (b) $(7x + 2)(x - 2)$
(c) $3(2x + 1)(x + 4)$ (d) $(2x + 3)(3x - 5)$
(e) $(x - 3)(4x + 5)$ (f) $(2x + 1)(x - 1)$
(g) $(x - 1)(x - 7)$ (h) $(3x - 1)(x - 1)$
3. (a) $(x + 3y)(a - b)$ (b) $(x - 7y)(a + b)$
(c) $(12a + d)(b - c)$ (d) $(8a - d)(b - c)$
(e) $(p + 2q)(4m + 3n)$ (f) $3(p - 3q)(2m - 3n)$
(g) $(5x - y)(3a - 2b)$ (h) $(11x - 3y)(5a + 9b)$
(i) $(5x - 8y)(8p - 3q)$ (j) $6(12x - 7y)(2a - b)$
(k) $(a - 2b)(5x + 3y)$ (l) $(2x + 5y)(m - 4n)$
4. (a) $(4x^2) - 2(4x)y + y^2$ (b) $(6y)^2 + 2(6y)1 + 1^2$
(c) $(3m)^2 - (2n)^2$ (d) $s^2 + 2s(3t) + (3t)^2$
(e) $(3x)^2 - 2(3x)1 + 1^2$ (f) $(2s)^2 - (6t)^2$
(g) $(4a)^2 + 2(4a)b + b^2$ (h) $(7m)^2 - 2(7m)2n + (2n)^2$
(i) $y^2 - 2(y)3 + 3^2$ (j) $(5p)^2 + 2(5p)2q + (2q)^2$
(k) $(2x)^2 - 6^2$ (l) $(4x)^2 - (3b)^2$
5. (a) $(4x - y)^2$ (b) $(6y + 1)^2$
(c) $(3m - 2n)(3m + 2n)$ (d) $(s + 3t)^2$
(e) $(3x - 1)^2$ (f) $4(s + 3t)(s - 3t)$
(g) $(4a + b)^2$ (h) $(7m - 2n)^2$
(i) $(y - 3)^2$ (j) $(5p + 2q)^2$
(k) $4(x + 3)(x - 3)$ (l) $(4x + 3b)(4x - 3b)$
6. (a) $(5a + 4b)(5a - 4b)$ (b) $(3m + 2n)^2$
(c) $(4p - 3)^2$ (d) $(x + 6)^2$
(e) $(7x - 3y)^2$ (f) $(6x + 7)(6x - 7)$
(g) $(5u - v)^2$ (h) $(9 + 8t)(9 - 8t)$
(i) $(1 + 15w)^2$ (j) $(x + 4)(x - 2)$
(k) $-4x$ (l) $(x + 4)^2$
(m) $(x + y)(x + z)$ (n) $(p^2 + q^2)(s^2 + r^2)$
(o) $(a + b)(b - 1)$ (p) $(a^2 + 1)(1 + a)$

(q) $(a-1)(b^2+1)$ (r) $(a-c)(d-a)$
(s) $(x-1)(x+y+1)$ (t) $(p+q-r)(p-q)$
(u) $(1+a)(1-a-b)$ (v) $(3x+z)(y-3x+z)$

Exercise 2.4 (p. 37)

1. (a) $\frac{2x+y}{4}$ (b) $\frac{2a}{15}$ (c) $\frac{5a+2}{6}$
(d) $\frac{8a}{5}$ (e) $\frac{a}{5}$ (f) $\frac{2a-3}{15}$
(g) $\frac{2(a-4b)}{15}$ (h) $\frac{8x-9}{15}$ (i) $\frac{31x+3}{20}$
(j) $\frac{17x}{12}$ (k) $\frac{12a-1}{20}$ (l) $\frac{7x+2}{4}$
(m) $\frac{2(y+x)}{xy}$ (n) $\frac{1+y^2}{xy}$ (o) $\frac{11}{4b}$
(p) $\frac{17y+16}{4xy}$ (q) $\frac{1}{a^2}$ (r) $\frac{11a-4b}{3c}$

2. (a) $\frac{3x+1}{(x-1)(x+3)}$ (b) $\frac{2(3x-5)}{(x-2)(x-1)}$
(c) $\frac{2-x}{(x-3)(x-4)}$ (d) $\frac{3(2x-3)}{(x-1)(x-2)}$
(e) $\frac{10x-1}{6(x-1)(2x+1)}$ (f) $\frac{-2x-5}{2(x+1)(x-2)}$
(g) $\frac{4x-5}{6(x+1)(x-2)}$ (h) $\frac{7}{18(x-1)}$
(i) $\frac{15x-61}{7(x-3)(3x-1)}$ (j) $\frac{2}{3x-2}$
(k) $\frac{2ab}{a^2-b^2}$ (l) $\frac{a^2}{a-b}$
(m) $\frac{-n}{3(3m+n)}$ (n) 0
(o) $\frac{2(x^2+y^2)}{(x+y)(x-y)}$ (p) $\frac{-4ab}{(b+a)(b-a)}$
(q) $\frac{3(2x+7)}{(x+2)(x+5)}$ (r) $\frac{4x+3y}{6x-10y}$
(s) $\frac{a^2+b^2+ab}{ab(a+b)}$ (t) $\frac{3x^2+14x+6}{x(x-3)(x+2)}$

Exercise 2.5 (p. 40)

1. (a) $\frac{a^2b}{3}$ (b) $\frac{x^2y}{6}$ (c) $\frac{3xy^2}{5}$
(d) $\frac{5}{6}$ (e) $\frac{3}{2}$ (f) $\frac{2}{3}$

2. (a) $\frac{1}{y^2}$ (b) a (c) $\frac{1}{q^4}$
(d) $\frac{u^5}{t}$ (e) $\frac{y^2}{x^4}$ (f) $\frac{b^2}{a^2}$
(g) a^8b^6 (h) x^8y^4 (i) $p^{10}q^2$
(j) q

3. (a) $\frac{6c^2}{b^2}$ (b) $\frac{6b^2}{a^2}$ (c) $\frac{8x}{3y^2z}$
(d) $\frac{18x^2}{y}$ (e) $\frac{x}{3z}$ (f) $-\frac{z^2}{2x^2}$
(g) $\frac{a}{2bc(a-b)}$ (h) $\frac{3x(3-2x)}{4yz(3+2x)}$

Exercise 2.6 (p. 42)

1. $x = 15$ 2. $x = 6$ 3. $x = -9$
4. $x = 4$ 5. $x = 5$ 6. $x = 6$
7. $x = -5$ 8. $x = 7$ 9. $x = 1$
10. $x = 6\frac{1}{2}$ 11. $x = 1\frac{7}{15}$ 12. $x = 1\frac{7}{26}$
13. $x = -\frac{2}{3}$ 14. $x = \frac{1}{27}$ 15. $x = -4\frac{4}{5}$
16. $x = -\frac{4}{15}$ 17. $x = 3$ 18. $x = 7\frac{1}{5}$
19. $x = 10$ 20. $x = 6$ 21. $x = 5\frac{1}{6}$
22. $x = 1\frac{11}{15}$ 23. $x = 1$ 24. $x = 3$
25. $x = -\frac{3}{4}$ 26. $x = -7\frac{1}{2}$ 27. $x = 2\frac{3}{4}$
28. $x = 1\frac{1}{3}$ 29. $x = 1$ 30. $x = 1\frac{2}{3}$
31. $x = 15$ 32. $x = 3$ 33. $x = \frac{1}{18}$
34. $x = 11$ 35. $x = \frac{2}{3}$ 36. $x = \frac{17}{12}$
37. $x = 5$ 38. $x = 1$

Exercise 2.7 (p. 45)

1. $\frac{2}{3}$ 2. 7, 9 3. 3, $\frac{3}{4}$
4. 9 cm by 8 cm 5. 33°, 57° 6. $1\frac{1}{2}$ kg
7. $1\frac{3}{8}$, $\frac{5}{6}$ 8. 42° 9. 30
10. 4.2 11. 40 12. 13
13. 1 200 14. 60

Chapter 3

Exercise 3.1 (p. 53)

1. (a) $x = \frac{q-p}{a}$ (b) $x = 1.54$

2. **(a)** $x = \dfrac{-s-q}{p-r}$ or $\dfrac{-(s+q)}{p-r}$ or $\dfrac{s+q}{r-p}$
(b) $x = -4.884$

3. **(a)** $x = \dfrac{q+n}{m-p}$ **(b)** $x = 8.06$

4. **(a)** $x = \dfrac{b-d}{a-c}$ **(b)** $x = -2$

5. **(a)** $x = \dfrac{ab-cd+e}{a+c}$
(b) $x = \dfrac{-ab-cd}{b-d-e}$ or $\dfrac{-(ab+cd)}{b-d-e}$ or $\dfrac{ab+cd}{d+e-b}$

6. **(a)** $x = \dfrac{s-pq-r}{p+1}$ **(b)** $x = \dfrac{pq+2r}{q-r-s}$

7. **(a)** $x = \dfrac{a}{c+b}$ **(b)** $x = \dfrac{b+c}{a}$

8. **(a)** $x = \dfrac{6abc}{2a+3b}$ **(b)** $x = \dfrac{30abc}{2b-3a}$

9. **(a)** $b = \dfrac{e-c}{a-d}$ **(b)** $d = \dfrac{ab+c-e}{b}$

10. **(a)** $a = \dfrac{d+c}{(b-e)}$ **(b)** $b = \dfrac{d+ae+c}{a}$

Exercise 3.2 *(p. 56)*

1. **(a)** 528 cm^3 **(b)** $h = \dfrac{3v}{\pi r^2}$; 21 cm

2. **(a)** 675 **(b)** $F = \dfrac{2S-NL}{N}$; 3

3. **(a)** \$115 **(b)** $r = \dfrac{100(S-C)}{C}$; 25%

4. **(a)** $V = 500 + 20T$ **(b)** 580*l*
(c) $T = \dfrac{V-500}{20}$; 75 min

5. **(a)** $w = \dfrac{A}{l}$ **(b)** $r = \dfrac{C}{2\pi}$
(c) $b = \dfrac{2A}{h}$ **(d)** $h = \dfrac{V}{\pi r^2}$
(e) $n = 2(E-a)$ **(f)** $h = \dfrac{2A}{a+b}$
(g) $h = \dfrac{A}{R^2-r^2}$ **(h)** $l = \dfrac{P}{2} - w$
(i) $h = \dfrac{s}{\pi r} - r$ **(j)** $S = 2px + s$
(k) $f = \dfrac{uv}{(v+u)}$ **(l)** $h = \dfrac{S}{2\pi r} - r$
(m) $u = \dfrac{2s-tv}{t}$ **(n)** $s = \dfrac{2p}{x} + 1$
(o) $p = \dfrac{x}{x-2}$ **(p)** $R = \dfrac{r}{T-1}$
(q) $u = \dfrac{fv}{v-f}$ **(r)** $t = \dfrac{v-u}{f}$
(s) $f = \dfrac{2(s-ut)}{t^2}$ **(t)** $s = \dfrac{v^2-u^2}{2f}$
(u) $t = \dfrac{r_1r_2}{(u-1)(r_1+r_2)}$ **(v)** $r = \dfrac{b}{h+k}$

Exercise 3.3 *(p. 59)*

1. 5, 3 **2.** 7, –1 **3.** $\frac{7}{2}$, 0
4. 5, –100 **5.** $-\frac{2}{3}$, 4 **6.** 2
7. 0, 3 **8.** 0, –7 **9.** –6, $\frac{11}{2}$
10. $\frac{5}{2}$, $-\frac{7}{4}$ **11.** $\frac{7}{3}$, $\frac{1}{4}$ **12.** 5
13. 2, 5 **14.** 7, 5 **15.** 3, –4
16. 5, –5 **17.** 3, –4 **18.** 9, –3
19. $\frac{1}{3}$, 4 **20.** $-\frac{3}{4}$, $\frac{3}{4}$

Exercise 3.4 *(p. 62)*

1. **(a)** $(x+4)(x-3)$ **(b)** $(x-7)(x+4)$
(c) $(x-16)(x+2)$ **(d)** $(x+27)(x-3)$
(e) $(x-16)(x-12)$ **(f)** $(x-10)(x-12)$
(g) $(x-17)(x+7)$ **(h)** $(x-36)(x+8)$
(i) $(x+10)(x-15)$ **(j)** $(x-8)(x-9)$
(k) $(x+19)(x-7)$ **(l)** $(x-17)(x+4)$

2. **(a)** $(x-48)(2x+1)$ **(b)** $(x+48)(2x-1)$
(c) $(x-24)(2x+2)$ or $2(x+1)(x-24)$
(d) $(x+24)(2x-2)$ or $2(x-1)(x+24)$
(e) $(x-16)(2x+3)$ **(f)** $(x+16)(2x-3)$
(g) $(2x-24)(x+2)$ or $2(x-12)(x+2)$
(h) $(2x+24)(x-2)$ or $2(x+12)(x-2)$
(i) $(2x+6)(x-8)$ or $2(x+3)(x-8)$
(j) $(2x-6)(x+8)$ or $2(x-3)(x+8)$
(k) $(x+6)(2x-8)$ or $2(x-4)(x+6)$
(l) $(x-6)(2x+8)$ or $2(x+4)(x-6)$

3. **(a)** $(x+1)(x-2)$ **(b)** $(2+3x)(1-x)$
(c) $(2x-1)(3x+4)$
(d) $(2x-4)(3x+5)$ or $2(x-2)(3x+5)$
(e) $(3x-3)(x+5)$ or $3(x-1)(x+5)$
(f) $(3x-2)(5x-1)$ **(g)** $(x-2)(5x-4)$
(h) $(2x+1)(3x-7)$ **(i)** $(1-4x)(3x+2)$
(j) $(4x-1)(-2x+6)$ or $2(x-3)(-4x+1)$
(k) $(x+2)(-x+3)$
(l) $(2x+3)(-2x+4)$ or $2(2-x)(3+2x)$
(m) $(2x-4)(2x+5)$ or $2(x-2)(2x+5)$
(n) $(3x+4)(3x-6)$ or $3(x-2)(3x+4)$
(o) $(2x-4)(3x-5)$ or $2(x-2)(3x-5)$

(p) $(2x+3)(3x-2)$ **(q)** $(1-2x)(1+5x)$
(r) $(2x+1)(4x+2)$ or $2(2x+1)(2x+1)$
(s) $(6x+1)(x-3)$
(t) $(2x-4)(6x+3)$ or $6(x-2)(2x+1)$
(u) $(2x-2)(x+5)$ or $2(x-1)(x+5)$
(v) $(6x+2)(2x-6)$ or $4(3x+1)(x-3)$
(w) $(2x+8)(3x-2)$ or $2(x+4)(3x-2)$
(x) $(x+1)(3x+3)$ or $3(x+1)(x+1)$

Exercise 3.5 *(p. 65)*

1. **(a)** $x = 0$ or $\frac{7}{3}$ **(b)** $x = 0$ or $-\frac{1}{2}$
(c) $x = 0$ or $-\frac{5}{4}$ **(d)** $x = 6$ or -6
(e) $x = \frac{7}{2}$ or $-\frac{7}{2}$ **(f)** $c = 3$ or $-1\frac{1}{2}$
(g) $d = -\frac{4}{3}, 2$ **(h)** $x = -\frac{1}{3}, 3$
(i) $p = -4, \frac{2}{3}$ **(j)** $a = -\frac{5}{4}$ or $-\frac{1}{7}$
(k) $x = 3$ or -3 **(l)** $y = -\frac{9}{4}$ or $-\frac{7}{3}$
(m) $y = -50$ or -60 **(n)** $p = -\frac{13}{3}$ or -7
(o) $c = \frac{1}{2}$ or -2 **(p)** $a = 6$ (repeated)
(q) $y = -\frac{1}{5}$ (repeated) **(r)** $x = 2$ or 3
(s) $x = \frac{2}{3}$ or 3 **(t)** $x = \frac{11}{3}$ or -1
(u) $x = \frac{3}{2}$ (repeated) **(v)** $x = -3$ or $-\frac{1}{3}$
(w) $x = 1$ or $\frac{1}{5}$ **(x)** $x = 11$ or $\frac{1}{7}$
(y) $x = 1$ or $\frac{2}{3}$ **(z)** $x = 1$ (repeated)

2. **(a)** $x = -3$ or 4 **(b)** $x = -\frac{3}{2}$ or $\frac{10}{3}$
(c) $x = 2$ or -1 **(d)** $x = -\frac{4}{5}$ or $\frac{5}{3}$
(e) $x = 1$ or $\frac{9}{5}$ **(f)** $x = 1$ or -2
(g) $x = -\frac{3}{2}$ or $\frac{1}{3}$ **(h)** $x = -\frac{2}{3}$ or 1
(i) $x = 1$ or $-\frac{2}{3}$ **(j)** $x = \frac{5}{2}$ (repeated)

Exercise 3.6 *(p. 66)*

1. 12 or –13 **2.** 17 or 0 **3.** –16
4. 12 cm **5.** 5 or –12 **6.** 8 or 4
7. 6 cm **8.** 11, 13 **9.** 7
10. 70 m, 40 m **11.** 7 m **12.** 9 days
13. 60 km/h **14.** $9

Chapter 4

Exercise 4.1 *(p. 76)*

1. $5 257.20 **2.** $126
3. $684 **4.** 38 *l*, $39.90
5. 137.5 km **6.** 600 km/h
7. 17 00
8. **(a)** $1\frac{1}{2}$ km/min **(b)** 25 m/s
9. **(a)** 275 min **(b)** 90
10. **(a)** $42\frac{1}{12}$ h **(b)** $319.83
11. **(a)** 07 31 **(b)** 2 km
12. **(a)** 9 min **(b)** 12 km/h
(c) 7.5 km/h
13. **(a)** 1.5×10^8 km **(b)** 2.59×10^3 s
14. **(a)** $96 **(b)** $3\frac{1}{4}$ h
(c) $16 **(d)** $103.55
15. **(a)** $1 260 **(b)** $650
16. 27 km
17. **(a)** 250 km **(b)** 3 h $7\frac{1}{2}$ min
18. **(a)** 100 km/h **(b)** 16 00
19. $36, $18, $9 **20.** *A*: $33, *B*: $55
21. $250, $350, $450 **22.** $8 000, $4 000, $2 000
23. 2 h 30 min
24. **(a)** $952 **(b)** 9 days
25. $18
26. **(a)** 9.3 kg **(b)** $330
27. 3 h **28.** $7\frac{1}{2}$ days
29. **(a)** 282 000 **(b)** 340 000
30. **(a)** 150 **(b)** 85%
31. **(a)** 15 cm **(b)** 324 cm^2
32. 15% **33.** 576
34. 22.2% **35.** **(a)** 35% **(b)** 36
36. 240 m*l* **37.** 30 g
38. 500 kg, 1 000 kg **39.** 12 %
40. 200

Exercise 4.2 *(p. 85)*

1. $91.00 **2.** 25% **3.** 81 cents
4. 12% **5.** Gain 20% **6.** $80
7. $220 **8.** 25% **9.** 20%
10. $20.40 **11.** $138

12. **(a)** 13% **(b)** 34% **(c)** 17%
(d) 28% **(e)** 31% **(f)** 37%
13. \$341.60 **14.** \$61.50
15. **(a)** 18 baht **(b)** \$57
(c) 86 ringgit **(d)** \$0.60
16. Electric oven \$42, Refrigerator \$180, Video recorder \$172
17. **(a)** \$15 **(b)** \$70
18. **(a)** 30 m^2 **(b)** \$750
19. **(a)** \$240 **(b)** \$80 **(c)** $33\frac{1}{3}\%$
20. **(a)** 180 m*l* **(b)** 22.5 m*l* **(c)** 8 days
21. **(a)** \$15.50 **(b)** \$3.50 **(c)** 23%
22. **(a)** \$4 160 **(b)** \$3 744
23. **(a)** \$119 **(b)** 14%
24. **(a)** \$2 600 **(b)** \$3 850
25. **(a)** 15% **(b)** \$9 184
26. **(a)** 642.24 **(b)** 550.08 **(c)** 136.65
(d) 289 075.04
27. **(a)** \$36 **(b)** \$3 400
28. **(a)** \$40 **(b)** **(i)** \$640 **(ii)** £500
29. **(a)** \$1.50 **(b)** \$630
30. **(a)** \$41.85 **(b)** \$85.93 **(c)** \$324
31. **(a)** \$3.50 **(b)** \$5.25 **(c)** \$192.50
(d) \$259.20 **(e)** \$60
32. **(a)** 960 km **(b)** \$864 **(c)** 768 km
33. **(a)** \$499.50 **(b)** \$26.50 **(c)** \$582.75
34. **(a)** 0.001 4
(b) **(i)** \$6 000 **(ii)** \$21 000
(iii) \$12 500 **(iv)** 168%
35. **(a)** \$187.50 **(b)** \$95.63 **(c)** \$27.40
(d) 11.3%

Revision Exercise 1

Revision 1A *(p. 96)*

1. 3.82×10^3
2. **(a)** \$3 **(b)** 60%
3. **(a)** $a = 5$ **(b)** $x = 0.8$
4. **(a)** $x = \frac{a}{b - c - 2a}$ **(b)** $x = \frac{2abc}{a + 2b}$
5. **(a)** $(7x - 5y)^2$ **(b)** $x(x + 4y)$
6. **(a)** $-\frac{3}{2}, -2$ **(b)** $-1, -\frac{1}{2}$
7. 10 cm, 4 cm
8. **(a)** 15% **(b)** \$178.50
9. **(a)** 155 min **(b)** 14 35
10. \$168

Revision 1B *(p. 97)*

1. **(a)** $x = 2z + y$ **(b)** $z = \frac{x - y}{2}$
(c) $y = x - 2z$
2. **(a)** 74 cents **(b)** \$120
3. **(a)** 4.5 m **(b)** 1 : 70 **4.** 93.17%
5. **(a)** 25% **(b)** 20%
6. **(a)** $\frac{3}{4}, 3$ **(b)** $\frac{2}{3}, -\frac{4}{9}$
7. **(a)** $\frac{x + 4}{12}$ **(b)** $\frac{61a - 48}{60}$ **8.** 3.59×10^2
9. **(a)** \$5 440 **(b)** $T = \frac{100(A - P)}{PR}$
10. 320 m

Revision 1C *(p. 98)*

1. 3.5×10^{-4} **2.** **(a)** $\frac{1}{7^{13}}$ **(b)** $\frac{3^2}{11^9}$
3. 35 days
4. **(a)** $3(a - 3b)(a + 9b)$ **(b)** $(6x - y)(6x + y + 2)$
5. 13 **6.** 8 000
7. **(a)** $\frac{x}{5}$ **(b)** $\frac{12x - 1}{20}$
8. **(a)** $\frac{5}{2a}$ **(b)** $\frac{6y^2 + 1}{2y}$
9. **(a)** $a = \frac{21}{b + 2}$ **(b)** $b = 8\frac{1}{2}$
10. \$940.80

Revision 1D *(p. 99)*

1. **(a)** 0.028 **(b)** 0.027 68 **(c)** $2.768\,4 \times 10^{-2}$
2. **(a)** 20% gain **(b)** \$150
3. **(a)** m^{12} **(b)** $a^{14}b^6$ **(c)** s^6t^2
4. 86 m, 72 m **5.** **(a)** $\frac{2x - 8y}{15}$ **(b)** $\frac{7a + 2}{4}$
6. **(a)** 60% **(b)** 12
7. **(a)** $60x^2 - 27xy - 60y^2$ **(b)** $2x^3 - 2xy^2 + 2x^2 + 2xy$
8. **(a)** $(x - y)(x + y - 3)$ **(b)** 4 680 007
(c) 25
9. **(a)** $t_1 = \frac{100(d - 100t)}{d}$ **(b)** $t = \frac{R - R_0}{aR_0}$
(c) $R_1 = \frac{RR_2}{R_2 - R}$
10. **(a)** **(i)** \$5.72/*l* **(ii)** 175 m*l* **(b)** \$11
(c) **(i)** 20% **(ii)** 4% **(d)** £12.80

Revision 1E *(p. 100)*

1. **(a)** $3(3m - 4t)(m + 2t)$ **(b)** $(k - h)(9x - 4y)$
2. **(a)** $\frac{12}{x}$ m **(b)** $2\left(x + \frac{12}{x}\right)$ m
(c) 24 m by $\frac{1}{2}$ m

3. **(a)** \$60 **(b)** \$280 **(c)** \$320

4. **(a)** $-4, 5$ **(b)** $-\frac{5}{4}, \frac{5}{2}$

5. **(a)** S\$15 **(b)** US\$17

6. **(a)** $6ab^3$ **(b)** $\frac{10}{7}ab$ **(c)** $3ab + 2ab^2$

(d) $\frac{ab}{3}$

7. $y + 1 = 2(x - 1)$

8. **(a)** $3x^4y - 9x^3y^3 + x^2y^2 - 3xy^4$

(b) $3xyz + 12xy^2 - 9x^2y + 3xy$

9. **(a)** $(x - y + 1)(x - y - 1)$ **(b)** 6

10. **(i)** \$14 **(ii)** \$185

(iii) \$579, \$93.24, \$91.20, \$731.64

Miscellaneous Exercise 1 *(p. 102)*

1. $-4\frac{3}{16}$ **2.** -24

3. **(a)** **(i)** 1 **(ii)** 9 **(iii)** 1

(iv) 9 **(v)** 9

(b) 3

4. $\frac{1}{3}$ or 1 **5.** 2.6 or 0.38 **6.** $x = 4a$

7. 5 **8.** $y + x + 3$

9. **(a)** -21 **(b)** **(i)** 49 **(ii)** 1

10. **(a)** 1

(b) **(i)** $x = 13, y = 4$ **(ii)** $x = 7, y = 3$

11. **(a)** $\frac{7x - 1}{3}$ **(b)** $\frac{7y - 3}{2}$

12. **(a)** **(i)** 6 **(ii)** 3 **(b)** 2 h 28 min

(c) 16 11 **(d)** 3 h 39 min

13. **(a)** 220 m*l*

(b) self-raising flour: 360 g, sugar: 273.75 g, butter: 86.25 g

(c) 3%

14. **(a)** **(i)** \$13 680 **(ii)** \$380

(b) 9.6% **(c)** 3.125%

15. **(a)** Square with 12, 14, 26, 28 at corners.

(b) Square with 5, 8, 26, 29 at corners.

(c) Rectangle with 13, 17, 27, 31 at corners.

Chapter 5

Exercise 5.1 *(p. 111)*

1. Q: $(-2, 3)$, R: $(-1, -1)$, S: $(0, -2)$, T: $(3, -3)$, U: $(0, 4)$, V: $(1, 0)$, W: $(-3, -1.5)$

3. (a), (b), (c), (d), (e), (f)

4. **(a)** rhombus **(b)** parallelogram

(c) trapezium **(d)** rectangle

Exercise 5.2 *(p. 115)*

3. **(a)** up-hill **(b)** up-hill

(c) down-hill **(d)** down-hill

(e) up-hill **(f)** down-hill

(g) down-hill **(h)** up-hill

(i) up-hill **(j)** up-hill

(k) up-hill **(l)** up-hill

(m) vertical **(n)** horizontal

Exercise 5.3 *(p. 117)*

1.

No. of correct answers	Score (Marks)
4	22.2
5	27.8
6	33.3
7	38.9
8	44.4
9	50
11	61.1
13	72.2
15	83.3
16	88.9

2.

Score (Marks)	Percentage
28	35%
60	75%
72	90%
50	62.5%
40	50%
64	80%
52	65%
42	52.5%

3. **(a)** $y = 1.4x$ **(b)**

x (US\$)	0	100
y (S\$)	0	140

(d) **(i)** S\$35 **(ii)** S\$112 **(iii)** US\$36

(iv) US\$111

4. **(a)** $y = 0.3x$

(b)

x (km/h)	0	100
y (m/s)	0	30

(d) (i) 2.7 km/h (ii) 2 km/h
(iii) 10.7 km/h (iv) 16 km/h
(v) 0.9 m/s (vi) 2.5 m/s
(vii) 3.4 m/s (viii) 4.7 m/s

5. **(a)** $y = \frac{32}{3}x$

(b)

x (litres)	0	18
y (km)	0	192

(d) (i) 128 km (ii) 192 km (iii) 267 km
(e) (i) 9 *l* (ii) 14 *l* (iii) 26 *l*

6. **(a)** $y = 1.5x + 50$

(b)

x (km)	0	100
y (dollars)	50	200

(d) (i) \$170 (ii) \$230 (iii) \$272
(e) (i) 28 km (ii) 52 km (iii) 144 km
(f) \$282.80

7. **(b)** \$20.80 **(c)** \$21.50
8. **(b)** \$1.38 **(c)** \$62
9. **(b)** 6.3 kg **(c)** 18 lb
10. **(b)** 12.4 *l* **(c)** $3\frac{1}{4}$ gal

Exercise 5.4 *(p. 122)*

1. **(a)** (i) 60 km/h (ii) 90 km/h
(iii) 60 km/h
(b) 11 20, 20 km, 10 min **(c)** 100 km/h, Yes
(d) 20 km, 11 22 **(e)** 50 min
2. **(a)** 80 km **(b)** 80 km/h
(c) 50 min **(d)** 48 km/h
(e) 20 km line at 11 45 for 15 min
(f) 24 km line at about 11 42
3. **(a)** 07 00, 11 00 **(b)** 4 h
(c) 20 km, 5 km/h **(d)** No
(e) 2 times, 1 h **(f)** 5 km/h, Yes
(g) starting (first 10 km)
4. **(a)** 50 km/h, 75 km/h, 60 km/h; Yes, all the speeds are constant.
(b) No **(c)** 50 km/h, 75 km/h
(d) 60 km/h **(e)** 09 49, 09 57
(f) 10 20 **(g)** 60 km/h
5. $29\frac{5}{11}$ km/h, $32\frac{2}{5}$ km/h, 14 04
6. **(a)** 9.15 **(b)** 15 km **(c)** 30 min
(d) 5 km/h **(e)** 40 km
7. **(a)** 82.8 km/h **(b)** (ii) 68 km
8. **(a)** 2 h 42 min **(b)** 1 500 km
(c) 556 km/h **(e)** 1 h 33 min
(f) 18 57

9. **(a)** *A* **(b)** *B* overtakes *A*
(c) (i) 200 m (ii) *B*
(d) (i) The distance between the cars increases from 200 km to 400 km.
(ii) equal
(e) 110 s **(f)** 166.5 km/h
10. 15 13, 14 38

Exercise 5.5 *(p. 130)*

1. $x = -1.2, y = -0.1$ **2.** $x = 1.3, y = 1.8$
3. $x = 2, y = 1.2$ **4.** $x = -0.8, y = 0.3$
5. $x = 0.1, y = -0.2$ **6.** $x = -1.4, y = 0.3$
7. $x = 1, y = 0.6$ **8.** $x = 0.3, y = -0.7$
9. $x = -0.1, y = -1.1$ **10.** $x = 0.2, y = 0.6$

Exercise 5.6 *(p. 133)*

1. **(a)**

x	–3	–2	–1	0	1	2	3	4	5
y	–14	5	18	25	26	21	10	–7	–30

(c) (i) $y = 15.9$ (ii) $x = 1.9$ or -0.6

2. **(a)**

x	–1	0	1	2	3	4
y	–10	–7	0	11	26	45

(c) (i) $y = 18$ (ii) $x = 1.4$

3. **(a)**

x	–2	–1	0	1	2	3
y	1	–5	–5	1	13	31

(c) (i) $y = 10.1$ (ii) $x = 1.4$

4. **(a)** (i) 2.5 (ii) 2.5, –3.5
(b) (i) 6.6 (ii) 2.2, –5.2
(c) (i) –6.6 (ii) 1.8, –3
(d) (i) –1 (ii) –0.6, –1.9
(e) (i) 14.9 (ii) 0.8, –8.3
(f) (i) 3.5 (ii) 0.6, –1.9

Chapter 6

Exercise 6.1 *(p. 141)*

1. $x = 5, y = 3$ **2.** $x = 3, y = 4$
3. $x = 4, y = 2$ **4.** $x = -2, y = 2$
5. $x = 3, y = 5$ **6.** $x = 5, y = 2$
7. $x = 1, y = 3$ **8.** $x = 3, y = -1$
9. $x = 3, y = 3$ **10.** $x = -1, y = -3$
11. $x = 2, y = -2$ **12.** $x = 4, y = 3$

Exercise 6.2 *(p. 144)*

1. $x = 5, y = 4$
2. $x = 4, y = 1$
3. $x = \frac{5}{8}, y = 4$
4. $x = 10, y = -9$
5. $x = 1, y = -\frac{1}{3}$
6. $x = 3, y = 0$
7. $x = -2, y = -3$
8. $x = 9\frac{6}{7}, y = 1\frac{5}{7}$
9. $x = \frac{1}{2}, y = 2$
10. $x = 6, y = -\frac{1}{3}$
11. $x = \frac{3}{28}, y = \frac{13}{14}$
12. $x = 2, y = 5$
13. $x = \frac{1}{3}, y = -\frac{2}{3}$
14. $x = 2, y = 3$
15. $x = 4, y = -2$
16. $x = 8\frac{1}{2}, y = -2\frac{1}{2}$
17. No solution
18. Infinite number of solutions
19. No solution
20. $x = 0, y = -\frac{11}{3}$
21. $m = -1, n = 2$
22. $p = 3, q = -2$
23. $a = 5, b = -3$
24. $r = -4, s = 3$

Exercise 6.3 *(p. 148)*

1. $x = 3, y = 2$
2. $x = 4, y = 3$
3. $x = 2, y = 4$
4. $x = 5, y = 2$
5. $x = 4, y = 1$
6. $x = 3, y = 4$
7. $x = 10, y = -9$
8. $x = -4, y = 9$
9. $x = 6, y = 4$
10. $x = 4, y = 2\frac{1}{2}$
11. $x = 2, y = 3$
12. $x = 4, y = 3$
13. $x = 5, y = 1$
14. $x = -1\frac{1}{2}, y = 0$
15. $x = 1.5, y = 1$
16. $x = -1, y = 5$
17. $x = -1, y = 9$
18. $x = 1, y = 1.5$
19. $p = 2, q = -1$
20. $c = 2, d = -3$

Exercise 6.4 *(p. 150)*

1. 16, 7
2. 37°, 53°
3. 21 cents
4. \$6.75, \$8.25
5. $\frac{33}{24}, \frac{20}{24}$ or $\frac{11}{8}, \frac{5}{6}$
6. 58
7. 18 boys, 8 girls
8. shorter piece: 9 m, long piece: 27 m, original piece: 36 m
9. 135°
10. length: 96 cm, width: 64 cm
11. $\frac{7}{16}$
12. speed of boat: 15 km/h, speed of current: 3 km/h
13. apple: 35 cents, orange: 30 cents
14. 10, –3
15. pencil: 5 cents, ruler: 15 cents
16. $\hat{B} = 145°, \hat{C} = 15°$
17. walking: 5 km/h, cycling: 18 km/h
18. normal rate: \$2 per h, overtime rate: \$3 per h
19. 37
20. 45 km/h, 60 km/h
21. 600 cm^3, 400 cm^3, 1 200 g, 1 200 g
22. 49 yrs old

Chapter 7

Exercise 7.1 *(p. 159)*

1. (a)
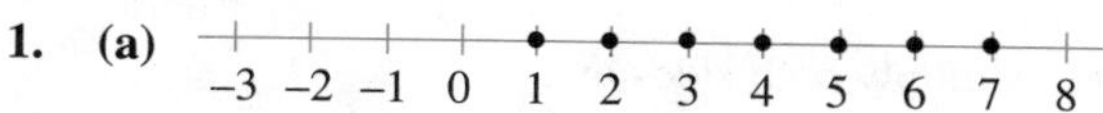

(b) –3 –2 –1 0 1 2 3 4 5 6 7 8

(c) –3 –2 –1 0 1 2 3 4 5 6 7 8

(d) –3 –2 –1 0 1 2 3 4 5 6 7 8

(e) –3 –2 –1 0 1 2 3 4 5 6 7 8

2. (a) –6 –5 –4 –3 –2 –1 0 1 2 3 4 5

(b) –6 –5 –4 –3 –2 –1 0 1 2 3 4 5

(c) –6 –5 –4 –3 –2 –1 0 1 2 3 4 5

(d) –6 –5 –4 –3 –2 –1 0 1 2 3 4 5

(e) –5 –4 –3 –2 –1 0 1 2 3 4 5

3. (a) –3 –2 –1 0 1 2 3 4 5 6

(b) –3 –2 –1 0 1 2 3 4 5 6

Exercise 7.2 (p. 162)

1. (a), (c), (d), (f), (g), (j), (k), (n)
2. **(a)** Add 3 to both sides. **(b)** Add –2 to both sides.
   (c) Add 3 to both sides. **(d)** Add 4 to both sides.
   (e) Add 5 to both sides. **(f)** Add –2 to both sides.
   (g) Add 4 to both sides. **(h)** Add –7 to both sides.
   (i) Add $-\frac{1}{2}$ to both sides. **(j)** Add $-\frac{2}{3}$ to both sides.
3. **(a)** Multiply both sides by $\frac{1}{2}$.
   (b) Multiply both sides by –1 and reverse the sign.
   (c) Multiply both sides by $\frac{1}{3}$.
   (d) Multiply both sides by $-\frac{1}{3}$ and reverse the sign.
   (e) Multiply both sides by $\frac{1}{3}$.
   (f) Multiply both sides by $-\frac{1}{2}$ and reverse the sign.
   (g) Multiply both sides by 2.
   (h) Multiply both sides by $\frac{3}{2}$.
   (i) Multiply both sides by 4.
   (j) Multiply both sides by $-\frac{1}{3}$ and reverse the sign.

Exercise 7.3 (p. 164)

1. **(a)** $x < 5$ **(b)** $x < 9$ **(c)** $x > 0$
   (d) $x > 19$ **(e)** $x < -2$ **(f)** $x \geqslant -19$
   (g) $x \leqslant 28$ **(h)** $x \geqslant 54$ **(i)** $x \leqslant 9$
2. **(a)** $x > -\frac{7}{6}$ **(b)** $x < \frac{17}{4}$ **(c)** $x > -\frac{14}{25}$
   (d) $x > \frac{19}{12}$ **(e)** $x < -\frac{15}{22}$ **(f)** $x \geqslant -\frac{1}{3}$
   (g) $x \leqslant \frac{3}{2}$ **(h)** $x \geqslant \frac{3}{32}$ **(i)** $x \leqslant \frac{37}{6}$
3. **(a)** $x > \frac{8}{3}$ **(b)** $x < -\frac{14}{5}$ **(c)** $x \geqslant \frac{19}{6}$
   (d) $x > -\frac{8}{7}$ **(e)** $x \leqslant -\frac{18}{5}$ **(f)** $x < -\frac{1}{4}$
   (g) $x \geqslant \frac{23}{9}$ **(h)** $x > -\frac{9}{4}$ **(i)** $x \leqslant -\frac{76}{45}$
   (j) $x \geqslant \frac{3}{4}$ **(k)** $x < -2$ **(l)** $x \leqslant -\frac{17}{9}$
   (m) $x \leqslant \frac{18}{7}$ **(n)** $x > -\frac{3}{4}$ **(o)** $x \leqslant \frac{3}{10}$
4. **(a)** $x \geqslant -\frac{4}{7}$ **(b)** $x > 1$ **(c)** $x \geqslant \frac{4}{3}$
   (d) $x \geqslant 16$ **(e)** $x > -\frac{21}{5}$ **(f)** $x < \frac{4}{25}$
   (g) $x \geqslant -\frac{18}{7}$ **(h)** $x > -\frac{15}{2}$ **(i)** $x \leqslant \frac{9}{8}$
   (j) $x \leqslant \frac{83}{28}$ **(k)** $x > \frac{34}{75}$ **(l)** $x \leqslant \frac{9}{10}$
   (m) $x > -\frac{87}{10}$ **(n)** $x \leqslant \frac{4}{77}$
5. **(a)** $\frac{22}{3}$ **(b)** 8
6. **(a)** 73 **(b)** 72
7. $x = 28$, $y = 35$; $x = 21$, $y = 42$; $x = 14$, $y = 49$; $x = 7$, $y = 56$
8. $x = 21$, $y = 21$; $x = 24$, $y = 15$; $x = 27$, $y = 9$; $x = 30$, $y = 3$

Chapter 8

Exercise 8.1 (p. 174)

1. **(a)** Yes, $\triangle ABC \equiv \triangle CDA$ (SSS)
   (b) Yes, $\triangle AOB \equiv \triangle DOC$ (SAS)
   (c) Yes, $\triangle ABD \equiv \triangle ACD$ (SAS)
   (d) Yes, $\triangle ABC \equiv \triangle EDC$ (AAS)
   (e) No
   (f) Yes, $\triangle ABC \equiv \triangle DEF$ (AAS)
   (g) Yes, $\triangle ABO \equiv \triangle CBO$ (RHS)
   (h) Yes, $\triangle PQR \equiv \triangle QPS$ (RHS)
   (i) Yes, $\triangle ABC \equiv \triangle FED$ (SAS)
   (j) Yes, $\triangle ABC \equiv \triangle BAD$ (RHS)
   (k) Yes, $\triangle LMN \equiv \triangle XYZ$ (SSS)
   (l) Yes, $\triangle ABE \equiv \triangle CBD$ (SSS)
   (m) Yes, $\triangle ALR \equiv \triangle QLR$ (SSS)
   (n) No
   (o) Yes, $\triangle ABC \equiv \triangle CDA$ (AAS)
   (p) No
   (q) Yes, $\triangle ABD \equiv \triangle BCD$ (SAS)
   (r) Yes, $\triangle ABD \equiv \triangle CBD$ (AAS or RHS)
   (s) Yes, $\triangle AOD \equiv \triangle COB$ (SSS)
   (t) No
   (u) Yes, $\triangle ABC \equiv \triangle BAD$ (AAS)
   (v) No
   (w) No
   (x) Yes, $\triangle DEF \equiv \triangle EGD$ (AAS)
   (y) No
   (z) No
2. **(a)** $x = 4.8$, $y = 42$ **(b)** $x = 16$, $y = 30$
   (c) $x = 69$, $y = 83$ **(d)** $x = 22$, $y = 17$
   (e) $x = 86$, $y = 64$
3. **(a)** Yes, $\triangle ABC \equiv \triangle XPG$ (SAS)
   (b) No
   (c) Yes, $\triangle ABC \equiv \triangle GPX$ (SSS)
   (d) No
   (e) Yes, $\triangle ABC \equiv \triangle PGX$ (AAS)
   (f) No

Exercise 8.2 *(p. 180)*

1. (a) Robert is constructing an angle bisector of $C\hat{A}B$.
   (b) $C\hat{A}D = B\hat{A}D$
2. (a) A perpendicular bisector of *AB* is being constructed.
   (b) The four triangles formed are right-angled triangles.
6. (a) Yes, AAS (b) (i) SSS (ii) SAS
7. (a) Yes, SAS (b) (i) SAS (ii) SAS

Exercise 8.3 *(p. 187)*

1. (a) Yes (b) Yes (c) Yes
   (d) Yes (e) No (f) No
2. (a) $\triangle EDC$ (b) $\triangle PMN$ (c) $\triangle WVU$
   (d) $\triangle ABC$ (e) $\triangle RUV$ (f) $\triangle AED$
   (g) $\triangle XYW$ (h) $\triangle RQP$
3. (a) Yes, $\triangle ADE$ and $\triangle ACB$ (b) Yes
4. (a) Yes (b) Yes (c) Yes
5. (a) $\triangle APQ$, $\triangle ABC$, QA; CA; $\frac{CB}{BA}$
   (b) $\triangle XLM$, $\triangle XZY$, XY; YZ, XY; XL; YX; XZ
6. (a) $x = 60$, $y = 50$, $z = 70$
   (b) $x = 30$, $y = 85$, $z = 65$
   (c) $x = 65$, $y = 40$, $z = 75$
   (d) $x = 110$, $y = 35$, $z = 35$
7. 8 units 8. 4 units 9. $\frac{12}{5}$ units
10. $\frac{20}{3}$ units 11. 6 units 12. 2 units
13. 3.6 cm 14. $x = 5.0$ cm, $y = 2.7$ cm, $z = 1.9$ cm

Revision Exercise 2

Revision 2A *(p. 197)*

1. (a) $x = -\frac{3}{2}$, $y = \frac{15}{8}$
   (b) No solution
2. 12, 6
3. (a) $x \geqslant \frac{23}{7}$ (b) $x > -\frac{21}{5}$
5. $112.50
6. (a) $y = 1$ (b) $x = 2.6, -3.1$
7. 34
8. (a) $1\frac{1}{3}$ cm (b) $9\frac{3}{5}$ cm (c) $3\frac{3}{14}$ cm
   (d) $6\frac{6}{7}$ cm (e) $11\frac{1}{4}$ cm (f) $10\frac{8}{9}$ cm
9. (a) (i) −1.9 (ii) 1 (b) (−1, 4.5)
10. about 17 days

Exercise 2B *(p. 198)*

1. (a) $x = \frac{20}{3}$, $y = \frac{8}{3}$ (b) $x = 2$, $y = -2$
2. 39 3. 4 units
4. (a) $x \geqslant -\frac{11}{15}$ (b) $x > 1$
6. (a) −3.75 (b) 10.1, −0.1
7. son – 8 years old
   father – 28 years old
8. $5 440 9. 120
10. (a) (ii) 45 km (b) $m = \frac{u^2}{u - f}$

Exercise 2C *(p. 199)*

1. (a) $x = \frac{3}{2}$, $y = 2$ (b) $x = -1$, $y = 2$
2. 36
3. (a) $\triangle CDB$ (b) $\triangle COD$ (c) $\triangle CBA$
   (d) $\triangle COB$
4. (a) 72 km (b) 43.2 km/h (c) 1 h 20 min
   (d) 60 km/h
   (e) 11 10 to 11 30, 60 km from its starting point, 20 min
   (f) 32 km from *A*'s starting point, 11 02
   (g) 11 10 to 11 30, 11 50 to 12 10
5. (a) $x \leqslant -\frac{5}{2}$ (b) $x \leqslant \frac{5}{8}$ 6. 4 : 3
7. (a) $6\frac{2}{3}$ cm (b) $8\frac{1}{3}$ cm (c) $2\frac{2}{5}$ cm
   (d) $9\frac{1}{3}$ cm
8. storybook – $7
   greeting card – $1
9. (a)

x	1	2	3	4	5	6	7
y	−1	0	3	8	15	24	35

   (c) 16.6 (d) 6.7
10. (a) $46.97
    (b) Same, since 3 × $8 × 103% × 90%
    = 3 × $8 × 90% × 103%

Revision 2D *(p. 201)*

1. (a) $x = 6$, $y = -\frac{2}{3}$ (b) $x = -2\frac{3}{31}$, $y = -\frac{23}{31}$
2. $\frac{13}{16}$
3. (a) $\triangle OAB$, $\triangle OCD$ (b) $\triangle OAB$, $\triangle ODC$
   (c) $\triangle OAB$, $\triangle OCD$ (d) Not possible
   (e) $\triangle OAB$, $\triangle OCD$ (f) $\triangle OAB$, $\triangle ODC$

4. **(a)** $x \leqslant \frac{11}{4}$ **(b)** $x < -\frac{7}{3}$ **(c)** $x > 1$

5. **(a)**

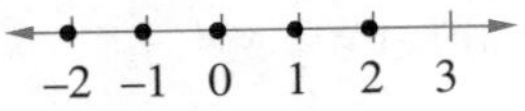

(b)

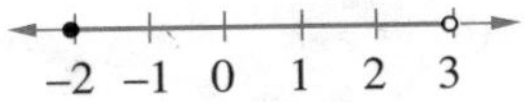

6. **(a)** 1 h 57 min **(b)** 11 33

7. **(a)** 52.5 km/h **(b)** 51 km/h
(c) 11 48, 56 km from *B*'s starting point
(d) 11 06, 32 km from *B*'s starting point

8. **(a)** 8 **(b)** 130

9. **(a)** $y = \frac{9}{5}x$ **(b)**

x (kg)	0	2.5
y ($)	0	4.50

(d) **(i)** $4.70 **(ii)** $13.00 **(iii)** $10.40
(iv) 5.6 kg **(v)** 6.4 kg **(vi)** 4.6 kg

10. $290

Revision 2E *(p. 204)*

1. **(a)** No solution **(b)** $x = 14\frac{2}{3}$; $y = \frac{17}{3}$

2. 20, 50

3. **(a)** $x > -\frac{7}{12}$ **(b)** $x \geqslant -\frac{2}{9}$

4. **(a)** $8\frac{3}{4}$ cm **(b)** $2\frac{1}{2}$ cm
(c) $13\frac{1}{2}$ cm **(d)** $4\frac{4}{9}$ cm

5. *X*: 17.5 km/h, *Y*: 7.5 km/h

6. Pen: 40 cents, Pencil: 10 cents

7. **(a)** *A*(–3, 0), *B*(0, –6), *C*(2, 0) **(b)** $2x + 1 = 0$

8. **(a)**

x	–3	–2	–1	0	1	2	3	4	5
y	17	10	5	2	1	2	5	10	17

(c) 7.3, 4.3, –2.4 **(d)** Yes

9. **(a)** 1st scheme: $2 500; 2nd scheme: $2 600
(b) $25 000

10. **(a)** 33 cm **(b)** 1 200 g **(c)** $L = 12 + \frac{3m}{100}$

Miscellaneous Exercise 2 *(p. 206)*

1. **(a)** F. Take $x = 2$, $2 > 2^2 > 2^3 > 2^4$ is false.
(b) F. Take $x = 0$, $0 < 0^2 < 0^3 < 0^4$ is false.
(c) F. Take $x = -1$, $-1 > (-1)^2 > (-1)^3 > (-1)^4$ is false since $-1 > (-1)^2$ is false.
(d) T. Take any positive proper fraction say $x = \frac{1}{2}$, $\frac{1}{2} > \left(\frac{1}{2}\right)^2 > \left(\frac{1}{2}\right)^3 > \left(\frac{1}{2}\right)^4$ is true.

2. **(a)** $\frac{18}{25}$ **(b)** 96 **(c)** 7

3. 7 **4.** **(a)** –1 **(b)** 1

5. **(a)** 16 **(b)** 9

6. **(b)** $5x - 4y + 4 > 0$ **(c)** $3\frac{1}{5} < x < 5$

7. **(a)** **(ii)** 12 45 **(b)** **(ii)** 55 km

8. **(a)** (4, 0) **(b)** **(i)** $x = 2$ **(ii)** (2, –4)
(c) (5, 5)

9. **(a)** **(i)** *x* stands for the number of apples and *y* stands for the number of oranges.
(ii) $90x + 25y = 740$
(iii) 6 apples, 8 oranges **(iv)** 16
(b) $a = \frac{5 - c}{8c - 1}$

10. **(a)** $x = 8$, $y = 6.4$ **(b)** $\frac{pm + qn}{px + qy}$

11. **(a)** **(i)** $\triangle ZXA$ **(ii)** 12.6 cm
(b) **(i)** $\triangle WBC$ **(ii)** $4\frac{1}{2}$ cm

Chapter 9

Exercise 9.1 *(p. 216)*

1. **(a)** 22 cm **(b)** 74 cm **(c)** 152 cm
(d) 37 cm **(e)** 90 cm **(f)** 156 cm

2. **(a)** 144 cm² **(b)** 359 cm² **(c)** 539 cm²
(d) 188 cm² **(e)** 462 cm² **(f)** 479 cm²

3. **(a)** **(i)** 13 cm **(ii)** 8 cm²
(b) **(i)** 11 cm **(ii)** 6 cm²

4. **(a)** **(i)** 47 cm **(ii)** 116 cm²
(b) **(i)** 27 cm **(ii)** 80 cm²

5. **(a)** 16° **(b)** 15° **(c)** 22°
(d) 43° **(e)** 327° **(f)** 300°

6. **(a)** 65° **(b)** 214° **(c)** 187°
(d) 320° **(e)** 18° **(f)** 24°

7. **(a)** 15 cm **(b)** 12 cm

8. **(a)** 68 cm **(b)** 36 cm

9. **(a)** 25 cm² **(b)** 21 cm² **(c)** 49 cm²
(d) 141 cm² **(e)** 450 cm² **(f)** 163 cm²

10. 9° **11.** **(a)** 0.25 kg **(b)** 0.056 kg

12. 82 cm **13.** 67 cm²

14. **(a)** 36 min **(b)** 22 cm

Exercise 9.2 *(p. 223)*

1. **(a)** 15 cubic units **(b)** 600 cubic units
(c) 616 cubic units **(d)** 196 cubic units

2. **(i)** **(a)** 754 cm^3 **(b)** 1 232 cm^3 **(c)** 4 714 cm^3 **(d)** 1 018 cm^3 **(e)** 1 006 cm^3 **(f)** 302 cm^3
(ii) **(a)** 943 cm^2 **(b)** 704 cm^2 **(c)** 1 886 cm^2 **(d)** 679 cm^2 **(e)** 629 cm^2 **(f)** 302 cm^2

3. 96 cm^2, 48 cm^3 **4.** 72 cm^2, 8.5 cm
5. 36 cm^3 **6.** $188\frac{4}{7}$ cm^3
7. 34π cm^2, 40π cm^3 **8.** 15 cm
9. 867 cm^3, 490 cm^2 **10.** 1 760 cm^3
11. 288 cm^3 **12.** $19\frac{1}{11}$ cm
13. **(a)** $8x$ cm^3 **(b)** 500 cm^3

Exercise 9.3 *(p. 227)*

1. **(a)** 408 cm^3, 266 cm^2 **(b)** 2 757 cm^3, 951 cm^2
(c) 19 852 cm^3, 3 545 cm^2
(d) 3 590 cm^3, 1 134 cm^2
(e) 6 879 cm^3, 1 749 cm^2 **(f)** 14 703 cm^3, 2 902 cm^2

2. **(a)** 7 cm, $1\,437\frac{1}{3}$ cm^3 **(b)** 2 cm, $33\frac{11}{21}$ cm^3
(c) 3 cm, $113\frac{1}{7}$ cm^3 **(d)** 21 cm, 38 808 cm^3
(e) 14 cm, $11\,498\frac{2}{3}$ cm^3 **(f)** 4 cm, $268\frac{4}{21}$ cm^3

3. 113 143 litres **4.** 12.2 cm
5. **(a)** 8 : 1 **(b)** 4 : 1
6. **(a)** 64 : 1 **(b)** 16 : 1
7. 374 million km^2 **8.** 1 047 cm^3
9. Volume increases to 8 times its original volume. Surface area increases to 4 times its original surface area.
10. Volume decreases to $\frac{1}{8}$ of the original volume.
Surface area decreases to $\frac{1}{4}$ of the original surface area.
11. \$200 **12.** 3 486 cm^3, 1 408 cm^2
13. 415 cm^2, 754 cm^3
14. **(a)** 452 cm^3 **(b)** 10.8 cm **(c)** 824 g **(d)** 10

Exercise 9.4 *(p. 232)*

1. **(a)** $\frac{9}{25}$ **(b)** $\frac{9}{16}$ **(c)** $\frac{49}{81}$ **(d)** $\frac{25}{64}$
2. 4 : 25 **3.** 9 : 1 **4.** 5 : 1
5. 136.11 cm^2 **6.** 5.56 cm^2 **7.** 33.75 cm^2
8. $5\frac{1}{2}$ cm^2 **9.** 33 750 m^2
10. 4 cm^2 **11.** $2\frac{2}{3}$ cm^2 **12.** 12 cm^2
13. $2\frac{2}{3}$, 6
14. **(a)** $C\hat{A}B = A\hat{B}D$ **(b)** **(i)** $\frac{AB}{AD}$ **(ii)** $\frac{AB^2}{AC^2}$
15. **(a)** $\frac{2}{1}, \frac{2}{3}$ **(b)** $\frac{4}{5}$
16. **(a)** 16 cm^2 **(b)** 18 cm^2
17. 7.5 km^2 **18.** \$36.45
19. **(a)** 37 km **(b)** 80 cm^2
20. **(a)** 4.6 cm **(b)** 5.6 m^2
21. **(a)** 93 cm **(b)** 14.5 cm^2
22. **(a)** 8 cm **(b)** 18 cm^2

Exercise 9.5 *(p. 238)*

1. **(a)** 8 : 27 **(b)** 27 : 125 **(c)** 27 : 64 **(d)** 27 : 343
2. **(a)** 12 cubic units **(b)** 7 cubic units **(c)** 2.2 cubic units **(d)** 160 cubic units
3. 101.25 g
4. The orange with diameter 6 cm.
5. **(a)** 800π m^3 **(b)** $\frac{2\,000\pi}{3}$ m^3 **(c)** $\frac{4\,400}{3}\pi$ m^3
(d) $3\,200\pi$ m^3 **(e)** $\frac{16\,000}{3}\pi$ m^3 **(f)** $\frac{25\,600}{3}\pi$ m^3
6. 9×10^{-4} m^3
7. **(a)** **(i)** $\frac{9}{25}$ **(ii)** $\frac{27}{125}$
(b) **(i)** $\frac{9}{16}$ **(ii)** $\frac{27}{64}$
(c) **(i)** $\frac{1}{9}$ **(ii)** $\frac{1}{27}$
8. **(a)** 2 : 3 **(b)** 675 cm^3
9. **(a)** 2 : 3 **(b)** 81 cm^2
10. 2 187 g **11.** 200 cm^2 **12.** 1 : 27 000
13. **(a)** 35 cm **(b)** $\frac{4}{25}$
14. **(a)** 7.5 cm **(b)** 8 : 27 **(c)** \$2.70

Chapter 10

Exercise 10.1 *(p. 253)*

1. **(a)** *AC* **(b)** *XZ*
2. **(a)** 10 **(b)** 12 **(c)** 24
3. **(a)** 24 **(b)** 17 **(c)** 63
4. **(a)** 12 **(b)** 9 **(c)** 13
5. **(b)** Right-angled triangle; $\hat{P}$
(c) Right-angled triangle; $\hat{X}$
(e) Right-angled triangle; $\hat{D}$
(f) Right-angled triangle; $\hat{M}$

6. **(a)** **(i)** 8.16 **(ii)** 25.7 **(iii)** 10.7 **(iv)** 263
(b) **(i)** 32.4 **(ii)** 43.3 **(iii)** 8.36 **(iv)** 15.7
(c) **(i)** 26.0 **(ii)** 67.9 **(iii)** 108 **(iv)** 4.02
7. 3 m 8. 3.1 m 9. 10 m
10. $h = 12$, $a = 20$ 11. $x = 36$, $a = 25$
12. $QR = 28$ 13. 8.5 m
14. $B\hat{F}H = 90°$, $BH = 13$ 15. 24 cm
16. 5 cm 17. 9 cm

Exercise 10.2 *(p. 259)*

1. 4.7 m, 1.7 m (Scale 2 cm : 1 m)
2. 355 m, 355 m (Scale 1 cm : 50 m)
3. 25 m (Scale 1 cm : 5 m)
4. 42 m (Scale 1 cm : 5 m)

Exercise 10.3 *(p. 262)*

1. **(a)** AC, AB, BC **(b)** PR, PQ, QR
(c) YZ, XZ, XY **(d)** RT, ST, RS
2. **(a)** $\sin y = \frac{ZX}{YZ}$, $\cos y = \frac{XY}{YZ}$, $\tan y = \frac{ZX}{XY}$
(b) $\sin z = \frac{XY}{YZ}$, $\cos z = \frac{XZ}{YZ}$, $\tan z = \frac{XY}{ZX}$
3. **(a)** $\sin A = \frac{m}{q}$, $\cos A = \frac{p}{q}$, $\tan A = \frac{m}{p}$
(b) $\sin A = \frac{p}{q}$, $\cos A = \frac{m}{q}$, $\tan A = \frac{p}{m}$
(c) $\sin A = \frac{m}{p}$, $\cos A = \frac{q}{p}$, $\tan A = \frac{m}{q}$
(d) $\sin A = \frac{q}{m}$, $\cos A = \frac{p}{m}$, $\tan A = \frac{q}{p}$

Exercise 10.4 *(p. 264)*

1. **(a)** 0.342 0 **(b)** 0.427 4 **(c)** 0.678 2
(d) 0.939 7 **(e)** 0.937 3 **(f)** 0.879 6
(g) 1.000 **(h)** 2.087 **(i)** 1.213
(j) 0.719 3 **(k)** 0.700 2 **(l)** 0.882 9
(m) 0.414 7 **(n)** 0.945 7 **(o)** 0.576 4
(p) 0.073 24 **(q)** 0.054 16 **(r)** 0.068 02
(s) 0.285 8 **(t)** 0.755 1 **(u)** 0.350 8
2. **(a)** 0.6° **(b)** 14.2° **(c)** 20.7°
(d) 5.1° **(e)** 17.1° **(f)** 89.2°
(g) 1.1° **(h)** 44.9° **(i)** 50.9°
3. **(a)** 71.0° **(b)** 45.2° **(c)** 19.5°
(d) 73.5°
4. **(a)** 0.396 0 **(b)** 0.490 9 **(c)** 0.165 0
(d) 0.513 1 **(e)** 0.663 1

Exercise 10.5 *(p. 266)*

1. **(a)** 25 **(b)** 43 **(c)** 190 **(d)** 15
2. **(a)** 13.81 **(b)** 12.78 **(c)** 27.23 **(d)** 10.39
3. **(a)** 64° **(b)** 42° **(c)** 58° **(d)** 70°
4. **(a)** 29.1° **(b)** 36.9° **(c)** 44.4° **(d)** 34.1°
5. 9 cm, 5 cm 6. 40 cm 7. 13 cm
8. $XY = 16$ cm, $XN = 12$ cm 9. 48°, 48°, 84°
10. **(a)** $p = 10$, $x° = 56°$ **(b)** $q = 23$, $t = 22$
(c) $m° = 38°$, $p = 11$ **(d)** $p = 35$, $m = 24$
(e) $r = 14$, $u° = 50°$ **(f)** $x = 32$, $y° = 71°$
11. 10 units, 162 sq units
12. **(a)** By Pythagoras' Theorem, $AB = 9$ cm
(b) **(i)** $\frac{9}{40}$ **(ii)** 102.7° **(iii)** 167.3°
13. $x = 43.2$, 0.729 m
14. **(a)** 4.24 cm **(b)** 21.2 cm^2 **(c)** 15.9 cm^2
15. **(a)** $9x^2 = 5^2 + 10^2 - 2 \times 5 \times 10 \cos 27°$ **(b)** 2.0

Exercise 10.6 *(p. 272)*

1. 5.20 m, 3 m 2. 212 m, 212 m 3. 11.5 m
4. 7 m 5. 34 m 6. 63°
7. 53.1° 8. 24 m 9. 35°
10. **(a)** 4.58 m **(b)** 66.4°
11. **(a)** 3 m **(b)** 3.56 m^2
12. **(a)** 4.2 m
(b) **(i)** $3.25 \text{ m} \leqslant \text{distance} < 3.75$ m
(ii) $45° \leqslant \text{angle} < 55°$
13. 109.8°
14. **(a)** 36 cm, 48 cm **(b)** 228 cm
15. 283 m 16. 49° 17. 502 m
18. **(a)** 36.0 m **(b)** 14.6 m
(c) 15.1° **(d)** 55.8 m
19. **(a)** 51.2 m **(b)** **(i)** 38.7° **(ii)** 50.2°
20. **(a)** $b = \frac{c \sin B}{\sin ECA}$ **(b)** 17.1 cm

Chapter 11

Exercise 11.1 *(p. 285)*

4. **(a)** (4, 2), (–1, 3), (–3, 4), (5, –2), (3, 0), (–4, 0)
(b) (–4, –2), (1, –3), (3, –4), (–5, 2), (–3, 0), (4, 0)

Exercise 11.2 *(p. 290)*

3. **(a)** $A'(-1, 1)$, $B'(-3, 3)$
(b) $C'(2, 1)$, $D'(3, 2)$, $E'(1, 3)$
(c) $F'(-1, 1)$, $G'(-1, 2)$, $H'(-3, 2)$, $I'(-3, 1)$
(d) $J'(2, 0)$, $K'(0, 2)$, $L'(-2, 0)$, $M'(0, -2)$
4. **(a)** $A'(1, -2)$, $B'(1, -3)$, $C'(2, -1)$
(b) (–1, –4), (–2, –4), (–3, –4), (–2, –2)

Exercise 11.3 (p. 295)

2. **(a)** $A'(2, 0)$, $B'(3, -1)$, $C'(4, -1)$
(b) $A'(0, -1)$, $B'(2, -2)$, $C'(2, -1)$
(c) $A'(-1, 2)$, $B'(-1, 1)$, $C'(1, 1)$, $D'(0, 2)$
(d) $A'(1, -1)$, $B'(1, -2)$, $C'(2, -3)$, $D'(2, -2)$
(e) $A'(3, 2)$, $B'(1, 2)$, $C'(1, 1)$, $D'(3, 1)$
(f) $A'(-2, -1)$, $B'(-3, -3)$, $C'(-1, -2)$

Exercise 11.4 (p. 300)

2. $A'(2, 2)$, $B'(6, 6)$
3. $\left(4\frac{1}{2}, 4\frac{1}{2}\right)$, $\left(1\frac{1}{2}, 1\frac{1}{2}\right)$, $(6, 3)$
4. $A'\left(\frac{2}{3}, 2\right)$, $B\left(\frac{2}{3}, \frac{2}{3}\right)$, $C'\left(2, \frac{2}{3}\right)$, $D'(2, 2)$
5. Multiply the coordinates by the enlargement factor.
6. **(a)** $A'(2, 6)$, $B'(2, 4)$, $C'(6, 2)$, $D'(8, 4)$, $E'(10, 8)$
(b) $A'(2.5, 7.5)$, $B'(2.5, 5)$, $C'(7.5, 2.5)$, $D'(10, 5)$, $E'(12.5, 10)$
(c) $A'(0.5, 1.5)$, $B'(0.5, 1)$, $C'(1.5, 0.5)$, $D'(2, 1)$, $E'(2.5, 2)$

Exercise 11.5 (p. 303)

1. **(a)** Rotation 90° clockwise about O followed by reflection in the x-axis.
(b) Rotation 90° clockwise about O followed by translation –3 units on y-axis.
(c) Enlargement by factor 2 followed by reflection in the y-axis.
(d) Reflection on y-axis followed by enlargement of factor $\frac{1}{2}$.
2. **(a)** **(i)** P – Reflection in the x-axis.
Q – Reflection in the y-axis.
(ii) Rotation 180° about O.
(b) **(i)** P – Reflection in the y-axis.
Q – Rotation 180° about O.
(ii) Reflection in the x-axis.
(c) **(i)** P – Enlargement by factor 3.
Q – Enlargement by factor $\frac{2}{3}$.
(ii) Enlargement by factor 2.
(d) **(i)** P – Translation by 8 units in the x-axis.
Q – Reflection in the y-axis.
(ii) Reflection at $x = -4$.
3. $A'(1, -2)$, $B'(1, -4)$, $C'(2, -4)$, $A''(-1, 2)$, $B''(-1, 4)$, $C''(-2, 4)$
4. $A'(-1, 0)$, $B'(-2, -2)$, $C'(-1, -2)$, $A''(-1, 0)$, $B''(-2, 2)$, $C''(-1, 2)$
5. $A'(2, 1)$, $B'(1, 2)$, $C'(1, 1)$, $A''(4, 2)$, $B''(2, 4)$, $C''(2, 2)$
6. **(a)** $(5, -6)$ **(b)** $(3, -2)$
7. **(a)** $A_1 = (5, 2)$, $A_2 = (3, 2)$ **(b)** $k = 1$
8. **(a)** $(-2, -2)$ **(b)** $(-2, -8)$

Revision Exercise 3

Revision 3A (p. 312)

1. 728 m **2.** $a = 49$, $b = 600$; Yes
4. **(a)** **(i)** 12 cm **(ii)** 4 cm^2
(b) **(i)** 26 cm **(ii)** 34 cm^2
5. $A'(0, -1)$, $B'(2, -1)$, $C'(2, -2)$
6. 120 cm^2 **7.** 88 cm^2
8. **(a)** **(i)** 20 cm^3 **(ii)** 45 cm^2
(b) **(i)** 33 cm^3 **(ii)** 63 cm^2
9. **(a)** 16 cm **(b)** 13 cm **(c)** $9\frac{1}{11}$ cm
10. **(a)** 10 cm **(b)** 31.42 cm **(c)** 157.1 cm^2

Revision 3B (p. 314)

1. **(a)** 1 099 cm^3, 515 cm^2 **(b)** 1 989 cm^3, 765 cm^2
2. **(a)** $DC = 2$ cm **(b)** $AD = 10$ cm
(c) $A\hat{D}B = 53.1°$
3. 10.9 m^2
4. $A'(1, 2)$, $B'(1, 1)$, $C'(2, 1)$
6. **(a)** **(i)** 34 cm **(ii)** 66 cm^2
(b) **(i)** 40 cm **(ii)** 79 cm^2
7. The circular pizza of diameter 32 cm.
8. **(a)** 270° **(b)** 141.3 cm
9. **(a)** 6 cm **(b)** 5 cm
10. **(c)** 24.8 m **(d)** $210.80

Revision 3C (p. 315)

1. **(a)** 16π cm^2 **(b)** 8
2. 0.5 kg, 123 cm^2
3. **(a)** 102.7° **(b)** 53.9 m
5. $A'(1, 4)$, $B'(3, 3)$, $C'(2, 2)$
6. **(a)** $P(4, 1)$, $Q(4, 4)$, $R(2, 4)$
(b) $3\frac{1}{2}$ sq units **(c)** $2\frac{1}{2}$ sq units
7. **(a)** 40 m **(b)** 3 m^3
8. **(a)** **(i)** 15.5 m **(ii)** 7.89 m
(b) 38.3°
9. **(b)** **(i)** 231 m **(ii)** 3 860 m^2
10. **(a)** **(i)** 78.5 cm^2 **(ii)** 942 cm^3
(b) 1 100 g **(c)** 30

Revision 3D (p. 318)

1. **(a)** 5 m **(b)** 9 m
2. **(a)** 120° **(b)** 1 440° **(c)** 75°
3. **(a)** 1.125 kg
(b) **(i)** 5 cm **(ii)** 150 cm^2
(c) 2.57 cm
4. $(-1, 2)$, $(-2, 4)$, $(-3, 3)$

5. **(a)** 37.71 cm^3 **(b)** 56.57 cm^3
6. **(a)** 4 times **(b)** 27 times
7. $A'(1, -1)$, $B'(1, -2)$, $C'(2, -2)$, $A''(-1, -1)$, $B''(-1, -2)$, $C''(-2, -2)$
8. **(a)** 15 cm **(c)** 6.2 cm
(e) **(i)** $\frac{1}{4}$ **(ii)** $\frac{2}{3}$
9. **(a)** 1 m 70 cm **(b)** 63
10. **(a)** **(i)** 20 000 cm^3
(ii) 0.02 m^3
(b) **(i)** 5 cm
(ii) 15 710 cm^3
(c) 78.55%

Revision 3E *(p. 320)*

1. **(a)** 54 cm^2 **(b)** 24.5° **2.** 233 m
3. **(a)** $V = 27\,000v$ **(b)** 0.6 m^2
5. 1 680 cm^3 **6.** Reflection in the x-axis.
7. **(a)** 678.67 cm^3 **(b)** 84.83 cm^3
(c) **(i)** $\frac{x}{3}$ cm **(ii)** $\frac{\pi x^3}{27}$
8. **(a)** 2.62 cm **(b)** 6.55 cm^2 **(c)** 7.14 cm^2
9. **(a)** 45 cm **(b)** 15 cm **(c)** 36 cm^3
10. **(a)** $\frac{9}{16}$ **(b)** $\frac{3}{7}$ **(c)** $\frac{40}{49}$ **(d)** $\frac{3}{7}$

Miscellaneous Exercise 3 *(p. 324)*

1. **(a)** T
(b) F. AA', BB' and CC' may not intersect at the centre of enlargement.
(c) T
(d) F. The ratios $\frac{A'O}{AO}$, $\frac{B'O}{BO}$ and $\frac{C'O}{CO}$ may not all be equal.
2. **(a)** 2 **(b)** $\left(5\frac{1}{2}, 4\frac{1}{2}\right)$
3. **(a)** **(i)** 7.6° **(ii)** 3 030 m
(b) 1 270 m **(c)** 42°
4. **(a)** 49 100 m^2 **(b)** 26.04°
5. **(b)** 60 **(c)** 21.49 l
6. 7 461 cm^3
7. **(a)** 37.5 m^2 **(b)** 1 h **(c)** 1.5 m
8. **(a)** **(i)** 12 cm **(ii)** 3 cm
(b) **(i)** 25 : 4 **(ii)** 13 : 4
9. **(a)** 113.62 cm^3 **(b)** 132.16 cm^3
10. 164 cm^2 **11.** $\frac{3}{10}$ **12.** 7 cm^2
13. **(a)** $\frac{4}{9}$ **(b)** $BE = 4\frac{1}{2}$ cm, $ED = 3$ cm
14. **(a)** 3 : 2 **(b)** $\sqrt{3} : \sqrt{2}$
15. 138 cm^2

Chapter 12

Exercise 12.2 *(p. 341)*

1. **(a)** 10 **(b)** 70 **(c)** 155
(d) 29.03% **(e)** 75
2. **(a)** 190 **(b)** 870 **(c)** Sec 1
(d) Sec 3 and Sec 4 **(e)** 18%
3. **(a)** 107 cm **(b)** 32 cm
(c) January, February, December
(d) June, July, August
(e) March, April, October, November
4. **(a)** 300 **(b)** 90 **(c)** 60
(d) **(i)** 415 **(ii)** 235 **(iii)** 36%
5. **(a)** 5 500 000 m^3
(b) Monday, 800 000 m^3
(c) Friday, 762 000 m^3
(d) Monday, Wednesday, Saturday, Sunday
(e) Thursday, Friday
(f) 10 000 m^3
6. **(a)** 1994 – 7 000, 1995 – 9 000, 1996 – 11 000, 1997 – 16 000
(b) \$1 750 000
(c) 45%
7. **(a)** Science – 2 200, Arts – 1 250, Commerce – 1 000
(b) **(i)** 1 150 **(ii)** 1 500 **(c)** 57%
(d) Science – 44%, Arts – 28%, Commerce – 28%
8. **(b)** 48.1%
11. **(a)**

Trumpet	French horn	Cymbals	Drum	Flute	Clarinet
11	10	5	11	10	12

Exercise 12.3 *(p. 348)*

1. Oranges – \$2 175, Apples – \$1 350, Bananas – \$1 050, Mangoes – \$825
2. Science fiction – 40, Short stories – 60, Classics – 30, Others – 50
4. **(b)** 38.9%
5. **(a)** boys – 200°, girls – 145°, teachers – 15°
(b) **(i)** 2 000 **(ii)** 1 450 **(iii)** 150
(c) 150°
6. **(b)** 27.8%
8.

	Others	Science	English	Mathematics
No. of students	45	90	135	810
% of students	4.2%	8.3%	12.5%	75%

12. **(a)** **(i)** 15 **(ii)** 25% **(b)** 480
13. **(a)** 146 **(b)** 900 **(c)** 15%
14. **(a)** 135 **(b)** 7 **(c)** 30%
15. **(a)** **(i)** 1 000 **(ii)** 96 **(b)** 650
16. **(a)** 72° **(b)** 36° **17.** 540
18. 40°, 120°, 200°
19. *A*: 120 tonnes, *B*: 160 tonnes, *C*: 200 tonnes
20. **(a)** 140° **(b)** 31

Exercise 12.4 *(p. 354)*

1. **(b)** 1985 – 1990
2. **(b)** From Monday to Friday, mostly tourists visit the zoo.
On Saturday and Sunday, the visitors include a large proportion of locals because of weekend family outings.
3. **(a)** A fixed fare was charged for the first kilometre.
After travelling 3 kilometres, there was a traffic jam but the fare meter still kept on running.
(b) The man married at 28 years old.
From ages 35–40, his children went to school, therefore he spent more.
He bought a car at age 40 and paid it off 2 years later.
From ages 44–55, his expenditure grew with the cost of living.
He retired at age 55 and enjoyed his pension.
(c) Between 7.30 a.m. and 10.15 a.m., only cars with a special label were allowed to pass this point to go into the city. The same thing happened between 4.30 p.m. and 6.30 p.m.
(d) The lift stopped at the 6th floor and 18th floor.
At the 2nd floor, the lift stopped for 30 sec before someone at the ground floor summoned it.
7. A poor and distorted representation.
The size is not proportional to the number.
It is better to represent it by different numbers of cups of the same size.
8. **(a)** *C* **(b)** *B*

Chapter 13

Exercise 13.1 *(p. 372)*

2. **(a)** 58 kg **(b)** one
(c) 60 kg
(d) **(i)** 12 **(ii)** 7 **(iii)** 2 **(iv)** 7
3. **(a)** 5 students **(b)** 11 marks
(c) 9 **(d)** 50 students

Exercise 13.2 *(p. 378)*

1. **(a)** mean = 2.83, median = 2.5, mode = 2
(b) mean = 6.2, median = 6, mode = 4
(c) mean = 5, median = 5, mode = 5
(d) mean = 6, median = 7, mode = 8
(e) mean = 66.7, median = 65, mode = 46
(f) mean = 10.1, median = 10, mode = 9.8

2. **(a)**

Grades obtained	1	2	3	4	5	6
No. of students	3	7	10	8	7	5

(c) mode = 3 **(d)** median = 3.5 **(e)** 3.6

3. **(a)**

No. of heads	0	1	2	3
No. of times	2	7	7	4

(c) mode = 1 and 2, median = 2
(d) mean = 1.65
4. **(c)** mode = 128 min, median = 127.5 min
(d) mean = 127.45 min
5. **(c)** mode = 58, median = 59
(d) 59
6. **(b)** **(i)** 90 **(ii)** 30 **(iii)** 30
(c) 150
(d) mean = 5.6, mode = 7, median = 6
7. **(b)** mode = 7, median = 7
(c) mean = 6.73
8. **(a)** 29 **(b)** 2 **(c)** 1
9. **(a)** 34 **(b)** Friday **(c)** 4.9
10. **(b)** **(i)** median = 4
(ii) mode = 2
(c) mean = 3.93
11. **(b)** 40
(c) **(i)** mode = 0 **(ii)** median = 0
(iii) mean = 1.425
12. **(b)** 143 children
(c) **(i)** median = 3 **(ii)** mode = 4
(iii) mean = 2.86

Exercise 13.3 *(p. 383)*

1. **(a)** mode or median **(b)** mean
(c) No, not exactly; Yes, misleading; answer varies
(d) answer varies
2. **(a)** median **(b)** 6% **(c)** 6%
3. **(a)** mean
(b) mode, mean (correct to the nearest dollar)
(c) Most students have more than $3.00. Although the idea of mode is implied, it is not exactly correct to say that the mode is more than $3.00.
(d) mode, mean (correct to the nearest dollar)
(e) mean
(f) median, mode

Chapter 14

Exercise 14.1 *(p. 391)*

1. (a) 2 (b) 3 (c) 1 (d) 6 (e) 0 (f) 0
2. (a) x^2 and x^2 (b) a^3 and $2a^3$ (c) $3xy$ and xy (d) $7x^4y^5z^3$ and $x^4y^5z^3$ (e) ab^3c^2 and $(-1)ab^3c^2$ (f) $3^3x^2y^2$ and $4^3x^2y^2$ (g) 2^3a^2b, 2^4a^2b and 2^5a^2b
3. (a) $x^4 + 3x^3 - 4x^2 - x - 3$ (b) $x^5 + x^4 + 8x^3 + 4x + 1$ (c) $x^5 + 3x^4 - 2x^3 + 8x^2 + x + 6$ (d) $x^6 - 2x^5 + 7x^4 + x^3 - 6$
4. (a) $5x^2 - x$ (b) $-3p + 11q$ (c) $10x - 4y + 9z$ (d) $2d^3 - 5d^2 - 3d - 1$ (e) $2x^2 - 3xy + 2y^2$ (f) $-16n^3 + 2n^2 - 2n$ (g) $-2y$ (h) $-2x^2 - 2x + 14$
5. $-3a^2 + 5a - 3$
6. $4x^2 - x + 1$
7. $5x^2 + 5xy - 3y^2$
8. $-6a^2 - 4a - 13$

Exercise 14.2 *(p. 393)*

1. (a) $21a^4 + 3a^2$ (b) $-10d^2 - 15d + 5$ (c) $-2b^3 + 2b^2 + 8b$ (d) $y^8 - y^6 + y^3$ (e) $-2n^8 + n^6 - 7n^5$ (f) $3t^2 - 2t^3 - t^7$
2. (a) $2x^6 + 4x^2 + 6x$ (b) $6x^2 - 5x - 6$ (c) $15m^2 + 7mn - 2n^2$ (d) $x^3 - 2x^2 - x - 6$ (e) $a^3 + a^2 - 2a + 12$ (f) $-4x^5 - 6x^4 - 2x^3 + 4x^2 + 6x + 2$ (g) $10a^4 - 9a^3 - 8a^2 + 9a - 2$ (h) $-6m^4 - 3m^3 - 11m^2 - 4m - 4$ (i) $21n^8 - 6n^7 - 7n^6 + 25n^5 - 4n^4 - 6n^3 + 6n^2 + n - 2$ (j) $-3x^5 + 2x^4 - 4x^3 - 8x^2 + 11x - 14$
3. (a) $6x^4 - 11x^3 + 8x^2 + 4x - 5$ (b) $4ab$ (c) $4y^5 - 21y^4 - 6y^3 - y^2 + y + 1$ (d) $x^5 + 7x^4 + x^3 - x^2 - 2$ (e) $x^4 - 3x^3 - 2$ (f) $x^6 + 3x^4 - 2x^3 - x + 1$

Exercise 14.3 *(p. 395)*

1. (a) $4x^3 + 10x^2 + 21x + 40$ R 81 (b) $2x^3 + 6x^2 + 12x + 27$ R 54 (c) $x^2 + 3x + 8$ R 17 (d) $4x^2 + 10x + 22$ R 41
2. (a) $2x^2 - 6x + 12$ R -22 (b) $x^3 - x^2 + x - 2$ R 8 (c) $3x^2 - 6x + 10$ R -22 (d) $2x^3 - 3x^2 + 3x - 3$ R 6
3. (a) $2x^3 + x^2 + x + 2$ R -3 (b) $x^3 + 3x^2 + x$ R 2 (c) $3x^3 + x + 6$ R 0 (d) $-x^2 - 2x + 3$ R 8
4. (a) $4x^2 - x + 2$ R 0 (b) $3x^3 - x^2 - 5x - 1$ R -4 (c) $2x^3 - 2x^2 - 1$ R 6 (d) $3x^2 - x + 4$ R 2

Exercise 14.4 *(p. 399)*

1. (a) $\frac{x-1}{x+1}$ (b) $\frac{x+1}{x-1}$ (c) $\frac{2x-1}{2(x+2)}$ (d) $\frac{2(x-2)}{x-1}$
2. (a) $\frac{1+x}{1-x}$ (b) $\frac{1-x}{1+x}$ (c) $\frac{2(x-4)}{x-5}$ (d) $\frac{2(2+3x)}{x(2-3x)}$
3. (a) $\frac{3x+1}{3(x+9)}$ (b) (i) $-\frac{1}{3}$ (ii) 2
4. (a) $\frac{3(x-3)}{2(x+1)}$ (b) (i) 3 (ii) 7
5. (a) $\frac{3x+4}{2x-3}$ (b) (i) $-\frac{4}{3}$ (ii) -7
6. (a) $\frac{x-1}{x-2}$ (b) (i) 1 (ii) $\frac{5}{2}$
7. (a) $\frac{3x-8}{2(x+3)}$ (b) (i) $\frac{8}{3}$ (ii) -4
8. (a) $\frac{37x}{(2x-5)(7x+1)}$ (b) (i) 0 (ii) $5, -\frac{1}{14}$
9. (a) $\frac{-5(x+1)}{(x+3)(1-3x)}$ (b) (i) -1 (ii) $-2, \frac{5}{3}$
10. (a) $\frac{2x-3}{x(x-1)}$ (b) (i) $\frac{3}{2}$ (ii) 2, 3

Exercise 14.5 *(p. 401)*

1. (c) Yes (e) Yes (g) Yes
2. (a) $a = 3, b = 2$ (b) $a = -4, b = 1$ (c) $a = 4, b = -3$ (d) $a = 0, b = -5$
3. (a) $a = 2, b = -1$ (b) $a = 1, b = -2$ (c) $a = 4, b = 5$ (d) $a = 15, b = -8$
4. (a) $a = 1, b = 0$ (b) $a = 2, b = 0$ (c) $a = 2, b = 3$ (d) $a = 2, b = 1$

Exercise 14.6 *(p. 403)*

1. (a) $x = y - 1$ (b) $x = \frac{y-1}{2}$ (c) $x = \frac{y+3}{5}$ (d) $x = \frac{3y+1}{2}$
2. (a) $y = 9z - 8$ (b) $y = 16z + 5$ (c) $y = 9z + 16$ (d) $y = 49z - 36$
3. (a) $x = \frac{y+5}{2}$ (b) $x = \frac{z+15}{4}$

4. **(a)** $x = \frac{y-7}{3}$ **(b)** $x = \frac{z-28}{9}$

5. **(a)** $x = \frac{y+6}{5}$ **(b)** $x = \frac{z+36}{25}$

10. **(a)** $\frac{37xy}{(2x-5y)(7x+y)}$

(b) **(i)** $x = 0$ **(ii)** $x = 3$ or $-\frac{5}{42}$

Revision Exercise 4

Revision 4A *(p. 407)*

1. 200°, 160°
2. **(a)** **(i)** 8 **(ii)** 308 **(b)** 6
3. 15% **4.** **(a)** 39 **(b)** 20
5. **(a)** 5 **(b)** 4 **(c)** 3.2
6. **(a)** $\frac{1}{3}$ **(b)** 105 **(c)** 37.5%
7. **(a)** $32a^5 + 12a^2$ **(b)** $2x^2 + 3x + 2$ R -3
8. **(a)** $2x^4 + 3x^3 - 4x^2 + 5x - 3$ **(b)** $x^2 + 7xy - 3y^2$
9. **(a)** $x = \frac{y+5}{3}$ **(b)** $x = \frac{z+5}{6}$
10. **(a)** $\frac{x-y}{2y-1}$
(b) **(i)** $y = 3$ **(ii)** $y = -1$

Revision 4B *(p. 408)*

1. **(a)** -4 **(b)** 12.5% **2.** 14
3. **(a)** 4 **(b)** 3 **(c)** 3.41
4. **(a)** bar chart **(b)** line graph **(c)** pie chart
5. **(a)** 75¢ **(b)** 50¢ **(c)** 55¢
6. **(a)** 7 **(b)** 68% **(c)** 90°
7. **(a)** $-4a^2 + 4a - 4$ **(b)** $5x^2 - x + 1$
8. **(a)** $-6x^4 - 5x^3 + 6x^2$ **(b)** $3x^3 + 2x^2 + 3x + 1$ R 5
9. **(a)** $b = \frac{a+6}{2}$ **(b)** $b = \frac{c+24}{6}$
10. **(a)** $\frac{3x-8y}{3(x+3y)}$
(b) **(i)** $x = \frac{16}{3}$ **(ii)** $x = \frac{1}{2}$

Revision 4C *(p. 409)*

2. **(a)** 8 **(b)** 6 **(c)** 7
3. **(a)** 2.5 **(b)** 30° **4.** 1, 2, 8, 9, 10
5. **(a)** **(i)** 50% **(ii)** 17.5% **(b)** 45
6. **(a)** 3 **(b)** 13
7. $-4a^2 - 2a - 14$
8. **(a)** $-6x^5 + 2x^4 + 13x^3 - 10x^2 + 11x - 24$
(b) $2x^4 + 3x^2 + x + 2$ R -4
9. **(a)** $m = \frac{3-p}{7}$ **(b)** $m = \frac{n-3}{14}$

Miscellaneous Exercise 4 *(p. 411)*

1. **(a)** **(i)** 1 **(ii)** 2 **(b)** 6
2. **(a)** 3 **(b)** 2 **(c)** 2.3
3. **(a)** 126 **(b)** **(i)** 225 **(ii)** $\frac{1}{3}$
4. **(a)** **(i)** 1 **(ii)** $1\frac{1}{2}$ **(iii)** 1.7
(b) **(i)** 18.7 **(ii)** $34 **(iii)** $187
5. **(a)** **(iii)** 5 **(iv)** 5.6
(b) **(i)** 5.2 **(ii)** No
6. **(a)** $\frac{1}{ab}$ **(b)** $-\frac{1}{ab}$
7. **(a)** $\frac{8x-3y}{xy}$ **(b)** $\frac{3x-1}{2(3x+1)}$
8. **(a)** $\frac{2ac+5ab-6bc}{abc}$ **(b)** $\frac{(a+c)(c-b)}{a^2}$
9. $x = 1$ **10.** $y = \frac{(a-b)^2}{a^2+b^2}$
11. $y = \frac{18}{3+x}$ **12.** $y = \frac{1+2x}{2+x}$
13. $z = \frac{11x-1}{11x-5}$
14. **(a)** $xy = ab$ **(b)** $x^2 + y^2 = b^2 - 2ab$
15. **(a)** $\frac{1+n^2}{n+3}$ **(b)** $\frac{1+m^2}{m+3}$

Assessment 1

Paper I *(p. 416)*

1. $(2a+3)(-2a+4)$ **2.** $x = -1$, $y = -\frac{9}{4}$
3. $x \geqslant \frac{83}{28}$ **4.** $x = 1$ or $-\frac{6}{7}$
6. 7.33×10^{-5} **7.** $a = -\frac{4}{15}$
8. *A*: $56, *B*: $40 **9.** 10
10. 48 cm^3 **11.** $x = 11$, $y = 5$
12. **(a)** 47 **(b)** $66\frac{1}{2}$
13. **(a)** $2x$ **(b)** 5
14. 3.36 pm
15. First boy: 9 km/h, second boy: 10 km/h
16. $12.50 profit

Paper II *(p. 417)*

1. **(a)** 3 : 4 **(b)** 270 cm^3
2. 349 cm^3, 332 cm^2
3. **(a)** 7 **(b)** 27
4. 9 sq units
5. **(a)** 10
   (b) 14 (or any integer > 13)
   (c) 10
6. **(a)** Food: 240°; Transport: 72°; Miscellaneous: 48°
   (b) $2 000
7. **(a)** 16.6°
   (b) 2.97 m
8. **(a)** **(i)** $(100x + 80y)$ cents
   (ii) $20(8x + 6y)$ cents
   (b) $x = 20$, $y = 25$
9. **(a)** **(i)** $10p + q$ **(ii)** $101p + 10q + 10r$
   (b) **(i)** 1 **(ii)** 5
   (iii) 7 **(iv)** 24

Assessment 2

Paper I *(p. 420)*

1. $\frac{7a + 2}{4}$ **2.** $x < \frac{4}{25}$
3. **(a)** $(5x + 4y)(5x - 4y)$ **(b)** $(3a + 2b)^2$
4. $x = 12$, $y = -5$
5. **(a)** -8 **(b)** $\frac{1}{9}$ **(c)** 1
6. **(a)** 36 **(b)** 15.75
7. **(a)** (3, 7) **(b)** (−3, 1) **(c)** (3, 1)
8. 4 cm **9.** 15% **10.** 4 hours
11. **(a)** 176 cm **(b)** 220 m
12. 33 **13.** 13 30 **14.** Gain: 26%
15. **(a)** similar **(b)** **(i)** 7.7 cm **(ii)** 8.4 cm
16. **(a)** 2 cm **(b)** 4 cm

Paper II *(p. 422)*

1. John: $200, Michael: $170
2. **(a)** 4.69 cm **(b)** 7.80 cm
3. $100\sqrt{3}$ cm^2
4. **(a)** 35 m **(b)** 41° **(c)** 60°
6. **(a)** 0.4 km **(b)** 62.5 cm **(c)** 4.8 km^2
7. **(b)** **(i)** 30 km/h
   (ii) The car is not moving.
8. **(a)** Divide by 2 and then add 3.
   (b) $U = \frac{S}{2} + 3$ **(c)** 55.6%
9. **(a)** **(i)** 115 **(ii)** 13
   (b) $19
   (c) $y = 12x + 19$
   (d) $m = 13n + 19$